ETERNAL QUEST

ETERNAL

QUEST

The Story of the Great Naturalists

by ALEXANDER B. ADAMS

G. P. PUTNAM'S SONS, NEW YORK

To
Elliott D. S. Adams
The winds and the waves and
the sounds of the forest at night
can all say it better than I can;
and because they can,
I will let them.

Contents

Illustrations follow page 256.

About This Book

At Cape Kennedy the earth trembles with the blast of rockets. Some swing by the planets, sending back pictures with amazing details; others probe the secrets of the moon's surface or spin around the earth at incredible speeds and heights. In the laboratories, physicists divide matter into smaller and stranger particles, engineers design calculating equipment that enables a single power line to do the intellectual work of thousands of humans, and biochemists dig deep into the structure of life, deeper than anyone had thought possible. On the flats of the desert, scientists huddle behind their barricades and hide their eyes from the blaze of light they have created, and in a factory, using another type of light, craftsmen sever a strip of steel with a slender, concentrated beam, then return home to watch signals bounced from a satellite flying overhead.

Truly it is an age of miracles. Yet the greatest is the miracle that has been with us unchanged for many millennia—the miracle of the interrelationship of all life-forms and of their dependency on their environments. The crops still die in the drought as they did in the time of the pharaohs; the largest liners, the swiftest airplanes, are stopped and tossed by storms just as the stagecoaches and coasting schooners often were; the hurricane blows, the lines come tumbling down, and the bulbs on the face of the computer go out (they are nothing now but pieces of useless glass); disease strikes, and man succumbs, not as often as before but often enough; and the blights still spread across our fields in spite of—or perhaps because of—what we attempt to do to halt them. Then, like Housman's country boy at the fair, we wake from our dream to find the world is the old world yet, and we become suspicious that technology may not be the sole determiner of life or death, conquest or defeat. Indeed, some

9

of us believe that technological advances, however innocent they may at first appear, can often lead to destruction.

Because man is slowly becoming more conscious of these delicate ties that bind him to the natural world and of the importance he should attach to them, my publishers and I thought it would be interesting to trace man's understanding of natural history through the lives of some of the naturalists who uncovered a few mysteries we do comprehend and to show how mankind has groped and fumbled toward the ultimate knowledge it has not yet attained.

In planning the book, the first problem was to define a naturalist. Dr. Richard A. Pimentel, an authority on this subject, has said that: "natural history is the study of a single thing, nature. Whether it is normally a science or an art is a matter of debate, but there is no doubt about its tremendous scope: all living and non-living things, their activities, and interrelationships. For practical purposes, the things and their activities are often separated into individual studies, field geology for the non-living and field biology for the living. In addition, the interrelationships constitute the field of ecology. However, these separate studies have a serious drawback—like an organism, nature as a whole is much more than the sum of its parts." This statement underlines the essential problem in picking out a naturalist from other scientists or thinkers, but Dr. Pimentel rightly emphasizes the two words "field" and "nature." These form the essence. The naturalist is one who studies nature and generally does so outside the laboratory, but even that definition is not quite complete. Darwin was a naturalist and went into the field, but his greatest thoughts came to him in the laboratory, as he examined his specimens and reviewed his notes. Cuvier most surely was a naturalist, too, within the definition I have used in selecting the characters to appear in this book. But he was far too busy to make many field expeditions and relied for the most part on the collections accumulated by others. So even the word "field" becomes difficult to apply under all circumstances.

And what constitutes the study of nature? This question is not susceptible to a single answer. It varies with the times. Aristotle's speculations on the composition of the universe, for example, just like Galileo's accurate and substantive observations, were a determining factor in man's attitudes toward nature. The field biologist's approach to the life around him underwent considerable change when he realized that he was only an insignificant part of the cosmos, not the center of it. On the other hand, more recent studies in astronomy, miraculous as they are, are more closely related to chemistry, mathematics, and physics than they are to natural history. So I included some astronomers and left others out and have followed the same course with other sciences.

Even among those persons who were indubitably naturalists, the choice was often difficult to make. There were hundreds of names, each deserving recognition, but I was not trying to prepare a textbook or a reference work. My goal was to write the story of man's discovery of his place in the natural world (insofar as he has discovered it) and to show the qualities and characters of some of the men who did the discovering. Bearing this in mind, I set up certain standards for the selection of the central figures in each chapter: Was the man's life interesting in itself? Did it reveal anything significant about the various ways that naturalists have performed their work? Were their results important? In this fashion, I tried to strike a balance, but even so, the choices were not easy: too many well qualified candidates deserved admission.

The people I have written about dealt with a large number of technical problems, and I have tried to simplify these as far as possible, although I am aware of the danger of oversimplification. In the appendices, I have included considerable material on classification and a timetable of geology. These two subjects recur frequently, and the appendices may be helpful to the reader who wishes to pursue them further. I have also included a list of the characters, both major and minor, appearing in this book, along with their dates and thumbnail sketches. The reader may occasionally wish to use this last to orient himself or for simple reference purposes.

So here they are, some of the great naturalists who have contributed so much to man's understanding of the natural world. They are a varied lot, some generous, some jealous, some good-natured and outgoing, others sharp-tongued and bitter. Some seized a gigantic truth in a single glance; others held the truth in their hands and never knew it. Often they arrived at the right conclusions, or almost the right conclusions, for the wrong reasons. In this, they are representative of all men's thinking, blinded by prejudice and preconceived ideas, yet driven by intellectual discontent and therefore continually searching. In these confused times we might well take to heart the lessons their lives so clearly reveal to us and learn that problems are conquered only by fresh and open minds. We might also respect what they have taught us about natural history: that man is not necessarily here to stay unless he can find a better means of preserving both himself and his environment.

ALEXANDER B. ADAMS

Westport, Connecticut
May, 1968

ETERNAL QUEST

1

In the Beginning

I

Many thousands of years ago, when the world was already old—its surface wrinkled with mountains and pockmarked by seas—a man stood at the mouth of a cave not far from the present site of Bordeaux, France. The air was colder than it is now, because the glaciers had not yet completed their retreat north, nor had the reindeer followed them; but the man himself was in many respects like a modern European, although he was shorter and physically far stronger. His large muscles rippled when he moved his arms or legs. He could run quickly, both to escape and to attack; he could find his way through the wilderness without a guide; he knew how to stalk game for food and how to find water; he could sleep in the open without serious discomfort; and in hand-to-hand combat, he was both ferocious and capable. Nevertheless, he spent much of his time in fear.

When the lightning cracked overhead, sending its bright shafts across the blackened sky, he was afraid. He had no way of knowing what lightning was, but he realized that it was the manifestation of unbelievable power. When the game suddenly disappeared and he was unable, for all his hunting skill, to obtain meat, he was again afraid. There was no easily understood reason for the animals' disappearance, no relationship in his mind between the effect and any possible cause. When the snow threw its muffling cloak over the earth and sometimes trapped him with its cold

15

or blinded him with its whiteness, he was again afraid. He recognized from experience that low temperatures often brought death in their wake, but how or why was beyond his comprehension. Nor could he understand the floods that sometimes followed extensive rainfalls or the hard, parching heat of a drought. He knew that berries appeared on certain bushes at one time of the year, but he had no name for the berries or the bushes and no realization of the true relationship between the plants and the seasons. When the berries failed to appear, he was again afraid. Some force, some evil power, had deprived him of food. Every so often a forest fire, kindled by lightning, raged through the land. The man saw the trees blaze in tall towers of flame, crash, and send sparks flying upward in streams of orange light. The fires came—that much he knew—but how they were started or why they destroyed life was outside his imagination. When he thrust a spear into the heart of an animal, blood poured out; the animal groaned in pain, then lost the capacity to act. Instead of a deer quickly racing over the ground, it was an inert mass. He could do with it what he wanted, sling it over his shoulder and carry it or tear its meat into bits and eat it. The deer could no longer resist. The man did not know what made the deer helpless when its blood poured out. He did know, however, that the same thing could happen to him.

In spite of the mysteries that surrounded him, the unanswerable questions that filled every day of his existence, he did not completely surrender to fear. He was far too knowledgeable and far too busy. He realized that panic meant an end to work and that an end to work meant an end to life. So he made garments out of skins to keep himself warm, he hunted to provide himself with food, and he performed all the duties man must perform to stay alive. These filled most of his days, but he still had time to think.

In the cave behind him, the man's thoughts were painted on the walls. In the great hall just inside the entrance an animal eight feet long and with straight, forward-thrusting horns was painted in color on the rock, and it was followed by other animals, principally bulls, horses, and deer, some of them larger than the first, some of them smaller. Many of them seemed to be dancing as though the whole great herd of animals were engaged in a ceremonial rite. For some distance, the right-hand wall was blank, the stone completely unworked. Then a passage opened through the rock, and the man could go down it and enter other rooms, also decorated with pictures of animals: horses, deer, a rhinoceros, and some bison, as well as a man.

Even to the modern eye, these pictures are magnificent, so beautiful that they bring not only anthropologists, but also art students, to Lascaux, where the man stood so many thousands of years ago. Some of the pictures are now flaked from the rock, and only their dim outlines can be seen; but others are brilliant and fresh, almost as though the artist who had created them had merely walked away for a few minutes to enjoy the sunlight, not as though he had died in the prehistory of the human race.

Beautiful as they are, these pictures have more than artistic interest. Like similar drawings found in other caves, they reflect man's early concern with his environment, his attempt to learn more about it and to record his knowledge and impressions.

The sum of what he knew was not great, but it represented a faltering step out of the blackness of ignorance. And the men of the cave, looking at the world around them and then placing their observations on the stone walls, were among the first of the great naturalists, the precursors of a long line of inquisitive seekers after truth.

II

The earth spun on its axis; the seasons, growing warmer as the glaciers withdrew into the north, came and went, and stretched out into years. The years turned into centuries; life was born, died, and was born again. The centuries became millennia. Some groups of men, unable to survive, faded out; some met other groups and exchanged ideas. In time they discovered they could capture animals, herd them, and raise them. Unlike the men in the Lascaux cave, they no longer had to hunt whenever they were hungry; they merely slaughtered the animals they already controlled. They planted seeds in the ground, making holes with long sticks they learned to weight with stones, and grew their own crops. Now they were no longer nomads—an important change if civilization was to advance—because only relatively large numbers of people settled permanently in one place could accumulate quantities of knowledge.

Even with this advantage, civilization was like seed scattered over indifferent ground. In some locations, it failed to take root; in others, it grew slowly and feebly; in a few, it flourished; and nowhere was its emergence more splendid and dazzling than in Greece.

Out of the north came a group of men who took possession of the peninsula and then, in the course of time, moved to the Aegean Islands and to the shores of Asia Minor. They mingled and bred with the men and women already there and infused them with a new quality: curiosity. For the Greeks were not content merely to know that a certain thing could be done or could happen; they wanted to know, as far as possible, how and why. This unprecedented lust for knowledge drove them into study, observation, and contemplation and produced some of the finest thinkers in the ancient world, men who laid the foundations of European culture: Thales, the successful merchant, who helped start men on the search for general scientific laws; his pupil, Anaximander, who became an excellent geographer; Pythagoras, who worked at philosophy and mathematics; Democritus, who believed that all matter was composed of indivisible "atoms" and the space between them; Hippocrates, who studied medicine and encouraged a rational, questioning approach to scientific problems; and Socrates and Plato, who studied the interrelations of people, sought ideal standards, and attempted to develop a perfect form of government. The list of such men is a long one, but one of the greatest, especially in natural history, was Aristotle, who was always inquisitive about the world around him—from the stars over his head to the animals that inhabited the seas at his feet.

Although his thoughts have survived the centuries, not many details are known about Aristotle's personal life, and a considerable number of the stories surrounding him are more legend than fact. Yet few persons have ever exerted a more profound or prolonged effect on human thinking.

He was born in 384 B.C. at Stagira, a city in Macedonia, where his father served as physician to King Amyntas II. When he was still in his teens, he was sent to study at Athens and came under the influence of Plato. On the death of the philosopher, Aristotle decided not to follow in his father's footsteps as a court physician but instead moved to a city in Asia Minor near Troy. Here, with his intensely inquisitive mind, he apparently became interested in two diverse subjects, marine biology and international politics. The first he pursued by collecting specimens along the shore; the second he absorbed through listening to the local inhabitants. The community, being close to the edge of the Greek world and under constant threat from the Persians, was strongly nationalistic, and when, a few years later, Aristotle moved to Mytilene on the island of Lesbos, he had become indoctrinated with Pan-Hellenism, the philosophy that also dominated the thinking of King Philip of Macedonia.

When Philip ascended the throne, Macedonia, which had remained for the most part outside the sphere of Greek politics, was besieged by enemies on every hand and had almost no means of defense. The new king, who was two years younger than Aristotle, quickly changed this. He strengthened the army, restored its discipline, and then embarked on a plan of conquest that was to make him the master of the Greek world.

At the same time, he searched for a tutor for his son, Alexander, and finally selected Aristotle. Exactly why he chose him is not certain, for Aristotle had not yet gained his later reputation as an intellectual. Probably he was influenced by the long service of Aristotle's family at the Macedonian court, by his excellent training at Athens, and by his interest in Pan-Hellenism. Yet the situation was a curious one. Aristotle was a man of thoughts; Philip, a man of action. Aristotle was no warrior (he preferred contemplation to battle); Philip, on the other hand, saw in the glitter of swords and spears the answer to all political problems, and his mind was obsessed with dreams of conquest. Greece lay before him like an apple ready for the picking, a temptation that he could not resist. So he spent his days plotting the subjugation of the independent states, which, not realizing their danger, were slow to unite against him. But death brought his career to an abrupt end, when, during the wedding festivities held for his daughter, he was murdered by a young nobleman.

The new king, Alexander, had spent years studying under Aristotle; but he was a true son of his father, a warrior, not a philosopher, and once he took command of the Macedonian forces, he was determined to continue with Philip's plans. Whether he and Aristotle fell into disagreement or whether Aristotle wisely foresaw no future for himself as adviser to the aggressive young king is not clear, but in any case Aristotle returned to Athens and opened his famous Lyceum, the school where he taught his pupils while he walked up and down a favorite corner of his garden. This was a peaceable life, much better than following the warlike Alexander in his overseas adventures, but it was halted by the king's death. For once Alexander's restraining influence was removed, the Athenians vented their pent-up hatred by persecuting the Macedonians. Aristotle, who had remained a citizen of Stagira—he always retained some measure of patriotic provincialism—became one of the Athenians' intended victims. They charged him with impiety, but before the trial took place, he fled for his life to Chalcis, a city some thirty miles north of Athens on the island of Euboea, and died there the same year.

Outwardly his life had been so quiet and scholarly that the historians found little to record, but inwardly it had been one of constant searching. Alexander attempted the conquest of the known physical world; Aristotle attempted the conquest of all human thinking. His mind ranged over a broad range of subjects—moral and political philosophy, the writing of poetry, and many others—and much of his thinking is still valid.

He was also a scientist and talked to his students about astronomy, physics, and biology, impressing on them the need for direct observations and for drawing conclusions from ascertainable facts. He did not, however, have the proper instruments for astronomical observations, and so in this field he unwittingly allowed his own skepticism to lapse and accepted two assumptions of previous thinkers: one, that matter was continuous; two, that the heavens operated under laws that were dissimilar to those on earth. Building on this feeble base, he constructed a cosmos consisting of a spherical world in the center, surrounded by rings of matter. Although he so strongly urged men to question all scientific concepts, his theory of the universe ironically remained unquestioned and therefore dominant for almost 2,000 years, seriously impeding independent research and thinking. A curious set of circumstances accounted for this unfortunate situation. One was Aristotle's great reputation; he had one of the finest intellects of all time, and this led him to be considered the supreme authority on every subject. The other was the support that his ideas eventually gained from the Christian Church. His concept of an indestructible, but finite universe, suited the theologians so perfectly that they condemned any efforts to criticize him.

In the biological sciences, he was able to make direct observations, and given this opportunity, he used it to the utmost. He studied his specimens minutely, thrust aside the temptation to speculate, insisted on detailed proof of every thesis, and produced remarkably accurate work. Among his numerous accomplishments were descriptions of the lives and breeding habits of a large number of animal specimens. He studied chicken embryos and the growth of squid and octopuses. He did anatomical studies of the digestive systems of certain animals, and he recognized the importance of the heart and the circulatory system. Also, like the greatest of the naturalists that followed him, he attempted to draw general conclusions from what he had seen.

He was handicapped in doing this, for although he assembled more information than any biologist before him, he still did not have enough facts to arrive at any important basic truths. That would take centuries and centuries of study; one man could not accomplish it in a lifetime. So if Aristotle is studied today for his philosophy, but not for his science, that is only because his ideas, unusual as they were for his age, have since been outdated, a fate to which scientists are particularly prone.

Yet even with the restrictions imposed on him, Aristotle reached some outstanding conclusions. He never, of course, realized that one form of life could emerge from another—man would have to wait centuries to discover that truth—but he came surprisingly close to it, for he recognized that it was difficult to draw a sharp line of demarcation between certain forms. He saw, too, that all life could be arranged in order, with man at the top, followed by the mammals, and on down to the lower plants. This concept later became known as his ladder of life, and although his arrangement did not stand up under closer examination, it was still a considerable achievement for a scholar living in the ancient world. He also developed certain philosophic attitudes toward nature. For one, he decided that each part of the body was designed to fill a particular need, and therefore, the body as a whole had to fill a need. In this, he was a teleologist—a word derived from *tēle,* meaning far off or end. Nature, he believed, did not have a purpose in the sense that men have purposes; nevertheless it was working toward ends. A chicken's egg, for example, was not to Aristotle simply an isolated combination of substances; it was the means of creating a chicken, and therefore it had an end. Later on, the theologians added the principle of design to Aristotle's teleology, arguing that everything in nature occurred according to a master plan established by God. The egg was then no longer limited to the purpose of creating a chicken; it was part of the complete plan. Aristotle, who failed to find direct evidence to support such a thesis, refused to admit any purpose in the workings of nature, but he laid the basis for an important aspect of Christian theology in the centuries to come.

During the Middle Ages his ideas, as interpreted by the church, represented the ultimate in authority. Particularly in astronomy, the sheer weight of his reputation and the church's endorsement prevented men from seeking better and more workable theories, and the few who had the courage to do so were reviled and criticized and sometimes imprisoned or put to death. Aristotle would have been horrified at the outcome of his work. He who desired truth above everything else eventually became one of the greatest obstacles to the search for truth.

When mankind finally broke free from his intellectual domination, his entire reputation as a scientist fell into disrepute. Men laughed at his conception of the universe, which they had been forced to accept so long, and in their laughter they included all his other scientific work. But when biology emerged as a distinct field and grew in importance, the naturalists again looked at the long neglected pages of Aristotle and were surprised by what they saw. Charles Darwin called him the greatest of them all.

III

The reign of Alexander the Great lasted for only slightly more than twelve years, but in the course of that short period and in spite of many difficulties, he changed the political map of the world. When he first ascended the throne, his father's subjects rose against him, and he was forced to put them down with violence. Then Thebes, forgetting the outcome of its earlier struggle, grew restive. Alexander quickly marched to the city's gates and demanded and received the citizens' submission. He then turned north to vanquish the barbarians beyond the Danube who were threatening his empire, and while he was away, a false report of his death spread across Greece. The Thebans mistakenly thought that the opportunity was ripe for another rebellion, but Alexander returned, took the city by storm, razed most of its buildings and either killed its inhabitants or sold them as slaves. This example of his wrath was so terrible that all thought of further resistance died out. Most of Greece accepted him humbly as its leader, leaving him free to pursue his plans for further conquest abroad.

With 35,000 men, he crossed the Hellespont. Resistance crumbled before his onslaught, as he swept across Asia into Assyria, Babylonia, Parthia, and beyond the banks of the Indus River. He added Egypt to the Macedonian Empire, but on a visit to Babylon, which he intended to make his capital, he caught a fever and died. Almost immediately the empire that he had put together with so much bloodshed began to fall apart.

No one general was strong enough to fill Alexander's place and control the others, so they divided the empire among them. Ptolemy took Egypt, the Seleucid family took Syria, Macedonia and its Greek satellites fell under other leadership, and several smaller kingdoms were established, such as that at Pergamum. But the ancient world was never the same again. Everywhere Alexander's armies went, they had carried with them Greek culture and ideas, and these were not forgotten even when the empire crumbled.

But after Aristotle's death, interest in natural history began to decline, and only a handful of scholars pursued it further. One of Aristotle's students, Theophrastus, turned to botany and studied this field in the same spirit as his former master. Since science had been hindered by the lack of a specific terminology, Theophrastus attempted to develop one of his own that could be used in describing plants. He tried, too, to distinguish between the sexes of plants, an idea that had first occurred to the Babylonians, but he was successful only with date palms. He also wrote a series of works containing many accurate botanical descriptions, which are considered among the best arranged biological treatises of the ancient world. Herophilus, who was a contemporary of Euclid, undertook public dissections of human bodies in front of students. He was followed by the physiologist Erasistratus, who contributed further knowledge of the nervous system, and by Crateuas, who used systematic drawings to represent the medicinal herbs with which he was concerned. But on the whole, except for medicine, the Alexandrians, who were the intellectual leaders, were not much interested in life sciences or natural history.

This was not occasioned by any lack of concern with the world around them. Just like the people in the Lascaux cave, the men of the Alexandrian world were influenced every day by natural forces. When the winds swept the Mediterranean and raised the great sea in waves, they lost their ships with valuable cargoes of glass or of grain grown in the soil of the Nile's valley. When the lightning cracked overhead, they were still afraid, not having any understanding of the source of its power. When the droughts came, they could only pray to their gods for rain; they had no means of knowing what caused the droughts. But there was so much to learn and discover that they could not do everything at once, and on the whole, they concentrated on physics, astronomy, and mathematics, hoping through these sciences to unlock the great mysteries of life and existence.

In the process they performed a service to every science. The Greeks, for all their brilliance, had linked philosophy and science together. Pythagoras, to name a single example, was both a philosopher and a mathematician, and to a considerable extent he confused one field with the other. The Alexandrians were more clearheaded than this. To them, philosophy was one subject, science another, and although they tended, like most men before and after, to answer unanswerable scientific questions by resorting to religion (as well as answering unanswerable religious questions by resorting to science), they attempted to keep them separate.

Although Greek intellectualism continued to predominate after the death of Alexander, Greek military and political influence fell into decline. The Romans first subjugated the Greek colonies in Italy and then turned their attention to their natural enemy, Carthage. In the three Punic Wars, which began in 264 B.C. and lasted until 146 B.C., the Romans and Carthaginians fought on land and sea, on the plains and in the mountains. Carthage had the larger population and the bigger fleet, but Rome had the better army and the wiser generals. In the end, Rome laid siege to Carthage and destroyed the African city. Its armies were then free for further conquests, and gradually, under a series of outstanding generals, Rome's boundaries expanded, until it finally emerged as an empire far bigger than anything even Alexander the Great had envisioned. But although it engulfed Greece physically, it failed to do so intellectually, and in philosophy and science the Greeks remained superior to their new masters. Roman scholars studied Greek and read Greek writings; the wealthy classes insisted on having Greeks as tutors for their children; but the Romans made little effort to widen the limits of Greek science or to encourage the Greeks to do so themselves.

The list of Roman naturalists is, therefore, short. Lucretius, the poet, wrote about natural history. Although he believed, like Aristotle, in a ladder of life and came close to developing a theory about the survival of the fittest, his work was not significant. In geography, the Romans did better, particularly because their conquests gave them a broader knowledge of the world. Strabo, from 63 B.C. to A.D. 24, traveled through part of the empire and then returned to Rome and devoted himself to map making. He was followed by Marcus Vipsanius Agrippa, who carried out a major portion of a worldwide survey ordered by Julius Caesar, and by Pomponius Mela, a Spaniard.

In botany, Pedanius Dioscorides, an army surgeon serving in Asia Minor, prepared a book on medicinal herbs, some of which he illustrated with pictures like Crateuas'. But the book was not well arranged in terms of the plants themselves, and Dioscorides made no attempt to draw any general scientific conclusions. His book, nevertheless, exerted great influence, because it became the primary basis of botanical research in the Middle Ages.

The leading anatomist was Galen, who came from Pergamum and went to Alexandria and then to Rome, where he studied physiology. Dissection of the human body was no longer approved, so he used Barbary apes and other animals. In his writings, he included the ideas of many previous scientists, as well as some new ones of his own, and although his work was not distinguished, it, like that of Dioscorides, influenced later thinkers. He was a teleologist but went much further than Aristotle, for he believed that nature worked not only toward ends but toward ends that were planned by God. This, of course, supported the theological beliefs of the Middle Ages, and so Galen's books were widely read long after they might otherwise have been forgotten. Seneca, the Roman philosopher and tutor to Nero, also exercised an influence on later science that his work did not merit. His book *Natural Questions* was largely a compendium of contemporary information, but Seneca believed that nature was designed to serve man. This, of course, also conformed with the thinking of the ecclesiastical authorities of the Middle Ages, and Seneca, too, was popular among them.

Of all the Roman naturalists, perhaps the most famous was Pliny the Elder. As a young boy, he went to Rome to study, received an excellent education, became a lawyer, and joined the army. He saw active service as a military commander and wrote books on the use of cavalry and on the history of the warfare between the Germans and the Romans. But he was not a warlike man and soon left the army for other government service, during which he traveled widely and devoted much of his time to study and writing. He was the author of *Natural History,* which he attempted to make a compendium of the knowledge of his time. It was an enormous task he set for himself, and he patiently consulted some 146 Roman and 326 Greek authors, as well as other sources. By doing this, he performed a valuable service, because he preserved the information they had collected, information that might otherwise have been lost as the original volumes disappeared.

What Pliny most lacked was the personal curiosity of Aristotle, but ironically, on one of the occasions when he did directly investigate a natural phenomenon, his action cost him his life. The event occurred in A.D. 79, when he was assigned to the Roman fleet in the Bay of Naples and Mount Vesuvius began to erupt. One August afternoon his wife called his attention to a strange cloud rising from one of the mountains, which one they could not be sure. It shot up in a straight column, which broke into branches at the top, making it look, according to one observer, like a pine tree. Sometimes the column was light, sometimes dark, depending on how many ashes and cinders it contained, and Pliny immediately ordered a small boat made ready so that he could observe it more closely. Before he put out, he received word that some of his friends who lived near the Bay of Naples were in danger, and so he decided to stop and rescue them at the same time.

As he approached the shore, hot cinders began to fall on his boat, followed by pumice stones and burning rocks. The tide was extremely low, and the boat was in danger of running aground or striking one of the gigantic rocks that had rolled down the mountainside and were now lining the shore. His pilot advised him to turn back, but Pliny refused to consider such a suggestion. "Fortune favors the brave," he said, and he continued on to his friend's house. When he reached it, he found that his friend, although not yet in direct danger, had already loaded his own boats and was prepared to flee; but the wind was blowing onshore, and they could not get off. So no choice remained but to spend the night.

In an effort to set an example for the others, who had become terror-stricken, Pliny took a bath, ate his supper cheerfully, and went to bed. His servants could hear him breathing deeply, but noticing that the court which led to his apartment was filling up with stones and ashes, they realized they must wake him while he still had a chance to escape alive from his room. On being aroused, he joined the rest of the household, which had not gone to bed, and discussed with them the question of whether they should stay in the house, the walls of which were now shaking, or go out into the fields, where they might be buried in the cinders and ashes. Finally, they decided on the latter course and tied pillows over their heads with napkins to protect them from the falling debris. It should have been daylight, but the sun was so obscured by the smoke they had to use torches as they walked to the seashore to see if the wind had changed direction. It had not, and the waves were now so high that flight by water was completely impossible. Still trying to calm the rest of the group, Pliny ordered a sail spread out and, with pretended indifference to the horror raging around them, attempted to sleep. Shortly after lying down, he asked for some water. Suddenly the flames and gases grew greater, and the other members of the party fled in terror. Pliny with the help of two of his servants raised himself from the sail to join them and abruptly fell back dead from the effects of what he had been through.

Although his desire for direct observation, as well as his brave consideration for his friends, brought about his death, Pliny did not apply the spirit he showed at Pompeii to the writing of his *Natural History*. At times he exercised independent, critical judgment, but more often he repeated as fact what some other author had written without attempting to test it himself. He was an encyclopedist rather than a scientist, an assembler of knowledge rather than a creator of knowledge. His book, however, had value for future generations. With all its mistakes and its legends—it refers to unicorns and to fish that can stop a ship from moving by sucking at its bottom—it still gives a clear picture of natural history in Pliny's day.

Pliny was a typically self-centered Roman in his attitude toward nature. He saw it almost entirely in its relation to man, and living things, he believed, were created principally for man's own use. There is a practicality about his approach to science that was common to the Romans, and this practicality brought about an increasing anti-intellectualism. By the beginning of the second century A.D., speculation and theoretical studies were widely derided, and scientific investigation had come almost to an end.

And yet the Romans had little else to offer their many subjects. The philosophy of the governing classes was Stoicism, a rational and fatalistic approach to life. One was supposed to do one's duty and accept what came. For victorious generals and wealthy senators and merchants, such a philosophy was adequate. What came to them was often good. But for the remainder of the population—the farmers, the slaves, the conquered peoples, the servants, the sailors—it was not sufficient. It answered no questions; it offered no hope. Like the men in the Lascaux cave or like the early Greeks, they were left in a threatening, dangerous world with neither scientific knowledge nor a faith to support them.

The people consequently had to turn to sources outside the structure of Roman society for comfort. Some found solace in the Hebrew religion, some in Christianity, some in various mystic beliefs imported from the East, and some in a philosophy later called Neo-Platonism, which consisted of a strange mixture of Persian ideas and a diluted form of Platonism. The clear vision of Aristotle and the rational approach of the Greeks to the problems of living in the natural world were replaced by a resort to mysticism. Slowly superstition replaced truth, and coincidentally, the decline of Rome hastened. By A.D. 476 a minor chieftain named Odoacer had ousted the Western co-emperor, Romulus Augustulus, and his replacement was not another Roman, but Theodoric, leader of the Visigoths.

The Roman Empire in the East, although greatly weakened, still stood, but in the West, the light of learning that had been flickering faintly during the last centuries of Roman rule finally went out. Intellectually, Europe was plunged into darkness.

IV

The collapse of the Roman Empire and the defeat of its legions left a void that nothing could fill, for the invading barbarians had little sense of order, discipline, or unity. Tribal chiefs came and went. Kingdoms were created, then conquered or dismembered by quarreling heirs. Some of the ruling classes, crude and unlettered, were also depraved. Other rulers, however, were more enlightened, and some, like Charlemagne, were able to maintain a semblance of order, although fresh dangers were threatening from the north and south.

In the Arab world toward the south, Mohammedanism sprang into being, and the words of the Prophet vitalized the people, setting them off on a march of conquest. In the east, Islamic forces beat at the doors of Byzantium and, in the west, crossed over to Spain and moved unchecked into France, until they met Charles Martel at Tours in 732. From the north came another group of invaders, the Scandinavians, who established themselves in Normandy in 911 and made England part of the Danish kingdom in 1016.

These turbulent centuries were not conducive to learning in Europe. A few works—Pliny's was one of the more popular—remained in use, but science did not flourish. In the Byzantine Empire, however, a few scholars who were still acquainted with classical Greek continued to catalogue and annotate the Greek writers. Among them were some of the Syriac-speaking peoples who lived in Byzantium. The latter also adopted the religious teachings of Nestorius, the Patriarch of Constantinople. As Nestorius' doctrines were later declared heretical, the Syriac-speaking peoples were persecuted and forced to leave Byzantium. They moved first to Mesopotamia and then to Persia, and in the Nestorian city of Gondisapur they served as the custodians of Western culture, preserving in Syriac the works of such men as Aristotle and Euclid. With the rise of Islam, the Nestorians were absorbed by the Arabs, who established a library and translating center at Baghdad, where they translated the Syriac versions of the Greek books into Arabic. These were translated once more by other scholars into medieval Latin and by this circuitous and inefficient route again reached Europe.

The Arabs made other important contributions. Standing at the crossroads of Persia, India, and Europe, they helped create a blend of East and West. From the Persians, they took ideas about alchemy, a science that was the forerunner of chemistry; from India, they adopted the Arabic system of numerals, which freed mathematicians from the limitations of the Roman system; and from the Syriac-speaking peoples, they received, of course, the knowledge of the Greeks. At first they simply absorbed the culture of other civilizations, but soon they produced thinkers and scientists of their own: Geber, the Syrian, who did exceptional work in chemistry; Rhazes and Avicenna, both outstanding physicians; Al-Khowarizimi, the mathematician; Al-Battani, the astronomer; and Al-Kindi, who wrote about meteorology, the tides, and optics. In the western part of the Arab world, other great thinkers arose, although somewhat later than in the eastern part: Maimonides, a physician, whose views on cosmology influenced Thomas Aquinas, and Averroës, another physician, who wrote a series of commentaries on Aristotle. Like other scientists of his day, Averroës believed that space was finite, but he propounded the daring idea that the world was eternal, thereby denying its creation as set forth by the Moslem, Hebraic, and Christian faiths and, in one speculative leap, coming closer to the ultimate truth than anyone supposed.

No such intellectual ferment took place in beleaguered Europe. There the church was the single remaining cohesive force, the sole custodian of the old ethics, and the only defender of the ancient cultures. All its strength and resources were employed in resisting the influx of the barbarians' codes of behavior, and although the church yielded on many points, adopting pagan rites, permitting its priests untraditional liberties, and becoming deeply involved in secular politics, nevertheless, it emerged triumphant, and that victory laid the base for the civilization of modern Europe.

In the course of its struggle the church gained a practical monopoly on education. Those who could read and write were generally clerics; the libraries were usually located in monasteries or church-founded universities; the priesthood dominated almost the entire educational system of medieval Europe. This resulted in both a service and a disservice to knowledge. The activities of the church kept learning alive; without the church the Dark Ages would have been truly dark. On the other hand, the church naturally used its monopoly to support its own theological views and was far less interested in science and pragmatic investigation than it was in promulgating the Christian philosophy. Many of the clergy were mystics, and all but a few of them placed faith above reason. They were not interested in independent research; they were concerned only with proving that the church was right. To accomplish this, they gave their full support to the science of the ancient world, particularly the science of Aristotle. This contained, in their opinion, all that mankind needed to know and nothing that was contradictory to the Christian faith as they expounded it. It was a comfortable position to assume, for it created a static base on which they could build their theology.

In spite of the church's acceptance of Aristotle as the supreme authority, the distance between the Greek scientist and the medieval theologians was great. In considering the cosmos, Aristotle had made several serious mistakes, but in his biological work he had observed and recorded accurately and had taken nothing for granted. This was the spirit and attitude that almost died out in the Middle Ages.

Yet science continued to make faltering progress. In addition to the great translators like Adelard of Bath, who helped introduce Arabic numerals into Europe, Robert of Chester, and Gerard of Cremona, there was Michael the Scot, who attacked the traditional astronomy of Europe, promoted the questioning beliefs of Averroës, and brought the biological works of Aristotle to the attention of the Western world.

Roger Bacon was another of the few who refused to accept tradition. Although he himself rarely conducted experiments, he argued for the need of experimentation. Tradition, he said, should be challenged by facts and observation. Like Aristotle, he opposed unskeptical acceptance of authority.

But such men were few, and their advances were slow and uncertain. They were like people wandering in the darkness, unsure, groping, and, more often than not, moving in the wrong direction. Barbarism and warfare had destroyed the learning of Europe, and the great promise offered by the activities of the Greek intellectuals had, after all these years, led to little of merit. Like a single tidal wave, rising in the center of the ocean, magnificent but lonely, it had dashed against the shore, then rolled back, spent and broken.

2

Some Inquiring Men

I

In the fifteenth and sixteenth centuries the light began to break again in Europe, and the Continent threw off the intellectual lethargy that had dominated it during the preceding years. Measured in terms of individual lifetimes, the period was long, but considered against the millennia of human history, it was remarkably brief. Suddenly man began to expand his knowledge of the physical world and to take renewed interest in physics, astronomy, and biology. The old traditions, firm but sterile, began to crack under onslaught after onslaught, as mankind began to gather both the information and the courage to throw them off. For it took courage to defy the accepted order. It meant flouting authority, particularly that of the church, an institution which could be deadly in its revenge. It meant destroying the tenets on which culture and faith had been built, leaving in their place only questions that seemed unanswerable. The foundations of life and living had to crumble to make way for the new, and for many, the resulting pressures and tensions were too much to bear. They went mad. For others, the conflict ended in intellectual triumph and physical defeat. They died in prison or at the stake. Others survived more happily, sometimes by couching their new findings in cautious words or by skirting the central issues on which tradition was most persistent. But together they moved learning ahead.

Inspired by a new alertness, men began taking another look at the world around them, and among the first to do so were the artists. As the pictures of plants in Botticelli's paintings demonstrate, some of the artists were remarkably accurate observers, but none more so than Leonardo da Vinci. With a mind that ranged far, he realized that when the "old moon is in the new moon's arms," the effect is caused by the reflection of light from the earth; he foresaw the development of airplanes and parachutes; he studied the flights of birds and drew plans for breech-loading guns; and he recognized that fossils were the remains of animals, not an entirely new idea, but one in opposition to the prevailing Aristotelianism. Unfortunately, Leonardo did not publish his findings, merely recording them in his private notebooks, so he did not influence his contemporaries as he might have. In his own time, his principal scientific contribution was his interest in anatomy and his dislike of sterile classicism. To paint well, he had to discover how bodies operated, not only human bodies, but the bodies of other animals as well. The anatomical drawings that he consequently made for himself and his students stimulated many artists to do the same and laid a base for improved work in medicine.

Even some officials of the church were swept up by the new spirit of inquiry that was stirring Europe. Nicholas of Cusa, who was a cardinal and a philosopher, did an outstanding botanical experiment on the weight gained by growing plants and also struck a telling blow at the cosmos of Aristotle. If the universe was a sphere, as Aristotle had argued, then there must be something outside that sphere. Since that is impossible, the universe had to be infinite, in which case the world could not be at the center. Unfortunately, Nicholas did not have enough knowledge of astronomy to go beyond this point or any means of proving himself correct. Consequently, his ideas were not widely circulated—only scholars knew about them—but before he died in 1464, he had glimpsed the truth that would be discovered and proved by Copernicus, who was born some nine years later.

Nicolaus Koppernigk (Copernicus is the Latin version of the name) was a successful merchant who lived for a while at Cracow and then moved to Torun, where he married one of the wealthy Waczenrodes. She bore him four children, the youngest of whom he named after himself. When the boy, who had been born in 1473, was only ten years old, his father died, and he was adopted by his uncle, Lucas Waczenrode, a church dignitary who shortly became Bishop of Ermland, one of the four dioceses of Prussia. A highly intelligent man, Waczenrode was determined that his adopted son should have the best possible education and, as soon as Copernicus was ready, sent him to the university at Cracow, one of the leading intellectual centers of Europe. Waczenrode intended his nephew to follow in his own steps and enter the church, but Copernicus soon developed other ideas. Cracow at the time was famous for its school of astronomy, and Copernicus spent more time listening to its faculty than attending the classes offered by the theologians.

When the boy had finished his studies at Cracow, Waczenrode sent him to Bologna to study canon law, a useful tool for a future clergyman and, while he was there, appointed him canon of the cathedral at Frauenburg. Thus, Copernicus' future was ensured, for he had both an education and a position. But he was in no hurry to return home and, since his family could afford the expense, went to Rome for a year and on to Padua, where he again studied canon law and obtained his doctorate, as well as taking courses in medicine. By this time he could no longer postpone the assumption of his clerical duties, so he went back to his uncle, but because it was now clear that he was more a scientist than a theologian, he became his uncle's private physician and personal assistant and lived at the bishop's palace at Heilsberg.

Although nepotism inspired his appointment, the post was no sinecure, for Ermland was endangered by the constant threat of invasion. The Teutonic Knights, who held lands surrounding it and much of the land within the state itself, wanted to gain complete control. Poland, on the other hand, was equally ambitious, and Ermland was an obvious target for its expansionist plans. Waczenrode, therefore, was constantly trying to play one enemy against the other as the only means of preserving his independence. Protracted and delicate diplomatic negotiations took up a large part of the bishop's daily life, and he entrusted many of them to Copernicus, who seems to have handled them capably.

Although his duties were heavy, Copernicus still had time to pursue a question that had bothered him for many years: the inability of Aristotelianism to explain many observable phenomena in the universe. His research was temporarily interrupted by the death of Waczenrode. With the loss of his uncle's protection, he was forced to return to Frauenburg and take up his responsibilities as a canon. Much of his time and energy, therefore, was devoted to administering the civic and church affairs of two communities, Allenstein and Mehlsack, and to protecting Allenstein from invasion when open warfare broke out between the Teutonic Knights and Poland. But the lessons he had learned from his uncle served him well, and he fulfilled his duties successfully. Although he led the busy life of a practical administrator and man of affairs, he never neglected his hunt for a better theory of the universe and, whenever time permitted, continued his calculations.

As a direct observer, he was not especially competent; indeed, he was not as good as some of the astronomers of the ancient world. But he brought to the subject an inquisitive, imaginative mind, unhampered by traditional thinking. If Aristotle's theories could not account for the universe's action, something else must, and starting with that premise, he continued studying his own records of the movements of the heavenly bodies and the records of those who had preceded him, examining them and reexamining them in a painful and prolonged search for the truth. After years of deliberation he finally decided that the earth could not possibly be at the center of the universe. What he reasoned was this: the sun was at the center; the earth turned on its axis once each day, and the moon revolved around it; Mercury and Venus circled the sun inside the earth's orbit, the other planets outside it; and the "fixed" stars—he still believed in fixed stars—were farther away. In substance, it was not a complicated theory—indeed, it retained many of Aristotle's ideas—and the facts are now so obvious that their discovery does not seem startling. But in Copernicus' day they struck at the roots of man's scientific, philosophic, and religious tenets. More than that, they destroyed man's conception of his dignity and importance. If the earth was not at the center, neither was man. Such findings may have frightened even Copernicus as he worked alone in the night watching the stars against the sky. Somewhere out in the black heavens was the God whom he had learned to praise as a boy in his uncle's palace. But if God no longer sat where his uncle had placed Him, where was He?

Copernicus wrote an abbreviated account of his theory and passed copies among his friends without publishing it. In this way, his ideas became known to a number of people, but none of them took him seriously. The concept was too ridiculous. (Even Luther, who should have welcomed such an attack on Catholic tradition, dismissed Copernicus as a fool who was trying to turn astronomy upside down. It was silly, Luther said, to suppose that Joshua had ordered the earth to stand still when the Bible clearly stated that He had halted the sun!)

Gradually the men Copernicus had known when he was young died, and he led a more and more lonely life. Yet he kept revising and adding to the now bulky manuscript that contained his complete theory without having any thought of publishing it. It was a strange situation—the discoverer of one of the most startling truths uncovered in mankind's history suppressing his findings. Perhaps he was one of those perfectionists who will not release their life's work until it is exactly what they want it to be. Perhaps he feared exposing himself to ridicule or to the anger of the church. In any case, the manuscript remained in his possession and was read only by those who came to see him. One of his visitors was a professor of mathematics at the university at Wittenberg, whose Latin name was Rheticus. Although he was a Protestant, he was interested in the new astronomical theory developed in the Catholic center of Frauenburg. To show his respect for Copernicus, he had brought with him a number of presents, including a copy of Euclid, and he finally gained Copernicus' confidence and a chance to read the manuscript, which so impressed him that he sent a short summary of it to a friend of his in Nuremberg. This summary was subsequently published with Copernicus' permission, but the *First Account,* as it was called, contained only the information dealing with the various motions of the earth. Then, suddenly, Copernicus, reversing his former attitude, gave the complete manuscript to Tiedemann Giese, Bishop of Ermland, who promptly sent it to Rheticus, who in turn placed it with a printer in Nuremberg for publication. Rheticus had intended to serve as editor, but because he received an appointment at Leipzig, he had to surrender the responsibility to a minister named Andreas Osiander.

Copernicus was now an old man and approaching his end. In 1542 he suffered a severe hemorrhage and stroke, which paralyzed him almost completely and brought him to the verge of death. But he lingered on that winter, as the pages of his book slowly came from the press. Gradually the snows melted, the cold gave way to the first warm airs of spring, the flowers broke through the ground, and life flooded around him, while his own life ebbed and his mind failed. By May, 1543, little was left of one of the most vigorous intellects in history.

On the twenty-fourth of that month the first printed copy of his book arrived from Nuremberg. There it was at last, the great theory that would shake the foundations of Aristotelianism, printed and bound and available to any library that wanted it.

They handed him the book. He was so sick he could hardly have been conscious of what he was receiving. And that day he died.

II

It is probably fortunate for his state of mind that Copernicus was far too ill to study the copy of his published book, for the editor, Osiander, had done his job badly. The manuscript from which the printer worked contained many changes that Copernicus had not authorized, but worse than that, Osiander had, without Copernicus' knowledge, added a second preface. In his own preface, Copernicus had taken certain precautions against the church's incriminations. Addressing himself to the Pope, he had carefully explained that several other cosmic theories had been advanced in the past, and no harm could result from proposing one more. He also expressed the hope that his studies would lead to the formulation of a better calendar, which he knew the Pope desired. But this statement was as far as he would go toward appeasing the church.

Earlier Osiander had suggested another course. The apparent motion of a planet as seen from the earth, he said, can be represented by several theories. Therefore, a purely artificial theory can be useful, as the Greeks had discovered, in preparing tables and making predictions.

Copernicus, he argued, should state that his theory was just such an artificiality, helpful in doing calculations but not actually true.

Copernicus had rejected this suggestion; but Osiander's second preface incorporated the idea anyway, and since it was unsigned, it could have been easily attributed to the author himself, not to a meddling editor. This second preface, which denied the basic validity of the theory, helped reduce the book's initial impact. Readership was generally limited to astronomers who were more concerned with its planetary tables than its basic ideas, and many years passed before its full import was widely understood.

In that restless, questioning age Copernicus was not alone in his attempt to revise traditional science. One of the prominent members of the movement was Andreas Vesalius, a Belgian. As a young boy, he became absorbed in anatomy; he read all the books he could find on the subject and taught himself to dissect animals. When he went to Paris to study medicine, he, therefore, had an advantage over the other students, particularly in this one field.

In those days the professors of anatomy followed a practice that had become established in the Middle Ages. They themselves never performed dissections but left this filthy, bloody work to ill-paid assistants, who operated with crude and limited instruments. Usually the assistants started by hacking open the abdomen and breast cavity with a knife, while the professor lectured on the parts exposed without turning around to look at them. He had no need to; his text was drawn directly from Galen, and who felt it necessary to confirm the classicist's statements by actual observation? After the abdomen and chest cavity had been described, the assistants started removing other organs, while the professor continued to drone away in the blind faith that Galen was right. Because the assistants were neither skilled nor well equipped, the corpse became a chopped-up mess, and the dissection soon stopped. Then the students went home, unless a debate broke out between the faculty of philosophy and the faculty of medicine. These debates always centered on one topic: whether Galen, the idol of the physicians, or Aristotle, the idol of the philosophers, was correct on a particular question. Since neither side really knew what it was talking about, the debates always proved fruitless.

Vesalius, however, showed such unusual initiative and became so expert that he was invited, while still a student, to perform dissections in public. After three years of study at Paris, he returned for a short time to Brussels, where he engaged in the macabre, but useful, task of putting together an entire human skeleton from the bones he picked up around the gallows. This accomplished, he went to Venice, where he completed his studies, and then accepted a professorship at Padua.

He had the usual assistants assigned to him to perform the dissections while he lectured, but he grew impatient with their clumsy hackings and decided to perform the work himself with the aid of his students. This was a revolutionary step, and it led to revolutionary results. In the first place, Vesalius recognized that additional instruments were sorely needed. As he walked through the streets of Padua, he constantly stopped to examine the tools used by various artisans, and he adapted many of them to surgery and also invented ones that were entirely new. (Many of the instruments used by today's surgeons can be traced directly back to Vesalius.) In the second place, when he realized that Galen's anatomy could not stand up under close examination, he began to revise it.

Each winter—the lectures were always held in cold weather, so the corpse would rot less quickly—Vesalius would stand before an audience of several hundred students and for a three-week period expound the new ideas he was developing. Although he retained many of Galen's principles, he corrected detail after detail that he found false and thus provided the foundation for modern anatomy. The lectures proved so popular he took a year's leave of absence and went to Basel to produce them in book form. The result was a folio volume of more than 700 pages and a summary published separately. The works appeared in 1543 and immediately created a furor. All the supporters of Galen's theories attacked these ideas, and they were not satisfied merely to denounce the books themselves; they also denounced Vesalius personally, accusing him of being godless and claiming he had dissected human beings who were still alive. The attacks were so sharp and bitter, the charges raised against him so severe, that he felt forced to resign his post at Padua. The question uppermost in his mind was where to seek safety. Charles I of Spain was now Charles V of the Holy Roman Empire, a man who had added greatly to the domains he had originally inherited and who had several times defeated the French. Although his empire was far-flung and beset by many problems, he was regarded as probably the most powerful personage in Europe. So when he offered Vesalius the position of court physician, Vesalius promptly accepted. Backed by Charles's patronage, he felt he would be secure.

But the protection did not last his lifetime. In 1556, Charles, wracked by the pain of gout and weary of the eternal struggles of governing, called a meeting in Brussels and announced his abdication in favor of his brother, Philip II. Moving to Spain, he took refuge in a monastery, where he died two years later. Vesalius remained with Philip a short time, but finding the court incompatible under the new monarch, he went back to Italy, hoping to obtain another professorship.

None was offered him, and lonely and friendless and with nothing else to do, he went on a pilgrimage to Jerusalem. What happened to him on this trip, no one knows. Whether he was killed in an accident, drowned, or murdered by robbers is still a mystery. He simply vanished from sight in the Near East, his death unrecorded, his grave unmarked.

The death of Giordano Bruno, on the other hand, was well documented. He was burned at the stake in Rome as the penalty for his heresies.

A native of Italy, he entered a monastery as a young man but was shortly forced to flee because of his disdain for authority and his criticisms of the church's views. He then made a precarious living lecturing on a system of logic that he had developed, visiting various universities like those at Lyons, Toulouse, Montpellier, and Paris. Apparently he was a disagreeable person, given to arguing and staying aloof from his fellows, and each time he left a university, his associates were glad to see him go.

In 1583 his wanderings took him to London, and the following year he published three small books in Italian, each bearing the false impress of Venice. These three books contained some of the most startling ideas of the century. Bruno was not a scientist but a philosopher. Yet he had carefully read the works of Copernicus and Nicholas of Cusa and purely by speculation wove out of them a theory of the universe that was surprisingly accurate.

The earth, he agreed with Copernicus, revolved around the sun, but the sun itself was not at the center. He also proposed the possibility that there were other worlds like ours and stated his belief that the universe possessed what he called a common soul, an argument that opened the way for the conceiving of universal natural laws.

If Bruno's ideas were accepted, Aristotelianism had to die, and with it the rigid tenets of sixteenth-century theology. The conflict that followed the publication of his three small books was typical. On the one hand was the man with the new idea; on the other, the powerful forces of traditional thinking. At no time—not even today—has the world granted recognition to thoughts that contradict its own beliefs, whether those beliefs are mythical or not, and the sixteenth century, in spite of its increasing liberality on scientific questions, was no exception. From 1583 on, Bruno was a marked man.

Unwisely he returned to Italy, where a patron had promised him a welcome. But the patron was not sufficiently strong to hold at bay the eager officers of the Inquisition, who had been waiting to lay their hands on this hateful heretic, this flouter of authority, this unchristian devil. They arrested him and kept him in prison for almost eight years, while they debated his case. He thought at the time that he had as few readers as he had friends, but this was not true. His ideas were permeating the thinking of Europe and helped give rise to a new order of science.

In 1600, at the opening of the new century, the officials of the Inquisition led Bruno in chains to the Campo de' Fiori, the Field of Flowers, in Rome. The stake was ready, the fagots stacked. Solemnly and self-righteously, they went about their duty, binding him to the post and touching their torches to the fuel. The flames crackled and leaped upward, licking at his body, while the priests prayed to a God who, if Bruno was right, could no longer exist in the form they believed He did. The air became heavy with the smell of burning flesh, and screaming with pain and unable to free himself from the bonds that held him, Bruno died.

III

The execution of Bruno was not an auspicious beginning for a century that, in spite of wars and revolutions, finally proved itself brilliant. Although these were turbulent years, with armies marching against one another across Europe and fleets firing at one another on the seas, some men still had time to think about mankind and its place in the world and the universe. One of these was Johannes Kepler, who bridged the sixteenth and seventeenth centuries.

He was born in Germany in 1571 of the most unlikely family that ever produced a genius. His grandfather was a man of some substance, mayor of the town of Weil der Stadt and owner of the house in which most of his descendants lived together. His grandmother, whom Kepler described as a violent troublemaker, bore twelve children, only a few of whom adopted a normal way of life. One of them joined the Catholic priesthood but, according to Kepler, "led a most impure life" and vanished somewhere in Italy or France. One aunt married beneath herself, squandered the little money she had, and ended a pauper. Kepler's father was a restless mercenary soldier and tavernkeeper, who narrowly escaped hanging and finally deserted his family and disappeared. Kepler's mother had been brought up by an aunt who had been burned as a witch. She herself, also liking to work charms, narrowly escaped the same fate.

Young Kepler was an unattractive child, given to putrid sores that broke out on his feet and hands, and suffered from frequent headaches and bad eyesight. His parents had so little money he could attend school only irregularly, and when he did, he made more enemies than friends among his classmates. Yet he early showed two rare qualities that marked him for distinction: he was extremely brilliant, and he had a great capacity for intellectual honesty. (Even when writing about himself, as he did some years later, he could be sharply critical and objective.) He never permitted emotion or even self-esteem to obscure the truth for which he was constantly searching.

The obvious career for such a bright, but unhealthy, child was the church, and so Kepler entered the seminary, where he won a scholarship to the university at Tübingen. His intention, of course, was to study theology, but he soon became distracted by astronomy, particularly by the ideas of Copernicus, which he defended publicly on several occasions. Before taking his degree, he received an offer to teach mathematics and astronomy at Graz in Austria and, after some hesitation, decided to accept. The courses that he offered were unpopular. The first year, he had only a handful of students; the second year, attendance at his classes dwindled to nothing. Kepler was frantic and unhappy, but the officials of the school took a broad-minded attitude and placed the blame not on the teacher, but on the attitude of the students. Furthermore, they were impressed by his abilities as the official astrologer of the area, a position that was usually assumed by the teacher of mathematics. (In his first attempt, he luckily predicted two events that actually occurred: warfare with the Turks and unusually cold weather.)

In July, 1595—he made a careful note of the date—he was drawing a geometric figure for his students when he was suddenly struck with the thought that the motions of the planets could be explained by assigning to the orbit of each one a specific geometric form. The idea was not entirely new, but the sudden inspiration launched Kepler on his life's work of searching for a logical means of explaining the planets' revolutions around the sun and thus carrying Copernicus' work farther. His first attempts, in the light of present knowledge, seem ridiculous. The orbit of Jupiter, for example, he thought was a tetrahedron and that of Venus an octahedron. After working on his theory for several years, he decided to publish it. The production of this volume, which appeared in 1596, posed numerous problems for an impecunious teacher, but Kepler faced his difficulties cheerfully. He had lost the physical and intellectual crassness of his youth and now seemed able to obtain support from many sources. (The Duke of Württemberg considered building a model of Kepler's universe as a drinking cup, but the project came to nothing, after Kepler had constructed several models in paper. The thing was too monstrous.)

But he was not happy even after the book came out. Catholicism was on the rise in Graz, and Kepler's school was Lutheran; it came under increasing attack and was finally dissolved. Kepler himself was fined for burying one of his children according to the Lutheran rites. But the real cause of his unhappiness was the failure of his complicated theory to explain the motions of the planets. As he worked and reworked it, he could find many discrepancies. What he needed above all else were more detailed records against which he could test and develop it, and he knew of only one person who had them, a Dane named Tycho Brahe.

In almost every respect, except for their common interest in astronomy, Tycho and Kepler were exact opposites. Tycho came from a wealthy family, had traveled widely, and had received an excellent education. He was also a favorite of the King of Denmark, who gave him many special privileges and greatly augmented his already large income. While Kepler was speculating on the planets' motions, Tycho was collecting the most accurate observations ever made. In doing this, he was assisted by his wealth, for there was no instrument he could not purchase or have constructed, no expense he could not go to. He had, however, no willingness to share the information he had gathered, because he hoped to draw up his own cosmic theories. Kepler's frustration must have been great. Tycho had what he wanted, but he could not accept Tycho's invitation to visit him—the cost of traveling was too much—and he could not hope to persuade Tycho to send him his records.

Then fate, in the form of Tycho's arrogance, intervened. Always a favorite at court, Tycho had assumed more and more power over the people in his district, rejecting the actions of the local courts when they went against his wishes and freely imprisoning his tenants when he cared to. Frederick II of Denmark was willing to accept such conduct; his successor, Christian IV, was not, and he was especially annoyed by Tycho's refusal to answer his letters. When he finally indicated that Tycho should leave the country, Tycho, who was growing restless anyway, accepted an invitation to become the astronomer at Prague. Some of his former assistants refused to go with him—they, too, were probably weary of his arrogance—and in casting around for new helpers, he fixed on Kepler. Kepler, of course, immediately accepted, and in the year that Bruno died at the stake, he moved from Graz to Prague.

The emperor, Rudolf II, had offered Tycho his choice of one of three castles to serve as his observatory and home, and Tycho had chosen Benatek (now Benátky nad Jizerou, Czechoslovakia), some twenty miles northeast of Prague. There Kepler joined him, expecting to find the great astronomer living the quiet life of a scholar. He must have been astonished, therefore, when he entered the castle and discovered it in the throes of physical and emotional turmoil. Tycho was completely rebuilding it, tearing down one wall, constructing another, and building a special gate for the emperor's use, and the dust and the clamor bothered Kepler's nerves. Seemingly oblivious to the confusion, Tycho was also debating heatedly with the emperor and his advisers over a question about the salary he was to have received. Nor did he and Kepler get along personally. Both were proud; both wanted something from the other—Kepler wanted Tycho's records; Tycho wanted Kepler's help in developing his cosmic theory—and they started arguing. On several occasions Kepler stalked out of the castle and let himself be persuaded to return only after he had extracted concessions from Tycho. Fortunately, the relationship was of short duration. In less than two years after Kepler's arrival, Tycho died, and the emperor appointed Kepler to his position.

The transition did not take place peacefully. Tycho's son-in-law declared himself the heir and grabbed the best instruments, which he promptly sold to the emperor. Since the emperor never paid for them and allowed him only the interest on the debt, the son-in-law kept them under lock and key, while they rusted. Kepler, however, seized control of Tycho's records and used them as his own in spite of the family's remonstrances. After all those years and many obstacles, he was still determined to find the laws governing the motions of the planets.

With endless patience, he reviewed his own observations and Tycho's records, sitting in his castle room, calculating and recalculating. The fault for any discrepancies, he believed, lay with his theory, not with Tycho's figures. For in spite of their many quarrels, he respected Tycho as an astronomical observer, and this confidence in his former employer was the keystone of his work. Without this faith, he might have been content with a less satisfactory theory than the one he finally produced. For putting his mathematics to its best use, he determined that planets did not move in circles, but in ellipses, and that their motion was not uniform.

He published these findings in 1609 under the title of *New Astronomy*. (Nine years later, he worked out a mathematical relationship between the time it took a planet to revolve and its distance from the sun.) Unfortunately Kepler's *New Astronomy* was written in rather poor Latin, and he buried the main points in a mass of detail that described everything he had done, not just the investigations that eventually proved fruitful. As a result, his book was not read as widely as it should have been, but it struck a further devastating blow at Aristotelianism. Not only did Kepler prove that Copernicus' basic conception was correct, but he also demonstrated that the whole idea of circular orbits was false.

In the year Kepler published his historic book, Galileo Galilei, who was teaching mathematics at the university in Padua, learned about the construction of telescopes in Holland, and when a friend in France confirmed the existence of these new instruments, Galileo decided to make one for himself. He first prepared a tube of lead and fitted it with two lenses. Looking through it, he computed its magnification as nine times. He then built two more, each more powerful than the last, and turned the best of them on the heavens. What he saw he reported in a small pamphlet that he published in the following year. Although it was only forty-eight pages long, it shook the intellectual world. The Aristotelians had always held that the heavenly bodies were spheres, becoming more nearly perfect the farther they were removed from the earth. Galileo announced that the moon was ridged and pockmarked like the earth. He also wrote about the hundreds of new stars that he had discovered and the four satellites revolving around Jupiter. These he called the Medicean planets in the hope that this honor to the Medici family would help him secure an appointment at Florence.

Kepler and Galileo had had only a slight correspondence, and Galileo had never commented on Kepler's books, but he now turned to Kepler for a favor. Would Kepler please write him a letter endorsing his new publication? It would be helpful in applying for the position at Florence. Kepler, although he had no way of directly confirming what Galileo had written, responded generously, thus contributing to Galileo's eventually leaving Padua.

The move was unfortunate. Earlier, as a result of some intrigue, he had been forced to resign a post at Pisa, and the Senate of Venice, under whose jurisdiction the university at Padua came, had taken him in. After he had presented the Senate with one of his telescopes, they had gratefully voted him a lifetime salary of 1,000 florins. This, combined with the income he earned by giving private instruction, made him comfortably off, but he resented the time required by his teaching. As he wrote to a friend, no one in a republic like Venice could exempt him from performing the duties for which he received wages. Only a despot could do that. This was true, but Galileo, for all his brilliance, overlooked an important point. The Senate of Venice was one of the most powerful and independent political forces in Italy, and it was the only one capable of defending a free-speaking scientist from the church. Galileo surrendered this protection when he moved to Florence.

At first his position seemed to have improved. True to his word, Cosimo de Medici, the Duke of Tuscany, gave Galileo the time he needed for his research, which included many aspects of physics, as well as astronomy. But as he spoke and wrote—he could be sharp and sarcastic in his writing, and he liked an argument—various groups began to join in opposition to him. In addition to his somewhat cantankerous personality, they objected to his espousing the works of Copernicus. Until then, few people had taken Copernicus seriously. His theory was too ridiculous, and besides, the second preface clearly stated that it was incorrect. But now Galileo, backed by the evidence he had discovered with his telescope, was proclaiming the validity of Copernicus' ideas.

The position of the church was clearly stated in a letter on the subject written by a cardinal. First, the cardinal said, there was no danger in stating the Copernican theory as a hypothesis and employing it as a device, but it should never be expressed as a positive fact. Second, the Bible cannot be interpreted according to Copernicus but must be considered solely in the light of what the Holy Fathers had said. Third, and here the cardinal somewhat repeated himself, the assumption that the sun is central may explain certain phenomena, but it is simply not true. After all, Solomon, one of the wisest men of all time, had said that the "sun also ariseth, and the sun goeth down, and hasteth to the place where he arose." Who would dare argue with Solomon?

Kepler, too, was beginning to run into difficulties. Emperor Rudolf was displaced, and Kepler was forced to leave Prague and accept a lesser post at Linz. He still, however, had time to work and write and produced more publications, but misfortunes dogged his remaining years. His wife died; his mother was tried as a witch, and he had to undertake her defense (the proceedings dragged on for years); he was excommunicated by the Lutheran Church; he was frustrated in his attempts to publish the astronomical tables he had constructed from Tycho's records; and he suffered during the two-month long siege of Linz, during which the printing shop where he was publishing his tables was set on fire. All the printed sheets were destroyed, but fortunately Kepler's manuscript was saved. He moved from Linz to supervise its printing in another town and, from then on, never had a permanent home. For a short time, he served as mathematician to General Wallenstein, who had won military fame by checking the Danish invasion. But Wallenstein was not interested in the motions of the planets except as they provided the basis for astrology. Since Kepler hesitated to submit forecasts of political and military events, Wallenstein finally used him only to supply information on the planets to more cooperative and also more imaginative astrologers. The two unlikely associates soon separated, and Kepler, with the little money he still had left, went to Ratisbon, where the Diet was sitting, in the hope that he could collect from the emperor the back salary owed him. This amounted to 12,000 florins. (The nag on which he rode to Ratisbon was worth only 2; it was the best horse he could afford.) While waiting for the financial relief that never arrived, he came down with a fever and died.

Galileo fared better, but not much. His quarrel with the church became more and more serious in spite of his efforts both to defend himself and to seek some sort of compromise. At last he secured permission from a friendly Pope to write his *Dialogues Concerning the Two Chief World Systems*. In this, it was agreed, he would discuss the traditional astronomy and also the Copernican theory, but he was to state categorically that Copernicus' ideas were merely hypothetical, following the line of thought expressed in Osiander's second preface.

To be fettered like this was humiliating, but Galileo had no choice except to accept the terms dictated by the Pope if he wished to write at all. As he worked on his new book, he tried to stay technically within the limits imposed on him, but when the book appeared in 1632, Galileo's enemies persuaded the Pope he had broken his word and had also ridiculed the Pope personally. The end of his freedom was drawing near.

He was ordered to Rome to appear before the stern judges of the Inquisition. No one in Italy was powerful enough to protect him, and the outcome of his trial was foreseeable. The church, unable to defend itself and its beliefs by logic, had resorted to the final argument of all—physical violence. Galileo was placed under perpetual arrest and forbidden ever to publish again. Silence or death. That was the Inquisition's response to the great revelations of Galileo's telescope.

But even the Inquisition could not check the wave of rising skepticism.

IV

The writings of Kepler and Galileo were like the giant cracks that appear in the ice's surface at the end of winter. The melting does not take place all at once. The sluggish mass of frozen water first begins to shift and shudder, then creeps downhill, and finally gives way in a rush. That last surge was some distance away, but the preliminary movement was starting to accelerate, and everywhere at least a few courageous men were questioning long-held ideas.

In England, Francis Bacon preached a new approach to science. Scholars, he said, should avoid oversimplification when dealing with the complex subject of nature, and they should free themselves of preconceived assumptions and concentrate on collecting facts. In France, René Descartes, mathematician, philosopher, and physicist, adopted the new ways of thinking and wrote about them brilliantly. Impressed by Galileo's troubles with the Inquisition, he expressed himself more cautiously, and this caution served the cause of science well. Descartes' books, being acceptable to the church, were widely read and played an important role in spreading modern ideas and ways of thought. This was also the century of men like Robert Hooke and Robert Boyle, who experimented with gases and chemistry, and of the incomparable Isaac Newton, whose effect on men's thought extended far beyond physics.

Newton's childhood was quiet and undistinguished. His father, who owned a small farm in Lincolnshire, died before Newton's birth in 1642, his mother remarried a few years later, and he led the usual life of a boy whose family is genteel but not well-off. He attended school locally and, at twelve, went on to the grammar school at Grantham, taking room and board with an apothecary. In his first year he was a mediocre student, just another country lad painfully obtaining a basic education. Then occurred an event that curiously aroused his dormant intellectuality. He did not fall under the influence of a particularly gifted teacher or come across a stimulating book that started him thinking. He got into a fight with a fellow student and whipped him. The other boy was bigger and older, and apparently Newton's victory against these odds gave him the self-confidence that he had lacked. From then on, he worked hard at his studies and shortly rose to the head of the class; he also spent much of his time building various mechanical contrivances, such as water clocks and windmills. But on the death of his stepfather, his mother withdrew him from school with the intention of turning his interest toward farming.

To William Ayscough, Newton's uncle, goes the credit for rescuing the boy—and science generally. He recognized his nephew's brilliance and persuaded his mother to send him to Trinity College on a scholarship. Newton, who matriculated in June, 1661, passed the following years quietly, devoting much of his time to mathematics, optics, and some astronomy, and after earning his BA degree, he obtained an MA and received a professorship.

His first significant recognition outside the university came in 1671, when he was proposed as member of the Royal Society. In accordance with custom, he presented a paper at the meeting at which he was elected, describing a reflecting telescope he had invented. It almost brought an end to his career. Although the Royal Society expressed appreciation of his work, several individual scientists subsequently attacked some of his conclusions concerning prisms. The effect on Newton was nearly disastrous. Unlike Galileo, who enjoyed controversy (except with officers of the Inquisition), Newton detested it. What was the point, he asked a friend, of coming out with a new idea and then spending the rest of your life as a slave in its defense? He resolved never to publish again. Fortunately for science, he did not keep to what he had said, for he was already formulating theories that would shake the scientific world.

During his undergraduate days, Trinity College had twice been closed because of the plague and the students and faculty sent home. On one of these enforced visits back to Lincolnshire, if Voltaire's story is to be believed, Newton was attracted to the study of gravity by a falling apple. In any case, early in his career he tried to determine whether gravitation was the force that kept the moon in orbit. But the results of his calculations were unsatisfactory, and he dropped the attempt.

In 1679, however, he became involved in another of those controversies that he so disliked, this time over the action of falling bodies, and decided to redo his calculations. As he had a more accurate measurement of the size of the earth, he now found that his original surmise was correct, but instead of rushing into print, for some reason he kept his discovery to himself.

A few years later, in 1684, Edmund Halley, the astronomer, visited Cambridge to ask Newton a question. If the force of attraction of the sun diminished as the square of the planet's distance from it, what would be the shape of the planet's orbit? An ellipse, Newton replied casually; he had already figured it out. But as he could not find his calculations, he told Halley he would do them again and send them to him. Out of this conversation came a paper, *De motu,* which was the forerunner of Newton's great *Principia.*

Halley was so impressed that he presented *De motu* to the Royal Society, became Newton's friend and patron, and did for Newton what Newton could not seem to do for himself. He encouraged him to write the *Principia;* he tried to persuade the Royal Society to pay for its publication; and when the Royal Society, after some delay, decided it could not afford to, Halley agreed to underwrite the publication himself, as well as serve as its editor. It was an unusually generous offer, for not only did it entail considerable financial risk, but it also took much time from Halley's own research. Instead of remembering him principally for the comet named after him, the world should recall that he gave it Newton's greatest book.

In 1687 he wrote Newton that publication was finished and that he was sending the author twenty complimentary copies and another forty that he hoped Newton would place with the local booksellers. The price he wished to obtain was nine shillings, but he was willing to give the booksellers a substantial discount. No book could be successful, he said, without the booksellers' support, and he was willing to pay them well to gain it. With humility, he added that he hoped Newton would not regret the time he had spent on such an important work. Few scientists have ever had a more loyal or considerate friend.

Halley's confidence in the book's importance was fully justified, not only by posterity, but also by contemporary opinion. Whereas Copernicus and Kepler had been read only in limited circles, Newton's book quickly sold out. Every scientist and many who were not scientists were discussing the *Principia.* What it did was bind together Copernicus, Kepler, and Galileo by providing them with a mathematical basis. Copernicus had observed that an earth-centered universe was impossible. Kepler had demonstrated that the orbits of the planets had to be ellipses. Galileo had confirmed their statements with his telescope. Now Newton, with his understanding of gravity, explained the why that had been previously missing, and he did so through universal laws and supported his conclusions mathematically. His contribution to science was great, but no greater than his contribution to general thinking. For he created the concept of a mechanically, rather than a spiritually, ordered universe. Just as the Alexandrians had helped separate philosophy from science, so Newton helped drive the church out of the fields in which it did not belong. From his day on, the Aristotelian theory of the cosmos could be neither successfully defended nor used as the basis of religion. It had crumbled against the reasoning of the Lincolnshire farmer's son.

Having produced his masterpiece, Newton might have been justified in resting on his laurels and enjoying his position as the foremost man of science in the world. But that was not his nature. His was the epitome of the truly intellectual mind that works for its own pleasure. Nothing could rush him, but on the other hand, nothing could stop him. He continued to produce more ideas and more publications, and his contributions to science were so many and so fundamental that his name is known to every schoolboy today. But his importance far exceeds the total value of his specific accomplishments, for he established concepts that applied to science generally. One of these was his belief in the existence of universal laws that applied equally on earth and in the heavens. This principle struck a final blow at the type of speculation in which laws were devised to support untested theories. From Newton's day on, the better scientists concentrated on developing theories based on demonstrable facts. Another of Newton's contributions was his constant search for general laws that would explain a wide variety of phenomena without having to be modified to fit a particular instance. This stimulated other scientists to do the same.

Newton was like a tremendous light whose brilliance drowns out all others nearby, but his country had difficulty finding him a position commensurate with his reputation. As a university professor, he was poorly paid, and he had no fortune of his own. An attempt to have him made provost of King's College failed when somebody discovered that the provost had to be a clergyman, and every other effort of his friends was similarly unsuccessful until Newton was in his fifties. Then he received the position of warden of the mint. The salary was good, 500 or 600 pounds a year, and the duties were negligible. Thus, it represented an excellent bit of patronage. Newton accepted it, while still retaining his professorship, but he threw himself into its duties more wholeheartedly than anyone expected, using his knowledge of mathematics and chemistry to assist in the recoinage that was taking place. A few years later he was appointed master of the mint, a position that paid between 1,200 and 1,500 pounds a year, and gained the financial independence he desired. (He still took his duties seriously, however, and prepared a detailed analysis of the metallic contents of foreign coins.) As his friends had expected, the arrangement was ideal. He earned the income he deserved but still had time to continue his own research and studies until his death in 1727.

Because of Newton, such sciences as physics leaped forward during the seventeenth century. Yet scientists in other fields, although less spectacular in their performances, had also been making advances and freeing themselves from the old traditions. Jan Baptista van Helmont, a Belgian, divided his time between research and the practice of medicine, for which he refused to take any fees. A curious person with a mystical approach to life—he frequently indulged in autosuggestion by gazing at a light—his writings sometimes became so obscure as to be almost meaningless. But although he had no real alternatives to offer, he was quick to expose the deficiencies of Galen and Aristotle, thus helping weaken their grip on mankind's thinking. He was not as effective, however, as William Harvey.

Harvey, who was born at Folkestone, went to Cambridge and, after some time spent in traveling, to Padua, where the iconoclastic tradition of Vesalius still persisted. There he earned his degree in medicine and returned to London, was elected to the London College of Physicians, gave lectures on medicine, developed a large practice, and served as court physician to James I and Charles I. During the Great Rebellion, he fled with the king from London, leaving behind his house and scientific collections, all of which were destroyed. Luckily he had some private wealth and also rich brothers, so he was able to exist in comfort after the royalists' defeat.

In spite of his large practice, Harvey had continued the research that he had commenced in medical school, and one of the points that interested him the most was the circulation of the blood. The classicists, following Galen, had always held that the liver was the center of the circulatory system. Here, they believed, food was converted into blood and then driven out into the body. (Some of the blood was also driven through the heart, where it received a vague, but supposedly necessary, *spiritus vitalis*.) Harvey was not content with this theory and looked at it from a practical point of view. He studied the valves in the veins and the two great arteries and found that their functioning did not support Galen's ideas; he examined the heart closely with similar results; he also analyzed the problem quantitatively. The heart, he concluded, holds 2 ounces of blood and beats approximately seventy times in a minute. Therefore, if the old theories held true, the liver would have to convert food into blood at a rate of 140 ounces a minute. As this was patently nonsense, Harvey began looking for a better answer and finally deduced that blood must circulate, going out from the heart through the arteries and returning through the veins. He then proceeded to back up his new theory with careful experiments. Of course, he was not able to solve every question—having no microscope, he never, for example, learned about capillaries—but he took physiology a long way forward at a single stroke. Furthermore, his experiments were decidedly modern in conception, for he tossed aside the usual philosophical speculation and came directly to grips with the demonstrable facts.

There were numerous other adventurous thinkers in the seventeenth century, and taken together, they form a diverse and curious group: Giovanni Alfonso Borelli, a Neapolitan, who applied the pragmatism of Galileo to biology; Claude Perrault, a French architect, who designed the Colonnade of the Louvre and who also studied the muscular motions of animals in the same spirit as Borelli; Thomas Bartholin, a quarrelsome, unpleasant professor at Copenhagen, who played an important role in the discovery of the lymph system; and the Swedish professor Olof Rudbeck, who argued with Bartholin that he had discovered the lymph system first.

Working together or sometimes fighting with one another, these men helped develop a realistic picture of the natural world. Yet many of them, living as they did in a period of transition, could not entirely free themselves of past superstitions, and the effect, both on themselves and on their work, was often startling. Thomas Willis was an example. The son of a British farmer, he became a physician and along with conducting his medical practice found time to study the brain and the nervous system. (One of his books was illustrated by Sir Christopher Wren, who turned, this time at least, from designing buildings to making anatomical drawings.) In many respects, Willis was typical of some of the better scientists of his era, a man caught in an intellectual tangle, unable to accept the beliefs of the past, yet equally unable to free himself from them. Harvey, for example, had discovered the truth about the circulation of the blood, but he still seriously believed in many of the quaintest concepts of Galen, and he once captured and dissected a toad that was supposed to be the familiar of a suspected witch. He wanted to find out if she really was one. In similar fashion, Willis could be clearheaded at one period, fuzzy-headed the next. Much of his work on the anatomy of the brain was outstanding, but he followed it with a publication that today can be called nothing but absurd. It concerned his search for a "vegetative soul," which might produce the animallike aspects of man and set in play his nervous reactions. The book, in utter contrast with his earlier publications, is pure speculation, a reversion to some of the worst type of thinking of the Middle Ages.

Yet his plight was better than Jan Swammerdam's, whose life was destroyed by the personal conflict raging within him between the old and the new. The son of a well-to-do apothecary in Amsterdam, Swammerdam studied medicine at the University of Leiden and then went to Paris. On his return home, he settled down in his father's house and continued his studies in anatomy, soon becoming one of the most brilliant anatomists of the era. He was also deeply interested in insects and other invertebrates and wrote outstanding descriptions of various species and conducted careful studies of their growth and development. One of his theories concerned the "preformation of the parts," for he held that each part of the body grew out of what was already there. This ran counter to much of the contemporary thinking, because it contradicted spontaneous generation and the old wives' tales that bewitched women could give birth to kittens or other monstrosities. But Swammerdam collapsed under the burden of his discoveries. His father, growing tired of supporting a son who would not support himself, cut him off financially. Instead of finding a university position that would give him the means of pursuing his studies or engaging in the active practice of medicine, he devoted himself to religious contemplation and finally joined the band of wanderers who followed a mystic named Antoinette Bourignon. A hysterical woman, she wanted to reform all Christianity, both Protestant and Catholic, and thereby incurred the hatred of every sect. Swammerdam went from country to country with her but never found the religious peace that he sought. On his father's death, he returned to Amsterdam, quarreled with his sister over their inheritance, and died at an early age, bitter, confused, and a victim of the struggle between old and new.

One of his few close friends was Nils Steensen, who became better known under the Latin version of his name, Nicolaus Steno. He, too, started out as a clearheaded, pragmatic scientist and ended as a religious fanatic. His father, a wealthy goldsmith in Copenhagen, was able to provide the best possible education for his son. Because Steno was interested in medicine, his father sent him to the university at Copenhagen and then provided him with the means to go to Leiden and Amsterdam for further studies. On his return home, Steno discovered that the better appointments at the university were surreptitiously reserved for the relatives of Professor Bartholin, and finally losing his patience, he went to Paris, where he studied the anatomy of the brain, then on to Pavia and Florence, where he accepted a position as physician to the Grand Duke of Tuscany. The duties were not arduous, and Steno had plenty of time to continue his independent studies, working primarily on glands and muscles. Of greater significance, however, was his interest in the many fossils that he found in Tuscany. He rightly supposed that these were the remains of ancient animals and, by combining his elementary knowledge of paleontology with his observations of rock structures, wrote an outstanding geologic study of the area, which drew new inferences about the origin of the earth. His ideas were a startling innovation, and his book was one of the first on geology that might be considered modern, but it attracted little contemporary attention. On the other hand, it had a profound effect on Steno himself. It was, of course, antireligious in terms of Steno's own day, and it apparently troubled him. Instead of pursuing his investigations further, the doubts they raised in his mind caused him to drop them altogether. Searching for relief from the spiritual quandary in which he found himself, he became a Catholic and returned to Denmark. This time the university authorities recognized his brilliance and offered him a well-paying appointment, but Steno's mental balance had been upset by his conversion. He refused the appointment, went back to Italy, and took orders. In a short time he became a bishop and was sent to Germany to spread the Catholic faith, which he did with all the fanaticism of a new convert. But this alone was not enough to satisfy his spiritual need. He also became a violent ascetic, and his mal-treatment of his own body undoubtedly hastened his early death at the age of forty-eight. His corpse was brought back to Florence and buried with great ceremony, and the ecclesiastical authorities erected a monu-ment to his memory at the Church of San Lorenzo. But his true monu-ment was the small book in which he pierced the truth about the past, looked at it for a few years, and then withdrew in horror at the unveiling of the mystery, his heart unable to support what his eyes and brain had told him.

V

Many scientists, however, were able to survive the emotional turbu-lence created by the destruction of old beliefs and traditions or not even to feel a touch of distress. Somehow they were naturally armored against the internal conflicts that others of the seventeenth-century scientists had to endure. Or in some cases, the subjects they chose to study, how-ever important in themselves, did not conflict with the tenets of religion. This was true of the microscopists like Marcello Malpighi, who is con-sidered one of the leading pioneer plant anatomists, and his friend, Ne-hemiah Grew, a British doctor. Together they closely approached some of the deepest secrets of life, for by studying the cells of plants, they re-vealed the essential structure of tissue. But by one of those curious twists that so often direct the trend of man's thinking, no one for many years went farther along the course they had charted. Their writings were widely admired for their exactness, but the true value of what they had accomplished was not appreciated.

Another of the microscopists who was unaffected by spiritual distress was the quiet, unassuming Dutchman, Antony van Leeuwenhoek. Born in Delft of parents who were reasonably successful tradespeople, he went to school for a short time and, after his father's death and mother's re-marriage, lived with an uncle who was the clerk of a small, nearby town. Apparently Leeuwenhoek considered following a similar career but made no attempt to learn either Latin or the law and certainly had no thought of obtaining a university degree. Following his stepfather's death, he moved to Amsterdam at the age of sixteen, entered a linendraper's shop, and became a competent draper and his employer's cashier. He remained in Amsterdam for six years and then went back to Delft, where he was to live for the rest of his long life. To the casual observer, he was simply a hardworking, practical young man following a conventional career in business. He married, he purchased a draper's shop of his own, and he obtained a town appointment with the unusual title Chamberlain of the Council-Chamber of the Worshipful Sheriffs of Delft. The duties of this position were nominal; he was in charge of the sheriffs' meeting room, keeping it clean, making sure that the fires were laid, and extinguishing the candles after the sheriffs had departed. The job paid well—a year's salary amounted to almost as much as he had originally given for the purchase of his shop—and he was apparently permitted to hire underlings to carry out the more menial duties. He also did some work as a surveyor and received a few other official appointments, including one as trustee of the estate of the bankrupt artist Jan Vermeer, who left his wife no money and some pictures which, although few in number, today are acknowledged among the world's greatest.

For thirteen years after he became chamberlain to the sheriffs, no one outside Delft ever heard of Leeuwenhoek. He was simply a moderately successful Dutch businessman, following a quiet and placid career. But in 1668 the editor of the Royal Society in London published an article describing a microscope constructed by an Italian, Eustachio Divini. This microscope, the article said, was the most powerful ever built, and it revealed wonders that had never been seen before. A Delft physician, Reinier de Graaf, read the article, and with commendable patriotism, announced that far better microscopes were being made right there at Delft. As proof, he enclosed a letter from Leeuwenhoek, describing some molds, various parts of a bee, and a louse, all of which he had observed through the microscopes that he had been building while working as a draper and chamberlain. The quiet tradesman and town official, with no university training, had moved ahead of anyone else in the construction of one of science's most important instruments.

Wisely, Dr. de Graaf realized that the publication of Leeuwenhoek's letter in the society's paper would not be sufficient to encourage him further, so he asked the secretary to start an official correspondence with Leeuwenhoek. Leeuwenhoek was both astonished and humble when the secretary's first letter arrived. He was, he replied, simply a businessman with no training in language, science, or the arts. Therefore, he had always resisted his friends' entreaties to write down descriptions of what he had seen through his microscopes. At the secretary's request, however, he was willing to submit drawings of the objects he had written about in his letter. But the secretary must realize that because he did not know how to draw, he had had to ask someone else to make the pictures for him. He was, he admitted, not pleased with the results—the proportions were far from accurate—but he hoped that they would satisfy the secretary's purpose. And would the secretary please remember that he was an amateur working by himself and, therefore, not take amiss anything he wrote?

It was an extraordinary beginning to an extraordinary career. For the remainder of his life, Leeuwenhoek devoted himself to the manufacture of microscopes and spent hours peering through them, examining various objects but most particularly what he called his little animalcules. He set down the results of his observations, not in scientific papers, but in a series of letters that he wrote over his lifetime. These were phrased in old-fashioned Dutch and opened with a formal presentation of his compliments. Then he would make several comments about some of his current experiments, followed by some personal remarks and afterward perhaps by a few lines on an utterly unrelated scientific subject. Fortunately, he rarely engaged in speculation, because when he did, he usually failed. His strength was in the power of his lenses and the accuracy of his eye, and as long as he restricted himself to what he actually saw, he occupied a unique place among the scientists of his time. He studied the capillary system, thus carrying on work originated by Malpighi; he investigated the fertilization of animals; he studied the structure of plants; he found out how ants reproduce. The list of subjects is almost endless, and although he did not make any important theoretical discoveries, he did contribute substantially to the development of the biological sciences.

As word of his achievements spread, more and more visitors knocked on his door, so many, in fact, that he complained about the interruptions and finally refused to admit anyone who did not bear a letter of introduction. The Czar of Russia came, as did many other members of Europe's nobility, but the linendraper remained the simple citizen of Delft. Even after his election as a member of the Royal Society in London—an honor that he greatly cherished—he could not find time to attend its meetings.

Perhaps he might have made an even greater contribution to science if he had been willing to part with some of the 400 microscopes and magnifying glasses he was reputed to have built, so that they could have been used by others, but this was asking too much of his generosity. He was the greatest microscope maker in the world, but as an amateur, not as a professional. He was willing to let visitors look through his instruments, although he usually reserved the most powerful for his sole use, but he had no intention of letting any of them pass out of his possession. On his death, however, his daughter, in accordance with the instructions given her by Leeuwenhoek, sent a cabinet containing 26 of them to the Royal Society. Thus, he repaid the members for the encouragement they had given him, encouragement that resulted in his being a re-membered scientist, not a forgotten linendraper. The society was greatly honored and carefully preserved the miscroscopes for 150 years, but then the legacy somehow disappeared and was never recovered.

Through his microscopes, Leeuwenhoek had narrowed the field of mankind's investigations and concentrated on what was smaller and smaller, objects so tiny that he had no means of measuring them except to compare them with another object like a grain of sand. Other men, however, were broadening the range of mankind's observations. The ships of Europe were crossing the Atlantic Ocean in increasing numbers and landing settlers and explorers on every coast from northern Canada to the shores of South America and the islands in between. The same ships ranged along Africa, touching here and there at ports on the vast, yet unknown continent, rounded the Cape of Good Hope, and set their sails for the Far East. Still others worked their long way through the Pacific, stopping at islands, visiting the continent of Australia, and dropping anchor in Canton and Singapore. For the most part, the men on board were driven by the desire for trade and empire, and on the passenger lists, the names of merchants, settlers, and soldiers predominated. But Europe's scientific curiosity was also aroused by the discovery of these far-off lands, and some of the passengers were men dedicated to scientific pursuits. Aside from geography, they were primarily interested in the discovery of new animal and plant specimens, and when they had collected these, they sent them back to the universities and societies of Europe for identification and further study. Under the burden of this mass of material, the systems previously used for identification and classification began to break down, and the need for some better manner of cataloguing the new discoveries quickly became apparent.

Several scientists gave most of their lives to this work. Augustus Quirinus Rivinus, who taught medicine at Leipzig, pointed out the failures of all the previous systems, but he lacked the ability to provide an adequate substitute. A contemporary of his, Joseph Pitton de Tournefort, did somewhat better, and although his system was not the final answer, momentarily at least it relieved the confusion that was beginning to overwhelm the great collections of Europe.

John Ray, the son of a well-to-do British blacksmith, was also greatly concerned with the problem of classification. Although his interests were broad, his principal work was a large book on plants. It ran for 2,860 pages and contained almost everything that was then known about botany. In order to put the material together, Ray had to develop his own system of classification, which, while also inadequate, was at least a substantial improvement over many of those used before, and the book was a great achievement. For years, it remained one of the standard authorities on botany, the work to which other students constantly referred.

Ray died just after the turn of the century in 1705, and the date of his death is significant, for his work epitomizes the accomplishments of the seventeenth century in the biological sciences and natural history: nothing especially brilliant, except for Harvey's discovery of the circulation of the blood; no universal truth that unlocked many of the mysteries of the natural world. In the physical sciences, mankind had done much better. The astronomers had rearranged the universe, finding its structure after the confusion caused by the traditions of the medievalists, and in doing so, they had helped crack the beliefs that not only were untrue in themselves, but also blocked the discovery of truth. The physicists, with Isaac Newton at their head, had helped make many phenomena intelligible and had demonstrated a new type of thinking, the search for laws that could be applied to a variety of situations and that were also based on the careful analysis of factual data. This method of thinking had also begun to be applied to the biological sciences. Borelli, for example, had studied muscular action in this manner, and Harvey had shown that the physical evidence did not support the classical theories of the blood. But their total findings had not been spectacular. Many old ideas had been overthrown; many new advances had been made. Ray, working quietly by himself and collecting all the information available about botany, typifies what was happening. The mass of material was accumulating, the scientific method was improving, and men like Steno and Malpighi and the others were catching glimpses of the truth. Yet these were only short flashes of light in the darkness.

A man who stood in Paris or London or Leipzig or Pisa on the night that the eighteenth century was born had moved far ahead of the man who had stood, thousands of years before, at the mouth of the cave, but not as far perhaps as he thought. Many of the old superstitions had been tossed aside, outmoded and proved false by the new research. Man now knew the earth was not at the center of the universe (at least he had the humility to accept that incontrovertible fact and also the dignity to endure it); gravity, as Newton explained it, not the spheres of Aristotle, held the heavenly bodies in their places; blood was pumped by the heart, not manufactured in the liver in an endless and prolific stream; but man still had little understanding of the natural world around him. He did not know what caused lightning; he had not yet discovered many of the great currents of the ocean; he was not certain how plants were reproduced; he had no understanding of how new life-forms developed; he had no real knowledge of the migration of birds, the history of the earth, the causes of the weather, the reasons for disease.

He also continued to think that he was unique, that there was no relationship between himself and the other living things in the world. He was one of them but did not realize it. He did not understand he was part of the whole web and structure of life, not an isolated unit, but something far grander—an integral piece of a miracle that was much greater than he knew.

As the old year died and the new century came into being, man stood on the threshold of fresh discoveries about himself and his world. For the time of the greatest naturalists had arrived.

3

Order Replaces Chaos

CARL LINNAEUS: 1707–1778

I

If ever a private citizen could be said to have started a major war solely through his own efforts, that man was Johann Reinhold Patkul.

The year of his birth was 1660; the place of his birth was the Stockholm jail, where his father was imprisoned on suspicion of treason. But the taint of his parent's crime did not cling to Patkul himself. He grew up a loyal citizen, enlisted in the army, and, by the age of twenty-nine, was serving as a captain in Livonia, the Baltic country that then was one of Sweden's vast possessions. He was a popular figure among the gentry there, and when they sent a delegation to Stockholm to protest the vigor with which Charles XI was recovering lands that had previously been alienated from the Crown, they twice chose Patkul to head it. The second time he lost his temper, and because of his abusive language, the king charged him with treason. Patkul fled to Switzerland and waited until Charles XII succeeded to the throne. He then petitioned the new monarch for pardon, but Charles was hard and cruel—he is said to have ordered sheep paraded through the halls of the palace so he could amuse himself by cutting off their heads—and he had no intention of forgiving Patkul's insults to his father. Patkul thereupon took an incredible course: he privately declared war on one of the greatest king-doms in Europe.

Under ordinary circumstances, he would not have had the slightest chance of success, but Sweden was ringed by enemies, and all they needed was a catalyst to bring them together. This was the role that Patkul as-sumed. In a relatively short time, he helped create an alliance between Frederick IV of Denmark, Augustus II of Poland, and Peter the Great of Russia, thus making possible the Great Northern War. By all logic, Sweden should have fallen before this array, but Charles XII quickly re-sponded to the threatening danger, and for the next several years, he continued like a meteor flashing across the skies of Europe. He struck here, he struck there, and victory after victory came to the Swedes. In the year 1707, seven years after the start of the Great Northern War, Charles XII had reached the pinnacle of his fortune, and, best of all from his point of view, he had captured Patkul. In October, 1707, Patkul was lashed to the wheel at Kazimierz, Poland. While he screamed in anguish, his bones were slowly crushed one by one, until at last the of-ficial torturer removed from the wheel the lifeless pulp that had once been a man. On the following New Year's Day, having revenged himself on his personal enemy, Charles XII crossed the Vistula with the intention of bringing Russia to its knees.

During this historic period, no one, except his own family and parish-ioners, paid any attention to the quiet and unheroic career of the curate of Råshult, a small parish in the south of Sweden. There was no reason why they should have, for although he was a good pastor, kindly and God-fearing, he served without distinction, one of the thousands who lead their lives, do their work, and then vanish into time. While Charles XII marched against the armies of Europe and sent shudders of fear through its chancelleries, the curate wrote his sermons and puttered in his well-tended garden, pulling a weed here, cultivating there, and in 1707, when Charles was rejoicing over Patkul's tortured body, the curate, Nils Linnaeus, was taking simple pleasure in the flowers he had raised that summer and in the birth of his first child, a boy named Carl.

As he grew older, Carl played in the garden and learned the names of his father's flowers. He rowed on nearby Lake Mockel watching the water lie flat and calm under the summer sun or become wrinkled with min-iature whitecaps at the touch of a breeze. He wandered through the mead-ows surrounding the community, picking blossoms and bringing them home to the vicar. He listened to the cuckoos singing and the sound of insects in the dusk. In the fall he saw the birds flock together, great swarms of them passing over the church and heading toward the south. In the spring he awaited their return and watched as they picked their nesting places.

As Carl grew up, the fortunes of Charles XII declined dramatically. Defeats followed the earlier victories, and about the time Carl began his formal education, first with a tutor and then at the school at Växjö, Charles XII returned to Sweden after a fourteen-year absence. Still uncrushed in spirit and young in body, he gathered a new army and launched an invasion of Norway. While Carl pored over his books and conjugated Latin verbs in the singsong tones of a child, a bullet entered the king's forehead. No one knows whether it was fired by a Norwegian or a disillusioned Swede, but it brought to a halt the country's militarism, and years of precarious peace followed the years of disastrous war.

II

Carl did poorly at the Gymnasium, which he entered in 1723. His father intended him to take courses that would permit him to enter a university and become a minister. But the studies that would best equip him for such a career were the ones that interested him the least. Greek, Hebrew, and similar subjects did not appeal to him. What did concern him were the various plants growing around Växjö and Stenbrohult, where his family now lived. He collected, pressed, and attempted to classify them.

Absorbed in his parish work and his garden, Nils Linnaeus was completely unaware of his son's deficiencies until he belatedly made a trip to Växjö to talk with his friend, Dr. Johann Stensson Rothman, the community's medical officer and a member of the school's faculty. Dr. Rothman told Nils the staggering news: Carl was better suited to be a botanist or doctor than he was a clergyman. Even in those days, a medical education was expensive, but it was not, as it is now, an almost certain route to a respected position and a good living. Theology, as everyone knew, could save a man's soul, but it was not sure medicine could save his body or even alleviate his pain. Ministers, therefore, received the better pay.

Nils pointed this out to his son but without success. Carl was determined to devote his life to botany, using medicine as a means of obtaining a living. Finally, Nils gave in and selected the university Carl should attend. For several reasons he chose Lund, which had been founded in 1688 by Charles XI. It was close by, which would reduce Carl's traveling expenses; it was reputed to have a good medical faculty; and Nils also had there a distant relative by marriage who was wealthy and might become interested in Carl and help the boy financially.

When Carl arrived at Lund, he was in high spirits, but as he wandered around the university, he met disappointment after disappointment. Sweden, impoverished by the wars of Charles XII, had little money to support its educational institutions. Lund, therefore, instead of possessing an outstanding medical faculty, had only a single professor, a poor, bewildered man who complained continually because he had no equipment. To make Carl's situation worse, the wealthy relative died shortly after his arrival, and so no help was available from that source.

At the conclusion of the first year, Linnaeus was discontented about his university career. In spite of his father's sacrifices, he was not getting the education he wanted, and the future looked bleak. That summer he discussed the problem with Nils Linnaeus and Dr. Rothman, and together they agreed that Carl should go to the university at Uppsala, even though it was far away—forty miles north of Stockholm—and consequently more expensive to attend.

Their decision was based on the reputation that Uppsala enjoyed throughout Sweden. Founded in 1477 near the site of an ancient heathen temple, it had been personally endowed by Gustavus Adolphus in 1624 with the income of 360 farms that belonged to him. Over the years it had gathered together an important collection of manuscripts, established a famous botanical garden which contained hundreds of plant specimens, and, in spite of a disastrous fire that swept the town of Uppsala in 1702, was regarded as the foremost university in the country. Furthermore, its medical faculty included two of Sweden's better-known scientists, Lars Roberg, and Olof Rudbeck, the younger, who had spent much of his life adding to the enormous botanical and zoological collections started by his father.

Yet after his arrival in the old cathedral city of Uppsala, Linnaeus quickly discovered that the university's reputation was based on its past, not its present. During the wars of Charles XII, both its faculty and its facilities, like those at Lund, had steadily declined. Roberg, who was in his late sixties, had lost all interest in teaching and merely enjoyed the benefits of his position without performing its duties. Rudbeck, on the other hand, was still working, but during the fire of 1702 his extensive collections had been destroyed. Discouraged by the effort necessary to rebuild them, he had turned his attention from biology to philology. Even the botanical garden had been badly neglected for many years. When plants died, no one replaced them, and since the university no longer had any real interest in botany, no new collecting expeditions were bringing in fresh specimens. As for the university's medical facilities, these, too, were in disrepair. The hospital was run-down and antiquated. In order to keep it going, its staff had rented part of the building as a tavern, and the laughter of reveling drinkers mingled with the moans of the sick and dying. The lectures in chemistry—there were not many —took place at the local apothecary's, because the university had no laboratory. Lectures in anatomy were rarely given, and when Linnaeus wanted to see a body dissected, he had to go to Stockholm, where a woman had been hanged. (Since the scientists found it inconvenient to perform the dissection on the date set for her execution, the execution was postponed, so the corpse would be fresh for them.)

To add to his despair, Linnaeus was soon in desperate financial straits. After paying his entrance fees and other initial bills, he had used up the money his father had given him, and, of course, he would receive no more. Yet Linnaeus was completely realistic about his situation. He realized that his choice did not lie between Uppsala and some better university; it lay between Uppsala or nothing. Either he learned botany here, or he never learned botany. So he stuffed his shoes with paper— the soles were worn out, and he could not afford to replace them—and visited the offices of the officials, begging for a scholarship. They were not much interested in this country boy from Stenbrohult, but they finally found a scholarship for him. It was tiny and barely satisfied his needs, but at least it was something.

He also made two good friends. One was a fellow student, Peter Artedi, poor and without influence, but with a lively mind. The other was a Doctor of Divinity, Olaf Celsius, who had a keen, although unprofessional, interest in plants. Their meeting occurred one spring day, when Celsius was walking through the botanical garden and noticed Linnaeus with pen and paper, writing scientific descriptions of some of the specimens. Celsius was so surprised to see a student actually studying in the garden that he stopped to talk to Linnaeus and learned of his deep interest in botanical classification and how he had started years ago building up his collection of pressed plants. On discovering that Linnaeus had about 600 specimens, more than the number in the garden, he asked him to bring them to his house, so he could examine them.

This chance meeting led to an invitation to live with Celsius, and since Linnaeus had successfully badgered the university officials into giving him a better scholarship and was also making money tutoring other students in botany, he was now comfortably off. Furthermore, he was slowly beginning to gain a reputation among the faculty, who, like Celsius, were finding for themselves that this was no ordinary student but a man of outstanding perception.

While he was living with Celsius, Linnaeus came across a review of a paper written by Sêbastien Vaillant, a Frenchman connected with the Jardin du Roi in Paris. This paper dealt with an important, but still relatively unknown, topic: the sexuality of plants. In the ancient world, scholars had studied the sex of date palms and knew that two palms of opposite sexes were needed to secure fruit, but in the intervening years, little more had been added to this field of knowledge. Linnaeus' excitement on reading the review of Vaillant's work was so great that he immediately began examining the pistils and stamens of the plants in his collection and started writing a paper on the subject. When he had finished it, he presented it to Celsius as a New Year's Day present. Celsius showed it to others, and the interest it aroused was sufficient to warrant making copies. These were circulated throughout the university, and one copy was presented at a meeting of the Royal Academy of Science, which ordered it printed.

As a result, Professor Rudbeck, who had been unsuccessfully looking for someone capable of lecturing on the plants in the botanical garden, decided to interview Linnaeus as a possible candidate for the position. (The garden came under the jurisdiction of the university's medical department because like most such gardens in Europe, it had been originally established to grow medicinal herbs.) Together the old professor and the young student walked down one path and up another. It was a crucial moment for Linnaeus. If he failed to pass Rudbeck's test, he might, for lack of funds, be forced to leave the university and abandon his proposed career. Although Rudbeck was deep in his studies of philology, he had not forgotten his botany, and his questions were sharp and discerning. Linnaeus answered them satisfactorily, drawing on his self-taught knowledge, and received the appointment and an invitation to live with the Rudbeck family.

Yet perhaps Linnaeus' success came a little abruptly, for he suddenly began to run into new problems. One was the jealousy of a man named Nils Rosén, who had been appointed assistant to the professors of the medical faculty but had taken a leave of absence. On his return, he regarded Linnaeus as a usurper and seized every opportunity to attack him and his work. Worst of all, Linnaeus had a quarrel with Rudbeck. No one knows exactly what happened. Perhaps Linnaeus, with his sudden success, grew overbearing. Perhaps Rudbeck simply wearied of this brilliant student. Linnaeus gave several versions of their falling out. But whatever the cause, Rudbeck asked his once-prized student to leave the house.

Linnaeus' mother was seriously ill, so he decided that after a three-year absence he would return home for a visit. In the winter of 1731 he appeared once more at the house at Stenbrohult. In addition to seeing his mother, he wanted to discuss the future with his father. For although he had been at the university for some time, he still possessed neither a degree nor any permanent way of making a living. What he needed above all else was something that would clearly raise him above the common scholars, and he had an idea. He would make an expedition to Lapland, the area that caps the northern part of Scandinavia.

Linnaeus already knew something about the country. The great collections of Rudbeck, collections that had been destroyed in the Uppsala fire of 1702, had been largely gathered by the professor and his father in Lapland, and although the destruction of his specimens had prevented him from completing his published studies, he was still probably the best-informed man in Sweden on the biology of the north. Whether he had explicitly suggested to Linnaeus that he undertake the trip or whether his own enthusiasm merely kindled his student's is not certain. But before leaving for Stenbrohult, Linnaeus had filed an application for financial assistance with the Royal Academy of Science, which was underwriting a series of expeditions throughout Sweden.

Today such a request from a student would appear presumptuous, but in the less formal atmosphere of an eighteenth-century university it did not. Yet the Royal Academy of Science failed to act. The months passed; Linnaeus remained in Stenbrohult, leaving his parents only to make a promised journey to Lund, where, after all, he found no one able to help him with mineralogy. Then, as the first signs of spring reached southern Sweden and the time approached when the north would again become accessible after the winter's snows, Linnaeus returned to Uppsala. Still nothing had happened. Apparently his request had been completely ignored. Instead of giving up—he was a tenacious man—he filed another application asking for a somewhat smaller amount of money. This time the academy made the grant, and in May, Linnaeus started on the road for Lycksele, Lapland.

III

Neither his appearance nor his equipment were impressive as he set out. He wore a loose coat, leather breeches, a round wig, a green leather cap, and a pair of half boots, while he carried with him "a small leather bag, half an ell in length, but somewhat less in breadth, furnished on one side with hooks and eyes, so that it could be opened and shut at pleasure. This bag contained one shirt; two pair of false sleeves; two half shirts; an inkstand, pencase, microscope, and spying glass; a gauze cap to protect me occasionally from the gnats; a comb; my journal, and a parcel of paper stitched together for drying plants." With this equipment, Linnaeus hoped to bring back specimens of the plants and wildlife of Lapland, as well as detailed descriptions of its natural history.

Lapland was not an entirely unexplored land. As early as the thirteenth century a group of men known as Birkarlians—from the word *birk*, meaning trade—had penetrated deep into the country, establishing outposts, reducing the Lapps to virtual slavery, and amassing large fortunes. In their wake had come churches, small Swedish settlements, and some mines. The roads, where they existed, were rough; Linnaeus often traveled by boat on the rapidly flowing rivers, and many times he had to wade through deep swamps, clamber up steep ridges, or find his way through thick forests. Once, when he was climbing a cliff, his Lapp guides, who were ahead of him, set loose two rocks, which came rolling down and nearly crushed him. Another time, the boat in which he was traveling broke in two, and although he was able to save his notes, he lost his collection of birds.

Once a Lapp fired a gun at him—the Lapps were always suspicious of strangers—and another time he had to walk through a forest that had recently been swept by a fire. The trees were still smoldering, and the smoke was so intense that the men had to keep moving in order to breathe. Without warning, a wind sprang up. It struck the weakened trees that were still standing. Their black forms swayed, then started crashing. One fell directly between Linnaeus and his guide but fortunately missed both men. It was a nightmare world, the wind blowing, the smoke surrounding them in swirls, the trees falling, sometimes far off in the distance, sometimes on the very route they were following. Yet both men kept their heads and, by remaining calm, escaped.

It was a dangerous journey and a rough journey, but perhaps neither as dangerous nor as rough as Linnaeus described it in his journal, for in those pages, written in his cramped, almost undecipherable handwriting, he revealed his mercurial temperament and his eagerness to dramatize himself. When the weather was fair and the going smooth, everything was wonderful. He was the young and adventuresome student, bringing to Sweden a knowledge of its land that the people had never before possessed. When the weather turned foul or the way became rough, his spirits fell. The countryside became gloomy and forbidding, his heart dark. In dramatizing himself, he left the impression in his journal that he was an explorer wandering into the complete unknown, not into a place that many Swedes had visited before him, and he was careful to bring back with him a Lapp costume, so he could wear it from time to time to impress other people with the extent of his travels.

But who can blame him? Ever since he had left home, he had struggled to overcome one obstacle after another: poverty; the inability of the university at Lund to provide him with the education he wanted; his first days at Uppsala, when he had roamed the streets with soleless shoes looking for recognition; his dismissal from the Rudbecks' household. These experiences had combined to make him feel uncertain, and although he had achieved success in spite of these obstacles, it was not a sure success. He had no degree, no place in the world, no means of making a living aside from his relatively unimportant teaching duties and the scholarships he received from the university. Everything he had accomplished could be swept away as quickly as the fire had swept over the forest through which he had passed.

Nor can one blame him for the fits of petulance that occur in his journal. Largely self-taught, he grew quickly impatient with some of the Swedes he met on his journey. In one instance, he talked to two ministers about meteorology and, finding that they knew little about the subject, derided them in his journal. "The clergyman, who is the schoolmaster," he wrote, "and the curate, tormented me with their consummate and most pertinacious ignorance. I could not but wonder how so much pride and ambition, such scandalous want of information, with such incorrigible stupidity, could exist in persons of their profession, who are commonly expected to be men of knowledge; yet any schoolboy twelve years of age might be better informed. No man will deny the propriety of such people as these at least, being placed as far as possible from civilized society." To the professors at Uppsala, when Linnaeus wanted something, he could be humble, but underneath his humility ran some of the arrogance of a self-made man. He boasted of the numbers of students his lectures had attracted; he had nothing but scorn for the ignorant ministers. "If I could do it," he asked in effect, "why cannot they?" It was an unattractive reaction but, given the circumstances under which he had lived, a reasonable one.

Yet the precious knowledge he was gaining in the north could not hold him in Lapland much longer. Whatever his personal feelings, whatever the state of his finances—and he was short of money—the question of when he would return was decided by a force with which he could not argue: the weather. As winter closed down, he made a rapid trip southward along the eastern coast of the Gulf of Bothnia, in what is now Finland, reached Turku, crossed the gulf by way of the island of Åland, and returned to Uppsala.

IV

On his arrival at the university, Linnaeus expected to be received as a young and able scientist, back from an important expedition with many new ideas to report. In fact, no one was even willing to assume the expense of publishing a full account of his journey. To make his situation worse, Linnaeus was in serious financial straits. In his second application to the Royal Academy of Science, he had reduced the amount of money he had originally requested, but his first estimate of the cost of the trip proved more nearly correct. Twice toward the end he had had to borrow funds, so he now had debts to repay. Also, his scholarship had expired, and under the university's rules he was eligible for no other. Sometimes, however, there was a surplus in another scholarship that could be given to needy students. Linnaeus asked for help from this source, but in such haughty terms that he was officially rebuked for his language. He had expected to be received as a returning hero. Instead, he found himself scolded for the manner in which he felt compelled to beg. But the university was not entirely heartless. The faculty did allow him to have the small surplus.

That Christmas he went back to Stenbrohult for a visit and, after the holiday was over, took up his studies once more at Uppsala, only to find that the university had even less to offer him than before. Rudbeck was still absorbed in his work on philology, Roberg was taking six months off to perform other duties, and the only courses in medicine that remained were the lectures on anatomy given by Rosén. Since Linnaeus knew everything that Rosén knew, he could gain little from hearing his rival speak, so once more he was left to his own devices.

For most students, this absence of formal instruction might have been a calamity, and surely Linnaeus himself must have sometimes yearned for the stimulus and discipline of regular courses. Yet the circumstances left him free to read critically the standard works on botany and to check their theories directly against his observations and experiences instead of being forced to accept the opinions of a professor. Fate, therefore, provided him with an early opportunity to apply the new scientific method exemplified by Vesalius and Newton to his studies, and he took full advantage of it.

His principal interest was classifying the objects of the natural world, particularly plants. He was a man who abhorred intellectual disorder and who liked everything placed in its appropriate relationship. Every specimen with which he worked had to be put in its proper cubbyhole with nothing left over, everything arranged as neatly and as logically as the inventory of a well-managed store.

At Uppsala, Linnaeus experimented with the various systems of classification. By himself he studied Ray and Rivinus and, most of all, Joseph Pitton de Tournefort, a Frenchman connected with the Jardin du Roi in Paris and the recognized authority in the field. Tournefort's system had provided a distinct service to science, being the best one yet devised, but it had several definite failings. Tournefort had done well in handling and defining the genera—the broad category now represented by the first of the two Latin names used to designate a plant or other form of life. But he had not done so well with the species, and so his system did not provide sufficiently fine divisions. He also used only the fruits and flowers of each plant in determining its classification, leaving out of consideration its stalk, leaves, and other characteristics.

As Linnaeus tested Tournefort's system, applying it to his collections of dried plants and to those that he was able to observe in the garden at Uppsala, he realized it was barely adequate. With the new masses of specimens being shipped to Europe's universities from all over the world, some better system had to be devised if order were to prevail and the material kept in useful, manageable form. Remembering his paper on the sexuality of plants, he attempted to develop a system based on the stamens and pistils. As he worked during those lonely days at Uppsala without formal direction from the faculty, he wrote down his thoughts on this subject, composing some fourteen short papers during the first part of 1733.

In the spring a new blow fell. The treasurer of the university had died, leaving his accounts in such poor shape that no one knew for certain whether any surplus existed in the scholarship fund that had been used to support Linnaeus. The university, therefore, refused to allow him any more money. Thrown back on his own resources, he announced a private series of lectures on mineralogy. Since no one else at Uppsala taught mineralogy, his lectures were well attended, and by the close of 1734 he had rescued himself from poverty and saved enough money to take a vacation.

In February, 1734, he returned to Uppsala and, planning to give private courses in botany, revealed his showman's instinct in arranging his room, which he laid out as a museum. He hung bird skins from the ceiling and a Lapland costume on one wall and displayed his racks of medical books, scientific instruments, and all his collections—some 3,000 pressed plants, 1,000 insects, and numerous samples of minerals. Everything was designed to attract and impress the other students, so they would not only come to his lectures, but pay for them. In addition to botany, he introduced a course on dietetics, a subject that dealt with food but in those days also verged on a philosophy of life. Yet Linnaeus was not content. To further himself, he needed more recognition than he had received so far, and he decided to propose an expedition through the area known as Dalecarlia. This region is in the middle of Sweden and slightly to the west, and it contains Lake Runn and Lake Siljan as well as the city of Falun. Linnaeus' idea was to do what he had done in Lapland: collect specimens; survey the flora, fauna, and mineralogy; and study the local customs of the inhabitants. The governor at Falun agreed to underwrite the cost. Indeed, unlike the Royal Academy of Science, he was willing to put up enough money to make the trip more comfortable. Linnaeus was also able to enlist seven other students to accompany him, each of whom was to pay his own expenses and perform certain specified functions. One, for example, was to serve as the official zoologist; another, as the quartermaster; a third, as the treasurer.

Compared with the trip through Lapland, this was truly an expedition, and the results should have been excellent, but they were not. For some reason, the group brought back little that was of real interest. They were not lazy, they were not unobservant, but they failed to find anything to excite the scientific world. Perhaps the country had little to offer. Perhaps Linnaeus had become slightly complacent. But the governor does not seem to have been disappointed. He invited Linnaeus to stay on with him as his guest, an arrangement that suited Linnaeus well, for the governor had an excellent library. In addition, Linnaeus could earn money at Falun by lecturing on assaying and, although he had no degree, by practicing medicine. But this life, pleasant as it may have been, did nothing to solve his basic problems. At the university he had reached an impasse. No openings were available to him as a teacher except those he created for himself, and he could find no publisher for the many papers he had written. As a doctor, he also had no future without a degree, but although the law permitted Swedish universities to confer a doctorate in medicine, custom did not. In Sweden it was generally believed such a degree had no meaning unless it had been obtained abroad.

After returning to Uppsala in 1734, Linnaeus decided that he had to go to Holland. He had saved some of the money he had earned lecturing, and the father of a friend and fellow student, Claes Sohlberg, offered to pay him, if he would take Claes along. The time, therefore, was opportune, and he left Uppsala in December of that year.

Instead of going directly south and west, he first visited Falun again, where, as he wrote later, "I was received with universal kindness. A physician named Moraeus resided there, who was esteemed rich by the common people. Indeed he was one of the richest persons in that very poor country. . . . He had a handsome daughter, besides a younger one, the former of whom was courted, but in vain, by a gentleman of rank and title. I was struck when I first saw her, and felt my heart assailed by new sensations and anxieties. I loved her, and she at length, won by my attentions, listened to my proposals, and returned my passion. I became an accepted lover." Having conquered the heart of the girl, Sara Lisa, Linnaeus next had to win over the doctor. "I addressed myself to her father," Linnaeus continued, "avowing, not without much confusion, my total want of fortune. He was favorable on some accounts, but had many objections. He approved of me, but not of my circumstances." And why should he? He knew from first hand experience that practicing medicine was not a way to make money in Sweden—his own fortune had come from sources outside his practice—and Linnaeus did not even have a degree. In the end, however, he consented to a three-year engagement, "after which he would tell me his determination."

Then Linnaeus started south, stopping at Lund, his first university; Växjö, his first school; and his home at Stenbrohult. It was almost as though he were reviewing his entire life before setting out on his new adventure.

V

The two students who took the boat at Hälsingborg were not an imposing pair. Claes was nothing but the moderately intelligent son of a rich man who was able to pay for the trip; Linnaeus, a scholar without a degree or a position. All he possessed were the papers buried deep in his luggage, papers that described his findings in Lapland and his system of classification and for which he could find no publisher. Perhaps somewhere on the Continent he would meet someone willing to risk the cost of typesetting and ink and paper. Perhaps not. Yet this and obtaining his degree in medicine remained his great hope as he climbed to the deck of the ship at Hälsingborg, sailed to Helsingor, from there to Lübeck, and by land to Hamburg, which was already an important shipping and trading center, rich enough to pay the enormous ransom demanded only a few years before by Frederick IV of Denmark, when he had threatened to attack the city. One of its great curiosities was the body of a seven-headed snake which was in the collection of Burgomaster Johann Anderson and his brother. This indeed was a rarity. It had been described scientifically, and it had once lain on an altar in Prague, revered by clergy and laymen. Frederick IV, the same Danish king who had extorted money from Hamburg, had offered to buy it. The offer was refused, but since then the price had fallen somewhat, for the burgomaster was now anxious to sell it. Linnaeus obtained permission to examine it and saw what it actually was: a weird combination of weasels' heads and claws, bound together by a snakeskin and intended by the monks of Prague to represent a dragon of the Apocalypse. With the lack of tact and the regard for truth that characterized him, Linnaeus promptly denounced the monstrosity as a fraud (although he examined it twice to make sure), the worth of the seven-headed dragon dropped to nothing, and Linnaeus moved on to Altona, where he boarded the boat for Holland.

After an uncomfortable voyage, during which they battled against head winds and passed through a violent thunderstorm, the ship dropped anchor at Amsterdam, where Linnaeus and Claes disembarked and made their way twenty-five miles east to Harderwijk, a fishing town on the Zuider Zee. Harderwijk contained an undistinguished university, but one that was well known in Sweden and attracted many Swedes. Its strength lay in its weakness. Having little in the way of a reputation to sustain, it raised few problems about giving degrees, and since a doctorate in medicine from Harderwijk was as good in Sweden as a doctorate in medicine from anywhere else, it was the place where students like Linnaeus naturally went, particularly if they were poor and could not afford months, or even years, of additional study.

As soon as he arrived in the city, Linnaeus introduced himself to the university's faculty and enrolled as a student. The same day he underwent a public examination in medicine, passed it, and presented his thesis, which he had foresightedly written before leaving Sweden. A member of the faculty read it and, according to the custom, ordered Linnaeus to have it printed. As soon as this was done, Linnaeus appeared to defend his thesis publicly, did so with success, and immediately received his doctorate. He could now formally practice medicine in Sweden, and the whole business had taken just a few days, indeed far less time than it had taken him to get to Harderwijk.

But his essential problems remained unsolved. He still had no money and no reputation, and the manuscripts he had brought from Sweden remained in his luggage, unpublished. Until they appeared in print, until his ideas were available to the world of scholars, he had no future ahead of him except a small medical practice in Sweden, and this was a future that he refused to accept.

As a consequence, he decided to go with Claes to Leiden, where he enrolled in the university. In some respects, this was a formality since he now had his degree, but it gave him the right to attend classes when he wished and also provided him with a certain standing in the academic community. Then he went about the business of trying to meet the right people. One of them was Dr. Jan Fredric Gronovius, a wealthy doctor who owned an excellent herbarium. Gronovius took an immediate liking to the Swedish scholar, and Linnaeus, who was not a person to miss an opportunity, dug into his luggage and brought out his unpublished manuscripts. One of them, *Systema naturae,* which dealt with his system of classification, particularly appealed to the doctor. He showed it to a wealthy Scotsman, Isaac Lawson, who was also in Leiden, and the two men, to Linnaeus' great pleasure, agreed to underwrite the cost of printing it.

While the manuscript was at the printer's, Linnaeus turned his attention to the fulfillment of another ambition: meeting Dr. Hermann Boerhaave, the best-known doctor of his day, not just in Holland, but throughout Europe. Gronovius suggested that Linnaeus write Boerhaave and request an appointment, for although the doctor was busy and wealthy, he was always interested in helping young students. Their first meeting was quickly followed by a second, and Boerhaave offered Linnaeus a job collecting specimens abroad, but Linnaeus declined. Instead, he thought that perhaps he should go back to Sweden, for although his first publication had not yet been printed, he was running out of funds. Boerhaave, however, refused to let him give up so easily. Before making a final decision, he insisted that Linnaeus consult with Johan Burman, manager of the botanical garden in Amsterdam.

Burman, like everyone else, was struck by Linnaeus' knowledge and offered him a job cataloguing a collection of plants from Ceylon, and at the same time, Claes' father sent one of the payments he had promised earlier. This combination of good fortune gave Linnaeus what he most needed at the time—money—and he agreed to stay for a while longer. Furthermore, he decided to publish two more papers, both of which he sent to the printer. He was gambling, and gambling heavily, on the worth of his ideas. But if they were as good as he thought they were, then his reputation would be made for all time.

Boerhaave, however, was not entirely content with the arrangement. He had won his first objective, delaying Linnaeus' return to Sweden, but he wanted something better for this scholar whom he had befriended. Among his patients was an extremely wealthy man, Georg Cliffort, director of the East India Company and an ardent botanist. Cliffort was also something of a hypochondriac and the owner of an enormous private botanical garden. In this combination, Boerhaave saw an opportunity for Linnaeus. What could be better for Cliffort than to have a physician constantly in attendance and, at the same time, a skilled botanist to supervise his garden? The way he put the idea to Cliffort made it irresistible, and in a short time, Linnaeus was installed on Cliffort's estate at Hartecamp, a small town outside Leiden. There he had a great garden to work in, a good salary, the facilities he needed to pursue his studies, and proximity to the university at Leiden.

Nothing could be better suited to his purposes, and to add to his happiness, he now had a personal friend in Holland. Peter Artedi, whom he had known so well at Uppsala, arrived in Amsterdam, still poor, still seeking knowledge, but still holding the theories he had shared with Linnaeus at the university. He had just come from England, where he had been studying fish—he and Linnaeus had formerly agreed that while the one worked on plants, the other would work on fish—and he wanted to stay in Holland, if only he could find a job. By now Linnaeus was sufficiently well established to help others as well as himself, and he took Artedi to see Albert Seba, a wealthy apothecary in Amsterdam, who owned vast biological collections, including a large number of fish he wanted to have catalogued. Linnaeus was unwilling to take on the job— he already had too much to do with his own work and his duties at Hartecamp—but he saw the perfect opportunity for Artedi. Taking his friend to the apothecary's house, he introduced the two men, and Seba offered Artedi the position.

It was good for Linnaeus to have this old and trusted friend in Holland, but tragedy struck almost immediately. Walking back to his lodgings from an evening spent with Seba, Artedi somehow lost his way. He wandered through the unfamiliar streets in the darkness, missed his step or was pushed by some thief, fell into a canal, and was drowned.

Overcome with grief, Linnaeus rushed from Hartecamp to Amsterdam, visited Seba, obtained some money from him, and made all the arrangements for Artedi's burial. But that was not the end of his obligation to the dead man lying in the strange house. For the stiffened corpse was only the shadow of the man; the true man was in his unpublished manuscript, those sheets of paper he had carried with him on his travels. They represented his life's work, the essence of all that he had thought and done, and Linnaeus was determined that they would be published. But the papers themselves were in grave danger. Artedi, on his death, had owed money to his landlord. The landlord argued with logic that the papers were his; Artedi had left nothing else. Linnaeus was desperate. In the landlord's hands, Artedi's work was valueless; his life, therefore, pointless. Linnaeus appealed to Seba, but Seba was unwilling to help. He did not know Artedi well, and he had already contributed to his burial expense. Then Linnaeus turned to Cliffort, and Cliffort paid off Artedi's debts. Linnaeus took possession of the papers, and later, as he had promised himself he would, he published them. Because of this, Artedi's name is known today.

This occurred in the fall of 1735, but it was the only touch of sorrow during Linnaeus' months in Holland. Otherwise everything had gone well. He had obtained his degree as doctor of medicine; he had made a place for himself among the professors at Leiden; he had a patron in Boerhaave and another in Cliffort; he had a position that paid well and yet gave him the leisure to further his own work; he had everything in short except fame—and the first of his publications was just about to come out.

VI

That publication and the others that quickly followed, although many were short, amounting to only a few pages, brought order to natural history. For what Linnaeus gave the world was a practical means of classifying and arranging the thousands of forms of life, of seeing their relationships to one another, a means whereby the expert could pick up an unfamiliar specimen and tell what it was.

Linnaeus' ideas, which he had been developing ever since he had studied in his father's garden, came at a crisis in the history of science. As explorers and adventurers came back from foreign lands, they brought with them an increasing horde of unidentified objects: strange shells, plants, fish, and animals, cases and crates and barrels of them, some of them directed to private collectors, some to public institutions. The mass of the material was overwhelming, there was enough to keep biologists occupied for years, and they might have gone down under the weight of it, unless they had a means of sorting and cataloguing it and keeping it in order.

Something of the problem can be illustrated by the discussion of beaver that had taken place before. At least one outstanding scientist had considered them along with fish, because they lived in the water. Indeed, he included all water-dwelling life in the same general category, and following the same reasoning, the church had at one time permitted beavers to be eaten on fast days. Another scientist, writing a work on zoology, started first with farm animals, because these were the best known, then discussed those that were less and less familiar to most readers, and an ornithologist in England in his book grouped together what he called "singing" birds, which placed the imported canary next to the British hedge sparrow. Such practices could lead only to confusion and scientific chaos. No one would be able to find anything, either in the museums or in the biology books, unless he knew the particular system used. Even more important, the relationships between different forms of life were obscured.

The work of Grew and Tournefort had certainly helped the situation, but Linnaeus had developed an even more practical system. To use an oversimplified simile, he was like a trained librarian who has walked into an ancient and great library filled with books and manuscripts and documents, all lying scattered on the shelves with no card catalogue, a book of philosophy standing next to a book on mathematics, a book of poetry wedged between a history of Greece and a text on chemistry. Instantly, he sees the need for order. This material has to be arranged in some fashion before it will become usable, and he shows how it can be done. The simile can also be carried a step further. Not only is it physically difficult to write a book on Greek philosophy if the proper volumes are not gathered together, but it is impossible to do so, unless the author can group Plato, Socrates, and Aristotle under the common heading "Greek philosophers." For not only does cataloguing produce order, but it also helps define relationships, and these definitions in turn can lead to concepts.

True, Linnaeus' system had faults. He relied on the sexual characteristics of plants and ignored others of equal or greater importance. Because of this, his system was labeled artificial, meaning that it was not based on actual relationships but only those that appeared after Linnaeus had imposed his artificial restriction. His ideas also worked better with plants than with animals. His method of handling insects, for example, was inadequate. In time, his system would be overturned and replaced with one that was more "natural" and used a wider range of characteristics. But at the beginning of the eighteenth century no system as comprehensive or useful had been devised, and Linnaeus appeared at the moment in history when the need was great.

Nor was this the total of his accomplishments. He gave more emphasis to the species, a finer division than the genus, than previous writers, thus providing for more subclassifications, and, of course, his publications were not limited only to the subject of his system. He probably knew more about the plants of Lapland than any other man in Europe, and he was a competent botanist in other fields as well. To have produced this work was no small feat for a man barely in his thirties. Linnaeus was one of those men who are destined to be great when they are young, whose ideas come to them almost whole, who arrive at giant concepts in a single leap, concepts so large they are all-embracing and encompass the details that compose the life's endeavor of lesser men.

VII

In the year 1736, as his publications began to appear and his ideas were gradually accepted by the scientists of Europe, Linnaeus could feel justified in his confidence in himself. Yet not everyone agreed with him or held a high opinion of his work.

That summer he made a brief trip to England, where he met Phillip Miller, the botanist who supervised the gardens at Chelsea. Miller took his guest among the plants and pointed them out, using their old names, while Linnaeus, seeing no point in trying to convert Miller to a new system of classification, kept silent. Miller mistook Linnaeus' quiet for ignorance and told a friend that Cliffort's botanist knew nothing about plants. Word of this comment came back to Linnaeus. He visited Miller again and this time described his theories. Miller was interested, but not convinced. Yet he shortly came to respect Linnaeus and realized that his first impression was mistaken.

Johann Jakob Dillenius had a sharper tongue, however. He was in charge of the botanical garden at Oxford and, in Linnaeus' presence, remarked that Linnaeus was the man who had "confounded" botany. The next day, when Linnaeus asked Dillenius the reason for his disparaging remark, Dillenius produced some of the press sheets from Linnaeus' unpublished book, *Genera plantarum,* which had been sent to him by Gronovius. Each page was marked several times with the letters *N.B.,* and when Linnaeus asked what they meant, Dillenius replied that they indicated serious errors in the book, places where Linnaeus' genera were false. Linnaeus asked Dillenius to defend his position and, in the ensuing argument, proved him wrong. But although Dillenius in time came to accept many of Linnaeus' ideas and although the two men entered into a long correspondence, Dillenius always held Linnaeus at some distance and often scolded him.

"I feel as much displeased with your *Critica botanica,*" he later wrote

Linnaeus, "as I am pleased with your Lapland *Flora,* especially as you have, without my deserving of such a compliment, or knowing of your intention, dedicated the book to me. You must have known of my dislike to all ceremonies and compliments. I hope that you have burthened but few copies with the dedication. Perhaps only the copy which you have sent me. If there be more, I beg of you to strip them of this vain parade, or I shall take it much amiss. At least I cannot offer you my thanks for what you have done. . . ."

Dillenius was not merely being crotchety. He was an important scientist, the holder of the first chair of botany at Oxford, and his views were typical of those held by many experienced men who saw the faults in Linnaeus' system and who also believed that he was trying to change classification too quickly. "We all know the nomenclature of botany to be an Augean stable," he explained to Linnaeus. The task of cleaning it "requires much reading, and extensive as well as various erudition; nor is it to be given up to hasty or careless hands. You rush upon it, and overturn everything."

On the other hand, in spite of his reservations, Dillenius could be encouraging. "I applaud and congratulate you," he wrote another time, "for having brought your premature birth to such perfection. You have accomplished great things, and that you may go on and prosper still more, let me exhort you to examine more and more species." Then he added the highest tribute one thinker can pay to another. "I do not doubt that you yourself will, one day, overthrow your own system." With those few words, Dillenius recognized an essential characteristic of Linnaeus, one that contributed to his greatness: he was a seeker after truth, not a defender of his own ideas.

Although Dillenius had certain doubts about Linnaeus' work, Boerhaave had none, and when he found that Linnaeus had dedicated to him the first edition of *Genera plantarum,* he was overjoyed. "Whoever reads your book must be struck with it, as a work of infinite attention, singular perseverance, and unrivaled science. Nor can I fully calculate the result of so valuable an undertaking. Ages to come will applaud, good men will imitate, and all will be improved. . . . You, in every instance, write nothing but what announces a man of experience, and a profound critic."

Neither the caution of Dillenius nor the enthusiasm of Boerhaave swayed Linnaeus one way or the other. He knew both men and how much to discount their opinions. Therefore, Dillenius could not discourage him or Boerhaave make him overconfident. He was gravely concerned, however, about the sharp pen of Albrecht von Haller.

A tragic figure in eighteenth-century science, Haller was so brilliant and talented he could not bring himself to concentrate on a single subject. When he died in 1777, he left behind approximately 650 published works, some religious, some scientific, and some poetical. He had been a doctor, a botanist, a professor of medicine, a member of the municipal council of Bern, and a diplomat for his native Switzerland. But when, as an old man, he looked back on his life, he did so with regret and melancholy. He had been good at many things, excellent at none.

Linnaeus had never met Haller, but knew the Swiss disliked his system of classification because of its artificiality, and he had written Haller in friendly fashion, encouraging him to improve the system if he could. He was writing again one spring day in 1737, when he received word from Gronovius that Haller was about to publish a full-scale attack on his system.

Instead of abruptly ending his letter, Linnaeus began writing again, this time pleading with Haller not to start a fight. In eleven numbered paragraphs he listed the reasons why a controversy between the two men would be unprofitable and in his emotionalism told much about himself and his philosophy. In his first two paragraphs, he expressed his desire for peace and his willingness to go to lengths to make amends for any wrongs he might have committed. "Let me know if I seem to have offended," he begged Haller, "and I will omit nothing to satisfy you." He agreed to accept any system Haller should devise if it proved better, he was willing to accept corrections from Haller, he praised Haller, he talked of his own reputation among other botanists, and in his sixth paragraph, he pointed out how time had mellowed him, how the experience of putting forth a new idea in a hostile world had made him regret his own sharp tongue. "Do but turn over the writings of botanists in general," he wrote, "and you will see, by their earlier performances, how they are puffed up at first with their own consequence, and scarcely able to keep from assaulting others; of which I myself have perhaps been guilty, which I greatly regret, having now learned better. But when these same people have passed a few years in the field of battle, they become so mild, candid, modest, and civil to everybody, that not a word of offense escapes them." The callow, short-tempered student, who had criticized the Lapp clergymen for their ignorance and had been rebuked by the university for his arrogant language, had become temperate. "What man," he asked, "was ever so learned and wise, who, in correcting others, did not now and then show he wanted correction himself? Something always sticks to him. . . . Look over the whole body of controversial writers, and point out one of them who has received any thanks for what he has done in this way." Then Linnaeus, in his eleventh numbered paragraph, concluded his plea for peace with a summary of his entire philosophy. "I dread all controversies," he said, "as, whether conqueror or conquered, I can never escape disgrace. Who ever fought without some wound, or some injurious consequence? Time is too precious, and can be far better employed by me, as well as by you. I am too young to take up arms, which if once taken, cannot be laid aside until the war is concluded, which may last all our lives."

Although his words had little effect on Haller, who continued to oppose him, they contained the essence of Linnaeus' belief. He had too much work to do to fight and quarrel. Let scientists everywhere work together; let them criticize one another's ideas, propose new theories, accept suggestions; but never let the discussion, the exchange of thoughts, degenerate into a battle with its defenses and offenses. Such struggles were demeaning to everyone concerned. They were even worse than demeaning. They wasted the strength of the contenders, strength that should be used advancing man's knowledge.

As for himself he was busy doing just that. In the same letter to Haller, he reported that "my *Critica botanica,* in octavo, is in the press, and the *Hortus cliffortianus* in folio." (The latter was a detailed catalogue of all the plants in Cliffort's garden.) In addition, "My *Genera* were finished early in the present year." But he still was not satisfied with his life. Pathetically homesick, he yearned for Sweden. His friends in Leiden managed, however, to persuade him to stay on awhile longer. Boerhaave offered him several appointments, the university gave him a position helping rearrange the botanical gardens, everyone opened his door to him, he could listen to lectures, he could talk with the city's most learned men, and all these inducements persuaded him to stay on. But not for long, for he received word that Dr. Moraeus, the father of his betrothed, was growing concerned over his prospective son-in-law's protracted absence. Did Linnaeus intend to return to Sweden, or was he going to spend the rest of his life in Holland? As the doctor pondered this question, a friend of Linnaeus began to court Sara Lisa, and the doctor looked on the courtship favorably. After all, his daughter could not remain bound to Linnaeus forever.

Linnaeus had reached a crisis. He could stay in Holland, where he did not feel at home—he had not even learned the Dutch language—or he could go back to Sweden and claim his wealthy bride.

Only a serious illness prevented him from leaving Leiden immediately. As soon as he had recovered, he was on his way, first making a visit to Paris to see the gardens and scientists there and then heading for Sweden, which he reached in the fall of 1738.

VIII

When Linnaeus returned to Sweden in the fall of 1738, the Hats, who took their name from the three-cornered hats that were the mark of a gentleman or an officer, were the rising political force. They were dedicated to opposing the chancellor, Count Arvid Bernhard Horn, who, recognizing the harm done Sweden by years of warfare, was pursuing a policy of peace at almost any cost. The Hats found this humiliating, but like most strong nationalists, they were confused. Instead of promoting a spirit of militarism, they might better have honored the obscure doctor in Stockholm who was unsuccessfully attempting to set up a medical practice. His carefully written papers would bring Sweden more glory than any number of victories on the battlefield, but his arrival home went practically unnoticed.

Describing his first months back in Sweden, Linnaeus wrote to a friend, "I settled in Stockholm, the laughing stock of everybody on account of my botany. No one cared how many sleepless nights and toilsome hours I had passed. . . . There was no one who would even put a servant under my care. I was obliged to live as I could, in virtuous poverty."

It was as though he had never been away, as though the struggle and hard work of the past years had gone for nothing. But he persevered as he had always done, and "now my adverse fate took a sudden turn, and, after so long a succession of cloudy prospects, the sun broke out upon me. I emerged from my obscurity, obtained access to the great, and every unfavorable presage vanished. No invalid could now recover without my assistance. I began to get money, and was busy in attendance on the sick, from four in the morning till late in the evening; nor were my nights uninterrupted by the calls of my patients."

One of his new patrons was Count Carl Gustaf Tessin, a leader of the Hats, a man somewhat wiser than other members of his party. He was familiar with Linnaeus' work and made an effort to meet him. The two men liked each other, and Tessin started using his influence on Linnaeus' behalf. He obtained a position for him as lecturer on botany and mineralogy at the Mining College, offered him free living quarters for a while, and also secured for him an appointment as a physician to the Admiralty. Thus, as Linnaeus wrote later, "I was enabled to present myself to the bride to whom I had been for five years engaged, and was honorably received as her husband," although he added ruefully, "My father-in-law, rather fond of his money, proved not very liberal to his son-in-law."

Although his medical practice was growing, he longed to return to Uppsala as a professor and in the early fall of 1739 wrote that "just now, both medical professorships are likely to become vacant. Professors Rudbeck and Roberg, both advanced in age, are about offering their resignations. If this takes place, probably Mr. Rosén [his old rival] may succeed Roberg, and I may obtain Rudbeck's appointment. But if I do not," he added, "I am content to live and die at Stockholm, nor shall I oppose the pretensions of any competitor."

A year later, however, his ambition had not been fulfilled. Writing to a friend in the fall of 1740, he said, "Professor Rudbeck, at Uppsala, having died this year, I was desirous of succeeding him. My whole summer has been devoted, though in vain, to this object. . . . It would have been suitable to my wishes to have removed to Uppsala, where I should entirely have given up the practice of medicine, and devoted myself exclusively to botany; but fate has decreed otherwise."

Rosén had taken Rudbeck's place on the faculty, but the same year, Roberg retired, so his place, too, became vacant. The appointment of Linnaeus should have been a foregone conclusion, but with the tendency of some academicians to wrangle over the inconsequential, the university authorities decided Linnaeus would have to show evidence of his competence to fill the post. Would the publications he had written be acceptable? No, they would not. How about a thesis specially written for the occasion? That would not be acceptable either. Linnaeus, certain faculty members argued, should be required to stand up and debate his ideas publicly. (Apparently they wanted to test his ability to speak and understand Latin.) The months went by while the faculty argued, and because of the delay, two more applicants entered their names. Finally, in the late spring of 1741, the dispute resolved itself in Linnaeus' favor, and he received the appointment, giving his first lecture that fall.

He did so, however, without receiving any salary. Roberg had retired, but under the procedures followed by the university, he continued to be paid, not a pension, but the full salary. This meant there was no money for Linnaeus. Financially all he could obtain were the various fees connected with the position, fees for giving examinations and performing other special duties. He was also entitled to charges for tutoring students and giving special lectures that were not part of the routine responsibility of a professor. He labored, however, under a disadvantage. His professorship was concerned primarily with medicine, in which he was not as interested or as proficient as he was in botany. Rosén, on the other hand, who was more of a doctor and less of a botanist, had received the professorship dealing with medicinal herbs and botany. The two, being practical men, discussed the problem and, with the concurrence of the university, agreed to exchange places. By 1742, therefore, Linnaeus had at last secured the position he wanted at Uppsala.

In time Sweden recognized his genius. Roberg died, and he received Roberg's salary. His lectures were well attended, he had plenty of special students to augment his income, he obtained funds for additional collecting expeditions, he was admitted to learned societies, and in 1761 the

Swedish government made him a noble. Having the right to place "von" before his name, he adopted the Swedish form, Von Linne. He became, in short, everything he had wanted to be.

As the years passed, he kept adding to his collections; he continued to write; he refined his system of classification until it became more and more effective. He also made another significant contribution to biology, for he developed what is known as binary nomenclature. Linnaeus had always emphasized the importance of the species, the subdivision under the genus, but he, like all other scientists of his day, required several words to describe each one. This was clumsy and impeded rapid classification. Why not, he asked himself, use a single name to describe the species, just as it was the custom to use one name to describe the genus? In this way, every living thing could be given its own particular designation consisting of only two names. Yet the two names would show where it fitted among other forms of life. Thus today, we call modern man *Homo* (the genus) *sapiens* (the species) to distinguish him from other men like *Homo erectus*. The two words tell the biologist exactly what he is dealing with.

It was just as though the countries of the world had had no specific names and, to reuse a simile, a librarian, trying to catalogue his historical section, had had to describe each one as best he could on his own. In designating a book on French history, for example, he would have been forced to write something like this: "History—country bounded by the Bay of Biscay, English Channel, and Mediterranean." Now, applying Linnaeus' principle, he could put down simply: "History—French." It was a brilliant bit of simplification—obvious, yes, but only after it was done. Until Linnaeus, no one had thought of it. This one idea lightened the task of biologists for all times, and binary nomenclature is still in use and makes possible the more orderly arrangement and cataloguing of living things.

But Linnaeus' truly basic work had been completed by the time he left Holland. At Uppsala, aside from the development of binary nomenclature, his research work was mostly that of refinement. He also spent much of his time improving the botanical gardens, which were among the world's best at his death, and he was an outstanding teacher, one who exerted unusual influence on the students that attended his classes. Years later they would talk about the courses they had taken under Linnaeus.

He was also personally popular with them, and often entertained groups of them at his house in nearby Hammarby. Sometimes the students would organize a dance, calling in a peasant to provide the music, and Linnaeus would stand watching them, smoking his pipe and occasionally joining in. At other times, he would talk to them about botany, and what they remembered, in addition to the subject matter, were his eyes, shining and lustrous. His figure, although powerful, was small, and a slight stoop made him appear even smaller than he was. But his eyes held their attention. They were the eyes of a man who had seen things no man had ever seen before, found relationships in the details of plants that no one had noticed, discovered simplicity where complexity had always existed.

With his fame and his secure position, he should have been happy, but he was not. Sara Lisa, the girl he had returned from Holland to marry, was not what he had imagined her to be. She fought with the wives of the other professors; she often quarreled with the guests that Linnaeus brought home. She did not have gentleness, and she apparently demanded much of her husband.

He had attained success early, but in doing so, he apparently burned himself out. His youthful exuberance faded away, he became easily subject to fits of depression and jealousy, and he began to keep a strange collection of notes under the title *Nemesis divina.* Although he was a man of science, he could not, like many others in this period of transition, entirely shake off the centuries-old heritage of superstition, and in the *Nemesis divina* he carefully recorded a number of curious stories, which he regarded as having significance. Before the birth of one of his daughters, the neighbors had seen strange lights in the house. The child died soon after, and Linnaeus thought that there must have been a connection between the two events. And again, his father had seen a figure wrapped in a sheet sitting by the fireplace. A few days later a friend died.

But the principal theme of *Nemesis divina* was Linnaeus' belief in divine vengeance. He was sure God stood by, watchful and ready to punish every sin, and Linnaeus collected anecdotes to support this philosophy, somewhat as he would have collected plants to develop a new botanical theory. Carefully he noted the rumor about the governor of Gotland, who fell in love with one of his servants and finally persuaded her to sleep with him. But a guest, noticing the girl's beauty, begged to take the governor's place that night, a request the governor granted. In the meanwhile, the serving girl had spoken to his wife, and the wife had agreed to substitute for the girl in the darkness. But the story, as Linnaeus put it down, was not told with the robustness of a Chaucer or a Boccaccio; it was an example of divine retribution.

The wife of a Lapland pastor sleeps with the quartermaster in the town where she lives. The pastor learns of it and takes to drink. The daughter is demoralized and becomes a whore. Everything is ruined for the one sin. Lisbon is struck by an earthquake because its citizens deserve punishment; a woman hits a servant for breaking a bowl and later breaks her own leg. On a large scale or a small, men labored under the shadow of nemesis. It was not a pleasant philosophy with its Old Testament overtones, and it did nothing to comfort Linnaeus in his declining days.

He took pleasure, however, in his son, Carl, more pleasure than the boy's abilities merited. Although Linnaeus hoped Carl would become a botanist, his son was more interested in women and a good time. Something of his character is revealed in his search for a wife. He pursued one young girl, then abandoned her when he found she had little money. He went after another and left her, too, because she had not had smallpox and he thought the disease might disfigure her in the future. He became interested in a third woman, who attracted him with her wealth and repulsed him with the scars left by smallpox. In his pursuit of women, Carl was a self-centered idler, as unlike his father as anyone could have been. Linnaeus, nevertheless, provided for his future by securing the right to appoint his own successor and then named Carl. Since Carl was neither capable nor popular, this act of nepotism diminished Linnaeus' standing among his colleagues.

To add to his distresses, his mind began to fail and his last years were marred by paralytic strokes. Death, when it came in 1778, was a release.

IX

The collections and papers he left behind were valuable. Carl, the younger, wanted them; so did Sara Lisa. They fought over them like two alley cats over a dirty piece of meat. Carl finally obtained them by renouncing his share of the remainder of the estate. On his death a few years later, they reverted to Sara Lisa, who was more interested in funds for herself and her daughters than she was in her husband's memory. Who would pay the highest price for the collections and for the library? Could she get 1,000 guineas for them? How quickly could she sell them? The King of Sweden was temporarily out of the country. If he came back before the sale was made, perhaps he would force her to sell them to Uppsala for a lower price.

A wealthy young Englishman, James Edward Smith, learned of Sara Lisa's intentions. As he wrote later, "The mother and sisters of the deceased were anxious to make as large a profit as they could of the museum." After examining the catalogue, he offered Sara Lisa her asking price, but she had now decided she might get more money elsewhere. Smith, however, made her hold firm to her original price, and finally, he was able to write, "I paid half the money down, and the rest in three months—and in October, 1785, received the collection in *twenty-six great boxes,* perfectly safe.

"I paid eighty guineas to the captain for freight, which was too much by half; but I was careful to avoid all delay. *For the ship had just sailed when the King of Sweden returned, and hearing the story, he sent a vessel after the ship, to bring it back; but happily for me, it was too late.*" Thus, the collections of Linnaeus, because of the avarice of his wife, passed from the Sweden he had loved so well into the hands of strangers.

Yet the tragedy was not as great as it might have appeared. Although Linnaeus would have wanted his possessions to remain in his own country, he could not have placed them in more friendly hands than Smith's. Although Smith sold the mineral collection and dispersed some of the others, he took the utmost care of the remainder, particularly the plants, and made them available to other students. He also served as president of the Linnaean Society, an organization devoted to the study of Linnaeus' work and to the advancement of science.

In Sweden, as the years passed, Linnaeus' memory became more and more revered. The botanical garden at Uppsala was kept in good condition; the house at Hammarby was preserved. The political boundaries drawn by Charles XII became nothing but lines on the pages of a historical atlas, but the ideas of Linnaeus continued to have impact. True, as Haller had predicted, the artificiality of his system of classification ultimately led to its replacement, but for many years it served the cause of science well, making it possible for biologists to handle the mass of material with which they had to deal. His binary nomenclature, with its great simplicity, is still used throughout the world.

Many years after his death, scholars everywhere still pored over his work, studying his ideas and benefiting from them. For he had lifted the natural world from the disorder in which men's minds had placed it and imposed on it unity and cohesion. That other naturalists could work with the masses of material arriving daily from abroad was largely to the credit of the curate's son, who had seen relationships so clearly and who had labored so long against the obstacles of poverty and ignorance.

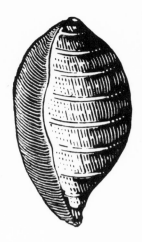

4

A Broader View

GEORGES LOUIS BUFFON: 1707–1788

I

Charles François de Cisternay Dufay (or du Fay), intendant of the Jardin du Roi in Paris, knew that he was dying, but like many men who have lived with a purpose, he was less interested in the approach of his death than he was in the future of the cause he had supported during his lifetime. That cause was the conversion of the king's garden into a scientific center capable of serving all France.

The garden had been established in the first half of the seventeenth century, when Louis XIII was king and Richelieu was first minister, and stood on the left bank of the Seine near the Pont d'Austerlitz, not far from the Sorbonne. Originally it had been planted with medicinal herbs, for the government had hoped to use it in instructing pharmacists and medical students in the values of various plants. But the doctors of Paris were hostile toward what they considered the government's attempt to interfere with their profession, so although they always insisted that a doctor be named intendant, they did little to provide proper management for the garden. Slowly, as any garden must under such circumstances, it fell into decay. The original plants withered and died, and few new plants were set in the ground to take their places. The winds of Paris swept over the city, picked up the seeds of weeds, and deposited them in the garden, where they took root and flourished, because no one was interested in pulling them out. Finally, after years of neglect, the place became so utterly useless and looked so disreputable that even the government agreed that drastic measures should be taken to improve it.

This was the moment for which many French scientists had been waiting. For a long time they had wanted a botanical garden, one that would become an important research center, and in the declining state of the Jardin du Roi, they saw their opportunity. Why not remove it from the control of the doctors, they argued, and place it under the supervision of a scientist? It could then be converted from a medicinal garden to one of general botanical interest.

The government listened to this argument and finally agreed. The next question was who to appoint as intendant. After the usual lengthy discussions surrounding a bureaucratic decision, the minister in charge selected Dufay. Although best known as a chemist, he was also skilled in anatomy, geometry, astronomy, mechanics, and botany and was recognized as an expert in each of these fields by the Academy of Sciences. In 1732 he received his appointment and immediately set about restoring the garden and expanding its collection of plants. His great plans, however, were cut short by ill health. In 1739, although he was only forty-one years old, he was dying, and the question uppermost in his mind was the choice of his successor.

For some time, the leading candidate had been Henri Louis Duhamel du Monceau, a young Frenchman who had already achieved a brilliant record in biology. Born in Paris in 1700, he quickly attained such eminence that the Academy of Sciences asked him to study a disease which was destroying the saffron plants in the Gâtinais, an area just south of Paris and slightly to the east. Monceau went to the Gâtinais, commenced his studies, and, by careful examination of the plants, was able to determine the trouble: a parasitical fungus that attached itself to the roots. This discovery was considered so significant that the Academy of Sciences elected Monceau to membership in 1728; and as he had continued his interest in biology, particularly in plant physiology, many members of the academy considered him a logical candidate to become intendant. But one member, Jean Hellot, a chemist, disagreed. He had a friend, Georges Louis Leclerc Buffon, who also wanted the post, and in his opinion, Buffon was better qualified. Knowing Dufay well and realizing that he was deeply concerned with finding the right person, Hellot called on the dying intendant and talked to him at length. There had been scientific differences between Dufay and Buffon. Yes, he knew that, but the time had come to overlook them. The question was not whether Dufay and Buffon agreed on all points; the question was: Who could best continue the work of improving the garden?

Because Dufay was an open-minded man, he listened with interest and, at the end of the discussion, was convinced. Monceau was an excellent person, but for the purpose of supervising the garden, Buffon would be even better. Being a man of action, Dufay immediately signed a document recommending Buffon to the king's minister, Maurepas.

How much effect would his deathbed request have on the court? Dufay did not know. He could only hope, because he himself would not be alive to find out.

II

Although Buffon had been born in the same year as Linnaeus and was also deeply interested in botany, no two men could have been more unlike in their backgrounds and their attitudes. Whereas Linnaeus was poor, Buffon was wealthy. Linnaeus did some of his most important work early in life; Buffon needed years of maturing before he embarked on his serious projects. Most significant of all, Linnaeus wished to constrict science, to set up boundaries within which it could work, to place everything in its proper rank and order. Buffon, on the other hand, consistently took the broad point of view. He had a philosophic turn of mind, his thought ranged over every aspect of natural science, and he wanted to free it of restrictions.

Part of the difference between the two men was certainly due to their upbringing. Buffon was born at Montbard, one of the principal cities of Burgundy. His father, Benjamin François Leclerc Buffon, was counselor to the Burgundian *parlement* and a man of considerable standing in the community. His mother, Anne Christine Marlin, was an intelligent and loving woman. Unlike Linnaeus' parents, they were able to supervise and to pay for their son's education, and because Buffon's father wanted him to become a lawyer like himself, Buffon was sent to the Jesuit college at Dijon, not far from Montbard.

He adjusted quickly and easily to life at the college, but although he adored his father and was always proud of his family's traditions, he rebelled against his father's wishes for his career. Instead of studying law, as his father wanted, he became fascinated by mathematics, particularly Euclid's geometry. As he remembered it in later years, he was an especially serious student. More than once, in the middle of the game that was called tennis, he would suddenly think of a problem in geometry, drop his racket, and disappear into some corner until he worked it out. On one occasion, according to his own account, he had indulged in a student's prank and climbed to the top of a clock tower. Sitting on his high perch, he suddenly became obsessed by a problem. Unable to find a solution and now deep in thought, he slid down a knotted rope without realizing he was tearing his hands.

Such reminiscences, however, reveal only one side of his conduct as a student. Certainly he was brilliant; he could not have done his subsequent work unless he had had an extraordinary intellect. But there is considerable evidence that he was something of a playboy, a typical son of a rich man enjoying the freedom of university life.

One of his closest friends was a fellow student, Evelyn Pierrepont, later the second Duke of Kingston, whom Horace Walpole once called the handsomest man in England and also the weakest. When Buffon decided to make a tour of France and Italy, he chose Pierrepont as his traveling companion. Their ostensible purpose was to improve their education, but like any young men off on a pleasure trip, they were more interested in parties and going to the theater than they were in studying. From Bordeaux, Buffon wrote with delight of the city's gaiety compared with Dijon's. "What you tell me," he said to a friend, "of the sterility of the pleasures of Dijon does not astound me. There one is often forced to spend the time of the carnival without any comedies or dances." How different it was at Bordeaux, he explained, as he described how he and Pierrepont were enjoying themselves.

Later, when they had reached Rome, he wrote in similar vein. "Rome at this time is at its best," he said. "The carnival has been going on for fifteen days. There are four magnificent operas and as many comedies without counting many small theaters." Then he reported with excitement the custom of using eunuchs in the roles of women characters. "The people of Rome ogle these geldings," he said, "and speak of their beauty just as we would discuss a pretty actress."

From Rome, the two students returned to France, where they separated. For Buffon, it had been a happy time, one given up almost entirely to pleasure and seeing new sights, but it had also, in an indirect way, served several useful purposes in his development as a scientist. He had come back from the journey in a more serious frame of mind than when he had left. Apparently his months with the fun-loving Pierrepont had sated his desire for the type of life his friend led. Furthermore, by seeing so much of Europe, from the glaciated country of northern France to the volcanic rocks of Italy, he had gained new insight into the forces that created the face of the earth, and with his curiosity aroused, he began asking himself questions.

So Pierrepont went on his own tragic, useless way—a few years later he ran off with the wife of one of Buffon's acquaintances—but Buffon turned to a more serious career. In 1733, shortly after his return, he wrote two papers dealing with mechanics and mathematics that were published by the Royal Academy of Sciences. Then, as he began improving the lands at Montbard, he studied forestry and gardening and became interested in the biological sciences. With his quick mind and ready enthusiasm, he soon established himself as somewhat of an authority in botany, a reputation that was enhanced in 1735 by the publication of his translation of Stephen Hales' work *Vegetable Staticks.*

In spite of its curious title, this book had considerable significance, for Hales was among the first scientists to apply the exact methods of physics to the study of biology. A graduate of Cambridge, where he had studied theology, he took holy orders and eventually became Vicar of Teddington in Middlesex. Although a capable priest, carefully watching over his parishioners, Hales also spent much of his time studying physics, chemistry, and botany—all subjects that had attracted his attention as an undergraduate. Among his interests, he was curious to learn more about the changes that occur in plants during their growth and devised an ingenious experiment, using the techniques of physics. First, he took a number of potted plants and carefully weighed them. Then he watered them regularly with predetermined amounts of water and weighed them again. By this means, he was able to discover how much water they absorbed each day. Then he measured the entire surface of each plant—both its stem and its leaves—and developed information about the relation between the water it needed and its total surface. He also conducted experiments on the plants' absorption of air and proved that plants, contrary to the general belief at the time, did absorb air through their leaves.

His book, therefore, represented an important forward step in the study of natural history, and Buffon added to his reputation both by recognizing its worth and by making it available to French readers. At the same time, he was continuing his independent studies, and in the following years, he published a number of original papers. Most of them were practical rather than theoretical and reflected the results of his work at Montbard. They dealt with the use of woods in tanning, the different effects of light and heavy frosts on plants, methods of increasing the strength of woods, and a study of the conservation of forests. Although not outstanding, they were worthwhile papers, and they qualified Buffon as a candidate for the post of intendant at the Jardin du Roi.

This, of all the positions in the world, was the one he wanted most. It seemed to offer him everything he desired, an opportunity to continue the experiments he had begun at Montbard and a chance to distinguish himself as both a scientist and an administrator. He was, therefore, willing to go to any honest lengths to obtain it. He importuned his friends to help him, he used every acquaintance of his father, he wrote letters, he pleaded, and he even persuaded his friend Hellot to visit the dying Dufay, thus securing the endorsement of the former intendant.

Yet in the summer of 1739 he wrote in reply to a question from Hellot, "I already knew of Dufay's death, which has truly saddened me. He is a great loss to the academy, for besides the honor he has brought it by his merit, he has such an excellent reputation both in society and at the court that he has been able to accomplish astonishing things for the Jardin du Roi. He has put it on such a good footing that it would be a great pleasure to succeed him in his position, but I believe the post will be much coveted. . . . I will beg my friends to speak for me and spread the word that I am suited for the post."

Without his realizing it, Buffon's vigorous campaign was taking effect. When Monceau, who had been away in England, returned to France, he found that he was no longer a candidate. Instead, he received an appointment as a marine inspector, a job that satisfied him and one in which his knowledge of the strength and durability of woods proved useful. One by one, the other candidates were also eliminated, and shortly after Buffon had written Hellot, the king's minister, Maurepas, made his announcement.

Dufay's deathbed wish had been granted, and Buffon was named the new intendant.

III

Although Dufay had done much to improve the garden and add to its collections, the Jardin du Roi still held little promise of becoming the important botanical center the scientists wanted. It was small, practically as small as when it had originally been laid out as an herb garden. In spite of Dufay's efforts, one-quarter of the land lay uncultivated, and two-thirds of the remainder were occupied by an orange grove and an elaborate labyrinth composed of dense plantings and twisting walks in which the visitor was expected to amuse himself by getting lost. The main building was small, one story high with a mansard roof, and contained the intendant's living quarters. A few professors and gardeners, who made up the staff, lived in another small building, and there were also a chapel, an amphitheater, and some greenhouses. The scientific collection amounted to nothing—400 or 500 vials filled with gums, resins, and medicinal drugs, all gathering dust in a small gallery. After practically 100 years of existence and in spite of Dufay's efforts, the Jardin du Roi was scientifically insignificant and a monument to bureaucratic neglect.

Buffon, however, was not in the least discouraged by the state in which he found it. Having visited it many times, he was thoroughly familiar with its disrepair. What he wanted was not a sinecure, but a challenge, and he saw in the Jardin du Roi a challenge that would last him a lifetime. Without the slightest delay, he set to work carrying out his plans to straighten out the gardens, increase the collections, and expand the staff.

The immediate change in his own character was enormous. He suddenly was no longer a playboy or even the gentleman farmer of Montbard, content to experiment with his own forests and gardens. Instead, he quickly became a serious administrator, determined to use his time and strength efficiently in completing the task he had undertaken. In later years, when the friends of his youth expressed surprise at the new habits he adopted and the strict routine he followed, he used to tell them that "in my youth I liked to sleep a lot and spent most of my time in bed. My poor Joseph [his valet for sixty-five years] was of great help to me in conquering this bad habit. One day, discontented with myself, I called him and promised to give him one crown each time he made me get up before six o'clock in the morning. The following day, he came to wake me up at the agreed-upon time; I answered him with insults. He came again the day after; I threatened him.

" 'You have earned nothing, my poor Joseph,' I said to him, when he served me dinner, 'and I have wasted my time. You don't know how to go about it. From now on, concentrate on the recompense I have promised you and pay less attention to my anger and my threats.'

"The next day he came again at the proper time and insisted I get up. I begged him to leave me alone; I told him I would fire him, that he was no longer in my employ. Without letting himself be intimidated by my anger, he used his strength and forced me to get out of bed."

This went on for a time, while Buffon tried to acquire new habits. One morning, when he was more stubborn than usual, Joseph, his patience exhausted, ripped off the bedclothes, poured a pitcher of cold water over his master's chest, and fled from the room. Shortly after, he heard Buffon's bell ring and answered it trembling. "Hand me my linen," Buffon said without anger, "but in the future, let's try to work this out better. We would both gain by it. Here are your three francs, which, this morning, you have certainly earned."

By dint of such measures, Buffon organized his life so he would have the time to manage the Jardin du Roi effectively, but he faced one immense obstacle: the king had little money to spend on the garden.

For some years, Britain and France had labored together in an uneasy alliance, both realizing that economic stability at home was dependent on peace abroad. But their ties were not strong enough to survive the strain when Britain declared war on Spain in 1739, because France feared the loss of the Spanish colonial market, if England won. To add to the confusion, Frederick the Great came to the throne of Prussia in the following year and began his reign by seizing some of the Hapsburg lands of the newly crowned Maria Theresa. This ignited the War of the Austrian Succession in which both France and Great Britain became involved. The

British colonists seized Louisburg, the French fortress near the Gulf of St. Lawrence; the French captured the British port of Madras in India and raided British commerce, doing comparatively little damage but greatly disturbing Britain's armchair patriots. In retaliation, the British raided French shipping and did even less harm. The French insured their shipping in London, where the rates were lower, and the London insurers, to protect themselves against losses, promptly warned the French of impending attacks. But in spite of these comic-opera overtones, the war created a serious drain on the purse of Louis XV, and he had little money to spare for the Jardin du Roi. As Buffon remarked to a friend, when thanking him for a contribution, "The war is the answer for everything."

Yet he refused to accept the war as an excuse for the failure of his plans. Instead, he took what funds he could obtain from the king and then tried to get everything else he needed free. Dufay had been in correspondence with many scientists and explorers, attempting to obtain gifts for the Jardin du Roi's collection, and he had demonstrated how successfully this could be done. Buffon immediately enlarged this correspondence, but he was even cleverer than Dufay. He persuaded Maurepas, the king's minister, to create the title of Correspondent of the Jardin du Roi, which could be awarded to particularly generous contributors, and devised other ways of appealing to his patrons. To some of them, he promised the support of his friends in the government; to others, he spoke of their glory and their scientific reputations. And he was completely successful. From all over the world, the packages poured in. Buffon stored the specimens here, and he stuffed them there, until finally every nook and cranny of the small buildings were filled. In 1745, only seven years after he had become intendant, he gave up part of his lodgings at the Jardin du Roi to make room for the growing collections. It was the only space left.

But Buffon was not content merely to build the Jardin du Roi into a scientific center with outstanding collections and a capable research staff; he also had another ambition—he wanted to write a book. The title he chose was a simple one, *Natural History,* but his idea was complex. He hoped to compress everything he knew and almost everything anyone else knew into a single work, containing not all the details, but the broad picture of natural history. It would require volume after volume and would take him many years to write, but this and his supervision of the Jardin du Roi would represent his life's achievement.

To accomplish all he intended, he needed time, and he set about using every spare hour and minute efficiently. Joseph, of course, had taught him to get up early and not waste time in bed, but that was not enough. He had to devise a program that would permit him a certain number of months each year at the Jardin du Roi for his work there and a certain number away from its distractions and interruptions so that he could write his book. Eventually he decided on four months a year in Paris and eight months at Montbard, with each day planned carefully in advance. As he liked to remark, "Genius is only a tedious patience."

As a result of his stringent schedule, the first three volumes of *Natural History* appeared in 1749. Volume I contained two essays, the first of which was entitled "On the Manner of Studying and Treating Natural History." In this, Buffon acknowledged the immensity of the task that he had undertaken. "Natural history," he said, "embraces all the objects the universe presents to us. This prodigious multitude of quadrupeds, birds, fish, insects, plants, minerals, etc., offers to the curiosity of the human mind a vast spectacle, of which the whole is so great that the details are inexhaustible." That statement contained the heart of Buffon's thinking as opposed to Linnaeus'. Buffon was interested in the broad sweep of natural history, the great majestic picture of the natural world with all its parts considered together. Linnaeus was interested in details.

Obviously, the ideas and attitudes of the two men were in sharp conflict, and Buffon opened his book with an attack on Linnaeus. After pointing out that every system of classification was based on artificial considerations, he said that nomenclature was becoming the most difficult part of botany; everything else was easier to learn. Indeed, he asked, why not continue to use Tournefort's system? "It is right," he wrote, "to conserve for M. de Tournefort the glory that he has earned by a work that is sensible and usable," and, he continued, "it is not necessary for men who have learned botany by De Tournefort's method to lose their time studying this new method in which everything is changed, even the names and surnames of the plants." Later in the same essay, he attacked Linnaeus even more bitterly for his classification of animals, and here he had greater justification, for this was Linnaeus' weakest point.

But the real cause of Buffon's irritation was not Linnaeus; it was the pedantry taking over science. "In the great number of authors who have written on natural history," he said, "very few have written well. . . . Nothing is more common than works filled with numerous and dry nomenclature, wearisome and unnatural methods for which the authors take too much credit, while nothing is so rare as to find exactitude in the descriptions, newness in the facts, and fineness in the observations."

Expressing his own attitude well, he went on to say that "the ancients who have written about natural history were great men and were not limited to a single field of study. They had lofty minds, wide and profound knowledge, and broad views. If, at first glance, they seem to us to lack exactitude in certain details, it is easy to see, on reading them with reflection, they did not believe that little things merit as much attention as we have recently given them."

Then he went on to state his personal philosophy. "When subjects are too complicated for us to use calculations and measurements to advantage, and that is almost always the case in natural history, it seems to me that the true method of conducting research is to have recourse to observations, put them together, make new ones and make enough of them to assure the truth of the principal facts . . . and above all, we must draw general conclusions and try to distinguish between the facts that are essential and those that are only accessory to the subject we are considering."

Compared with Linnaeus, Buffon might seem an undisciplined thinker, and in fact, his methods brought him to many erroneous conclusions. On the other hand, his freedom of thought made it possible for him to dispense successfully with many traditions that constrained the scientific thinking of his time, and he demonstrated this in the second part of the same volume, the section entitled "History and Theory of the Earth."

"The general history of the earth must precede the history of what it has produced," he said. Without understanding how the earth came into being and how it has been shaped during the ages, man cannot understand the lives and habits of the animals and other creatures living on it.

He, therefore, started at the beginning. His cosmogony added little to what had been stated before; indeed, most of what he had to say was simply a restatement of ideas that were already current. When he discussed the actual shaping of the earth, however, he wrote sentences that shocked the more conservative minds of France. "In effect," Buffon began, "it appears certain that the earth, now dry and inhabited, was formerly under the waters of the sea. These waters were above the summits of the highest mountains, since we find on these mountains and even on their peaks the remains of sealife and of shells which, compared to shells now living, are the same. We cannot doubt their perfect resemblance or the identity of their species." In other words, he recognized fossils for what they actually are—remains of forms of life—and he used them as the basis for his theories of geology.

In the sixteenth century a French glass painter and surveyor, Bernard Palissy, saw what might well have been a piece of Chinese porcelain— he thought it was a white enameled cup—and was so inspired by its beauty he decided to learn how to duplicate it. He never did, but in the course of his studies, he became one of the best-known potters in France. His interest in pottery was also coupled with an interest in natural history, and he often turned to nature for ideas for designs. Some of his most familiar works are his large plates and vases decorated with realistic pictures of shells, reptiles, fish, and plants. While hunting for new objects that he could use, he came across some fossils near Paris. These were ideally suited to his purposes, because he could easily make casts of them to incorporate in his pottery. Consequently, he used them frequently and often compared them with the shells that he always had on hand. These comparisons soon led him to believe that the fossils had been formed from living objects.

Nicolaus Steno, the geologist who turned religious zealot, was among those who carried Palissy's ideas even further. Although no one defended Steno's book when it was ridiculed at the Royal Society of London and other seats of learning, his thinking nevertheless persisted among a small group of farsighted men who took up the same theme. By Buffon's time, however, the truth had not yet generally prevailed. Even while Buffon was working on his book, he came across an anonymous publication, *Italian Letter*, which had originally been a communication to the Academy of Bologna. In it the author scoffed at the idea that fossil fish proved that the sea had once inundated parts of the earth. Sarcastically the writer said, "It is more natural to suspect that these fish were carried by a traveler, became spoiled, were thrown away, and then became petrified in the course of time. . . ." In this way, he accounted for all the fossils found in the Alps. As for those discovered in France and said to resemble life found in the waters off Syria, the author pointed out that they were probably shells brought home by pilgrims and Crusaders. To think that the seas had brought them was preposterous. Although he admitted that fossils were once living things, he refused to accept them as having any role in interpreting geology.

When Buffon read the article, which was a direct attack on his own theories, he was furious and for once let his temper run away with him. Why, he wrote, did not the author go a step further and claim that monkeys had carried the shells to the summits of the mountains, where it was difficult for man to go? "That," he added, "would have spoiled nothing and would have rendered his explanation more probable."

With these sharp words, Buffon disposed of the author's ideas. He had no time for such nonsense. Any fool should be able to see the truth. But the author of *Italian Letter,* although he wrote anonymously, was no fool. Buffon, without knowing whom he was attacking, had rebuffed one of the cleverest men in France, Voltaire, who had written the paper. For all his iconoclasm and refusal to condone established forms merely because they were traditional, Voltaire could not bring himself to believe that fossils had any geologic significance, and many others shared his disbelief. Buffon, therefore, was upholding a radical point of view when he used fossils as the basis for his geologic theories. His thinking, although not original, was at least courageous, and he was willing to quarrel with the sharp-tongued Voltaire to sustain it.

It did, however, lead him astray on at least one important point, for his concentration on fossils made him place too much emphasis on the action of the waters and not enough on faults and uplifts, those gigantic movements of the earth's crust. "There are two causes which produce earthquakes," he wrote. "The first is the sudden crumbling of cavities in the earth; the second, which occurs more frequently and violently than the first, is the action of subterranean fires." But these were usually local, he said, and "what produces the largest and most widespread changes on the surface of the earth are the waters of the heavens, the rivers, the streams, and the torrents." Water, he thought, was the only important factor in the shaping of the earth.

In this he was mistaken, but his further speculations led him to a conclusion that, for his age, was both daring and dangerous. "If we propose," Buffon wrote, "that during the Flood the shells must have been raised from the bottom of the sea and carried to all parts of the earth, we are upholding a supposition that it is difficult to establish. It is also clear, since we find these shells incorporated and petrified in the marbles and rocks of the highest mountains, that we must then believe these marbles and rocks were all formed at precisely the same moment as the Flood and, furthermore, that before this great change, there were on earth neither rocks, marbles, chalks, nor any other material that today contains the remains of sea life."

This was a revolutionary statement. It demonstrated that the formation of the earth's surface was a continuous process—not one that had happened at a particular moment in time. It therefore demolished the ecclesiastical tenet that only two epochs existed: the Creation and the Flood. He was not only willing to dispute with Voltaire; he was also willing to battle the church.

The book, when it appeared, was a great success. As Buffon wrote to a friend, "The first edition of the work, although printed in large numbers, was entirely exhausted in six weeks; we are now making a second and a third edition, one of which will appear in eight or ten days, and the other in a month. . . . The work has already been translated into German, English, and Dutch." But he was not happy in his mind, because a few months later, he also wrote, "I hope there will be no question of putting my book on the Catholic Index, and, to tell the truth, I have done everything I could to prevent this from happening and to avoid theological bickerings, because I fear them much more than I do the criticisms of the doctors and the mathematicians."

Every month the Faculty of Theology at the Sorbonne met to hear complaints about books which might damage the public's morality or which threatened the established dogma. These complaints were brought by an official who spent his time reviewing books as they appeared. If the faculty found a book dangerous, they might order the book burned. In extreme cases, such as occurred when Jean Jacques Rousseau wrote *Émile,* the archbishop might even publish an official statement refuting the book's bad doctrines. Buffon was right; the doctors and mathematicians might criticize him, but the theologians could prevent his book from being read.

Nothing happened for weeks, but then Buffon received formal notice that his *Natural History* had been examined by the Faculty of Theology and was found to contain "principles and maxims that do not conform to those of religion." He now faced a dilemma. Should he take time from his already heavy schedule and fight the church? Or should he meekly submit and thus sacrifice his reputation as a scientist? It was not an easy choice, but as he debated which course to take, he saw a middle way. In a conciliatory letter to the faculty, he asked for a list of the specific statements they thought objectionable and promised to prepare a satisfactory response to their complaints. This move put him in good favor with the church.

"We are not able, sir, to give too great praise to such a Christian resolution," the faculty replied, "and in order to make it possible for you to execute it, we are sending the extracts from your book that have appeared to us contrary to the beliefs of the Church."

Buffon wrote a ten-paragraph response, which was a masterpiece of diplomacy. Without retracting a single one of his basic ideas, he reaffirmed his faith in the church in general terms. "I declare," he wrote, "that I had no intention of contradicting the text of the Scriptures, that I believe strongly in everything that is reported on the creation of the earth, whether it has to do with the order of time or the circumstance of events, and that I abandon the material in my book concerning the formation of the earth and, in general, everything that appears contrary to the narration of Moses, having presented my hypothesis on the formation of the planets only as a purely philosophic supposition."

For ten paragraphs, he dodged and maneuvered and tried to placate the ecclesiastical wrath. "When I said that the truths of morality have for their object and end only expediency and probability, I did not mean to speak of the real truths" of religion, he explained, but the morality established by men in their laws. "The objects of our faith are very certain," he said, "without being evident." His entire ten paragraphs were filled with such comments, all of them submissive to the church and none of them really contradicting anything he had said. Furthermore, he added, he would be more than willing to include these statements and his exchange of correspondence with the faculty in all subsequent editions.

His stratagem proved successful. The faculty, failing to see what he was doing, expressed their approval of his apparent submission, the book continued to be widely read, and Buffon was free to devote his full time to his work.

But although in public he gave the appearance of submitting to the church and although he always believed ardently in God, he had little use for the priests. When the controller general of France, as a financial measure, asked them to submit inventories of their ecclesiastical property, Buffon was delighted at their embarrassment. "All honest people," he wrote to a friend, "admire the kindness of the king and cry out against the pride and disobedience of the priests, who have flatly refused to make a declaration of the goods they possess." But, he added, taking vengeful pleasure in their discomfiture, the government will force them to do it.

IV

Having skillfully avoided an open quarrel with the church, Buffon could concentrate on the improvements he was making at the Jardin du Roi and on the next volumes of *Natural History,* which were to deal with animals. Yet these two tasks, great as they were, did not fully occupy him, for his attention was caught by Benjamin Franklin's speculations on the possible relation between lightning and electricity.

Only a few years before, in 1746, Pieter van Musschenbroek had discovered the principle of the Leyden jar and, by giving scientists a means of storing electricity, had also provided a way to experiment with it. For the first time, the learned men of Europe and America hoped to discover what electricity really was.

Benjamin Franklin was particularly intrigued by the problem, and for a number of years, whenever his other duties permitted, he conducted a series of experiments with the mysterious force. He helped design a frictional electrical machine for making sparks. He killed a turkey with electricity. He also nearly killed himself. While performing an experiment before a group of friends, he let their conversation distract him, and he inadvertently grounded two large condensers. There was a flash of light and a sound like a pistol shot, and the discharge knocked Franklin unconscious. Afterward he was ashamed of his carelessness and said that he was like the Irishman who tried to steal some gunpowder by drilling a hole in the cask with a hot iron. But in spite of the discomfort, which lasted until the next day, he continued his experiments and came to the conclusion that lightning was an electrical discharge.

This was not a new thought. Many other scientists, including Isaac Newton, had believed so, too. But Franklin went a step further than the others; he proposed a practical experiment for determining whether his theory was true. What was needed, he said, was a thirty-foot iron rod. This should be placed on the top of a tall building and insulated from both the building and the ground. Perhaps it could be mounted on a glass stool or a pad of resin. If, during a thunderstorm, the clouds overhead were actually charged with electricity, they would charge the rod by induction, and the theory would be proved correct. If, on the other hand, the rod did not become charged, it was apparent that lightning was something other than electricity. The only problem, as he saw it, was that the experiment would require a tall building, and there was none high enough in Philadelphia.

Always more interested in science than in personal acclaim, Franklin had no hesitation about sharing his ideas with others. As a consequence, since he could not conduct the experiment himself, he wrote a series of letters to a friend in England, Peter Collinson, telling him what should be done and urging him to interest the Royal Society of London. Collinson read Franklin's proposals to the society, but the members refused to carry out the experiment. Nevertheless, Franklin's letters were published, and in this form, his ideas reached France.

Buffon read the proposal with interest and immediately saw one point Franklin had overlooked: a tall building was not necessary; a long rod mounted on the ground should serve just as well as one on a tower or a church steeple. This, of course, would make the whole experiment easier, and Buffon decided to conduct it. Years before, Louis XIV had built a château at Marly-le-Roi, a small town that was close to Versailles. Originally, he had intended it to be a refuge from the court, but he soon made it so sumptuous and magnificent that it became one of the scandals of his reign. Louis XV rarely went there (it was eventually torn down), but being near Versailles and easily accessible to Paris, Marly seemed like a good place for the experiment. With Buffon acting as the guiding spirit, another Frenchman, Thomas François d'Abilard, constructed an iron rod, which was about forty feet long and tipped with brass. Since Franklin's idea of mounting the rod on a glass stool did not seem practical and since they had no resin pad, they decided on a much simpler system. They placed the rod upright on a table made from a wooden plank and insulated from the ground by the use of wine bottles for legs.

By early May, 1752, the device was in place with the long rod pointing toward the cloudless spring skies overhead. At two thirty on the afternoon of the tenth, clouds formed, and a single clap of thunder burst over the French countryside, its sound echoing around the newly sown fields. D'Abilard was not in Marly at this historic moment, but he had left a former dragoon named Coiffer in charge, and Coiffer knew what he was supposed to do. If Franklin's thesis were valid, that lone clap of thunder would mean there was electricity in the sky. And if there were electricity in the sky, the rod would be charged.

He approached it cautiously and, as he had been told to do, held out a wire that had been connected to the ground. Immediately sparks came streaming from the rod. In great excitement, Coiffer shouted to a small child who was nearby to run and fetch the Prior of Marly. The child went off running, but the prior, having heard the thunder, was already on his way. Suddenly a hailstorm broke, the stones clattering against the roofs of the houses and barns. Somehow the child's report became distorted, so most of Marly thought that Coiffer had been killed, and they ran out to see the corpse. Finally, Coiffer and the prior were able to quiet the crowd, and the prior picked up the wire himself and held it toward the rod. Once more sparks shot forth, and for the first time men knew with certainty that lightning was electricity.

The excitement was great. The prior wrote a report that D'Abilard read to the Academy of Sciences. The king himself came to see the experiment, and on his personal order the news was sent to London. Now that the experiment had been proved successful, the British were anxious to carry it out, and all that summer, in England, France, and Belgium, men erected insulated rods and marveled at the streams of sparks that poured forth during every thunderstorm. As Buffon wrote to a friend, "We are conducting fine experiments with thunder all the time. I am the one who made known the necessary information and executed the first one."

Franklin himself knew nothing about what was happening. In France he was widely hailed as "Prometheus"—after all, he had drawn fire from the sky—but in the United States he kept trying to figure out a way of proving he was right without the tall building he thought necessary. In June of the same year, about a month after Buffon's experiment, Franklin stepped out into a storm with a silk kite in his hands. Casting it upward, he caught it in the summer winds and, jerking on the string like any small boy, watched it rise in the air. For some time he let it fly in the skies without seeing any sign that it was becoming charged, and he was almost ready to bring it back down in discouragement, when he noticed that some of the loose threads on the hemp kite string were beginning to stand up straight. At that moment he touched his knuckle against the metal key he had tied to the end of the string. To his great satisfaction, a spark flew out.

To Franklin, of course, goes all the credit for the discovery. He was the one who devised the experiment and eventually carried it through, and Buffon always acknowledged that it was Franklin's thinking, not his own, that lay behind the iron rod at Marly. But to Buffon goes the credit for being the first man actually to prove that lightning is electricity.

That summer he was also busy making preparations to marry a young girl named Marie Françoise de Saint-Belin, who was a boarding student at the Ursuline convent at Montbard. Buffon's sister was the mother superior, and when he was in Montbard, he went to see her regularly. In this way, he met the girl, who was then scarcely eighteen years old. He fell in love with her almost immediately and soon was visiting the convent even more often than before. His sister was concerned about a scandal, but Buffon insisted he intended to marry the girl as soon as she was a few years older. All his acquaintances were horrified. The girl, it was true, came from an old family, but she had no money and no connections. In what way could she advance the career of the intendant of the Jardin du Roi? He should marry someone who had either a personal fortune or influence at court. But Buffon was not to be put off by any such arguments. He loved the girl, and that was that. As he wrote to a close friend, he planned to pay as little attention to the critics of his marriage as he did to the critics of his book.

In the early fall of that year, when the experiments with lightning were finished and the thunderstorms over France were growing fewer and fewer, he and Marie Françoise were married, the middle-aged, distinguished scientist standing beside the young and unknown girl. In an age that was often cynical, it was a marriage of love on both sides.

All this while Buffon had not neglected any of his other tasks. The Jardin du Roi was continuing to flourish under his direction, becoming more nearly the type of intellectual center the scientists wanted it to be, and the manuscript pages for his next volumes were beginning to pile up. When he worked on his book, he spent months collecting the information he needed. Then he wrote and rewrote, trying to make each of his volumes clear and intelligible—more than that, the type of book that people generally would want to read. Their relatively large sales testified to his success, and he soon became known in France as a prominent author, as well as a famous scientist. As a consequence, he was considered as a candidate for membership in the French Academy.

This body, known as the Immortals, has been ridiculed as often as it has been praised, but it has always played an important part in France's cultural life. Founded by Richelieu, its principal purpose is to safeguard the French language, and with this aim, the members have devoted much of their energy to preparing a series of dictionaries, most of which have tended to be slightly out of date by the time they were issued. In part, this has been caused by the natural conservatism of the academy. Ever since Richelieu's day, it has had a protector—who is always the head of the state—and the protector has the right to blackball any proposed member. This has kept out many radical thinkers, and as a result some of France's most illustrious men—Proust, Zola, Rousseau, and Diderot among them—have never been admitted.

But for all its shortcomings, the academy has always wielded influence, and election to membership is a great honor. Vacancies are created only by death, and when the Archbishop of Sens died, Buffon's name was proposed, and he was elected. On the day of his admission, he had to deliver an address, and up until a few weeks before the ceremony, he was still trying to decide on a subject. Although he was a scientist, one of the most noted in France, science was not a suitable topic for the occasion, so he decided to speak on his other great interest, writing.

In late August, when Paris was drowsing in the summer heat and many of its citizens were away in the country, Buffon stood up in the hall of the French Academy and began speaking in terms that were unusual for a scientist. "How can I fulfill the duty that is imposed on me today?" he asked. "I can only offer you what you have given me—some ideas on style that I have borrowed from your works." Throughout history, he continued, some men have always known how to command others through the power of words, but there is a vast difference between the spoken and the written word. When a man speaks, he can use every movement of his body to supplement what he is saying. He cannot do this with writing; the writing stands alone. What makes the writing speak for itself is its style.

"Style," he said, "is only the order and movement that the writer puts into his thoughts." But before deciding on the proper order, he should first consider only the major ideas that he wants to present and leave out all the others. In this way he can distinguish between sterile thoughts and fruitful ideas, abandoning the one and stressing the other. Once the writer has done this, his thoughts will fall into order. "It is for lack of a plan, for not having thought enough about his subject that an intelligent man finds himself troubled and does not know where to begin his writing. He sees a large number of ideas all at once, and since he has neither compared them nor subordinated some of them to the others, nothing helps him determine between them. Consequently he remains perplexed. But once he has made a plan, once he has assembled and put in order all the thoughts essential to his subject, he will easily see the place at which he should start. . . . His ideas will follow each other easily, and his style will be natural and graceful. Warmth will come from his own pleasure in writing and will give life to each of his expressions. Everything will come alive, the tone of the writing will be raised, its objects will take on color."

Eliminate the unnecessary, he said. Do not strive for fine phrases that have no real bearing on the subject. They are nothing better than metal leaf, which may have the brilliance of gold or silver but none of their solidity. "Nothing is more opposed to quality in writing than the trouble some people take to express ordinary and common ideas in an unusual and pompous manner; nothing more degrades the writer."

Today Buffon's discourse on style remains as fresh and meaningful as when he delivered it on that August day during the ceremony at the academy. "Well-written works," he told his audience, "are the only ones which will pass into posterity. The quantity of knowledge, the singularity of the facts, even the newness of the discoveries they contain is not a sure guarantee of immortality. If the works that contain them are written without taste, nobility, and genius, they will perish, because knowledge, facts, and discoveries can be easily removed and transferred to a work written by more skillful hands, and they will even gain in the process. These things are outside the man; style is the man himself. The style cannot be removed, or transferred, or altered. If it is noble and sublime, the author will be admired in every period, for that is the only truth that can last and even be eternal."

No wonder Buffon spent so much time in the writing of his volumes. The members of the academy might call themselves the Immortals, but Buffon knew better. Immortality was conferred, not by membership, but by the quality of the work performed by the individual.

V

In 1753, the year he became a member of the French Academy, Buffon brought out the first of the volumes of his *Natural History* devoted to animals. Just as he had promised the church, it contained his correspondence with the faculty of theology—their accusations and his recantation, which did not suggest a single change in the earlier text. He had now acquired a collaborator, a Montbard doctor named Louis Jean Marie Daubenton. This lightened Buffon's task somewhat, and by 1758, when his daughter was born, the third volume on animals had appeared. The Buffons' baby died the following year, but in spite of the sadness in his heart, Buffon kept up his rigorous schedule.

In the fall of that year, however, he wrote a friend, "You will have to excuse me. . . . I rarely write, so as not to tire my eyes which have become very feeble during the past year. You doubtless know about my sorrows. I have lost a child, who had just begun to speak, which is the same thing as beginning to love. Her mother has also been in the greatest danger and is still only convalescing."

Regardless of his personal troubles, he willingly followed the example of the king and gave his silver plates and dishes to the mint, for France was again in serious financial trouble. The War of the Austrian Succession had ended without settling any issues, and when their negotiations were over, France and Britain sat back and glowered at each other.

The years of uneasy peace did not last long. By 1756 they were at it again, but like dancers at a party, they had switched partners. The French had become disenchanted with Frederick the Great, who kept opening up secret negotiations behind their back, so they joined forces with the Hapsburgs of Austria. The British, who had become equally disenchanted with the Austrians, turned to Frederick the Great. With these realignments completed, they started the Seven Years' War. The French, who were trying to fight both in Europe and overseas—the British left the European fighting to Frederick the Great—found themselves hard pressed physically and financially. Finally, the situation became so bad that the government found it almost impossible to borrow money and had to suspend payments on many of its obligations. At this moment, Louis XV stepped forward, and he offered his own silverware to the mint. This was done with considerable ceremony, and the implication was clear: those who wanted to stay in the king's favor should do likewise. The patriots did so willingly; others were reluctant and held back as much as they could. Buffon was a patriot and gave gladly. "I have just sent my silver plates and dishes to the mint," he wrote. "It is much better for the government to ask for silver from the well-to-do than to overtax the poor."

In spite of the sacrifices of men like Buffon, the French continued to lose battle after battle. Then, at the peace convention held in Paris in 1763, their diplomats made up for their generals' and admirals' mistakes. By playing on the fears of the British planters, whose markets had been flooded by sugar from the captured French colonies, the negotiators persuaded Great Britain to return the territory that had been lost in the West Indies. They also got back their more important possessions in India and Africa. Once more everything was just about what it had been before.

To Buffon, working at Montbard on his books or returning to Paris to supervise the development of the Jardin du Roi, such events had little significance. He was a true Frenchman—his sacrifice of his silver, his sympathy for the poor, and his desire for the scientific eminence of France, all demonstrated that—but he stayed aloof from the main current of affairs. He had his interests—his family, his book, his studies, and, of course, the Jardin du Roi—and these absorbed all his time. While others visited the court frequently and went regularly to the famous salons of Paris, he stayed for the most part at the Jardin du Roi or Montbard, quietly continuing his work and rejoicing both in his wife and in his son, who was born in 1764.

His eyes were weak, a serious problem for any writer, and his health was poor; but his spirits remained high. In 1765, he wrote a friend, "I fully intend, although I was fifty-eight last September, on finishing the entire *Natural History* before I am sixty-eight, that is to say before I have commenced to talk drivel. Here are the steps I have taken to do just that. I will do still six more volumes, the material for which is almost all ready. These six volumes will contain, after the history of the quadrupeds, that of the cetaceans and cartilaginous fish, then those of the oviparous quadrupeds and the reptiles, and finally some information on plants and minerals. Thus I will have done—with black and white illustrations—all those animals whose shape is alone sufficient for us to recognize them easily. At the same time, I am having colored plates prepared for all those birds who need to be presented in color in order to be identified and whose colors constitute at least a half of their descriptions. . . . That will make a work in folio of four or five volumes, which will have for its title: *Continuation of Natural History*, by M. de Buffon."

It was an ambitious project for a man who, by the standards of his times, was getting old, particularly as he continued to improve the gardens at the Jardin du Roi and add to its collections. Originally these had been housed in two narrow, dimly lighted halls. A third room in the same building contained the skeletons, which were never exhibited to the public. (All plant specimens were in the hands of the lecturer on botany.) This, with the addition of part of Buffon's living quarters, had provided sufficient space, but the collections had grown so under Buffon's direction that something drastic had to be done. Buffon decided, therefore, to move out of the garden entirely and rent a house nearby. "My wife," he wrote a friend in the early fall of 1766, "has remained in Paris to settle us in a new house close to the Jardin du Roi, where I have given up my lodgings in order to enlarge the space used for the collections. The government has treated me honestly for my moving expense, but not *magnificently* . . . and to tell the truth, personal interest has played no part in any of this. My only determination is to give a certain degree of consistency and usefulness to the establishment that I have formed. Everything was piled up. Everything was being ruined for lack of space. It would have cost us two hundred thousand livres to erect a building. The king is not rich enough for that. His controller general has taken this course of action, which will cost only forty thousand livres for everything."

The remodeling took some time. Four exhibit halls were created. The first two contained the collection of animals; the third, mineral specimens; and the fourth, plants. Twice every week the doors were opened to the public. The rest of the time the collections were reserved for the use of students. With this major project out of the way and with his volumes on animals finished, Buffon was able to spend more time on his bird book.

Daubenton had given him considerable help with the animals, particularly with respect to their anatomy, but Daubenton and Buffon had had a quarrel that made further collaboration impossible. Yet Buffon knew that he could not finish his work alone. He had to have assistance. He turned, therefore, to another close friend, Guéneau de Montbéliard, but he asked more of him than he had asked of Daubenton. This time he wanted help not only with certain details but with the book generally. It was a happy arrangement, and it left Buffon free to pursue some of his other interests.

One of these was his iron works in Montbard. These were large enough to be used commercially—he employed 300 or 400 workers—but Buffon had not erected them to make money. He wanted them as a laboratory, where he could conduct experiments in metallurgy. Some of these involved the ability of metals to conduct heat. Another was an effort to reduce the weight of the cannons used in the French Navy.

But the subject that was most on his mind was the sickness of his young wife. "We are in deep affliction in our house," he wrote to a friend early in 1768. "My wife is seriously ill and will be so for a long time, and unfortunately she is in pain. Her situation, which demands all my cares, upsets my plans." He did everything he could for her. He even covered the road to Montbard with sand, so that if she had to go out, she would not suffer from the jolting of the carriage. But none of his efforts availed, and she died in March, 1769, at the age of thirty-seven.

Buffon was desolate. This was the woman whom he had wooed when she was a young girl in a convent school, married when he was past middle age, and had always adored. She had had no fortune to bring him, no connections at court; but she had given him herself, and that was all he had wanted. Sadly, he wrote to a friend, "I have known you too long to doubt the sincere interest that you take in my grief. First, it was a cruel shock; today it has become an illness which I regard as incurable and which I must learn to support as a necessary evil. My health is altered by it, and I have abandoned, at least for the time being, all my occupations."

The affection he had had for his wife was now lavished on his son. He worried about the boy's education; he worried about his upbringing; he wrote friends for advice; he hired tutors and supervised their work; he made arrangements for the boy to stay here, then there. And best of all, he obtained from the king a promise that on his own death, the boy would succeed him as intendant of the Jardin du Roi. This fulfilled one of Buffon's greatest ambitions, to have the management of the garden remain in the family, and it also assured the future of this boy he loved so well.

But the triumph was brief, for about a year later, Buffon became seriously ill, so ill his doctors feared for his life. As soon as this news spread, the usual intrigues started at the court. If Buffon were to die—and it seemed likely that he would—the intendancy would become vacant. Buffon's son was still too young to fill the post. The king, therefore, might be persuaded to renege on his promise to Buffon and, instead of holding the intendancy open until young Buffon was ready, give the survivorship to someone else. Among those who thought this way was one of the most skillful courtiers of Louis XV's reign, Charles Claude Flahaut, Count de Billarderie d'Angiviller. He had become director general of the king's buildings, an office that would not seem to hold much promise of influence but that, in D'Angiviller's hands, did. He saw to it that his duties brought him constantly before the king; indeed, he met with the king as regularly as the first minister. Using this opportunity, he had ingratiated himself and become one of the court favorites.

Although he was a member of the Academy of Sciences—he was a member of everything he could get into—he was not a qualified scientist. A collection of minerals represented his only scientific attainment. But he saw no reason why this should prevent him from becoming the new intendant. Working carefully through the dauphin, with whom he was also a favorite, he presented his case to the king, and the king acceded. Supposedly the agreement was to be kept secret until after Buffon's death —Louis XV had at least that much feeling—but secrets were difficult to keep at court, and soon everybody knew what had happened. The news inevitably reached Buffon, and he protested as best he could. But D'Angiviller's hold over the king was too great. "He has been my friend for twenty years," Louis XV wrote Buffon. "He is an excellent man, and I do not know anyone more virtuous." Perhaps, he suggested with the attitude of a politician, this was the best course after all. D'Angiviller would succeed Buffon. Then, when D'Angiviller died, Buffon's son would be old enough, and he could become intendant.

Buffon was furious, but helpless. He had given his life to France; he had transformed the Jardin du Roi into an important scientific center; he had carried out experiments for the government at his ironworks at Montbard; he had devoted years to writing *Natural History,* which had brought fame to his country. All he wanted in return was the survivorship of the intendancy for his son, and it had been promised to him. Now it was denied him.

Even the king was a little embarrassed by what had happened and as a recompense decided to elevate Buffon. With lofty language about the encouragement France owed to the sciences and to men of all talent "who help and adorn the nation," he pronounced Buffon a count. On the July day when the news became official, Buffon, who had now recovered from his illness, held a small party at Montbard for some of his friends. It was not a happy occasion, because they knew that the title was a sorry substitute for what Buffon really wanted.

Among the guests was Buffon's collaborator, Montbéliard. During the festivities, he called for silence; he had a little song he wanted to sing. What title, the song asked, was as good as the name Buffon? The person who had been really honored in life was the king. After all, his curate had named him Louis at his christening. And Louis was the Christian name of Buffon.

VI

In 1774, on the death of Louis XV, the throne passed to Louis XVI. The change of monarchs had little direct effect on Buffon. Although he depended on the government to support his work at the Jardin du Roi, he rarely went to Versailles and even treated the court with a certain disdain. One day, for example, while he had been working in his office, a fast courier arrived from Versailles, demanding Buffon's immediate appearance before one of the royal princesses. It was Lent, and someone had placed an unfamiliar dish in front of the princess. She had eaten it. The question, therefore, arose: What was the food, and had the princess broken her Lenten fast? Buffon was to come immediately and tell her. Buffon merely smiled and said no and returned to his work. When the king heard of the incident, he smiled, too, for Buffon had created a unique place for himself in France. Except for the intrigue over the survivorship, no one interfered with him, and he was not expected to play the usual role of a government administrator or a courtier.

Yet he could not make friends with Voltaire, who had quarreled with him before his first volume had appeared and had continued quarreling with him ever since. They each had backed different candidates for membership in the French Academy, Voltaire had attacked several friends of Buffon, and he had also written a number of caustic remarks about Buffon, his work, and his book. Buffon had answered him only the first time, but the differences between the men were so basic it was difficult for them to be anything but enemies.

Montbéliard decided to effect a reconciliation and persuaded Buffon to write Voltaire. The letter was couched in flattering terms. "To Voltaire, the First," it began. "If you look, sir, at the address of my letter, you will see that, among the small number of people of the first order, I think very truly and with great faith that you are the first. . . . There will never exist a Voltaire, the Second." Along with the letter went a new edition of *Natural History*.

As a messenger, Montbéliard chose a niece of Voltaire who was passing by Montbard. She took the letter and the book to her uncle, who was so pleased that he gave her a gold watch in return for her trouble. From that day on, according to a woman who knew both men, "they became two powerful allies, but never two powerful friends. They differed on every point. Made to admire each other and to respect each other, they were not made to love each other."

Buffon, who had always avoided quarrels, now needed as many friends as possible, whether they were Voltaires or ministers of the king, because he was about to embark on another important undertaking: the physical enlargement of the Jardin du Roi. Until now he had contented himself with improving the gardens, building up the collections, enlarging the working area, and developing a well-informed professional staff. But he felt the time had come to increase the lands owned by the Jardin du Roi and to extend them all the way to the banks of the Seine.

He had several important friends at the court who could help him: Maurepas, who was still minister; the financier Jacques Necker, who was controller general of finances; and Amelot de Chaillon, minister of the king's household, who had direct supervision over the Jardin du Roi. Furthermore, Buffon was a considerable figure in France and commanded influence in many circles. He thought, therefore, that the project could be accomplished, although it would not be easy.

Some years before, when he had moved out of the intendant's quarters, he had purchased a house. The first step was to sell this to the government. This accomplished, he turned his attention to acquiring the largest tract of land separating the Jardin du Roi from the Seine. This tract belonged to the Abbey of St.-Victor, which had rented most of it to a family named Bouillon on a life lease. This troubled Buffon, because it meant that not only did he have to purchase the land from the abbey, but he also had to indemnify the Bouillons, making the total cost prohibitive. While he was pondering a solution to this problem, he purchased several smaller pieces of property adjoining the garden, paying for them himself with the understanding that he would be reimbursed later by the government. He also bought a large tract to the south of the garden, not expecting to use it but hoping that he could persuade the Abbey of St.-Victor to accept it in trade for its land.

Then he had an idea. Almost a century before, Louis XIV, thinking someday the garden might be enlarged, had forbidden the construction of any buildings on the lands between the Jardin du Roi and the Seine. This order had long been ignored, but Buffon saw no reason why it should not be revived and enforced. Using his connections at court, he talked the king into reaffirming the order and thus gained a trump card in his negotiations.

He turned his attention back to the Abbey of St.-Victor. Why not exchange the new lands he had just bought for the lands the abbey already held? he asked. But the abbey demurred; the new lands were not as valuable. But they were, Buffon insisted. Under the revived law the abbey could no longer construct buildings on the land it already possessed. Using this sort of pressure, Buffon finally got the abbey to agree, but he still had to contend with the Bouillon family, who refused to negotiate with him on any terms he could afford. He, therefore, left this question up to the abbey, playing on the abbey's annoyance over the low rent paid by the Bouillon family. The abbey finally brought suit to break the lease, claiming fraud had been involved. Since the abbey won, the exchange was effected.

This was not the end, however. There were other lands to be acquired or traded. (Some had to be obtained from the city of Paris.) It was a complicated business and took years to finish, but Buffon saw it through, handling the real estate transactions with skill, financing some of the purchases himself or, when necessary, borrowing money from others, and all the while playing a diplomatic role that ensured him the continued support of the court.

He had already demonstrated he was an outstanding writer and scientist. He now demonstrated that he was also a capable businessman.

VII

In spite of his concern with the Jardin du Roi, Buffon had no intention of delaying his book. He still spent about eight months of each year at Montbard working, and he obtained an additional collaborator, Gabriel Léopold Charles Aimé Bexon, a young abbot. Bexon had twice called at Buffon's house in Paris and each time had been refused admittance. Not at all discouraged, he returned again, this time asking to see Buffon's secretary. He had with him a long box containing his mineral collection, which he wanted to show Buffon. The secretary, influenced by his frankness and his enthusiasm, tried to persuade Buffon to see him, but Buffon refused. Too many people came to see him, pretending they wanted to give him some important information but actually hoping to gain his influence on their behalf. The secretary finally prevailed. Buffon agreed to see Bexon, took an interest in him, and out of the meeting sprang a lifelong friendship. Buffon guided the young abbot's studies and obtained a church appointment for him. In time, when he needed more help than Montbéliard could give him, he selected Bexon as an assistant.

One reason he needed additional help was his desire to increase the scope of *Natural History*. After each volume came out, he inevitably learned more about the subjects that he had discussed, so he decided to issue a series of supplements.

One of these was called *Epochs of the Earth,* in which he expanded his original theories about the earth. Remembering his previous difficulties with the church, he opened this book with a profession of faith. "Before going any further," he wrote, "let us hasten to forestall a serious objection. . . . How do you reconcile, someone might ask, the great age that you give to matter with the sacred traditions that allow the earth an age of only six to eight thousand years? However strong your proofs, however well founded your reasonings, however evident your facts, are not those reported in the sacred text more certain? Is not contradicting them the same as failing God, who had the graciousness to reveal them to us?

"I am always afflicted," he went on, "every time we abuse the great and holy name of God. I am wounded every time man profanes it or prostitutes the idea of the First Being by substituting for Him the phantom of his own opinions. The more I have penetrated into the center of nature, the more I have admired and deeply respected His authorship. But a blind respect would be superstition. True religion on the contrary presupposes an enlightened respect. Let us try then to understand wisely the basic facts that the Divine Interpreter has given us on the subject of the Creation. Let us gather with care the rays that have escaped from the heavenly light. Far from obscuring the truth, they can only add a new degree of brilliance and splendor to it."

It was a skillful performance. But the question remained: Would he get away with it? The answer was no. As one contemporary said, "For a long time, the devout shuddered at the thought of another book by Buffon circulating among the public with approbation and privilege without drawing any counterattack from the theologians. Now we have the *Epochs of the Earth,* a daring book that deals with the formation of the earth and absolutely destroys the story told in Genesis." Once more charges against Buffon were read before a meeting of the Faculty of Theology, and once more Buffon wrote a letter of apology. This time, however, he was not sure the church would accept it. Other writers had followed his earlier example, making a public retraction that was not really a retraction, and the church had begun to take a firmer stand. If a book should be censored, the theologians argued, the author should not be allowed to escape merely by publicly proclaiming his faith. In Buffon's case, however, they eventually decided not to censor *Epochs of the Earth.* Buffon had too many friends and too much influence, but one priest published a denunciation of it.

By now Buffon was seventy-two years old and was growing weary of working on his book, particularly the volumes dealing with birds. He had never liked details—his was the kind of mind that prefers a broad subject—and he wrote to his collaborator Bexon, "Although I am not as tired as you are of this work, it nevertheless weighs on me heavily, and I wish as much as you do to be quit of it and no longer have to work on feathers."

The task of encompassing all natural history in a single book seemed endless, but he was not prepared to give up. He still kept the routine he had followed for years, going to Paris for approximately four months to supervise the Jardin du Roi and direct his expansion program and remaining at Montbard for eight months to work on his book. Each morning he went to his office located at the end of the last garden terrace. It was built on the ruins of an old tower, which had once formed part of the fortifications of the original château, and considering Buffon's wealth, it contained relatively little furniture: a marble-topped table, some chairs, a bed where he could rest, and some pictures on the walls. All his books and reference materials were kept in his library, which was housed in another building some distance away. Because his eyesight was so poor, Buffon did little writing himself. Instead, he dictated his book to one of his secretaries, whc then read it back to him while he made corrections. It was a laborious, cumbersome way to work, particularly for an author who constantly rewrote what he had done, but Buffon's secretaries were well trained and able to help their employer. In addition, they read the new material that constantly flowed into the library at Montbard—books, reports, letters, and articles—selecting what would interest him and storing the rest away for possible future use.

During the morning Buffon never permitted anyone to disturb him. No guest—no matter how important—was allowed to interrupt the master of the house when he was in his study. At dinnertime Buffon emerged. The table was always set with twenty-five places, and the cook was the best-paid servant, for Buffon liked his dinners and made the most of them. Having worked all morning, he was now ready to relax, and what he most enjoyed was hearing his guests' conversation. Occasionally they would trap him into discoursing on a subject. Then he would stop himself abruptly, saying, "Come, we're not at the academy," and turn the talk to something else. After dinner he would busy himself with his many other concerns, his correspondence, which was voluminous, with his ironworks, or with some of the experiments in which he was interested.

Under such conditions, the volumes had kept pouring forth, one after another as the years passed. Inevitably he made some serious errors. For example, he believed strongly in spontaneous generation, that living matter could be created out of inert matter. He also underestimated the value of what Linnaeus had done. Right from the beginning, he had ridiculed Linnaeus' system of classification, calling it artificial, which it was and which Linnaeus recognized. But what he substituted was far less useful in every respect. In dealing with animals, for example, he first discussed donkeys, horses, and cattle, because these were the animals best known to man. Therefore, according to Buffon's logic, they should be treated before less familiar animals, and he could see no point at all in trying to establish relationships between animals that lived on different continents and were similar to one another only in the minutest details. Linnaeus was irritated by Buffon's criticism and took his revenge in a scientific manner. The discoverer of a new species is, by custom, permitted to name it after someone he likes—or dislikes. One day Linnaeus came across a swamp plant that he thought looked particularly repulsive and that also had an offensive odor. With great delight, he named it *Buffonia*. The insult, however, did not affect Buffon's judgment. When he had finished with the animals and started writing about birds, he began to realize he had been wrong. There were too many birds to be discussed without some system of classifying them. He could, for example, start with a chicken and move on to a pigeon, using the same method he had applied to the animals, but this approach broke down under its own weight and led to endless confusion. Therefore, with some grace, Buffon began retracting his former criticism of Linnaeus, and the references he made to the Swedish scientist became more and more respectful.

In spite of its inevitable errors, Buffon's book was a monumental achievement and remained for many years the recognized authority in its field, the cornerstone of every library devoted to natural history. Whatever question arose, a naturalist's first reaction was to consult a copy of Buffon. But the book was considerably more than a compendium of information, for its author was an original thinker and investigator.

If he had done nothing more than issue his challenge on the age of the earth, he would be remembered today. This one act alone removed a substantial obstacle to the advancement of man's understanding. Until scientists knew they were dealing with a period of time far greater than 6,000 to 8,000 years, they were unable to explain many of the phenomena of life. Buffon, of course, was not the first to question the church's position, but he was such a popular well-known figure that his voice carried more influence than most.

He also showed, again carefully and respectfully, that the earth was not formed in two distinct periods—the Creation and the Flood, as the church held—but that the process had been continuous. This concept, which today is accepted as a matter of course, was dangerous and revolutionary in Buffon's time. To advance it required courage, and to make it more widely accepted eased the work of other scientists.

He made other important contributions in his book. In his discussion of animals, he considered man as one of them, an important and decisive step forward that has made many regard him as the true founder of anthropology. Man's anatomy and physiology had been studied long before Buffon's time, but Buffon was one of the first to examine the development of man from childhood to maturity, to study the causes of death at certain ages, to draw up mortality tables, and to look at man in relation to his environment. True, he believed man had two sides, one spiritual and one material, which had to be observed separately. This may have been a concession to the church, or the thought may have come from his own pessimism. (He wondered, for example, why love brought only happiness to animals and so much unhappiness to men.) Nevertheless, he saw men as physical beings that should be studied as such.

He also laid down some general principles of research that still hold valid. Opposed as he once had been to the best in Linnaeus, he also saw the danger of overspecialization in science, of fragmenting it, and of dividing it further and further into small pieces. To Buffon, the aim of science was to provide generalizations based on careful experimentation, to do in biology what Newton had done in physics, not to lose sight of the whole in the pursuit of the minute.

In the realm of purely scientific thought, these contributions were great, but he also accomplished something no one had ever done before: he made the study of biology popular. With his careful writing, with his constant emphasis on style, with his ability to describe nature more graphically than most men, he succeeded in producing what amounted to a best seller. Every educated person in France read Buffon's volumes—priests, as well as courtiers, noblemen, merchants, shipowners, and also their wives. And so, too, did other important Europeans. Because of Buffon, the life sciences were something to know about, at least by those who wished to be fashionable.

And, of course, he had conducted his experiments in metallurgy, drawn the lightning from the skies, encouraged many younger scientists, and developed the Jardin du Roi into the center Dufay had envisioned. Its collections were now enormous, its buildings in good shape, the botanical gardens well cared for, and its staff of researchers and teachers one of the best in Europe. Students and scientists came from many countries to study there and listen to the lectures. Indeed, on every count, the dying intendant, Dufay, had chosen his successor well.

VIII

For all the eminence he enjoyed in France and throughout Europe, for all his scientific accomplishment and the pleasure he felt at the improvements in the Jardin du Roi, Buffon's last years were not happy. Fame and success did nothing to relieve the racking pain from which he suffered. As early as 1779, the Duke d'Orléans, noticing how he was tortured by the jolting of a carriage, lent him a special litter to use in making the trip from Montbard to Paris, and in 1783, Mme. Necker, wife of the financier and a close friend of Buffon, gave him a carriage that was designed to ride more smoothly than most and save him agony when he was traveling. The pain was caused by gallstones, and although his condition would sometimes improve, each day of relief was later paid for by a more serious attack. He took the advice of everyone except doctors, and he tried every remedy except those the doctors offered him. He had no use for medicine, even though he was a man of science.

To add to his sadness, he watched his collaborators, men younger than himself, die before him. First, in 1784, Bexon, the young abbot whom he had befriended; then the following year, Montbéliard. These were the people with whom he had worked the most closely, the men whom he had trained and helped and who, in turn, knew what he wanted and how he wanted it done and had shared in the preparation of his book. At the time of life when he was weary and most needed their help and companionship, they were gone.

His greatest satisfaction was in Georges Louis Marie Leclerc Buffon, the son born of his happy marriage to the young, but penniless, love of his middle age. He fretted and worried over the boy's upbringing, placing him with that friend or this and selecting his tutors, one of whom was Jean Baptiste Pierre Antoine de Monet, Chevalier de Lamarck, and a member of the Academy of Sciences at the age of thirty-five. Together Lamarck and young Buffon traveled through Europe, visited the famous botanical gardens, and talked to other scientists, for Buffon had not yet completely abandoned the hope that he could regain the survivorship of the Jardin du Roi from D'Angiviller. This, next to finishing his book, represented his greatest ambition.

After studying with Lamarck, young Buffon made a trip to Russia, where he was favorably received at court, and then to Prussia, where the name Buffon was well known to Frederick the Great and opened every door to him. But the right of survivorship continued to elude his father, and Georges Buffon was forced to find a career in the Army. As some compensation, however, he made a marriage that delighted his father, because the girl was both charming and rich.

He, in his turn, was a devoted son. Whenever he could, he joined his father at Montbard, and when his father was ill, he served him as a tender, loving nurse. Nothing his father asked was too much for him to give, and in a gesture which today seems sentimental, but then was appropriate, he erected a statue to his father in the garden at Montbard. It was a surprise, done while his father was away, and a sincere acknowledgment of his father's greatness.

But even this happiness in Buffon's life was shattered. The young couple, whose marriage had first seemed so brilliant, now became strained. They spent less and less time with each other, and Mme. Buffon went more and more often to the court of the Duke d'Orléans. It was well known she was one of the duke's favorites; her engaging ways had caught his eye. In time, she inevitably became his mistress. At first, the liaison was kept secret, but soon the relationship was common knowledge at the court, then common knowledge throughout France.

To the young husband, the blow was bad, but since his love was already dead, not as bad as the blow to his father. He who had done so much for France, who had so great a pride in his family and his name, now found his son cuckolded by a nobleman against whom Buffon could not protest. Writing to his son about his financial arrangements, he said in his intense bitterness, "You know that you must, at the same time, remit fifteen hundred francs *to your dead wife.*"

In 1788, Georges Buffon became a major, partly because of his own performance, partly because of his father's efforts. That year Buffon, who was now eighty-one, was back at Paris and again supervising the work being done at the Jardin du Roi, when he became seriously ill. Although his friends had little hope he would recover this time, he had several wishes to fulfill. One was to visit the Jardin du Roi again. In the warmth of an April sun, with the light gleaming on the trees, he entered the garden on the arms of two servants. He stood for a moment or two on the path, looking around him at the plants he had cared for, the flowerbeds he had laid out, the grounds he had enlarged at so much effort. Then he nodded to the servants, and they led him slowly back to his sickroom. It was his last visit.

His other unfulfilled wish was still to obtain the survivorship for his son. He had notaries brought to his bedside and dictated to them a touching plea addressed to the king. Louis XV, he was sure, had meant to give the survivorship to D'Angiviller only if his son was too young. "But now his father finds him worthy of the position, and hopes that His Majesty, after fifty years of loyal service, will not let the survivorship fall into any hands but these."

It was a futile attempt. Louis XVI refused to reverse the earlier decision favoring D'Angiviller. Frustrated in his last wish, Buffon died that spring, while the first warm breezes rustled the leaves in the Jardin du Roi he had loved so well.

IX

One of Buffon's associates at the Jardin du Roi was the Count de Lacépède, whom he had befriended as a young man. Lacépède had written an article on electricity, and Buffon read it and invited him to join the staff of the Jardin du Roi. There he moved ahead under Buffon and in 1788, the year of Buffon's death, published his own book, *The Natural History of Oviparous Quadrupeds and Serpents*. Buffon did not like the book but said that since Lacépède was a friend, he would not criticize it.

Buffon's son joined with Buffon's brother, who was executor of the estate, in persuading Lacépède to do the writing needed to complete the dead man's book. They did not know Buffon's feelings or that in a letter, found years later at the Jardin du Roi, he had specifically named another man to finish his work.

Shortly after Buffon's death, the fires that had been kindled under Louis XV and nourished by Louis XVI's incompetence broke into open flame. The wave of change swept over France. Old traditions were thrown aside, and divorce was permitted. Buffon's son took advantage of the new laws to free himself of Orléans' mistress and marry a younger woman, whom he loved.

But the wave was a tidal wave. There was no way of checking or stopping it once the mobs had tasted freedom, and it engulfed Buffon's family. His possessions were declared forfeit to the state, and the crowds came to Montbard to demand his silver—the replacements he had bought for the silver he had so gladly given his country years before.

And they executed his son, killed him like hundreds of others on a scaffold in Paris.

But before the blood-streaked blade descended on his neck, he shouted one last defiance at the angry crowd. He had already reminded his executioners that he had served the Revolution in its early stages, had held a commission in the republican army, and had renounced all his titles. But they would not listen. The time had passed when men were willing to listen. They could only hate. Now he hated, too, but his hatred was tempered with pride, and he had one last sentence to utter—one tribute to pay his father, one honor to claim for himself.

Standing on the ugly platform in the Place de la Révolution, he cried out as loud as he could, "Citizens, my name is Buffon!"

5

A Glimpse of a Truth

JEAN LAMARCK: 1744–1829

I

In 1761, while Buffon was fretting over the effect of the Seven Years' War on the government's financing of the Jardin du Roi, his son's future tutor, Lamarck, was a young soldier trying to win glory for himself on the battlefields of eastern Europe. It seemed to him the only possible way to escape the undistinguished life into which he had been born.

His father was a former French army officer, one of thousands who had fought for the court at Versailles and, after eluding death, passed the remainder of their years on a small pension. In addition to his military income, he owned some lands in Picardy, a part of France that touches on the English Channel almost directly north of Paris. But these lands were small, too small to support a large family, and his two-story house could barely accommodate the many children he had sired. It is extremely doubtful, therefore, that in 1744 he welcomed the birth of his last and eleventh child, Jean Baptiste Pierre Antoine de Monet, Chevalier de Lamarck.

The little influence he wielded with the army had already been exhausted in obtaining appointments for his older sons, so the church appeared to be the only career possible for the youngest. As soon as Lamarck was old enough, he was enrolled in the Jesuit college at Amiens to

prepare for the priesthood. There he received a reasonably good education at no cost to his family. His school records have long since disappeared, but he had a good mind, and it is unlikely his studies caused
him much difficulty. Nor is it probable that he was bothered by the aus-
tere conditions in which the students lived. Surely they were no worse
than those that he had known at home. But he was restless and troubled
by his desire to get away from the priests and their books and join the
army. All his life he had heard his father talk about war—Lamarck's
father had little else to talk about—and he had watched his brothers
march off and, when they returned, listened to their tales of adventure.
More than anything else in the world he wanted to be like them.

Two years after his father's death, he discussed his longings with his
mother. She gave him her consent and obtained for him a letter of introduction from one of her neighbors to a Colonel de Lastic, one of the
officers serving under the Duke de Broglie. In the late spring or early
summer of 1761, Lamarck started eastward on his search for glory, not
knowing that the war was nearly finished.

When Lamarck presented his letter of introduction to Colonel de Lastic on July 14, 1761, the French armies were preparing for the Battle
of Vellinghausen, and the colonel spoke bitterly about Lamarck's neighbor, who had placed such a burden on him by sending him a boy in the
middle of a campaign. Still grumbling, he offered Lamarck some food
and a place to sleep in his tent and dashed off to headquarters to receive
his orders without giving him a further thought. Next morning he was
surprised to find that Lamarck, without De Lastic's permission, had assigned himself to a company of grenadiers and was marching off with
them to the battle.

Their assigned position was behind a hedge. In front of them was a
deep ravine, which protected them from a direct assault by the opposing
army, but not from enemy gunfire. The bullets rattled through the
hedge, snapping off twigs as they flew toward the grenadiers, and the
men could see puffs of smoke each time a cannon was discharged and a
ball sent in their direction. For someone who had never been in a
battle before, it was a bloody baptism by fire. One by one the grenadiers
fell, clutching their chests or their entrails in a futile attempt to stop the
spurts of blood. A cannonball roared through the hedge, struck the company's captain, and blew his head from his neck, spattering his brains
over Lamarck. Then the lieutenant was killed and finally all the officers and all the noncommissioned officers. Only fourteen men were
left alive, and although the ravine still protected them from an infantry
charge, the scorching gunfire continued.

From their position behind the shattered remains of the hedge, Lamarck and the grenadiers could see the other French soldiers forced

to leave the field, but they themselves, being left without any officers, did not know what to do. Finally, they decided to elect their own commander and, for some reason, chose the newest recruit of all. At the age of seventeen and toward the close of his first battle, Lamarck found himself in command of the remnants of the company, who, of course, expected him to take the responsibility for ordering their retreat. To their surprise, he refused. They had been given a position to hold, and according to Lamarck, they would continue to keep it until they either were dead or had received orders.

By the time the French army had completed its withdrawal and formed new lines, Colonel de Lastic realized he still had one company left on the battlefield and sent an adjutant to find it. The adjutant slipped as quietly and unobtrusively as he could through the woods and finally reached a spot where Lamarck could see him but the enemy could not. Waving a handkerchief in the air, he caught Lamarck's attention and indicated to him that he should retreat and join the rest of the troops. Somehow Lamarck was able to lead his handful of men through the enemy's lines and back to the French army, where he was enthusiastically greeted by Lastic. In fact, the colonel was so pleased with the performance of his new recruit that he almost immediately asked that he be commissioned. A short while later, on August 1, the orders arrived, and he became an ensign in the French army.

II

Lamarck soon learned that military glory, while it can be quickly earned, is just as quickly forgotten. He had been a hero and received his reward, but the undistinguished campaigns fought by the French armies in the succeeding months gave him no further opportunity to demonstrate his courage. He rose in rank from ensign to sublieutenant, but with the signing of the peace treaty early in 1763, his opportunities for advancement came to an end. He spent five more years serving in various garrisons such as Toulon and Monaco and then suffered a severe accident. What the accident was nobody knows, although there is evidence to believe his fellow officers violently disliked him and attacked him in an effort to drive him out of the regiment. In any case, he was incapacitated, and the army surgeons were unable to cure him. He therefore resigned his commission and went to Paris for medical treatment. There a doctor discovered he had an abscess below his ear. After he had lanced it, Lamarck recovered.

The cure, however, did not settle Lamarck's future. He still had no career, and the small inheritance he received on his mother's death was not enough to support him. For a year he tried working for a banker but, finding this unsatisfying, took up the study of medicine. The change was not as surprising as it might appear. During his years of garrison duty, he had developed an amateur's taste for the sciences, particularly botany, and his studies gave him a chance to indulge it. Whether he finally obtained a medical degree is not certain, but he learned botany— there was a botanist attached to the medical school to teach the students about herbs—and finally took courses in the subject under Bernard de Jussieu, one of the staff members of the Jardin du Roi. Jussieu, a believer in Tournefort's method of classification, was rearranging the Jardin du Roi's collection and eventually used Lamarck as an assistant. This gave Lamarck the part-time employment he needed to bolster his finances and also an opportunity to develop his own system of classification, which was a combination of Linnaeus' and Tournefort's. Although the system was never universally adopted, it proved practical for his own purposes.

His fellow students, however, joked about it. In reply, he challenged them to bring him a plant that he could not identify. This led to a demonstration at the Jardin du Roi. Lamarck occupied the center of the stage, while the other students were ringed around him, prepared to discredit him. Each of them held specimens for him to examine, and one by one he named them correctly. His outstanding success in meeting this test prompted him to drop his other scientific interests—even meteorology, on which he had written a short paper—and concentrate on botany.

To establish himself in his new field, he wrote a book, *French Flora.* Unlike his inconsequential paper on meteorology (it proposed a theory that the atmosphere was similar to the ocean with waves and tides affected by the moon), *French Flora* was a highly competent piece of work, a guidebook to the plants of France.

Buffon liked the manuscript and assigned his assistant, Daubenton, to help write an introduction to it. He also arranged to have the book published by the Royal Printing Office at no expense to Lamarck. As all the copies were delivered to Lamarck, he could even make a little money selling them. Furthermore, the work attracted considerable attention, and in 1779, the year after it appeared, Lamarck was elected to the Academy of Sciences as an assistant botanist. This was the lowest rank of membership, but since there were only twelve such positions, it was an achievement for Lamarck to have obtained one.

Nevertheless, he still had difficulty finding regular employment, although Buffon acted as his patron, giving him various jobs around the Jardin du Roi. None of these, however, appears to have been on a steady basis, and Lamarck must have wondered where his next meal was coming from. Aside from the short-lived glory brought by the publication of *French Flora,* he led a grubby, obscure existence, so little noticed that almost nothing is known about either his personal or his professional life. Presumably his home was near the Jardin du Roi, so he could trudge back and forth to his work. Presumably he was married, because the records show he eventually had three wives, all of whom died before him. Also presumably he totted up his accounts at the end of each week, trying to figure out how he could get through the next. Nothing relieved the dull grayness of his poverty, and although his book had carried him into the academy, it took him no farther. Like his one act of heroism in the army, its effect was limited.

Buffon, however, had not lost interest in him and, in 1781, offered him the position of tutor to his son during a tour of Europe. Lamarck was delighted to accept. To travel through Europe with the letters of introduction that Buffon would give his son! To see the leading scientific centers on the Continent under the auspices of Buffon! To carry notes of recommendation to the French ambassadors in the principal cities! It was as though his old world had suddenly been dissolved and replaced with another, as though with one bound he had ascended from almost the bottom to near the top of the social scale.

Off they went, the older man and the young boy whom Buffon hoped would become the intendant of the Jardin du Roi. At Vienna, they found the French ambassador out of town but were cordially received by his assistant, the Marquis de Barthélemy, who arranged meetings for them with everyone of consequence. At Prague, they were the guests of the emperor, who was on maneuvers with some 45,000 men. Young Buffon was invited to eat at the emperor's table—the records do not show whether Lamarck was included in the invitation—and talked with the leading generals. They visited Germany, Hungary, and Holland, touring the museums, looking at the botanical gardens, and visiting several important mines. (In those days, mines had a scientific interest that they do not have today. They provided an important means of studying the earth's structure.)

The trip was a good experience for Lamarck, and he would have liked to have gone farther, particularly to Italy, but he could not get along with young Buffon. According to his version of their differences, which he related many years later, the boy was haughty, opinionated, vain, and thoughtless. Furthermore, he resented having Lamarck look after him. This is a different picture from that painted by some of Buffon's correspondents, who wrote that everyone was impressed by his son's appearance, knowledge, and graciousness. Undoubtedly the truth lay somewhere between the courtiers' praises and the tutor's bitter condemnation.

One day, according to Lamarck, the boy wanted to go out alone; Lamarck insisted they go together; they began to argue; finally, in a fit of anger, the boy picked up a bottle of ink and poured it over his tutor's clothing. When he was seventy-five years old, Lamarck still told the story with anger, and the insult must have hurt him even more at the time. Here he was, a man who had risen from the ranks during the war and proved himself a hero under fire, a man who had been appointed to the Academy of Sciences and written a consequential book on the flora of France, a man who had done all this strictly on his own merits without an influential father to assist him. Was he to take insults, real or implied, from a young boy? The answer in Lamarck's mind was no. He tried to assert his authority. The boy rebelled. At last, the quarrel grew so great that Buffon called them both back home.

Later, when Buffon sent his son to Russia, Lamarck remained in Paris. He had lost his great opportunity to visit more of the scientific and cultural centers of Europe, and there is also little doubt he had lost the esteem of Buffon. As long as Buffon lived, Lamarck was never able to obtain permanent employment at the Jardin du Roi.

III

Still seeking the glory he had looked for on the battlefield, still frustrated in his efforts to make an important place for himself in the scientific world, Lamarck found himself forced to accept whatever work might be offered him and eagerly accepted the authorship of a botanical dictionary.

This dictionary, which was to appear in several volumes and form part of a larger encyclopedia, was a commercial venture, and Lamarck was completely subject to the desires of the publisher. On the publisher's orders, he abandoned his own system of classification, the one he had successfully defended at the Jardin du Roi, and adopted the method used by Linnaeus. He was not even allowed to arrange the plants according to their genera and species and had to place them in alphabetical order. This must have been a blow to his professional pride, because he strongly believed that collections, whether they were in museums or presented on the printed pages of a book, were useful only if they demonstrated the relationship between one plant and another. But he had no choice. The botanical dictionary was his sole means of livelihood, and the publisher's instructions were firm.

In spite of this, the book had great merit. In it, Lamarck attempted to describe and classify every known plant. It was a tremendous undertaking and required him to search through all the available written material, talk to other botanists, and obtain as many new specimens as possible. Several of the staff members at the Jardin du Roi assisted him, especially Jussieu, and he was fortunate in meeting a traveler from the Far East who had brought home with him a large collection of plants. He had supposed this collection would be extremely valuable to the botanists of France, but no one paid any attention to it except Lamarck. Annoyed at the others, the traveler gave it to him.

There were few other bright moments in his life. He was still poor and driven by an ambition he could not satisfy, and he could not obtain a salaried position. Then, in 1788, Buffon walked for the last time in the Jardin du Roi, which he loved so deeply, returned to his room, and died. His last-minute efforts to obtain the intendancy for his son were, of course, unsuccessful, but D'Angiviller, who should have succeeded him, decided to pass the job on to his own son. Apparently he felt some embarrassment over the way he had acted and was unwilling now to assume the position himself. The change of administration was not beneficial to the Jardin du Roi—young D'Angiviller was no more a scientist than his father—but it helped Lamarck, for in June, 1789, he received an appointment as keeper of plants. The salary was only 1,000 livres a year, which was modest even in those days, but it was the first regular salary Lamarck had received since resigning from the army.

At last he had security, but the security was almost immediately threatened by the collapse of France's economy. Ever since the reign of Louis XIV, the country had been on the verge of bankruptcy. The nobles refused to pay their share of the taxes or even to cultivate their lands properly. The hierarchy of the church, like the courtiers at Versailles, was much more concerned with its privileges than with the responsibilities it should have borne. Instead of trying to relieve the poverty it saw everywhere, it spent its time augmenting its holdings. The army and navy had also proved expensive. The various wars in which France had engaged, including its participation in the American Revolution, had created an enormous drain on the treasury, until, in 1788, the budget showed a deficit of 126,000,000 livres. But even worse than the deficit itself was the necessity of using more than one-half of the total national budget to pay the interest charges on money already borrowed. A genius might have been able to rescue the country from disaster, but Louis XVI was not one.

The people of Paris were already in a frenzy. Unemployment was rampant, because a reduction in the tariffs had flooded France with British goods. During the winter preceding Lamarck's appointment, the Seine, which carried so much of Paris' commerce, froze over. Grain could not reach the city, and when the spring sun of 1789 unlocked the water again, prices soared two to four times above what they had been before. Rioting broke out in the streets, and when the Estates-General met at Versailles —it was the first time it had met in 175 years—the stage was set for a battle between hereditary privilege and human dignity. Always before, each estate's vote had been counted as a unit. Thus, the First Estate—

the clergy—and the Second—the nobility—could outvote the Third Estate, composed of commoners. But this time the Third Estate revolted. When Louis XVI refused to change the procedure and permit each man's vote to be counted individually, it went into separate session and swore it would never adjourn until the king gave in. Under such pressure, Louis XVI ordered the clergy and nobility to join the commoners, and the National Assembly was thus formed.

One of its first responsibilities was to examine the country's finances, not only to produce more revenue, but also to reduce costs, and before the summer was out, it called on D'Angiviller's son for an accounting of the expenses of the Jardin du Roi. The intendant was a pathetic figure at a time of crisis. He knew his way around the court, how to smile on people of influence, how to reach the king's ear. But he did not know how to deal with a legislative body acting on its own. In a panic, he suggested changes that might be made at the Jardin du Roi. One of those changes was to eliminate the job he had just given Lamarck.

Whatever his faults—an inability to get along with people seems to have been one of them—Lamarck was no coward. He had already demonstrated his bravery on the battlefield; he now demonstrated it in political infighting. No sooner had the intendant recommended the elimination of his job than Lamarck responded by sending two petitions directly to the National Assembly.

In the first, he described his book, *French Flora,* and told how it "had greatly popularized the study of botany in France." He mentioned his travels with Buffon's son, although he carefully omitted all reference to his responsibilities as a tutor. Writing about himself in the third person, he said, "His ardor for botany and all natural history increasing more and more, he wished in 1780 to visit the leading botanical gardens of Holland and Germany, also the natural history collections and the commercial mines in those countries, as well as in Hungary. Because of this, he was given by the late Count de Buffon an order from the king creating him a correspondent of the Jardin du Roi and was instructed to travel and do research on rare objects and also to collect as many of them as possible for the Jardin du Roi." The ink-stained, frustrated tutor had undergone a metamorphosis; he was now an official undertaking a commission for his government. But no one can blame Lamarck. He had truly held the title of correspondent of the Jardin du Roi; he had visited the mines and botanical gardens; he had brought back whatever he could collect to the Jardin du Roi. Was it necessary, when he was fighting for his economic life, for the security he had at last attained, to tell the whole truth?

When it came to describing the botanical dictionary, he saw no reason to explain that this was a commercial venture, arranged in a manner he did not approve. Instead, he proclaimed its virtues. "No one," he wrote, "has undertaken an enterprise of this nature; no one has tried to give descriptions of all the known plants." Ending his petition with a summary of his own merits, he said the intendant's recommendation "would be a crying injustice; but the Assembly has not committed it, and it is difficult to believe that it would commit it."

Having stated his qualifications in his first petition, Lamarck in his second one explained why his functions as "Keeper of Plants" were important. "The best-informed specialist on animals—in a word, one who knows the quadrupeds, birds, fish, insects, and worms—would certainly have only vague and insufficient knowledge of plants, and a botanist who really knew his own field would not know much about minerals and animals." No, he argued, instead of just a botanist as keeper of plants, the Jardin du Roi should also have a zoologist and mineralogist as well. Nor could the duties of the people like himself, who were assigned to arranging the collections, be carried out by the professors of the Jardin du Roi.

On August 20, 1790, the subject was debated by the National Assembly. Some members favored eliminating Lamarck's position, as well as the job held by one of his friends, in order to effect the necessary savings. Others, however, suggested eliminating D'Angiviller's job instead. This was a complete reversal of D'Angiviller's original proposal and demonstrated the speed with which public opinion—and public power —had shifted. As long as the king ruled the country firmly, D'Angiviller's father, with the king's assistance, could take the survivorship of the intendancy away from Buffon. In the late summer of 1790, however, the king's assistance was worthless. In fact, it was even less than worthless: it was a positive detriment, and D'Angiviller, instead of being on the offensive, was forced into the defensive. Buffon, if he had been alive, would have laughed at the discomfiture of his old enemies, but D'Angiviller was not defeated completely. After the debate, the members of the Assembly agreed on a compromise. They kept Lamarck and his colleague on the staff of the Jardin du Roi but deducted the amount of their salaries from the salary of the intendant.

Emboldened by this success, Lamarck sent the National Assembly another petition concerning the collections of the Jardin du Roi, suggesting some changes that would make them "truly useful." He thought there should be six curators, four of them handling the zoological collections, and one each for the plants and minerals. He proposed that visitors should be allowed to hold and examine the specimens that interested them, instead of being forced to look at them through glass, and he even got into such details as the hours when the halls should be open to the public. It was an arrogant document. Lamarck, after all, was a minor official with no real authority, and yet he was taking it on himself to tell the National Assembly how the Jardin du Roi should be organized. But this was in the spirit of the times. Although Lamarck called himself the Chevalier de Lamarck—there is some question whether, as the youngest son, he had any right to do so—he was one of the thousands in France who had pretenses, but no influence. They were a sad group of people, proud of their families, but with little means of satisfying their ambitions. After the summer of 1789, when the National Assembly was formed and the Bastille taken by the angry Paris mobs, they at last dared speak out and tossed aside all their diffidence.

These circumstances explain Lamarck's action, but not his final remarks. After concluding a proposed set of articles to govern the collections, he went on with unbelievable haughtiness: "After what has been said above, it is doubtless superfluous to add that the articles which have just been suggested . . . are all essential to the true interest of this public institution. Without them, this same establishment will always be reduced to being nothing more than a magnificent object, just as it has been until now." So much for D'Angiviller! So much for Buffon! So much for Buffon's son, who had thrown the ink at him! So much for every bureaucrat who had stood in Lamarck's way over the years, the officers in the army, the professors at the Jardin du Roi, the courtiers who had kept the nation's best positions for themselves! He was, by this time, a bitter man and at last free to vent his feelings.

Indeed, the whole staff of the Jardin du Roi was given an opportunity to air their grievances and make suggestions, for the National Assembly had requested them to prepare a set of recommendations for the future organization of the institution. They met on August 25. D'Angiviller was present, but no one paid attention to him. He was in theory the king's representative and appointee, but they passed him over when they chose a president to direct the preparation of the report to the Assembly. Daubenton, Buffon's former collaborator, was the person selected.

On September 9 the staff met again to approve its committee's report. The recommendations were radical. The Jardin du Roi and its collections were to be dissolved as an institution. In its place, the government should create a natural history museum. This museum would have no officers; everybody would be a professor, and everybody would teach. All nominations for vacant positions would be made by the staff, although the king would retain the privilege of formally making the appointments. Last and most important, the museum would be governed by an assembly made up of its own professors. Had not the National Assembly only a few days before declared that men are born free and have equal rights? The rules proposed for the new museum put that declaration into effect.

The National Assembly was anxious to reform the Jardin du Roi just as it was anxious to reform everything else in France, but centuries of abuse and injustice could not be repaired in a single stroke. The problems that submerged the Assembly were enormous. The Duke of Brunswick, against whose army Lamarck had fought his first battle years before, marched from the east and threatened to torture any Frenchman who laid a hand on the royal family. The Jacobins, far more extreme in their views than those who had launched the revolution, maneuvered to destroy the Assembly and replace it with a more radical group. This attempt succeeded in the late summer of 1792, when the National Convention was elected, and a few weeks later, the French army defeated Brunswick at Valmy. But order did not grow out of disorder. Once released, the forces of freedom moved like a flood away from freedom into anarchy. Those who had opposed the arbitrary acts of the king now became arbitrary. Mobs broke into the prisons, held kangaroo courts, and summarily executed those they considered guilty. Who, in those months of crisis, had time to distinguish between innocence and guilt? Who had time to reason, to think, to seek truth out? Who had time to control emotion, to question Danton's words—strange words from a minister of justice—"audacity, more audacity, always audacity." Who, in the midst of such turbulence, had the leisure to consider the future of the Jardin du Roi?

No one except its staff, who struggled along as best they could. D'Angiviller, acknowledging the opinion against him, had resigned as intendant in 1791. To fill his place, the staff selected Jacques Henri Bernardin de Saint-Pierre, as unlikely a choice as they could have made. Bernardin de Saint-Pierre had written a book, *Nature Studies,* which was a highly moralistic interpretation of natural history and a novel, *Paul et Virginie,* which struck a new low in sentimentality. (At the end of the book, Virginie is on a sinking ship. A sailor tries to rescue her, but she demurely refuses to take off her voluminous clothes and swim, preferring to sink to the bottom with her petticoats still on.) Under Bernardin de Saint-Pierre's direction, the Jardin du Roi continued to operate without any further drastic changes. Lamarck published a few papers on botany and quarreled with the other members of the staff over the classification of herbs, for which he was publicly rebuked by Bernardin de Saint-Pierre.

Early in 1793 the National Convention took up the problem that had been left unresolved by the National Assembly: How should the Jardin du Roi be reorganized? Daubenton again presented the staff's recommendations. These were substantially the same as those made a few years earlier, but the Convention did not feel it necessary to have four professors of zoology—which Lamarck had originally proposed—when two would do, one for the vertebrates and one for the invertebrates. Even these two positions might be difficult to fill, particularly the second, since none of the staff was qualified in the subject.

Earlier, when he had been defending his position as keeper of plants, Lamarck had argued hard for specialization. "A botanist who really knew his own field," he had stated, "would not know much about animals and minerals." But now his problem had been reversed. It was no longer a question of holding onto his old post, but a matter of obtaining a new one, and Lamarck, like many other men in similar circumstances, quickly forgot what he had said before. He knew nothing about zoology. That he admitted. But there was no reason, he argued, why he could not learn. Because no one else was better qualified, the authorities agreed, and in 1793, the year that Louis XVI went to the scaffold and the Place de la Révolution reeked with the blood of decapitated victims, Lamarck became professor of the natural history of insects and worms at the newly constituted National Museum. The salary was 2,500 francs, the largest he had ever received. And the title? What they meant by the title was professor of invertebrate zoology.

They could not use the word "invertebrate," because Lamarck had not yet coined it; he did that later. In the fall of 1789, at the age of forty-five, he knew nothing at all about the subject.

IV

Lamarck's debt to the Revolution was great. Without the turmoil it created, he could never have shattered the social barrier that, under the king, had prevented him from rising to a higher place. In his next publication, a work on physics, he spoke out with fervent republicanism, dedicating his book to the people of France in these terms: "Accept, magnanimous People, who are victorious over all your enemies, People who have known how to retrieve the sacred and inalienable rights that you have received from nature; Accept, I say, not the flattering homage which, under the old regime, the grovelling slaves offered the Kings, the Ministers, and the Nobles who protected them, but the tribute of admiration which your virtues and your energy, developed by the wisdom and the intrepid constancy of your Representatives, have earned for you." There was more of the same, along with a special letter to the National Convention calling attention to his patriotism and his desire to serve his country through science.

But he did more than write words of praise to the National Convention; he was determined to show his appreciation for his new appointment by his actions. France, as he saw it, had at last given him a chance. In return, he would give France the best he had to offer, his scientific judgment and experience. From then on, he became active in the administration of the National Museum, holding various positions and rarely missing a meeting of its staff, and he plunged into his new field of invertebrate zoology, examining the large, but poorly arranged, collections at the museum and studying the writings of other scientists.

He quickly discovered that this was a sadly neglected field. Linnaeus had dismissed all invertebrates by dividing them into two groups—insects and worms, the latter classification containing any invertebrate that was not obviously an insect. Since no one had done much to improve this system, it was practically impossible to put the collections of the museum into any sort of working order. Furthermore, there was no great interest in invertebrates. Insects had been studied to some extent, but none of the others. Later, in his book *Zoological Philosophy,* Lamarck explained why. "When the world really started to cultivate natural history," he said, "and each kingdom gained the attention of the naturalists, those people interested in the animal kingdom concentrated on animals with vertebrae, that is to say, mammals, birds, reptiles, and also fish. These groups of animals, because the species are generally larger and have better developed parts and faculties and also because they are easier to describe, seem to offer more of interest in their study than those that belong to the division of invertebrate animals. In effect, the extreme smallness of most of the animals without vertebrae, their limited faculties, and the fact that their organs are less closely related to man's than to those of the more perfect animals, have caused them to be scorned as vulgar; and until our time, they have aroused only a very mild interest on the part of most naturalists."

In other words, the division of the museum assigned to Lamarck was considered one of the least important. Invertebrate zoology was a subject no one particularly cared about—except Lamarck. He saw challenge in it. Until then, he had gained a reputation as a competent botanist, but this was a popular field. As a botanist he had to compete with the reputations of experts like Linnaeus and Buffon. He might, with years of work, approach them, but probably he could never surpass them. Invertebrate zoology, however, offered a chance to the man who would seize it, who could look at these animals with a fresh view.

Lamarck was that man. As he told his classes later, the extreme number of these small animals and their immense diversification provided a means of discovering many truths, particularly the progress of nature and the means it has used to give existence to all the living organisms that we now know.

V

Over the years the number of students who attended the lectures of the newly appointed professor varied greatly. At one time they dropped to a low of 7, at another, they rose to a high of 128, but Lamarck never became truly popular. Perhaps his somewhat shabby appearance put the students off. He barely made enough money to support his family, and consequently he never attained the glamor of his wealthier associates. What probably disturbed them most was his offensive manner. He was absorbed with his own ideas and had no use for any others. When he lectured, he spoke with warmth, vivacity, and conviction, but if a student raised an objection to one of his statements, Lamarck would stop, listen, and then, without replying, simply continue with what he had been saying before. He had no interest in the give-and-take of discussion, no willingness to let the students exercise their own minds, no desire to hear their thoughts. Yet the lectures were worth attending, because Lamarck, for all his arrogance, began developing some revolutionary ideas.

In 1802 he published, under the title *Hydrogeology,* a book on geology, which also set forth his philosophy of science. "Men with small vision can concentrate only on small objects, and yet they are the majority. Now, as a consequence of the value each man places on what he himself can do, ordinary people scorn or disapprove of big objects and great ideas." But, he asked, "must we always evade considering the larger questions just to busy ourselves incessantly gathering all the little facts that are discovered without ever trying to find general truths, of which the little facts are only the final results?" Like Buffon, he had imagination and breadth of vision.

Sometimes these qualities led him astray. For example, he developed a curious theory about the formation of the granites. This had occurred, he said, "at the bottom of the seas and resulted from deposits of their composite molecules, brought there by the waves slowly enough to allow them to aggregate." Coarser-grained rocks like gneiss were merely precipitated more quickly.

But along with a few other inaccurate ideas, he introduced some thoughts that were startling in his age. Like Buffon, he realized that the earth must be much older than the theologians would admit, but he carried this thought to greater extremes than Buffon had dared. "Oh," he wrote, "how great is the antiquity of the terrestrial globe. And how small are the ideas of those people who think that only six thousand and a few hundred years have passed since the formation of the earth and our present time.

"The naturalist and the geologist, in this regard, see things very differently. One looks at the fossils spread over every part of the earth from the greatest heights to the greatest depths. The other, the number and disposition of the layers of rocks. . . . Why cannot they see from this that the antiquity of this globe is so great that it is absolutely ouside the power of man to understand it in any way?"

This was a dramatic challenge to the accepted beliefs of the early eighteenth century. But Lamarck went even further. "How much greater the antiquity of the earth will seem to man, when he at last forms a correct idea of the origin of living bodies, as well as the causes of the development and gradual perfecting of the organization of these bodies, and also when man realizes that, time and circumstances having been necessary to give existence to all living species as we know them today, he himself is the final result and the present *maximum* of this perfecting process. The length of time taken to do this just cannot be known."

Buffon had walked on dangerous ground, but Lamarck simply hurled himself into the volcano. His ideas, of course, should have set traditionalists against him, but two factors worked in his favor and protected him from their wrath. For one, the Revolution had somewhat liberalized thinking in France. For the other, almost no one read his book. Buffon, when he had fought with the faculty, had been one of the nation's outstanding figures, a popular writer and a leading scientist. Lamarck was merely a minor professor at the museum. Even his colleagues did not pay much attention to his ideas, and he escaped condemnation largely because he had never really escaped the obscurity that had originally driven him to join the army.

His ideas in zoology were also a curious mixture of the true, the half-true, and the untrue. He believed, as Buffon had done, in spontaneous generation. In his book, *Investigations into the Organization of Living Bodies,* he admitted that "it has never happened, and never will happen, that lifeless, unorganized materials, no matter what they are, have under any circumstances formed an insect, a bird, a rabbit." Such forms of life could only be produced by generation. On the other hand, he argued that the world was filled with a mysterious fluid, "of a pasty and gelatinous consistency," that could give rise to life. Indeed, he believed that new animals were constantly being created out of this fluid, although these animals were limited to the very simplest forms.

Like Linnaeus, he originally believed that no new species was possible, but he was not a rigid thinker, and as he worked with the collections at the museum, he began to gain new insight into zoology. Each year in his course, he would summarize some of his thinking, and on May 11, 1800, as he stood before his class, he announced some new concepts. One of these had to do with what he called the degeneration of the organs in a body. When one started with man, the highest living form of life, it was possible to trace each part backward down the scale of life and observe that the organ became simpler and simpler and often disappeared altogether. This led him to state that various forms of life could be listed in a series. He made it clear that neither was this series a straight line nor could it be divided into species and genera. It was something more vague and irregular than that and dealt only with the major classifications, not the minor. Nevertheless, if such a series were drawn up, the most complicated form of life would be at the top and the least complicated at the bottom. Such a statement implied a direct relationship between one form of life and another.

He also developed two other interesting ideas in his class. One of these had to do with the variety of life. Nature, he said, needed both time and circumstances to give existence to its productions. The amount of time available was almost endless; he had made that point in his work on geology. As for the circumstances, these, too, were limitless. Thus, for example, there was a place in the world for water birds and their specially equipped feet. What was more, he told his class, he could have gone through the lists of every genus and every species and shown that "their organs, their faculties, etc., etc., are entirely the result of the circumstances in which the race of each species has been placed by nature." The second idea he proposed to his class concerned overpopulation. Each species, he pointed out, produced far more than enough of its own kind to survive. Yet no one species predominated. Nature had accomplished this feat by providing certain checks: the simpler animals, which reproduced more rapidly, had shorter lives than the more complicated animals. Some animals preyed on others and destroyed them. Some animals were limited by the climates in which they could survive and thus were not free to roam the world. This, of course, was an extremely oversimplified statement of the way in which nature's balances work, but Lamarck did recognize that such balances existed.

Most of his students probably listened with some interest to these remarks—some of them probably yawned—but it is doubtful that any of them had the slightest conception of the direction in which Lamarck's thinking was leading him. If he could only put together these isolated conceptions—the relationship between all forms of life, their adaption to their environment, and the struggle of each individual to survive against the checks provided by nature—he might produce a startlingly new theory. And that is what he proceeded to do.

VI

During his lifetime Lamarck published many works; but the three that contain his principal thoughts on evolution were *Investigations into the Organization of Living Bodies,* which appeared in 1802, *Zoological*

Philosophy, in 1809, and *Natural History of Invertebrate Animals,* which appeared in several volumes from 1815 to 1822. (In the last book, he coined the word "biology" just as he had sometime earlier coined the word "invertebrate.")

Zoological Philosophy, which is the most famous of the three, contains the essence of his theory. Here is how he described his own contribution to science: *"Conclusion generally accepted until today:* Nature (or its Author), in creating animals, has foreseen all the possible sorts of circumstances in which they will have to live and has given to each species a constant organization, as well as a determined and invariable form, which forces each species to live in the places and climates where we find it. . . .

"*My own particular conclusion:* Nature, in successively producing all the species of animals and, commencing with the most imperfect or the simplest in order to end its work with the most perfect, has gradually complicated their organization, and after these animals spread into all the habitable places on the globe, each species has received the influence of the circumstances in which it is found, the habits that we know belong to it, and the modifications in its parts which observation shows us." In one bold stroke, the professor at the museum knocked aside the Creation and what was known as the fixity of the species. Instead, he said life had developed from simple beginnings and, through a long chain, although certainly not in a straight line, had reached the highest forms. Furthermore, its adaptations had been influenced by the conditions around it.

In saying this, he did not deny the role of God. "Nothing," he wrote, "exists except by the will of the sublime Author of all things. But can we not assign to Him rules in the execution of His will and determine the method He has followed in this regard? Has not His infinite power been able to create an *order of things* which successively gave existence to all that we see . . . ?" But he was not willing, as other naturalists were, to reserve a special place for man in God's order. "If man is distinguished from animals," he wrote, "only with relationship to his physical makeup, it is easy to show that the characteristics which make him a separate family have all been produced by former changes in his habits, changes that have become particular to his species."

Lamarck also mentioned again the checks and balances that he had talked about to his classes. "The multiplication of the small species of animals is so considerable, and they renew their generations so promptly, that the little species would render the globe uninhabitable to the others, if nature had not put a limit on their prodigious multiplication. But as they serve as prey to a multitude of animals, and as they have short lives and die from sharp drops in the temperature, their quantity always maintains itself in the proper proportions for the conservation of their own races and all the others."

Far ahead of his time, Lamarck had with astonishing originality developed a theory of evolution. He saw clearly that one form of life was not just related to another, but that one form had come out of another, starting with the simplest. He recognized that mankind, instead of being separate, was an integral part of the chain of life. He saw the relationship between various forms of life and their environments. And he realized that nature went through an enormous elimination process. Unfortunately, he missed part of the significance of what he said. Nevertheless, it was an astounding performance, and except for his inability to communicate his ideas and the basic weakness of his theory, he might be better known today as the first evolutionist.

The weakness, which made it possible for less imaginative scientists to attack him, was summarized in the four laws that he wrote about in the *Natural History of Invertebrate Animals.* "*First law:* Life, by its own forces, tends continually to increase the volume of every body which possesses it and extends the dimensions of its parts up to a limit that is appropriate to itself." This statement really made no difference to the overall value of his conclusions. It was in the next three laws that he went badly wrong. "*Second law:* The production of a new organism in an animal body results from a new need that continues to make itself felt and a new movement which that need creates and extends. *Third law:* The development of the organs and their strength of action are constantly in proportion to the use of those organs. *Fourth law:* Everything that has been acquired or changed in the organization of individuals during the course of their lives is conserved by generation and is transmitted to new individuals who come from those that have experienced the changes." It sounded formal, it sounded impressive, but it undermined his entire theory.

For he was simply saying this: that a giraffe has a long neck because it wants to eat the leaves on the upper branches, not that giraffes have long necks and can therefore survive by eating from the upper branches. And to make the damage even worse, he argued in his fourth law that characteristics acquired during the lifetime of an individual can be passed on to succeeding generations. Applying this to man, for example, he argued, in effect, that certain individuals wanted to see farther. Therefore, they stood up. This created changes in their bodies making it easier for them to stand. These acquired changes were then passed on to the next generation; this, of course, was wrong. He had somehow in his reasoning got the horse behind the cart, although he had recognized many of the factors actually involved. Instead of grasping the importance of nature's program of changes and eliminations, he left evolution up to the individual and the individual's will. One animal, one form of life, might wish to do something, do it, acquire the characteristics needed to do it well, then pass those characteristics on to the next generation.

This does not detract from the greatness of his thinking. He had broken through the barriers imposed by theology and scientific tradition. He had left Linnaeus and Buffon and the others far behind in the search for universal laws, and although other scientists ignored him, he had pointed a way for them to follow.

VII

Some men seem destined to go through life unnoticed and unloved. No matter how obsequious they are, they gain little patronage. No matter how warm they try to be, they acquire few friendships. No matter how brilliant their ideas or actions, fame eludes them. Lamarck was one of those.

He had been a hero on the battlefield and won only a low commission. He had praised the National Convention in excessive terms and obtained only a minor professorship. He spoke eagerly to his classes and barely held their interest. He produced the most dramatic and imaginative idea of his times in biology, and hardly anyone bothered even to discuss it. When they did, they attacked it.

Some quality was missing from his personality. He seems to have been unable to communicate with other people. The social and the wealthy lined the walls of their libraries with editions of Buffon's works; they probably had never heard of Lamarck. Buffon rarely went out to social events, not because he was uninvited, but because he could not afford the time; Lamarck rarely went out, because no one wanted him. Buffon was constantly besieged by young scientists asking for his help and approval; few students cared what Lamarck thought of them.

And so he continued his lonely way during the years after he became a professor. He went to the museum to do his remarkable work on invertebrate zoology and give his lectures. Then he went home again. The cold winds of fall blew the dead leaves across the Place de la Concorde, rattled the branches of trees in the Tuileries. In winter the housewives of Paris lit their scanty fires of coal and wood and waited for spring to come. Then the flowers burst forth in the Bois de Boulogne; the heat of August oppressed the city, driving its wealthier inhabitants into the country. Once more the dead leaves fell and covered the cobbled walks, and once more the housewives gathered their bundles of fuel. So the months passed and became years, and the years became decades, and Lamarck remained in comparative obscurity.

He was desperately worried about money. When the National Assembly offered bonuses for special services to the country, Lamarck applied for one, spending hours writing long appeals. He received enough money to help, but not enough to make him comfortable. He seems to have had no particular joy in his wives—even their deaths remain obscure— and his children do not appear to have brought him comfort. Only one of them married and gave him grandchildren.

He founded an annual publication on meteorology. In it, he published the times of sunrises and sunsets and the phases of the moon, as well as his own weather predictions. It was rather like the almanacs that became so popular in America during the nineteenth century, and it represented a serious attempt on Lamarck's part to collect meteorological information from all over the country and develop a technique for long-range forecasting. All he succeeded in doing was to irritate Napoleon.

There are several versions of what happened. According to one, Napoleon held a reception for the academicians of France. Each brought with him his latest publication as a present for the emperor, and Lamarck, too, had a book, probably his *Zoological Philosophy*. When his turn came, he stepped up to Napoleon and held out the volume. Napoleon snatched it from his hand, asked him if it was another of his ridiculous books on meteorology, berated him for publishing such nonsense, and said he would accept it only out of deference to Lamarck's years. Lamarck tried to explain that he was presenting a book on natural history, then, unable to contain himself, burst into tears.

He was haunted, too, by one of his colleagues, Baron Cuvier. Personally much more like Buffon than Lamarck, Cuvier commanded wide respect in the scientific world and was held in esteem by the government. When he spoke, France listened. He respected Lamarck's work in botany and the classification of invertebrates, but he had no use for Lamarck's theory of evolution, and he was influential in destroying its effect on contemporary thinking. Lamarck was no match for this younger, stronger enemy. Cuvier had prestige; Lamarck had none. Cuvier was wealthy; Lamarck was poor. Cuvier was eloquent and persuasive; Lamarck had difficulty even lecturing to his students. Cuvier's opposition, therefore, was insurmountable. Lamarck's ideas on evolution could not prevail against it.

In the last years of his life, Lamarck's troubles increased. For some five years, he knew the horror of cataracts, the slow, painless, but inevitable, dimming of sight. First, there was just the slight blurring as he studied a specimen with his magnifying glass, the thought that perhaps the glass was not clean. Then the realization that the fault lay, not in the lens, but in his eyes. Then the hope that, since he was an old man, the process would be slow and that his body would not outlive his eyes. But it did. During his last years, he groped his way through the museum's corridors like the blind man he was.

When he died in 1829, his friends held a service for him at St.-Médard Church in Paris. It was December, and the weather had turned cold. Smoke was rising from the chimneys of the houses, and the students at the museum had on their heavy garments. After the service, a few people followed the hearse during its slow funeral procession to Montparnasse. At the grave, two scientists gave short eulogies. One represented the Academy of Sciences; the other, the museum. It was a routine burial. Even his colleagues' tributes were routine.

The grave into which they lowered him was rented only on a temporary basis; at the end of five years the body had to be removed. It was all his estate could afford. When the gravediggers came the second time, his work was still unrecognized. No one knows where they placed the body. No one cared enough to find out.

Several of his children had died before him. Those who remained sold his furniture, his books, and his collections. They had to; these were his only assets. The professors at the museum petitioned the minister of the interior to pay Lamarck's pension to his older daughter; they found a job arranging dried plants for the other. Lamarck's son, Auguste, became an engineer of bridges and dikes and apparently a good one. But none of them ever found the fame and fortune that had also eluded their father.

He was an ill-fated man. His scientific work had gained him only a small professorship. His theory of evolution, dramatic, daring, and imaginative as it was, earned him nothing but scorn except from a few of his associates, and their voices were drowned out by men like Cuvier. The final irony came years later, when Darwin's writings made scientists reconsider Lamarck's. By then it was too late. Darwin resurrected Lamarck from obscurity but at the same time destroyed him. For Darwin's theory was much better conceived.

Yet to the young army officer who later became professor of invertebrate zoology goes the credit for having briefly lifted the veil hiding one of the great truths of the natural world. Sadly almost no one was looking when he did so.

6

Reconstructing the Past

GEORGES CUVIER: 1769–1832

I

If Baron Cuvier had shown the slightest enthusiasm for Lamarck's theories or if he had even suggested that they be studied and discussed further, the history of the discovery of evolution might have been changed, and Lamarck would have died a famous man. But Cuvier did just the opposite. Everything Lamarck said or wrote about evolution contradicted his own belief that each species was fixed. There could be, and were, minor variations in different forms of life, Cuvier recognized, but he thought these variations did not lead to the creation of new species. Lamarck's whole proposal, therefore, was absolutely ridiculous, and so, instead of encouraging his colleague, Cuvier continually attacked and derided him. Yet in one of the great paradoxes of science, Cuvier gave the later evolutionists one of their most important tools, for he helped perfect the study and reconstruction of ancient fossils, and many consider him the founder of modern paleontology.

Like Lamarck, he was the son of a retired French army officer, but he was not a French citizen. Montbéliard, the town where he was born in 1769, was not then a part of France but was ruled by the Duke of Württemberg, and it was to the duke that Cuvier and his family owed their allegiance. The town was a pleasant place with a handsome castle, a good

138

school, and an unusually tolerant and intelligent population, composed mostly of Lutherans. But as Cuvier's father had found out, it was not large enough to provide him with an acceptable living. Consequently, he followed the example of many other men of good, but poor, families, and joined the army—in his case a regiment of Swiss mercenaries who had enlisted in the service of the French king. For some forty years, he fought for the glory of France, taking part in the War of the Austrian Succession and in the Seven Years' War. Then he returned to Montbéliard with a medal and a small pension to pass the rest of his days living in the narrow three-story house, where his son was born.

At the christening, he named the new child Jean Léopold Chrétien Frédéric Dogobert, but the boy's mother almost immediately started calling him Georges after another son who had died earlier, and that was the name he retained the rest of his life. The two of them, mother and boy, were unusually close, and even in his old age, Cuvier always enjoyed receiving a bouquet of red stocks, because those had been his mother's favorite flowers. But although she was affectionate, she did not spoil him. She recognized that he would have a difficult time making his way in life and that the world offered little opportunity to the son of a retired army officer and a citizen of the small community of Montbéliard. The only means of overcoming this double handicap was a thorough education, and she began teaching him to read as soon as he was old enough. When he entered the elementary school, she walked with him each day, making him repeat his Latin lessons over and over again, so that he soon won a reputation as the best-prepared student. (This was quite a feat on the part of Mme. Cuvier, because she knew no Latin.) She also made him learn his catechism and the Psalms of David. Most important, she was careful to see that the house was always filled with good books for him to read.

At the age of ten, he entered the Gymnasium. Montbéliard's citizens had always been interested in education and intellectualism, and the quality of the school reflected this. Its faculty was excellent, and its head had an enlightened attitude toward teaching. To memorize facts, he said, was not enough. The students should also learn to think. In addition, he believed that most schools spent too much time on the classics and not enough time on contemporary, practical learning. These were advanced ideas, but they worked to Cuvier's advantage. For he learned sufficient Latin to stand him in good stead all the rest of his life—he could always read and write it with ease—but he also received instruction in mathematics and natural history, which formed the basis for his later scientific career. His natural history teacher, in particular, was lively and imaginative. Instead of keeping his students in the classroom, he led them on frequent field trips into the surrounding countryside and developed various experiments for them to conduct. He had them, for example, collect caterpillars and observe them as they went through their life cycles. Teaching such as this stimulated Cuvier, but like Buffon before him, he was not obsessed by science to the exclusion of other subjects. He was also extremely interested in writing and did well in both composition and rhetoric, thus gaining the ability to communicate his ideas to others.

He soon showed that he had a practical mind and a quick eye and that he was not easily swept away by the romantic or the exaggerated. On at least one occasion, his forthright attitude caused considerable embarrassment. He was attending a party given by his uncle, who had hired an itinerant magician to perform. Two of the magician's most startling tricks featured a fountain that he could apparently make flow or stop by the sound of his voice and a dagger that he could drive into his arm and withdraw covered with blood. All the children and most of the adults, too, were amazed, but while they gasped and applauded, Cuvier watched the performer quietly and intently. When the magician was finished, Cuvier stood up and explained to his relatives exactly how the tricks were performed and even drew diagrams of the mechanisms involved.

Cuvier enjoyed more at his uncle's house, however, than visiting magicians; he also found a set of Buffon's *Natural History* which his uncle, like many other people in Europe, was buying volume by volume as they were published. At first, Cuvier examined the books just as casually as the other children did and exclaimed with them over the fascinating pictures and strange descriptions. But on subsequent visits he began to study the volumes more seriously and to make copies of the black-and-white illustrations. After that, he attempted to color his drawings, an effort that required him to read the descriptions more seriously. Some of the species in the book were not illustrated, and when he also tried to draw their pictures, he was forced to study the text even more closely and thus gained considerable knowledge of natural history.

His highly developed intellectual curiosity, as well as his excellent performance at school, made him a favorite of his grandfather, who held him up as an example to the other grandchildren. But Cuvier also had his weaknesses, one of which brought about a change in the career his mother had planned for him. She wanted him to enter the church—she considered it a better alternative than the army—and the necessary education should not have been difficult for Cuvier to obtain. Each year scholarships were awarded to the two top classics students, and Cuvier obviously was capable of winning one. But before judgment was passed by the professors, Cuvier came across a French translation of Pliny's *Natural History* and became so intrigued with it he neglected Virgil and Cicero. This irritated his teacher, who took revenge on him by ranking him third in his class. Although in his later years Cuvier continued to feel that he had been badly wronged, the teacher had actually done him a favor. By closing the doors of the church, he forced Cuvier to select another field and thus drove him against his will into work he was better equipped to perform.

At the moment, however, it seemed a disaster. Without an education, Cuvier had no prospects for the future, and without a scholarship he had no chance of obtaining an education. By a stroke of fortune, the Duke of Württemberg happened to visit Montbéliard. Some time before, the duke had founded a military school, which he later transformed into the Caroline Academy at Stuttgart. Becoming more and more interested in education, he had built the school into a university authorized to offer degrees in every field except theology. Hearing about Cuvier's brilliance and his problem, he agreed to accept him as a student.

The academy was separated into two general divisions. One prepared its students to become "men of the world"; the other offered courses in specific skills, such as forestry, finance, medicine, law, and business. Much of Cuvier's time during his first year was spent in learning German, which he had not known. Then, since he had to make his own living, he entered the second of the two divisions. The variety of courses he took was wide. Of course, he studied mineralogy, botany, and zoology—one of his professors introduced him to the works of Linnaeus—but he also added several courses in what today would be called public administration, including police organization, financial law, and civil architecture. In 1787 he received an award given each year to the highest student in the class, but when he was graduated in 1788, the year in which Buffon died, he was disappointed not to receive a government appointment from the duke, who usually employed the brightest students. Having no further reason to remain at Stuttgart, Cuvier returned to Montbéliard.

II

Through a fellow student, Cuvier heard of an opening as a tutor in the household of the Count d'Héricy and obtained the position. In a short time he was bound for Caen, which lies on the Orne some seven or eight miles from the English Channel. His pupil, he discovered, was a good-looking thirteen-year-old boy, agreeable and pleasant, but not in the least studious. The count, who expected to inherit a large fortune on the death of his own father, the marquis, was less agreeable, but his wife was a delightful woman of thirty. (Cuvier, writing to a friend, found it almost impossible to describe her beauty, her fine nature, and her great virtue.) He took pleasure, too, in the social life of the Héricy family. For the son of the old soldier at Montbéliard, it was a giddy experience to meet counts, former generals, and at least one friend of Voltaire, and it was valuable to him, because he gained the social ease that later helped make him so popular.

He also began to be interested in French politics. The world Buffon had known was rapidly crumbling, as the king at Versailles futilely tried to save the monarchy with a small compromise here and another there, none of them sufficient to check the growing tide of liberalism. Even when the Count d'Héricy moved his family out of Caen and took them to the quiet countryside at Fiquainville, Cuvier's interest did not lessen. He studied French political history so he could better interpret current events, and he closely followed Necker's reports on the nation's finances.

By early 1789 rioting had broken out in Normandy, and Cuvier reported in detail in a letter how a group of servants had attacked some university students, killing one and wounding several others, and how the students had retaliated by attacking the nobles, who were saved only by the arrival of a detachment of troops. But it was not the bloodshed that attracted his attention as much as the intellectual aspects of the prerevolutionary days. With care and thought, he analyzed the nation's problems. As a result of his studies, he became more of a revolutionary, and the attempt of the king and queen to flee the country in 1791 disgusted him. How could anyone respect a king who, having sworn to uphold a constitution, tried to slip away at night and seek refuge among his country's enemies? This, for Cuvier, spelled the end of any sympathy for the monarchy.

In spite of his concern about politics, he did not neglect his scientific studies. He collected as many plants as he could and examined the rarities he found in the botanical gardens at Caen and in the gardens of his pupil's grandfather, the old marquis. Nor did he limit himself to botany. He corresponded with other scientists he had known as students, read Linnaeus and Buffon carefully enough to make corrections in their works, learned more about birds, hunted for fossils, and also worked on the anatomy of fish.

One of the scientists he came to admire was Félix Vicq-d'Azyr, a French physician. Vicq-d'Azyr had always been interested in anatomy and had given lectures on the subject in Paris, but although he had aspired to be professor of anatomy at the Jardin du Roi, he was passed over for the post by a government that seemed intent on making him practice medicine rather than do the work he preferred. He was assigned to various parts of the country as a public health officer to control epidemics, became permanent secretary of the Royal Society of Physicians, which he helped found, and was appointed personal physician to Louis XVI. (When the Revolution broke out, this appointment worked to his disadvantage.) Although his life was short and his days occupied with government business, he tried to improve comparative anatomy by combining the ideas of Haller, Linnaeus' critic, and Daubenton, who had been Buffon's collaborator. The final results were fragmentary—Vicq-d'Azyr did not have enough time to perfect his methods—but he fired Cuvier's imagination, stimulating him into trying to carry the work further. How busily Cuvier set about doing this is indicated by a letter he wrote from Caen in 1790, describing how he had prepared descriptions of 420 seashells, 110 fish, 11 amphibians, 14 sea urchins, 18 corals, and 30 butterflies.

The Count d'Héricy, foreseeing political trouble, had been wise to move from Caen to Fiquainville and to let himself and his household slip into the obscurity of the countryside. Here he was simply the head of another family, not a member of the nobility forced to take sides in the great disputes raging throughout France. Cuvier benefited from this circumstance. He had time to study the political situation without having to partake in it and leisure to work and to think. But in 1793, while the Terror was shaking the social and moral foundations of the nation, a series of events took place that changed the course of Cuvier's life. His mother died, an event which, in view of their close relationship, was a particularly severe blow to him; France annexed Montbéliard, automatically making him a French citizen and no longer an alien who could remain aloof, and the commune of Bec-en-Cauchois, a small town near Fiquainville, selected him as secretary of its general council. He who had been an observer of politics now became a participant.

The position he accepted had many responsibilities. Most of the members of the council were illiterate, so Cuvier not only kept all their records, but also wrote most of their pronouncements, such as a discourse celebrating the recapture of Toulon. He also had to deal with the national agent assigned to the commune. This man, who represented the government at Paris and therefore had extraordinary power, was both a drunkard and a brute and fell into the habit of abusing several members of the council. One night he appeared at a meeting and started shouting at some of the members and finally struck one. This was too much, and Cuvier, who always had a strong feeling for human decency, helped prepare a stinging official rebuke. He also intervened in a dispute over the taxes imposed on the town to support the troops quartered there. Deciding that the suggested plan for taxation was entirely arbitrary, he refused to sign the necessary papers until he had forced the government to accept his revisions.

As the Revolution became more moderate in tone, Cuvier considered leaving Normandy for Paris, where he would have more opportunity for advancement. He talked to a friend, Henri Alexandre Tessier, who had been a member of the Academy of Sciences but had fled to Normandy during the Terror. Now that the worst of the Revolution was over,

Tessier was no longer afraid to reveal his whereabouts, so he agreed to help Cuvier find employment. In glowing terms, he described Cuvier to many of his former associates and in a short time convinced them that Cuvier deserved a place in Paris. But Cuvier, with his native shrewdness, was not willing to give up his position in Normandy unless Tessier's friends could offer him a definite job. This they were finally able to do. On the strength of their recommendations, Cuvier was offered the professorship of natural history at the central school in Paris, and in the first half of 1795 he left Normandy and headed south for the capital.

III

Unlike Lamarck, who entered Paris untrained and unknown, Cuvier's reputation had preceded him, and he had already gained enough skill in anatomy to justify everything Tessier had written about him. Important scientists readily received him at their houses, and when the professor of anatomy at the Jardin des Plantes, the postrevolutionary name for the Jardin du Roi, died that same year, the staff named Cuvier to the post, although he was only twenty-six years old.

Cuvier immediately moved into a small house that was made available to him at the garden. The first floor he used for living quarters. A dining room and a drawing room on the second floor gave him a place to entertain guests. The third floor, which was under the mansard roof, became his office, where he immediately set to work organizing the skeletons that had been collected by Daubenton. Buffon had been proud, and rightly so, of all that he had done for the Jardin du Roi in extending its grounds and enlarging its display space, but now Cuvier was shocked by what he found. The bones, he said, were piled up like fagots, and he had to straighten them out and arrange them before he could start enlarging the collection and continue his work, which he had begun in Normandy.

At the same time he collaborated on a paper with another staff member of the Jardin des Plantes, Étienne Geoffroy Saint-Hilaire, who was professor of zoology. A man of great personal courage—during the massacres of 1792 he had rescued a number of priests at the risk of his own life—he was also highly gifted and had an imaginative turn of mind. For some time, he had been studying the work done by Buffon and Daubenton in comparative anatomy and was continuing it. In Cuvier, he found an excellent and enthusiastic collaborator and coauthor. Cuvier also published by himself a paper dealing with the classification of Linnaeus' "worms," using their nervous and circulatory organs as two important features. One of his colleagues was Lamarck, who was just as impressed with Cuvier as Geoffroy Saint-Hilaire was and who adopted many of Cuvier's ideas.

Cuvier did not limit his interest to living organisms. As early as 1792, while he was still in Normandy, he had begun to collect and examine fossils, and in January, 1796, still less than a year after he had arrived in Paris, he read an important paper on elephants. "The fossil bones of elephants," he started out, "are those that have been dug up the most and have generally received the greatest attention from observers and even from the public. Their enormous mass has made them noticed and collected everywhere; their extreme abundance in every climate—even in climates where the species could not exist today—has caused astonishment, and has made people dream up an infinite number of hypotheses to explain them; but people should have put as much energy into determining the conditions and nature of the problem as they did into their efforts to solve it. And perhaps this negligence in fixing the basis and fundamental terms of the problem has been one of the causes which has made most of the solutions so unfortunate.

"I mean that people have been very slow to consider the subordinate questions, which need to be answered before we test our minds on the great problem.

"Are our present elephants the same species? Supposing there are several species, then are the elephant fossils from different countries the same? Or are they scattered in different countries according to their species? Or are they different and lost species?

"It is evident that we cannot say anything demonstrable about the problem before having resolved these preliminary questions, and yet we hardly possess the necessary information to solve some of them.

"The studies of elephant bones published up until now contain so little detail that even today a scientist cannot say whether they belong to one or another of our living species, and of the enormous quantity of fossil bones about which so many writers have spoken, we have good drawings of only two or three." This was a brash statement for a young scientist who had just come to Paris, but Cuvier could be outspoken. He even named some of those who he thought had done careless work. "Daubenton," he said, "who had a skeleton from Africa before him, did not perceive the enormous differences between its molars and the molars of fossils, and he confused the fossil femur of an animal from the Ohio River with that of an elephant."

Cuvier's purpose was not merely to criticize; he had definite beliefs about scientific thinking he wished to express, and these beliefs formed the keystone of his work and attitude. He opposed broad theorizing and speculation without a solid foundation of factual evidence. Even though the process was slow and long, he favored the accumulation of numerous small facts that could be checked and rechecked and used to take a forward step in man's thinking. Buffon had intrigued him as a child, indeed had aroused his interest in natural history, but Buffon's way was not his way. On the other hand, he agreed completely with Buffon that fossils were not freaks of nature formed by some strange geological occurrence. He recognized that they were the remains of once-living animals and should be treated as such.

In this, he was comparable to most scientists of his time, for the ideas that Buffon had expressed so well were rapidly becoming more generally accepted. Where Cuvier differed from many of his contemporaries was in the care with which he studied fossils and the philosophy he brought to this study. He expressed this philosophy later in a discourse on the revolutions that he thought had taken place on the surface of the earth. "In my work on fossil bones," he wrote, "I set myself the task of recognizing the animals to which the fossil debris spread throughout the earth really belonged. It was an attempt to go down a road on which others had hazarded only a few steps. As a new type of antiquarian, I had to learn how to restore these monuments of the past and make sense of them; I had to collect and put into order the fragments of which they were composed, to reconstruct the ancient beings to which these fragments belonged, to reproduce them with their proportions and their characters, to compare them finally with those that live on the surface of the globe today. This was an almost unknown art, which presupposed a science that had scarcely been developed before, the relationships which prevail between different parts in all organized beings. I then had to prepare myself for these researches by longer research on existing animals; an almost complete review of all present life could alone give proof to the results of my work on ancient life." Cuvier was undertaking far more than an accurate and more detailed study of anatomy; he was trying to develop a scientific means of reconstructing former life from the fossil fragments that remained.

He was helped in this by his early interest in physiology, as well as in anatomy. When he had worked with Geoffroy Saint-Hilaire, he had already decided that animals might be classified according to certain physiological characteristics, and this interest led him to become a functional, rather than a formal, anatomist. To the formal anatomist, a leg is a leg, or a tooth is a tooth, and the object is interesting and significant in itself. The functional anatomist, on the other hand, wants to know what the part is used for. The leg, of course, is for locomotion, but what kind of locomotion? Does the animal run, leap, or merely waddle? Or a tooth? Is it used for tearing meat or grinding grass? While Daubenton had been interested in describing what an animal is, Cuvier wanted also to know what the animal did with the parts described.

In his thinking, he was also a teleologist, one who believes that events are working toward a purposeful end and are not behaving in an irrational and accidental manner. Although he avoided carrying this line of thinking to the extremes of the theologians, he did believe nature was acting purposefully.

This led him to a conclusion he later expressed in his book, *Animal Kingdom*: "Natural History has, moreover, a principle on which to reason, which is peculiar to it, and which it employs advantageously on many occasions; it is that of the conditions of existence, commonly termed *final causes*. As nothing can exist without the concurrence of those conditions which render its existence possible, the component parts of each must be so arranged as to render possible the whole living being, not only with regard to itself, but to its surrounding relations, and the analysis of these conditions frequently leads to general laws, as demonstrable as those which are derived from calculation or experiment."

In many respects, this was what Aristotle had said, but Cuvier was determined to use the principle for fresh purposes. Each organism, he thought, was specially designed to live under its own conditions and was a functional unit, each part of it being used in support of the others. This idea, later known as the correlation of parts, became the keystone of Cuvier's most important work.

He expressed these thoughts in his work *Discourse on the Revolutions of the Surface of the Globe*. Fossil shells, he pointed out, presented almost no difficulties to naturalists, because they were usually preserved in their entirety. Therefore, they could be easily compared with specimens in existing collections. Fish also presented a relatively simple problem. Generally, their skeletons were preserved whole, and the scientist could "almost always distinguish the general form of their body, and more often than not their generic and specific characters. . . ." But fossilized quadrupeds presented an entirely different problem. Even when it was possible to find a complete skeleton, the scientist still had no clues about "the skin, the colors, and other marks that vanished before encrustation." Moreover, he said, "It is infinitely rare to find a fossil skeleton even partway complete; isolated bones, tossed about pell-mell, almost always broken and reduced to fragments, that is all that the layers of rocks furnish us, and the only resource of the naturalist.

"Happily," he continued, "comparative anatomy possessed a principle which, if developed further, was capable of clearing up the problem. That principle was the correlation of the parts in organized beings, by means of which each sort of being can be recognized by each fragment of each of its parts.

"Every organized being forms a whole, a unique, closed system, whose parts correspond mutually and lead to the same definitive action by a reciprocal reaction. None of the parts can change without the others changing, too, and consequently, each one of them, taken separately, indicates what the other parts are." In other words, as he explained: "The least bit of bone . . . has a character determined in relation to the class, order, genus, and species to which it belongs to such an extent that every time one has only the extremity of a well-preserved bone, one can, with application, the use of a little analogy, and effective comparison, determine all those points as assuredly as if one had the entire animal." What is more, he proved his thesis. "I have," he wrote, "experimented with this method many times on portions of known animals before placing my trust in using it on fossils; the method has always been so successful that I have no doubt about the certainty of the results it has produced for me." This is a far cry from the purely descriptive anatomy of Daubenton. Cuvier was not content merely to describe and classify; he had developed a means of using anatomy to reconstruct the animals of the past.

One of his earliest attempts at reconstruction concerned an animal he called *Palaeotherium medium,* a heavyset creature that lived about 15,000,000 or 20,000,000 years ago and that left many fossilized fragments in the gypsum beds at Montmartre. No complete or even nearly complete fossils were available, however, so Cuvier set to work with what he could obtain, beginning with the teeth. Sorting through a large number that had been found, he was finally able to divide them into two sets, thus establishing that the remains of two animals had become intermingled. One of these animals, he decided, had twenty-eight molars, twelve incisors, and four canines. Furthermore, it was herbivorous and must have had some resemblance to a modern tapir and a modern rhinoceros. It did not have a rhinoceros' horn, however, because the nose bones were too light to support one. He then took the other set of teeth and assigned them to another genus, *Anoplotherium.* This genus, he decided, had no canine teeth. Next, he began sorting out other fossil bones that he had, including leg bones and bones from the heads. The problem now was to assign the proper heads to the proper legs. This he did on the basis of their relative abundance and finally created out of the bones a description of the *Palaeotherium* that was so analogous to a modern tapir that he was sure he was right. In the end, he established four species of *Palaeotherium* and three of *Anoplotherium,* and his final drawings were remarkably close to what scientists believe today.

In actual practice, his theories were perhaps not quite so perfect as he liked to claim, because he found himself forced from time to time to use plain common sense and his general knowledge of anatomy. But he had successfully devised a method of rebuilding the past and permitting man to see what had come before.

I V

During those early years in Paris, Cuvier, busy as he was and obsessed by his new scientific thoughts, did not forget his family in Montbéliard. He had a brother, Frédéric, who had gone to the Gymnasium for a few years, but the family had not had sufficient funds to keep paying his tuition. Because watchmaking was suddenly thriving, his father decided that he should be apprenticed to a watchmaker at Strasbourg. There, in addition to learning his trade, he became interested in natural history, and as soon as Cuvier had established himself in Paris, he sent for his brother. Frédéric came to the capital and at first devoted himself to chemistry and physics, doing well enough to make a small place for himself in the scientific world. A few years later, he became keeper of the menagerie at the Jardin des Plantes and switched his interest to zoology. Although never as distinguished as Georges, Frédéric became a competent scientist in his own right and an extremely helpful collaborator. He also brought to the household at the garden a touch of Montbéliard.

But Cuvier never allowed his affection for his family or for his many friends to interfere with his work, and he busily continued to teach his classes, write papers, and make further investigations into comparative anatomy. In 1800 he published the first volume of a five-volume book entitled *Lessons in Comparative Anatomy,* which is often considered the first real attempt to produce a complete work in the field. Previous anatomists like Daubenton and Vicq-d'Azyr had compared the anatomy of particular groups, but Cuvier discussed basic ideas that would apply to them all.

Meanwhile, Cuvier, gracious, polished, and with a considerable name in scientific circles, had attracted the attention of Napoleon. Napoleon liked men who added to France's renown, and whereas Lamarck only irritated him, Cuvier pleased him. In 1802, Napoleon named him one of the six general inspectors of studies who were charged with reorganizing the French school system. Napoleon was criticized for making the appointment. Why, some people asked, did he give Cuvier an assignment that would only distract him from his other work? But Napoleon knew his man. He had given Cuvier the position, he said, so Cuvier could get some rest, because he was the type of person who can never stop working and whose sole relaxation comes from changing what he is doing, not merely sitting idle.

Cuvier's first assignment was to establish a new school at Marseilles, checking on the space available, recruiting a faculty, and ranking the students. He went about the task just as methodically as he went about solving a scientific problem, gathering the information he needed, weighing it, and finally taking action.

While away from Paris, he kept in close touch with his friends in the city. He had worked hard to establish himself, and he did not want to be forgotten during his prolonged absence. When the French Institute was being staffed, his friends talked about him as a candidate for the office of perpetual secretary of the Academy of Sciences. Since Napoleon himself was involved in making choices, the esteem in which he held Cuvier could work only to Cuvier's advantage. On Cuvier's urging, his friends rallied to his support, and he received news of his appointment while he was in Marseilles. Although he had wanted the job and had done everything possible to obtain it, he did not return to Paris immediately. His original assignment called for him to go from Marseilles to Bordeaux and set up a school there. Always conscientious in fulfilling his duties, he resisted the temptation to drop everything and leave for Paris. Instead, he continued on to Bordeaux, finished his work there, and only then went back to his home.

His house at the Jardin des Plantes had become far too small to encompass all the activity in which Cuvier was engaged, so he persuaded the administration to purchase another, larger building on the adjoining property. Then he cut a door between them, so that he was able to walk directly from one to the other without going outside. The new building contained a large hall, which Cuvier divided with partial partitions. Each section was then devoted to some particular job. By this means and with the help of assistants, he was able to continue the enormous amount of work he had undertaken.

In 1804, the year after he came back from Bordeaux, he married Anne Marie Coquet du Trazaille, the widow of a man guillotined during the Revolution. She was five years older than Cuvier, had lost her money, and had four children; but Cuvier was deeply in love with her, and his love was not misplaced. They were married in the Swiss Embassy—there was no Lutheran church in Paris—and Mme. Cuvier immediately entered into her husband's work and interests. She organized the household to fit in with his habits; she served him as a clerk, making copies of his writings and other documents, and listened closely to his public lectures. Yet she did not let Cuvier's fame interfere with their family life. (They had four children of their own, three of whom unfortunately died young, leaving only a daughter, Clémentine.) Mme. Cuvier reserved every Saturday for the family. On that day they filled the house with young people and friends, and Cuvier set aside his work and joined in the merriment.

He was a gregarious person. He liked people, and they liked him. Lamarck's lectures, in spite of the astonishing ideas they contained, drew a relatively small audience. His stubbornness and his intensity did not win loyalty from his students. Cuvier, on the other hand, lectured in a large amphitheater that was almost completely filled. He spoke in a strong, sonorous voice that filled the entire hall, and although he did not write out his lectures in advance, but worked from copious notes, he never hesitated even slightly while he was speaking, always using the right word, always expressing his thoughts in eloquent terms. Years later, many students still recalled their studies with him as a high point in their careers, and Cuvier's contemporaries considered him an excellent professor.

In 1806, two years after his marriage, he had dramatic proof that his anatomical theories were correct. From a few fragmentary bones he had reconstructed *Anoplotherium*. Now someone discovered an almost complete skeleton and brought it to him. Cuvier examined it closely in the large hall where he did his anatomical work. To his great gratification, he found that this skeleton and the one he had reconstructed were so similar that all his conjectures were verified.

Along with his research, he continued his interest in public service, particularly in education, and in 1808 became councilor of a new university founded in Paris. A year later he accepted an assignment to study public education in the new departments formed on the other side of the Alps and went to various Italian cities, including Pisa, Sienna, and Florence. In each one, he examined the qualifications of the faculty, the courses taught, and the materials used.

He made a similar inspection trip to Holland in 1811. There he found the state of primary education so excellent that he advised France to adopt some of the Dutch ideas. From Holland, he was ordered to go to the Hanseatic cities and the new departments of South Germany. While he was in Hamburg, which Linnaeus had visited so many years before, he learned that Napoleon had made him a chevalier, but he did not allow his new honor to influence his judgment. Napoleon had expressed a strong dislike for Germany, but Cuvier praised Germany's public education highly and pointed out to the French government that the cultures and habits of each country should be taken into account in setting up an educational system. Napoleon liked uniformity; in education at least, Cuvier was opposed to it, and although he got along well with the emperor, he was no sycophant and not afraid to state ideas that were in opposition to what the emperor preferred.

In spite of these long travels and the heavy load of administrative work they imposed, Cuvier went on with his scientific studies and in 1812 brought out his book entitled *Investigations of Fossil Bones*. This was by far his most important publication until then, and it contained the results of all his examinations of fossils. Preceding the main part of the text was an essay entitled "Preliminary Discourse," which he later rewrote for a new edition and then published separately under the title *A Discourse on the Revolutions of the Surface of the Globe*. In this, he briefly discussed the various theories that had been advanced concerning the formation of the earth. Among others, he mentioned Buffon's, although he pointed out that Buffon had largely adopted the ideas of the German lawyer, mathematician, and philosopher Gottfried Wilhelm Leibniz. What bothered Cuvier was the diversity of the theories and the reason for this diversity. "How is it possible," he asked, "that men can come to such opposite solutions, when they start with the same principles to solve the same problem?

"Could it be that the conditions of the problem have not been entirely taken into consideration, which has made it remain, until now, undetermined and susceptible of several solutions, all equally good when such and such a consideration is set aside; all equally bad when a new condition is made known, or when our attention is directed to some condition that was known, but neglected?"

The key, he thought, might lie in using fossils. "Other scientists studied, it is true, the fossil remains of organized bodies; they have gathered and presented them by the thousands; their works make up collections of precious material; but, more occupied by animals and plants considered as such than with a theory of the development of the earth, or looking on these petrifications or fossils as curiosities rather than historic documents . . . they have almost always neglected to do research on the general laws governing the position and connection of the fossils with certain layers of rocks.

". . . Why has not anyone seen that fossils alone gave birth to a theory about the formation of the earth, that without them, no one would have ever dreamed that there were successive epochs in the formation of the globe?" He then explained that the study of minerals, "while not less necessary and of greater commercial value," held less promise of revealing the past than the study of fossils. But the field was so immense that a single man could investigate only a small part of it. Therefore, he had decided to concentrate on the quadrupeds, which he considered more accurate and detailed indicators of what had taken place in the past than Lamarck's invertebrates.

"What was most important," he continued, "and the essential object of all my work and what establishes its true relationship with the theory of the earth, is to know in which layers of rock each species is found and if there are general laws relative to this. . . ." Such laws, he believed, could be discovered. For example, he continued, "it is certain that oviparous quadrupeds appeared much sooner than viviparous quadrupeds, that they are even more abundant, stronger, and more varied in the old layers of rock than on the present face of the earth." He then went on to demonstrate that the study of fossils revealed that there had been a succession of organic lives on the earth; that many ancient animals were unlike modern animals; that some animals had become extinct, others continuing to live. The remaining problem was to write this history and to relate the animals that had been reconstructed to the type of environment in which they must have lived.

But there were certain limits to Cuvier's thinking. "Why are not present races, someone will say to me, modifications of those ancient races we find among the fossils, modifications that would have been produced by local circumstances and changes of climate, and carried to extreme lengths by the long succession of years?" Cuvier's answer to his rhetorical question firmly disposed of such a suggestion. If the species have changed by degrees, he argued, "we should be able to find traces of these gradual modifications. Between the *Palaeotherium* and the species of today we should be able to discover some intermediary forms, but up until now that has not happened.

"Why have not the entrails of the earth preserved the signs of such a curious genealogy? Because the former species were just as constant as today's species." He did not deny that variations could occur within a species. That would have been to deny the obvious. But he held that these variations were minor. He cited as examples a number of domestic animals and placed special emphasis on dogs. Of all animals, they bore "the most marked effects of the influence of man." They varied in color, in abundance of hair, in the size of their tails, in the shape of their ears, noses, and necks. "But in all these variations, the relationship of the bones remains the same, and the form of the teeth never changes in an appreciable manner. . . . There are then, in animals, characteristics that resist all influences, whether natural or whether caused by humans, and nothing shows that time has, in this respect, any more effect than climate or domesticity."

Indeed, he was thoroughly opposed to those scientists who thought anything could be accomplished if a sufficient amount of time were available. "I know that some naturalists," he wrote, "count heavily on the thousands of centuries they accumulate with a stroke of their pen. But we are hardly able to judge what a long period of time will produce except by multiplying in our thoughts what a lesser period of time will produce. I have therefore attempted to gather together the oldest documents on the forms of animals, and there are none of greater abundance and antiquity than those of Egypt. They offer us not only pictures but also the bodies of the animals themselves embalmed in their catacombs.

"I have examined with the greatest care the figures of animals and birds engraved on the numerous obelisks brought from Egypt to ancient Rome. All the figures, taken as a whole, bear a perfect resemblance to the species as we see them today."

He went on to consider the human race, using it, too, in support of his thesis. "It is certain that we have not yet found human bones among the fossils, and that is even further proof that the fossil races have not varied, since they were never submitted to the influence of man." Cuvier, like many thinkers before and since, had used a logical, orderly process to arrive at the wrong conclusion. He did not have enough specimens to see that one species could actually develop from another, and he was unwilling to accept the effects of time without more factual evidence than was available to him. He had a clear, accurate mind, he wanted to document every point, and he refused to speculate. So, working with the material he had, he concluded that the species could not vary. This, of course, brought him into direct conflict with Lamarck. If Cuvier had proved that the species were immutable, then Lamarck's ideas must be utter nonsense.

It was a curious paradox. Lamarck, in his investigations, had come closer to the general truth, although he could not support his conclusions, because they were based largely on his own speculations. Cuvier, on the other hand, was further from the ultimate truth, although his contribution toward modern science and the discoveries of the later evolutionists was far greater. What he deduced from his studies was not particularly significant. He believed that the earth's surface had suffered a series of catastrophes or revolutions, the last of which had occurred about 5,000 or 6,000 years before and had shaped the world as he and his contemporaries knew it. (In his writings he argued at some length that no civilization could be as old as many people believed.) These catastrophes had come suddenly—how else, for example, could mastodons be quickly frozen?—but they had not resulted in the extinction of every species, because they had not necessarily been worldwide. Man, therefore, could have survived the Deluge; this was perfectly compatible with Cuvier's thinking and in line with the traditions of the church.

In all this, his ideas were not especially original. They were essentially those of many other thinkers of his time. But his methods were new. He had, to an extent no one had ever done before, blended taxonomy, anatomy, and geology to create the science of paleontology.

V

The year 1812, in which Cuvier published his *Investigations of Fossil Bones,* was the year Napoleon commenced his disastrous Russian campaign. Inevitably the French army reached Moscow, but it was greatly weakened and demoralized and soon was forced to start the long retreat back over the ground it had conquered. The cold did not set in immediately; indeed, the frost came later than usual that year. Even when the army reached the Berezina on November 26, the river was not frozen over, but panic had struck the troops. Although they could have forded the river, they rushed for the bridges like men trying to escape from a fire, trampling hundreds of their fellows underfoot. By the time they reached Smolensk, only 50,000 soldiers were left of the hundreds of thousands who had started out. If Napoleon were to salvage his European empire, he had to return to Paris and raise a new army.

One of the people he called on during the following desperate year was Cuvier. First, he asked him to go to Rome to examine the state of public instruction. That was an unusual act, to send a Lutheran to the center of Catholicism, but once again Cuvier accepted the assignment. While he was in Rome, he learned that he had been named master of requests to the Council of State.

Meanwhile, Napoleon once more had launched himself against his enemies, driving them from the field at Lützen and Bautzen, but was unable to win a decisive victory. Finally, he agreed to a six-week suspension of the war, time in which he could consolidate his men and place them in more favorable positions, but that autumn, when hostilities recommenced, Napoleon suffered a defeat at Leipzig and began his retreat back toward France. Cuvier had returned to France, and Napoleon assigned him to the imperial commission charged with preparing the defenses on the eastern borders of France. Once more Cuvier accepted. He was a man of science, not a man of war, but if the emperor thought he could be useful, he would try to be so. Fortunately, his abilities were not brought to a test. The invasion never took place, and Cuvier was free to go back to Paris.

During the year 1814, Cuvier was so distracted by current events that he accomplished little scientific work. By April the allies had occupied Paris, Napoleon had abdicated and gone to Elba, which he was given as a "possession," and the Bourbons were beginning to return. Cuvier, who had supported both the Revolution and the emperor, was fearful for his position. As he wrote to a friend, he realized he had no chance of further advancement, but he hoped somehow he could retain the position he had reached after twenty years of work. This hope was based not only on his personal desire, but also on his interest in the future of science. He wished to be allowed to continue his studies.

His reputation as a scientist and as a public servant was so great that he was reconfirmed in many of his posts and also given additional duties. By 1815, although the year was one of political upset during the 100 days of Napoleon's return and final defeat at Waterloo, Cuvier was concentrating on his scientific studies at the Jardin des Plantes and was serving France as a member of the Royal Council of the University and as a councilor of state assigned to the committee on legislation. Over the years his interest in government had changed. During the Revolution he had been a fervent republican and had taken, at least in a small way, an active role, but he had welcomed Napoleon, who he thought would restore order. But as Napoleon became more despotic, Cuvier, always concerned with fundamental human rights, turned more moderate. He also realized his temperament equipped him better to be an administrator and adviser than a politician, and he refused to run for elective office, preferring to serve in appointive positions instead.

In 1816 he received a unique opportunity to exercise his talents. Louis XVIII, lethargic, gouty, and fat, was nevertheless a sensible statesman. He realized the government would be foolhardy to try to reestablish the monarchy as it had existed before the Revolution and instead had recommended a constitutional monarchy in the charter he proposed in 1814. The nobility, however, was not generally in agreement. After years of exile and the bitterness that went with it, the nobles wanted to regain their original powers and formed a party that opposed much of what the king wanted. By 1816 they had gained sufficient control of the Chamber of Deputies to try to force through a reform of the election law, which they thought was too liberal. Their majority was such that it appeared their attempt would be successful. Worried by this turn of events, Cuvier asked to be heard as a representative of the king. Dressed in black velvet, he mounted the rostrum and, pacing backward and forward, delivered an eloquent plea in defense of the people's rights and the maintenance of the former, more liberal law. The effect on the Chamber was startling. In later years many of the members still remembered the eloquence with which Cuvier spoke and the impression that he made on his audience. One of those present said that when Cuvier stepped up to the rostrum, the election law was in serious danger of being repealed; when he got down, the law was saved.

But he did not permit his public duties to interfere with his private research, and the year after his successful appearance in the Chamber, he published his work *Animal Kingdom*. Writing about it later, an English commentator said, "Perhaps no book was ever so soon, so generally, and with so little envy, admitted to take its place at the head of that department of knowledge to which it belongs, as the *Animal Kingdom* of the illustrious Baron Cuvier. This is a high, but just, tribute, both to the work and to the author; for it at once showed that the former is what had long been required, and that the latter was as much admired for the comprehensive range and unprecedented accuracy of his views as he was beloved for the kindness and urbanity of his manners."

The commentator went on to say that "it must, indeed, be admitted that, until Cuvier's great work made its appearance, we had no modern systematic arrangement of animals which applied equally to all the Classes,

Orders, and Families;—which brought the extinct species into their proper positions in the living catalogue, and enabled every discoverer of a new animal, or part of an animal, instantly to connect it with its proper tribe or family."

The last statement was perhaps an exaggeration, but the four volumes did contain the largest collection of zoological facts that had yet been published in one book. Furthermore, these facts were so arranged that a reader could acquaint himself with the overall structure of the animal kingdom and could also learn in detail about any particular species. As a first step, Cuvier divided the animal kingdom into four types into which all known animals could be divided. Within these four types, as he said in his preface, he had attempted to provide "a kind of abridged system of animals, in which I should present their divisions and subdivisions of all degrees, established in a parallel manner upon their structure, both internal and external; where I would give the indication of well-authenticated species that belonged, with certainty, to each of the subdivisions. . . ." This was followed by detailed descriptions of certain species which were either especially abundant, harmful, or useful. "I hoped by so doing," he continued, "to prove useful to young naturalists, who, for the most part, have but little idea of the confusion and errors of criticism in which the most accredited works abound, and who, particularly in foreign countries, do not sufficiently attend to the study of the true relations of beings; I considered myself as rendering a more direct service to those anatomists, who require to know beforehand to which orders they should direct their researches, when they wish to solve by comparative anatomy some problem of human anatomy or physiology. . . ." It was a large undertaking but, considering the material and knowledge available to him, one he accomplished extremely well.

He also gave credit to Lamarck for what he had done: "So far as the shells and corals are concerned, I could depend on a work just published by M. de Lamarck, in which will be found all that the most ardent desire for information can require." Nevertheless, he clearly stated his belief that the species were fixed and separate. "To anticipate a remark that will naturally occur to many, I must observe that I have neither pretended nor desired to class animals so as to form a single line, or as to mark their relative superiority. I even consider every attempt of this kind impracticable. . . . I regard my divisions and subdivisions as merely the graduated expression of the resemblance of the beings which enter into each of them; and although in some we observe a sort of passage or gradation from one species into another, which cannot be denied, this disposition is far from being general. The pretended chain of beings, as applied to the whole creation, is but an erroneous application of those partial observations, which are only true when confined to the limits within which they were made; and, in my opinion, it has proved more detrimental to the progress of natural history in modern times than is easy to imagine."

Practical and pragmatic, Cuvier refused to be drawn into speculation. He needed definite proof before he would accept an idea. He agreed that sometimes "we observe a sort of passage or gradation from one species into another," but the evidence was too slim to convince him. He had gathered together what was perhaps the greatest collection of zoological facts in history, he had catalogued those facts accurately and well, he had developed a technique for reconstructing animals from small fragments and had applied this technique to fossils, and he had related fossils to the story of life on earth. But for any concept of evolution, he had no use. The idea seemed impossible to him.

VI

In 1818 Cuvier was offered the ministry of the interior, but he declined. He thought the additional responsibilities would interfere with his scientific work, and he also thought that his being a Lutheran would cause difficulties. He did, however, speak out, this time unsuccessfully, against further restrictions on the freedom of the press; he became a member of the French Academy; and he was named a baron and president of the Committee of the Interior of the Council of State. But all his acumen could not keep him from falling into political difficulties.

The ultras, those who wanted to return to the despotic government of the past, had been steadily gaining strength, and by 1820 they were again ready to change the election law Cuvier had defended a few years before. As a commissioner of the king, he was expected to argue on behalf of the changes before the Chamber. This was repugnant both to him and to his liberal friends, who wrote urging him to resign his post. As they pointed out, he had become an important symbol of French liberalism, and for him to defend the proposed changes would be a blow to the cause. Cuvier was greatly tempted to follow their advice, but there were other considerations. The president of the Council of State was a close personal friend and also a generous financial contributor to Cuvier's museum. He told Cuvier he could not simply withdraw and stand to one side as a neutral. Even if he said nothing one way or the other, his resignation would be interpreted as opposition. He had accepted the government's appointment; therefore, he should fulfill the responsibilities it imposed. Representatives of the government also began to call on him, each of them asking for his support. Cuvier still resisted their appeals, although the pressure was wearing on him, and he spent long hours pacing the floor of his library, trying to decide what to do. It was a torturous position for a man with his sense of honor and order. Although he recognized the truth of the president's arguments and felt under obligation to perform his governmental duties, he resisted repudiating his own liberal philosophy.

Then Louis Pierre Louvel, a saddlemaker who had sworn "to exterminate the Bourbons," tried to put his oath into effect. On February 12, when the Duke de Berry, nephew of Louis XVIII and son of the king's conservative brother, was attending the opera, Louvel was lurking in the darkness outside. As the duke left, Louvel attacked and killed him. The news, of course, was all over Paris the next day, and Cuvier was sickened by it. The government had told him that revolutionary forces were sweeping France and that they would resort to violence, unless the government was given firmer controls. Here was proof the government was right. That day he sat down at his desk, picked up his pen, and wrote that he was "at the orders of the king." His action aroused considerable resentment. His old liberal friends thought of him as a traitor to the cause he had once defended so ably, and the government, knowing his long period of hesitation, did not regard him as a truly loyal supporter. For years afterward he was criticized for what he had done, and few of his critics understood his dilemma. A lover of justice, a man of conscience, and a person who desired order in France after the decades of turmoil, he had done what he thought was right. In the light of history his judgment was wrong, but his decision was honorable.

This political misfortune, although it cost him some friendships, did not lessen his prestige. He was still regarded as one of France's finest intellectuals, a world leader in science, and a person who could be counted on to help with government problems. So he continued his endless round of activities, his blond hair whitening, his stomach becoming slightly larger as a result of his sedentary life, his shoulders a little stooped. He was somewhat nearsighted, so he had to squint when he was looking at close-by objects, but he was still an impressive figure. According to his contemporaries, he had a remarkable face, a high forehead, and a somewhat hooked nose. But like Linnaeus, his eyes were his dominant feature. They showed intelligence, vivacity, and gentleness.

When John James Audubon, the American ornithologist and bird painter, visited Paris in 1828, he saw Cuvier, and after their first meeting, he wrote in his journal, "I looked at him, and here follows the result: age about sixty-five; size corpulent, five feet five, English measure; head large; face wrinkled and brownish; eyes gray, brilliant and sparkling; nose aquiline, large and red; mouth large, with good lips; teeth few, blunted by age, excepting one on the lower jaw, measuring nearly three-quarters of an inch square. Thus . . . ," he added jokingly, "have I described Cuvier almost as if a new species of man."

Audubon saw Cuvier several times while he was in Paris and wrote his impressions of both the man and his house. A friend of his was painting Cuvier's portrait, and Audubon went along with him. "The footman asked us to follow him upstairs, and in the first room we caught a glimpse of a slight figure dressed all in black, that glided across the floor like a sylph; it was Mlle. Cuvier [Clémentine], not quite ready to see gentlemen; off she flew like a Dove before Falcons. We followed our man, who continually turned, saying, 'This way, gentlemen.' Eight rooms we passed filled with books, and each with a recessed bed, and at last reached a sort of laboratory, the *sanctum sanctorum* of Cuvier; there was nothing in it but books and skeletons of animals, reptiles, etc. Our conductor, surprised, bid us sit down, and left us to seek the Baron. My eyes were fully employed, and I contemplated in imagination the extent of the great man's knowledge. His books were in great disorder, and I concluded that he read and studied them, and owned them for other purposes than show. Our man returned and led us back through the same avenue of bed-chambers, lined with books instead of satin, and we were conducted through the kitchen to another laboratory, where the Baron was found."

The series of rooms that Audubon observed were part of the secret of Cuvier's ability to carry on so much work, for he had his possessions arranged as carefully as the species in the *Animal Kingdom*. Across the street was the natural history museum, and the building next door to his house served as a museum of anatomy. Within his house he had his library dispersed throughout several rooms, each one containing all the books that he owned on one particular subject: icthyology, ornithology, law, or any of his other interests. When he was doing extensive research on a particular subject, he would have a stove moved into the appropriate room and stay there for as long as necessary. His principal workroom was set up on a similar basis. It contained eleven desks at which he could stand and two at which he could sit. Each desk was completely equipped with an inkstand, pens, and paper, the reference works he was using for a particular topic, and his manuscript. During the course of the day, when he was not in one of his libraries, he moved from desk to desk as he switched from one task to another.

Another secret of his great output was the intensity with which he worked. He had agreed to review Audubon's book and asked Audubon to meet him at the French Institute at one thirty. Audubon arrived promptly, but Cuvier did not appear. The minutes ticked by, with Audubon growing more and more nervous. Several people advised him to go to Cuvier's house, but he decided to continue waiting. Then suddenly, after more than an hour, "I heard his voice, and saw him advancing, very warm and apparently fatigued. He met me with many apologies, and said, 'Come with me'; and we walked along, he explaining all the time why he had been late, while his hand drove a pencil with great rapidity, and he told me that he was actually *now* writing the report on my work!

"I thought of La Fontaine's fable of the Turtle and the Hare; I was surprised that so great a man should leave till the last moment the writing of a report to every word of which the forty critics of France [the members of the French Academy] would lend an attentive ear. For being on an eminence he has to take more care of his actions than a common individual, to prevent his fall, being surrounded, as all great men are more or less, by envy and malice. My enormous book lay before him, and I shifted as fast as lightning the different plates that he had marked for examination. His pencil moved as constantly and as rapidly. He turned and returned the sheets of his manuscript with amazing accuracy, and noted as quickly as he saw, *and he saw all.* We were both wet with perspiration. It wanted but a few minutes of three when we went off to the Council room, Cuvier still writing, and bowing to everyone he met. I left him, and was glad to get into the pure air."

Audubon was younger than Cuvier and a hard worker himself. Day after day he would rise early in the morning, take a walk, return to his rooms as soon as it was light, and paint until dark or handle his enormous correspondence. Or he went on trips from city to city, calling on strangers and trying to sell copies of his book. But even he was exhausted by the pace Cuvier maintained.

As the years passed, Cuvier kept on producing new publications: a second edition of the *Investigations of Fossil Bones,* completely revised, then a third; a five-volume book entitled *History of the Progress of Natural Science from 1789 Until Today* (which represented a continuation of Buffon's work); an eight-volume book, *The Natural History of Fish*; and several others.

He also found time to keep in touch with many leading scientists, not only in France, but throughout the world. He saw Audubon; he knew Louis Agassiz, the Swiss who was studying fossil fish; Alexander von Humboldt, after whom the Humboldt Current is named and who also drew one of the geological diagrams for the *Investigations of Fossil Bones*; Charles Lyell, the English geologist, and many others. Of course, to accomplish all this, he had to use assistants and collaborators, but he never had a large staff, much preferring to employ a few people who were skilled and aware of what he wanted than large numbers who were not.

But in spite of the success of his scientific work and the high position he continued to occupy, he had the sorrow of seeing throughout France the decline of the political ideas that he had, with one exception, so vigorously defended. In 1824, Louis XVIII died, and the Count d'Artois, father of the assassinated Duke de Berry, came to the throne of

France as Charles X. He had none of the statesmanship of his brother and immediately tried to sweep away the last vestiges of the liberties won during the Revolution.

At home, Cuvier was further saddened by the death of his daughter, Clémentine. He had always been devoted to her, and she was the last of his four children. After her death, when people called on him, he simply said, "Excuse me. I am a father, and I have lost them all." Sadness overwhelmed him, and even bitterness. His only solace was work.

VII

The efforts of Charles X to reestablish the old order in France ended in failure. Instead of gaining control of the country, he lost it. His new legislation merely aroused the resentment of the people without strengthening Charles' authority. In 1830 the liberal opposition in the Chamber of Deputies, increasingly angered by the king, declared illegal his appointment of the conservative Prince de Polignac as first minister. Charles dissolved the Chamber and ordered a new election. The opposition won. Meanwhile, to divert the public's attention from domestic issues, Charles had launched a war against the Dey of Algiers, whom he had conquered, thereby laying the foundation for France's future holdings in North Africa. On the strength of this victory, he believed himself sufficiently popular to ignore the Chamber. He again dissolved it and ordered a new election and, without the approval of the legislature, issued regulations further restricting the press and disenfranchising many of the bourgeoisie. The students of Paris rebelled. They threw up barricades in the streets, captured the City Hall in Paris, and demanded a democratic republic. The liberals in the Chamber of Deputies, however, wanted a constitutional monarchy, and because they had great political skill, they got it. Charles X abdicated, and the Duke d'Orléans, Louis Philippe, ascended the throne.

In the midst of this political turmoil, Cuvier found himself embroiled in the most bitter scientific dispute of his career. Étienne Geoffroy Saint-Hilaire, the botanist, had befriended Lamarck and continued to uphold Lamarck's ideas after Lamarck's death. There was, he held, a uniformity in life; species were related to one another. Cuvier did not argue with him. Always anxious to avoid personal disputes, he simply continued his studies and became more and more convinced that the species were fixed and that it was useless to make comparisons between types in an effort to establish a relationship.

Then Geoffroy Saint-Hilaire submitted a paper to the Academy of Sciences. This paper attempted to link the cephalopods, particularly cuttlefish and squid, with the vertebrates and was completely contrary to

Cuvier's thinking. He would probably have ignored it, however, if it had not contained a specific attack on him. This passage was deleted when the paper was published, but it had been read before the academy, and therefore, Cuvier felt obliged to reply. He did so with a detailed comparison of the cephalopods and vertebrates and, with his great knowledge and accurate eye, was able to prove that Geoffroy Saint-Hilaire's conclusions were wrong. At the same time he gracefully acknowledged Saint-Hilaire's work in comparative anatomy and his studies in embryology, but he also sharply attacked his basic philosophy that there was a rational unity underlying the structure of the animal kingdom.

Cuvier's response annoyed Geoffroy Saint-Hilaire, who decided to continue the debate. Although he abandoned his comparison of the cephalopods with the vertebrates, he took sharp issue on several other points. In the first place, he ardently maintained that he was proposing a new approach to comparative anatomy, not merely, as Cuvier claimed, an adaptation of Aristotle's well-known ladder of life. Furthermore, he could not agree with Cuvier that the various types of life were separate. They all were, he stated, interrelated.

The battle continued in a series of discussions at the Academy of Sciences. Geoffroy Saint-Hilaire upheld his and Lamarck's position as best he could, but he was no match for Cuvier in an argument. He presented his speculations, but without being able to substantiate them, particularly in the face of Cuvier's practical, detailed analysis of what evidence he did muster. Cuvier even found factual errors in Geoffroy Saint-Hilaire's work, pointing them out to the academy and thus discrediting his opponent. In the end, Geoffroy Saint-Hilaire, unable to defend himself against Cuvier's astonishing technical knowledge, was completely routed, and any hope that Lamarck's original ideas would be considered seriously was gone.

VIII

Cuvier celebrated his sixty-third birthday the year he argued with Geoffroy Saint-Hilaire. In his heart, he must have felt easier about the state of France. In Louis Philippe he saw, or at least thought he saw, what he had always wanted: a man who would bring to France a limited constitutional monarchy, capable of maintaining order but also protective of human rights. He died before Louis Philippe fell.

New honors came to Cuvier. He was asked to receive the king in the Upper House, and he was made president of the Council of State. His popularity increased; students flocked to his lectures; the government listened to his advice. In 1832 an outbreak of cholera struck Paris, and Cuvier's lectures at the College of France were suspended, as were other meetings where large numbers of people might congregate. On May 8 the suspension was lifted, and Cuvier once more resumed his teaching. In the opinions of many of his students, the lecture he gave that day was particularly memorable. The subject of his course was the history of science, and after the long interruption, he felt it desirable to review everything he had said so far. His lecture amounted to a summary of his entire scientific thinking and a reiteration of his basic belief that each form of life contains within itself the means of living according to the conditions in which it has to exist, that belief which had led him so far into the past.

The next day, May 9, 1832, he had trouble closing one hand. He did not go to a meeting of the Council of State that had been scheduled and at mealtime realized that he could not pick up a cup of liquid. His hand was too uncertain. On the tenth he grew worse. Believing that nothing could be done to help him, Cuvier dictated his will, which he was unable to sign. (He called in witnesses to attest to it.) On the twelfth he was visited by a friend who brought him the best wishes of the French Academy for his recovery. He was apparently not in pain. On the following day he spoke of his work and all that he yet wanted to accomplish, but that evening at eight o'clock his strength failed him. At nine forty-five he was dead.

He had asked to be buried with a simple ceremony alongside the body of his daughter, Clémentine, but France did not agree to his request. His coffin was carried by students representing various schools and was followed by deputations from the French Academy, the Academy of Sciences, the Polytechnique School, both legislative bodies, and the Council of State. At least seven orations were given over his grave, one of them by Geoffroy Saint-Hilaire. Although there had been scientific differences between them, Geoffroy Saint-Hilaire could forget them at the moment of death.

All France felt a sense of loss. Cuvier had been more than an excellent scientist: he was a symbol of the nation's culture, a man of thought who could also be a man of affairs.

Only a few years afterward, his critics would condemn him for having opposed Lamarck, for not having glimpsed the great truth that Lamarck saw, even if only vaguely. But Cuvier could not have done the work he had if he had also been capable of accepting Lamarck's speculations. It was his clear thinking, his demand for positive proof, his sober-minded approach to every theory that made his great contributions possible. And in the end, those contributions were vital to the evolutionists in their great discoveries.

7

The Collectors

ALEXANDER WILSON: 1766–1813
JOHN JAMES AUDUBON: 1785–1851

I

On September 4, 1828, Baron Cuvier was as usual busily occupied meeting the demands of his heavy schedule at the Jardin des Plantes when two strangers knocked at his door. Almost as a matter of routine, his servant abruptly refused them admittance, for casual visitors and self-seekers were too frequent for the baron to permit so many interruptions.

One of the strangers, however, was John James Audubon, the American ornithologist and artist and a man of extraordinary persistence. After the servant had shut the door in his face, he knocked again and insisted with considerable firmness that Cuvier be notified of the presence of himself and his companion, an English naturalist. This time the servant disappeared to consult his employer; and when he returned, he escorted the two callers upstairs, where Cuvier greeted them cordially. Although Audubon had not yet established his later reputation, Cuvier, in his wholehearted fashion, invited both men to dinner the following Saturday and, during the remainder of their stay in Paris, proved to be their friend by writing an admiring review of Audubon's book *The Birds of America* and arranging introductions to people who might purchase it.

Although Cuvier, except in his dealings with Lamarck, was a gen-

erous person, his courtesy to his two visitors arose not only from his innate kindness, but also from his curiosity about the New World, a curiosity that he shared with many other Europeans. Everyone, from the
lowliest shopkeeper to the highest prince, was eager for firsthand information about the new lands that were being opened up in Asia, Africa,
and the Americas—merchants who sought opportunities for trade,
government officials who dreamed of empire, common people who
thought of becoming settlers, and intellectuals who hoped to find there
the material necessary to support old theories or develop new ones. Because of this demand for information, the early explorers were often accompanied by scientists, usually botanists, zoologists, geologists, or geographers, who observed their surroundings, collected specimens, and,
in effect, took inventory of what they saw. (When Sir Walter Raleigh
employed a scientist, Thomas Harriot, to describe the natural history of
Roanoke Island, he was not unique; he was merely following what became
the custom.)

The Europeans' interest helped stimulate the scientific investigations
of the permanent inhabitants, and by the time Audubon appeared at
Cuvier's door, the Americans, for example, could count as part of their
culture a considerable number of outstanding scientists, many of whom
not only held respected positions in their professions but also played a
prominent role in public life: Benjamin Franklin, whose scientific reputation was worldwide; Samuel Latham Mitchill, a member of Congress and a physician whose scientific interests extended far beyond
medicine; and, of course, Thomas Jefferson, whose knowledge of natural
history was more professional than amateur in spite of the time he devoted
to politics. Although the Revolution drove some scientists out of the country—to name two, Alexander Garden, the botanist, and Benjamin
Thompson, later Count Rumford—the aftermath of political and economic freedom also attracted others, such as Thomas Cooper, the chemist,
and Joseph Priestley, one of the discoverers of oxygen.

Among these scientists were the men who served as the collectors,
traveling throughout the country, often at great hardship to themselves,
and attempting to find out what the land contained. John James Audubon
was one of them, a man who had made it his business to know the country and the animals and plants living in it. Even Cuvier, famous and renowned as he was, had not seen what Audubon had seen—the trees
bending under the weight of flocks of passenger pigeons; the enormous
catfish in the Ohio River; the bald eagles winging their way up the valley
of the Mississippi; the raccoons that climbed the trees around the farmer's cabin; the giant ash trees the trappers used for firewood when they
made a winter encampment. Cuvier was a man of the laboratory,
brilliant, imaginative, and a mighty contributor to man's knowledge of his

surroundings. But he could not exist without the collectors, the men who gathered the raw material he needed.

Audubon, of course, was not the only collector. There were many others who provided a similar service to science: John Bartram, who operated a botanical garden on the outskirts of Philadelphia and sent many specimens to Europe, and his son, William, who continued his work; Thomas Say, who traveled far and wide in search of insects; Constantine Samuel Rafinesque, who studied fish and died a pauper; and that curious determined figure, Alexander Wilson, who by dint of perseverance and little else, made a reputation for himself as the father of American ornithology.

II

Nothing about the circumstances of Alexander Wilson's birth and early life indicated that he would become a leading scientist in the New World and one of the foremost naturalists of his time. His upbringing was humble, and his formal education stopped when he was ten years old; but he had both pride and determination, and these compensated for his handicaps.

His father was a reformed smuggler, who, at the request of his wife, had given up that trade for the more respectable, but less romantic, business of weaving the cloth for which Wilson's birthplace, Paisley, Scotland, was famous. Wilson's mother was a law- and God-fearing woman, who not only converted her husband from his lawbreaking, but made up her mind that her son should become a minister. She encouraged his regular attendance at the Paisley school and saved her pennies for his future education, but tragically in 1776, when he was nine years old, she died.

Once her restraining influence was removed, Wilson's father reverted to his old ways. But when it came to choosing a career for his son, he decided on something less dangerous and bound him out as an apprentice weaver. The choice, although reasonable, was not a happy one for Wilson. He had inherited his father's restlessness and dislike of authority and found the days at the loom endless and boring. Nevertheless, he patiently mastered his trade and obtained work as a journeyman.

But the future looked gloomy. No matter how hard he labored, he could never earn much more than a pound a day, the rate paid the best weavers, and he would never be able to rise in social position. Being highly ambitious, he pondered his problem as he stood before his loom and finally evolved a plan of escape. To provide himself with an income, he would become a peddler, for although the open road might be uncomfortable when the Scottish mists rolled across it and the wind blew over the moors, being a peddler was preferable to the boring, monotonous hours at the loom. And to provide himself with the fame he so much desired, he would write poetry. Already he had acquired something of a local reputation as a poet, and Robert Burns' dramatic success made it seem easy to gain worldwide recognition by writing verses in dialect.

Wilson had such confidence in his ability that in 1789 he ordered the publication of 700 copies of a book containing seventy-two of his poems, and although this act put him into debt, he borrowed further to obtain a peddler's stock, thinking he could sell these wares and his book at the same time. Unfortunately, like many hopeful plans, Wilson's was ill conceived. As he soon wrote to a friend, "Since I left Paisley, I have met with some encouragement, but I assure you, sir, that my occupation is greatly against my success in collecting subscribers. A *Packman* is a character which none esteem, and almost every one despises." Yet in the midst of his frustration he was able to laugh at himself just a little. "I can't for my life say whether mirth or sorrow would be most predominant in your mind; whether a burst of laughter would convulse your nerves, or the tear of pity steal from your cheek," he also wrote, and the words illuminate a significant aspect of his character. Throughout his life, even at some of his most despairing moments, he could always step outside himself and see the humor of his situation before returning to his sorrow. But his attempted laughter could not obscure the brutal truth. He would have to consider resigning himself to weaving, now and forever.

The following month his interest in poetry revived, for he received an invitation to paticipate in a literary contest at Edinburgh. Each contestant was to present either an essay or a poem upholding one of two designated writers as the better Scottish poet. After the authors had read their compositions, the audience would vote for the one they liked best.

Wilson opened by saying he was only an old Scottish farmer who had been lured into entering the contest because of the prize money but who was shocked at being charged the sixpence admission fee. Continuing in verse along this vein, he skillfully and humorously wove his argument in support of one of the two poets and, when he was finished, received an ovation. But the prize was snatched away from him. Another contestant had had the foresight—and also enough money—to bring with him forty friends and thus pack the house with a bloc in his favor. When the count was taken, Wilson had lost by seventeen votes.

III

In 1792, the year after Wilson's defeat at Edinburgh, all Europe was trembling with the social and political unrest ignited by the upheavals taking place in France. At first, many of the liberal elements elsewhere had sympathized with the country's efforts to curtail its despotic monarchy and irresponsible nobility. But as the excessive nature of the Revolution began to reveal itself, even the moderates became alarmed, particularly by France's influence among the workingman's clubs in Great Britain.

Wilson, who had returned to the trade of weaving, was naturally a radical. He regularly attended the club meetings held in Paisley, and when the members wanted a resolution phrased properly—these resolutions often had to do with political affairs—they soon found he was the man with the barbed pen. In addition, he wrote for them at least three poems that were printed anonymously and distributed as handbills, all of them satirizing the millowners of the city. Then in a curious incident, the threads of which have never been completely unraveled, he overstepped himself.

On May 23, 1792, William Sharp of Paisley, owner of the Long Mills, appeared with his attorney at the office of Sheriff Orr. In his hand, he had two documents. One was a poem entitled "The Shark, or Lang Mills Detected." Written in dialect and containing many technical terms, the poem on the surface seemed nothing more than a description of the weavers' hard existence, but buried in the text was a dangerous and inflammatory accusation. Mr. Shark of Lang Mills, the poet charged, used inaccurate measures in determining the amount of cloth manufactured each week by his weavers. Since the weavers were paid on a piece-rate basis, this meant he had been fraudulently underpaying his workers for years. The similarities between "Shark" and "Sharp" and between "Lang Mills" and "Long Mills" could not be overlooked. Mr. Sharp had been libeled.

The other document added to the immensity of the crime. It was a letter signed with the initials A. B. and was addressed to Mr. Sharp. In it the writer said that the enclosed poem had fallen into his hands under strange circumstances and that the author was about to sell it for five pounds. If Mr. Sharp or anyone else wanted to stop its publication, they had to offer only five guineas, instead of five pounds. The money should be addressed to A. B. care of the bookseller in Paisley, and it should be delivered in three hours. The poem was libel; the letter was blackmail. Both documents were in the handwriting of Alexander Wilson.

The act was unlike anything Wilson had ever done before, in both its immorality and its stupidity. Smuggling, in which he had certainly helped his father from time to time, was merely a battle of wits with the Crown's revenue officers. Blackmail was something else altogether. Furthermore, the conception of the offense ran against Wilson's usual common sense on two counts: Why did Wilson fail to disguise his handwriting? And why did he establish such foolish conditions for the payoff, conditions that would inevitably lead to his arrest and conviction? No one, including Wilson himself, ever answered those questions.

As soon as he had read the documents, the sheriff ordered five men to seize Wilson when he returned from Glasgow, where he had gone for the day. After Wilson had been held in jail for several months and then released on bail, the magistrate levied a fine against him of ten pounds and ordered him to pay Sharp fifty additional pounds in damages. The total was just about a year's earnings for a weaver, and unless Wilson could borrow the money, the sentence from a practical point of view amounted to life imprisonment.

Because Wilson failed to appear before the court to hear his sentence, he was held in contempt and fined approximately a pound more. But on learning that he had no lawyer, the sheriff appointed counsel to represent him. In January, 1793, the sheriff changed Wilson's sentence for contempt. He was, according to the new order, to serve two more weeks in jail and to burn his poem in public. Even after he had done this, the case continued to drag on while Wilson hoped to reduce the damages and fine he was to pay. In May, approximately a year after his original arrest, they were lowered to a little more than twelve pounds. Still on bail, Wilson went to live quietly with a friend and work out his debt.

In January of the following year he was arrested again under circumstances that were especially disturbing. He was charged with having written an announcement of a meeting of the Friends of Liberty and Reform, although the meeting had been held six months previously, and there was no evidence that Wilson was in any way involved. Evidently the officials of Paisley regarded Wilson as a dangerous radical who should be harassed and persecuted whenever possible.

Their attitude placed Wilson in a difficult position. To secure his release from jail on the new charge, he was forced to ask another friend to go bond for him, and in view of the obvious hostility of Paisley's officialdom, no one could tell when either bond might be declared forfeit. Unwilling to have his friends undergo such a risk in his behalf, Wilson made up his mind he could no longer live peaceably in Scotland and decided to emigrate to America.

To obtain the money for his passage, he saved every shilling he could, and the authorities, apparently glad to be rid of him, raised no objections to his plans. On May 16, 1794, in the company of his nephew, William Duncan, he left Paisley for the last time. Behind him were the shattered dreams of the fame he had hoped to gain with his poetry, the bitter memories of the Paisley jail, and the humiliation he had suffered when compelled to burn his poem in public. Perhaps in the New World, he thought, all this would be changed.

IV

Wilson and William Duncan sailed to Belfast, where they found a ship ready to leave for the United States, and reached New Castle, Delaware, on July 12. They immediately started hunting for work but quickly found the New World had little need of weavers. Wilson wrote his family that "after we had spent every farthing we had, and saw no hopes of anything being done that way, we took the first offer of employment we could find. . . ." Wilson's job was with a copperplate engraver, with whom he stayed until he located a position at a small textile mill some ten miles outside Philadelphia. He worked there until the spring of 1795, when, almost a year after his arrival in America, he resigned and went off on a peddling trip in northern New Jersey, taking with him some of the cloth he had woven.

On his return, he accepted a position as teacher at a school in Bustleton, Pennsylvania, where he remained until, at the end of one term, he received a better offer from a school at Milestown, about twenty miles from Philadelphia. This new post was not an easy one for an uneducated man to fill. Since most of the students came from Pennsylvania Dutch families and spoke only German, Wilson was required to teach them English. With his characteristic determination, he started learning German and mathematics, too, becoming so proficient in the latter that he was able to obtain part-time work as a surveyor. This schedule kept him so busy he had little time for friendships until the end of his first year at Milestown, when he began to collect a small circle of acquaintances, which included Alexander Lawson, a Philadelphia engraver from Scotland, and Charles Orr, a teacher of penmanship who originally came from Paisley. With friends like these, Wilson spent what hours he could spare outdoors, taking walks, going hunting, and observing the countryside.

He also watched with concern the growing crisis between the United States and France. The American commissioners assigned to negotiate a treaty with the French had been approached by three agents, X, Y, and Z, who said that a favorable treaty would be written only after the payment of a substantial bribe. Charles C. Pinckney replied with the now-classic phrase "Millions for defense, but not one cent for tribute," and John Adams made the whole intrigue public by turning over the pertinent correspondence to Congress. Public opinion was aroused and bitter. Wilson, after commenting on an outbreak of the plague in Philadelphia, wrote his father, "But a still worse scourge is likely to fall on us soon—that monstrous mother of almost every human evil—War. . . . But indeed," he went on in a revelation of his philosophy, "it is needless to spend the little time we have in thinking on the badness of the times, for I am persuaded while the world remains there will be tyrants and freemen, reformers and revolutionists, peace and war, till the end of time; and he is only the wise and happy man who, in following a peaceful employment through private life, intermeddles with politics as little as possible."

Putting this philosophy into practice, he decided to join with Duncan in buying a farm. They had heard of some land between lakes Cayuga and Seneca in New York State that they might be able to afford. Duncan went out to look at it, and finding the soil rich and the game plentiful, he and Wilson purchased 150 acres at five dollars an acre, even though they had to borrow the money. The plan they intended to follow was that of thousands of young partners without capital: Duncan was to clear the ground and start the farm; Wilson was to stay in his paid position and earn the cash they needed.

At the same time, in spite of an earlier resolve to the contrary, he once more became involved in politics. Jefferson was running for the Presidency against the Federalists, and Wilson was one of the many Americans who were convinced that John Adams intended to establish some sort of monarchy. So Wilson took up his pen and again began to write and speak in favor of the liberal side, doing so with considerable success and gaining recognition around Milestown as a concerned and influential citizen. Wilson now possessed much of what he had come to America to seek. He had a respected position as a teacher, considerable standing among his neighbors, and, if the farm worked out, a financial future.

Suddenly, on May 1, 1801, he wrote a short note to Charles Orr inviting him to come out to Milestown and stay with him. "I have matters to lay before you that have almost distracted me. Do come. I shall be so much obliged. Your friendship and counsel may be of the utmost service to me. I shall not remain here long. It is impossible I can. I have now no friend but yourself, and *one* whose friendship has involved us both in ruin or threatens to do so." Orr immediately responded and found Wilson practically incoherent in his distress and alarm. Although no one knows precisely what had happened, Wilson had probably fallen in love with the wife of one of his Milestown neighbors and feared the affair would become known. Orr spent the day with him and returned to Philadelphia. That night, abandoning almost all his belongings as well as the position he had worked so hard to attain, Wilson fled some fifteen miles away to Wrightstown, New Jersey. After a short stay there, he moved on to New York, where he remained for several weeks, with Orr serving as his only contact with the world. Even his nephew, William Duncan, did not know where he was.

In July he wrote Orr that he had moved to Bloomfield, New Jersey, and was living "six miles from Newark and twelve miles from New York, in a settlement of canting, preaching, praying, and sniveling ignorant Presbyterians. They pay their minister 250 pounds a year for preaching twice a week, and their teacher 40 dollars a quarter for the most spirit-sinking laborious work, six, I may say twelve times, weekly. I have no company and live unknowing and unknown. I have lost all relish for this country. . . ."

Emotionally distraught and disliking Bloomfield intensely, Wilson returned to Philadelphia, where he lived in seclusion, until he was offered a position teaching at a school a short way beyond Gray's Ferry, Pennsylvania. Although he accepted the post, Wilson was not happy. "I shall recommence that painful profession once more," he wrote, "with the same gloomy sullen resignation that a prisoner re-enters his dungeon or a malefactor mounts the scaffold; fate urges him, necessity me." Then he closed his letter with these words: "But perseverance overcometh all things."

V

So far Wilson's life had consisted of minor victories and major defeats. Now he was starting over again, heavy of heart and "with the same gloomy sullen resignation" of a condemned prisoner. But the key to his character was his belief in perseverance, and he was determined to make a success of himself at his new school.

Gray's Ferry was a congenial place, and being in the country again did much to revive his spirits. By July he was busy reexamining all his poetry, both published and unpublished, with the thought of bringing it together in one volume. And that summer he was excited, too, by the news that his sister, Mary, and his brother-in-law, William Duncan, were coming to the United States to take up residence on the New York farm.

Wilson visited the farm during the summer of 1802, and when he returned to Gray's Ferry, he found Mary and her six children waiting for him, but not her husband. At Belfast, Duncan had spent his passage money on liquor and was forced to remain behind. So Wilson now had to provide for his sister and her children, as well as for himself. Furthermore, as the weeks passed, it became apparent that Duncan had no further interest in his family and was leaving them in Wilson's charge. But their presence gave Wilson more incentive than he had had before, and his outlook improved accordingly.

He had always liked the out-of-doors, and during this period his interest in natural history, particularly in ornithology, increased. He watched the birds at Gray's Ferry change with the seasons, he captured some and kept them in cages so he could observe them closely, and he slowly gained a reputation in the neighborhood as an amateur ornithologist. People brought bird specimens for him to identify, and gradually a new thought occurred to him: If he could not gain fame with his poetry, perhaps he could do so by producing an illustrated book on the birds of America.

It was a wild idea since he lacked training in either science or art, but not so wild that he did not receive some encouragement. He had become a frequent visitor to Bartram's Garden on the outskirts of Philadelphia, and William Bartram, the botanist, thought the idea might be feasible. First, of course, Wilson must learn to draw, and Bartram was willing to criticize his pictures for him. As he always did, Wilson threw himself wholeheartedly into his new effort, although, as he wrote Bartram, "the duties of my profession will not admit me to apply to this study with the assiduity and perseverance I could wish. Chief part of what I do is by candle-light; and for this I am obliged to sacrifice the pleasures of social life. . . ."

In the early spring of 1804 he wrote the engraver Alexander Lawson that "I am most earnestly bent on pursuing my plan of making a collection of all the birds in this part of North America. Now I don't want you to throw cold water, as Shakespeare says, on this notion, Quixotic as it may appear. I have so long been accustomed to the building of airy castles and brain windmills, that it has become one of my earthly comforts, a sort of rough bone, that amuses me when sated with the dull drudgery of life." But being a practical man, Lawson pointed out that the expense of printing the illustrations would be prohibitive. Including the necessary copper and the engraver's work, each plate would cost between $50 and $80, and that was only the beginning. Every individual print in every copy would have to be colored by hand. The charge for this was usually 25 cents apiece. Even if Wilson divided the book into volumes containing only ten illustrations each, he would have to make an initial investment of more than $2,000 to obtain 500 copies of the first volume. Where was he going to get the money? His salary as a teacher was modest, and every cent he could save went to Mary and the farm.

But Wilson had to have some means of casting a light of hope on his future. At least until the book proved a failure, he could live in his "airy castle." So in spite of Lawson's warnings, he went ahead. How little he knew about what he was doing is revealed in a letter he wrote William Bartram in March, 1804. "I send for your amusement," he wrote, "a few attempts at some of our indigenous birds, hoping that your good nature will excuse their deficiencies, while you point them out to me. . . . I am almost ashamed to send you these drawings; but I know your generous disposition will induce you to encourage one in whom you perceive a sincere and eager wish to do well. They were chiefly coloured by candle-light."

Having asked Bartram for artistic criticism, he also looked to him for scientific help. "I have now got my collection of native birds considerably enlarged; and shall endeavour, if possible, to obtain all the smaller ones this summer. Be pleased to mark on the drawings, with a pencil, the names of each bird, as, except three or four, I do not know them." Probably no potential scientist was more ill equipped than Wilson. Not only was he unable to draw the illustrations that were essential, but he could not even identify most of the birds he portrayed.

Yet he persisted. His attitude toward his new work and the method by which he trained himself are set forth in another letter he wrote to Bartram: "While others are hoarding up their bags of money, without the power of enjoying it, I am collecting, without injuring my conscience, or wounding my peace of mind, those beautiful specimens of Nature's works that are forever pleasing. I have had live crows, hawks, and owls —opossums, squirrels, snakes, lizards, &c, so that my room has sometimes reminded me of Noah's ark; but Noah had a wife in one corner of it, and in this particular our parallel does not altogether tally. I receive every object of natural history that is brought to me, and though they do not march into my ark from all quarters, as they did that of our great ancestor, yet I find means, by the distribution of a few five-penny *bits,* to make them find the way fast enough. A boy, not long ago, brought me a large basket full of crows. I expect his next load will be bull-frogs, if I don't soon issue orders to the contrary."

As the months passed, he kept on collecting birds and animals and both studying and drawing them. Friends like Bartram helped him whenever they could, and as a result of their assistance and his own efforts, he became more proficient as an artist and more competent as a scientist, gradually making himself into an authority on American birds.

Two of his students were the sons of Samuel Bradford, a Philadelphia publisher and bookseller, who was the grandson of the printer who gave Benjamin Franklin his first job in the city. Bradford was much impressed by the serious teacher and offered him a job as editor of a new edition of *Rees's Cyclopedia.*

As the two men talked together, Bradford became intrigued with Wilson's contemplated book on birds, which he had decided to call *American Ornithology* and which, as a result of his extraordinary self-education, he now felt prepared to write. As the two men saw it, the book would consist of ten volumes, each with ten plates and selling for $12 or a total price of $120 for the set. Bradford and his father-in-law would underwrite the expense of publishing 200 copies of the first volume and of preparing an advertisement for it. If Wilson could obtain 200 subscriptions, they would then continue with the remainder.

Wilson could now laugh at Lawson's skepticism. In approximately four years of study he had learned enough about both art and ornithology to prepare his book. And what was most important of all, he had found a publisher to produce it. "Perseverance," he had written, "overcometh all things," and he had proved he was right.

VI

On April 8, 1807, Wilson sent William Bartram a proof of the prospectus. Twenty-five hundred copies were to be printed, he said, and Bradford intended to appoint "an agent in every town in the Union." Meanwhile, he himself, in addition to working as assistant editor on *Rees's Cyclopedia,* was still busy collecting and observing birds. That very morning, he wrote, he had started "by peep of day, with my gun, for the purpose of shooting a nuthatch. After jumping a hundred fences, and getting over the ankles in mud (for I had put on my shoes for lightness), I found myself almost at the junction of the Schuylkill and the Delaware, without success, there being hardly half an acre of woodland in the whole *neck;* and the nuthatch generally frequents large-timbered woods. I returned home at eight o'clock, after getting completely wet, and in a profuse perspiration, which, contrary to the maxims of the doctors, has done me a great deal of good." After this energetic beginning to the day—and it was not unusual—he had to report at Bradford's office to take up his regular work.

But in spite of his efforts, subscriptions did not sell well. Even the 2,500 prospectuses failed to attract sufficient buyers, and the "agent in every town in the Union" proved to be merely another of Wilson's "airy castles." People were interested, but they thought the price was too high. So in the fall of 1807 Wilson set out on a selling trip through New Jersey, New York, and New England.

He rode in the stagecoach as far as Princeton, New Jersey, where, as he wrote later, "I bade my fellow travellers good-bye, as I had to wait upon the reverend doctors of the college. I took my book under my arm, put several copies of the prospectus into my pocket, and walked up to this spacious sanctuary of literature. I could amuse you with some of my reflections on this occasion, but room will not permit. Dr. Smith, the president, and Dr. M'Lean, Professor of Natural History, were the only two I found at home. The latter invited me to tea, and both were much pleased and surprised by the appearance of the work. I expected to receive some valuable information from M'Lean, on the ornithology of the country, but I soon found, to my astonishment, that he scarcely knew a *sparrow* from a *woodpecker.* At his particular request, I left a specimen of the plates with him; and from what passed between us, I have hopes that he will pay more attention to this department of his profession than he has hitherto done."

From Princeton, Wilson went to New York, where he walked the streets so long and often trying to sell his book that people came to recognize him. Then he caught the packet and sailed up Long Island Sound to New Haven, Connecticut and went overland to Boston, returning by way of Dartmouth, New Hampshire, and Albany, New York. But the long trip was only partially successful. As Wilson wrote Lawson from Albany, "In short, the book, in all its parts, so far exceeds the ideas and expectations of the first literary characters of the eastern section of the United States, as to command their admiration and respect. The only objection has been the sum of *one hundred and twenty dollars* [the price of a complete set], which, in innumerable instances, has risen like an evil genius between me and my hopes. Yet I doubt not but when those copies subscribed for are delivered, and the book a little better known, the whole number will be disposed of, and perhaps encouragement given to go on with the rest. To effect this, to me, most desirable object, I have encountered the fatigues of a long, circuitous, and expensive journey, with a zeal that has increased with increasing difficulties; and I am sorry to say that the whole number of subscribers which I have obtained amounts only to *forty-one*."

The task Wilson had set for himself could be divided into several components: first, the collection of specimens; next, their identification; then the preparation of the drawings, followed by checking the plates, and examining the individual coloring of each picture (because each was done by hand, there could be serious deviations, and Wilson had to watch his artists' work closely); and finally, the writing and printing of the text, which included a description of the bird and its habits, all based largely on Wilson's observations, although he drew from other authorities when he could. This represented a full-time job, but he also had to be his chief salesman.

Yet Wilson persisted. With one journey completed, he immediately set off on another, this time southward. At Annapolis, the Maryland legislature considered subscribing but, on hearing the price, unanimously decided against it. In Washington he had better luck. He had corresponded several times with President Jefferson, who had already taken a subscription, and when Wilson called at the White House, the President received him. This endorsement helped him to sell seventeen subscriptions in the city before he started off again. He visited Norfolk, Virginia, and continued south, stopping here and there to interest potential subscribers and to observe the many new birds that he saw. About twelve miles north of Wilmington, North Carolina, he shot his first ivory-billed woodpecker, those giant birds that are now close to extinction. As Wilson later described the incident in *American Ornithology,* "This bird was only wounded slightly in the wing, and, on being caught, uttered a loudly reiterated and most piteous note, exactly resembling the violent crying of a young child; which terrified my horse so, as nearly to have cost me my life. It was distressing to hear it. I carried it with me . . . under cover, to Wilmington. In passing through the streets, its affecting cries surprised everyone within hearing, particularly the females, who hurried to the doors and windows with looks of alarm and anxiety. I drove on, and, on arriving at the piazza of the hotel, where I intended to put up, the landlord came forward, and a number of other persons who happened to be there, all equally alarmed at what they heard; this was greatly increased by my asking, whether he could furnish me with accommodations for me and my baby. The man looked blank and foolish, while the others stared with still greater astonishment. After diverting myself a few moments at their expense, I drew my woodpecker from under the cover and a general laugh took place."

Wilson, who wished to draw the bird, left it in his room, while he went out to care for his horse. The woodpecker, with his sharp, long bill, was, as Wilson discovered when he returned an hour later, capable of considerable destruction. "It had mounted along the side of the window, nearly as high as the ceiling a little below which he had begun to break through. The bed was covered with large pieces of plaster; the lath was exposed for at least fifteen inches square, and a hole, large enough to admit the fist, opened to the weather-boards; so that, in less than another hour, he would certainly have succeeded in making his way through. I now tied a string around his leg, and, fastening it to the table, again left him. I wished to preserve his life, and had gone off in search of suitable food for him. As I reascended the stairs, I heard him again hard at work, and on entering had the mortification to perceive that he had almost entirely ruined the mahogany table to which he was fastened, and on which he had wreaked his whole vengeance."

After paying his hotel bill, including reimbursement to the innkeeper for the woodpecker's damage, Wilson continued his journey. He went as far south as Savannah, Georgia, where he took a ship to New York. Returning directly to Philadelphia, he immediately started working on the second volume. But although his book was a scientific success, he found himself besieged by financial problems in producing it. Bradford was becoming disenchanted with the agreement he had made with Wilson, for the initial outlay was high, and the payments slow in coming back. (The subscribers were not required to send in their twelve dollars until the end of the year in which they received their copy.) The problem was further aggravated by the hand coloring, which meant that there was relatively little reduction in unit cost even with an increased number of sales. As Bradford's interest waned, Wilson found more and more of the burden falling on his own shoulders, and he finally established the book as a separate department of the firm, ordering his own plates and employing his own artists. Meanwhile, the costs were eating up the small profit. In August, 1809, Wilson wrote Bartram: "I assure you, dear friend, that this undertaking has involved me in many difficulties and expenses which I never dreamt of; and I have never yet received one cent from it. I am, therefore, a volunteer in the cause of Natural History, impelled by nobler views than those of money."

He scheduled the publication of the second volume for January, 1810. As soon as it was out, he intended to take another trip in hope of obtaining more specimens and more subscribers, and by the last week of February, 1810, he was in Pittsburgh, where the Monongahela and the Allegheny rivers join to form the Ohio. The shores were lined with flatboats, keelboats, and rafts, all ready to start the downward trip as soon as the ice broke. Wilson, however, decided that he would purchase a skiff and make the trip by himself. "I considered this mode," he wrote, "with all its inconveniences, as the most favourable to my researches and the most suitable to my funds. . . ." His entire stock of provisions consisted of some biscuits and cheese and a bottle of cordial that had been given him in Pittsburgh; his equipment was merely his gun, trunk, greatcoat, and a can he could use for both bailing and drinking. The current, he estimated, carried him about two and a half miles an hour, and his rowing added about three and a half miles an hour more. Every time he passed a town, he would go ashore, obtain what information he could concerning the birds of the region, and try to sell some subscriptions.

In this painful fashion, he traveled from February 24 to March 17, 1810, covering 720 miles and arriving at last at Bear Grass Creek, the landing place for Louisville just above the Falls of the Ohio. Strong as he was, the journey had tired him, and his hands were so stiff from rowing he thought it would be weeks before they became limber again. The day after his arrival he sold the skiff to a man who was surprised at the name Wilson had given it. The *Ornithologist,* the buyer supposed, must have been an old Indian chief or warrior.

Wilson spent several days in Louisville, talking to various people, and learning that one of the local merchants, John James Audubon, was considered something of an authority on birds, he walked to the unimpressive store operated by Audubon and his partner, Ferdinand Rozier, and introduced himself. Writing many years later, Audubon said, "One fair morning I was surprised by the sudden entrance into our counting-room of Mr. Alexander Wilson, the celebrated author of the 'American Ornithology,' of whose existence I had never until that moment been apprised. This happened in March, 1810. How well do I remember him, as he walked up to me! His long, rather hooked nose, the keenness of his eyes, and his prominent cheek bones, stamped his countenance with a peculiar character. His dress, too, was of a kind not usually seen in that part of the country,—a short coat, trousers, and a waistcoat of gray cloth. His stature was not above the middle size. He had two volumes under his arm, and as he approached the table at which I was working, I thought I discovered something like astonishment in his countenance. He, however, immediately proceeded to disclose the object of his visit, which was to procure subscriptions for his work. He opened his books, explained the nature of his occupations, and requested my patronage.

"I felt surprised and gratified at the sight of his volumes, turned over a few of the plates, and had already taken a pen to write my name to his favor, when my partner, rather abruptly, said to me in French, 'My dear Audubon, what induces you to subscribe to this work? Your drawings are certainly far better, and again, you must know as much of the habits of American birds as this gentleman.' Whether Mr. Wilson understood French or not, or whether the suddenness with which I paused disappointed him, I cannot tell; but I clearly perceived that he was not pleased. Vanity and the encomiums of my friend prevented me from subscribing. Mr. Wilson asked me if I had many drawings of birds. I rose, took down a large portfolio, laid it on the table, and showed him, as I would show you, kind reader, or any other person fond of such subjects, the whole contents, with the same patience with which he had shown me his own engravings.

"His surprise appeared great, as he told me he never had the most distant idea that any other individual than himself had been engaged in forming such a collection. He asked me if it was my intention to publish, and when I answered in the negative, his surprise seemed to increase. . . . Mr. Wilson now examined my drawings with care, asked if I should have any objections to lending him a few during his stay, to which I replied that I had none; he then bade me good-morning, not, however, until I had made an arrangement to explore the woods in the vicinity with him, and had promised to procure for him some birds of which I had drawings in my collection, but which he had never seen."

In relating the incident years later, Audubon undoubtedly permitted some distortion of the truth. Since he lived on a flyway that Wilson had not yet explored, he certainly had collected some birds that Wilson had not observed, but he did not know "as much of the habits of American birds as this gentleman," to use the words he put into Rozier's mouth. Nor is it likely that Rozier objected to the purchase of *American Ornithology* merely because he thought Audubon's pictures were better. The firm was doing badly financially, and it is reasonable to assume his objections were based on the unnecessary expense.

Nevertheless, Audubon spent some time with Wilson, going out hunting with him and trying to find new birds for him. He also lent him some of his own pictures to copy. Then Wilson, having failed to sell any subscriptions in Louisville, started south again. He continued to solicit sub-scriptions in every large town that he visited and to collect birds in the woods and fields and along the waterways, adding to his notes and his drawings. Strange as his appearance must have been, riding by himself with his gun and his tame bird, he was engaged in a truly important sci-entific expedition, and by the time he reached New Orleans, he was cer-tainly the world's outstanding authority on North American birds. No one else in the country had traveled so widely in search of new species or labored so systematically, collecting, identifying, and making notes of his field observations. He now had far more information than anyone else. All that remained was to get everything he knew into print.

VII

When Wilson sailed from New Orleans on June 24, 1810, he had every reason to be pleased with the results of his journey. Expensive as it had been for him to travel so far even in the simple fashion he did, he had sold many new subscriptions, obtained many new birds, and made many new friends. Particularly in New Orleans, he discovered that his fame as an ornithologist had preceded him and that he had access to some of the most important people in the city. The voyage back to New York was also useful, because it gave him a chance to observe the sea-birds of the southern coast.

Yet on his return to Philadelphia, he found himself faced with a seri-ous economic problem, the root of which lay in his agreements with his subscribers. They received the volumes as they came out, but, of course, by the terms he had established, they did not have to pay for them until the end of the calendar year in which they were issued. So far, Wilson had published Volume I in 1808 and Volume II in 1810. To obtain the working capital he needed, he should have produced Volume III in the same year, but he did not allow enough time. The book failed to come out until February, 1811, thus delaying payment until December. From that point on, Wilson was never able to catch up with his schedule, especially because the subscribers were unwilling to buy more than two volumes in a single year.

In an effort to increase his collection of birds more rapidly, Wilson sent out word that he would welcome help from other observers, and one of those who responded was a wealthy and eccentric Philadelphian, George Ord. (One of his eccentricities was the preparation of a diction-ary of obsolete words. He offered it, unpublished, to Noah Webster, who earned Ord's undying hatred by refusing it.) Ord was not an ornitholo-gist, but as an enthusiastic sportsman, he had spent many days in the field and, therefore, thought himself qualified to ply Wilson with information. Furthermore, he took an inexplicably possessive attitude toward Wilson. He had to know him better than anyone else, give him more advice, and be more intimate with him, centering his own life on Wilson's.

But even Ord's exaggerated attentions could not distract Wilson from his work. He made several visits to the New Jersey coast and in 1812 took another trip through New England. Back in Philadelphia that fall, he returned to his usual routine. Volume VI was distributed to the subscribers in November, and in April, 1813, he wrote William Bartram that "I have been extremely busy these several months, my colourists having all left me; so I have been obliged to do extra duty this last winter. Next week I shall publish my seventh volume; and I shall send you your copy with the earliest opportunity. I am now engaged with the ducks, all of which that I am acquainted with, will be comprehended in the eighth volume."

It had been a prodigious performance. In 1804 he had written his letter to Alexander Lawson proclaiming his intention of writing a book on the birds of the United States and asking Lawson not to laugh at his "airy castle." Nine years later he had published the seventh volume of his work, which was regarded as the authority in its field. It illustrated and described far more American birds than any other book, and no ornithologist could afford to be without it.

Now at last, the promises of fortune seemed about to be fulfilled. He was recognized as the nation's leading ornithologist, and once the book was finished, he would be relieved of the necessity of constantly reinvesting his earnings in additional volumes. When that point came, he might begin to realize the profit for which he had struggled so hard and long. He was exhausted, but the end of his labor was in sight. On July 6, 1813, he wrote, "I am myself far from being in good health. Intense application to study has hurt me much. My 8th volume is now in the press and will be published in November. One volume more will complete the whole. . . ."

He did not live to see the eighth volume off the press. On August 19, 1813, the doctor was called to the house where Wilson was living. Wilson was seriously ill and, after the doctor left, wrote his will in which he named that possessive eccentric George Ord an executor. Four days later he died. He had just turned forty-seven.

VIII

In 1810, when Wilson walked into the shabby, ill-stocked store of Audubon & Rozier in Louisville, John James Audubon, as he himself said, had no thought of publishing a book on the birds of America. Instead, he was intent on making a fortune as a businessman.

Unlike Wilson's, his family had been wealthy. His father, a former sea captain, had made a small fortune in the colony of San Domingo, where he had worked as a merchant and slave trader. While living there, he had taken two mistresses, one of whom was John James' mother, and the other, the mother of a girl, Rosa. On his return to his wife in Nantes, he brought his two illegitimate children with him, and Mme. Audubon, instead of rejecting them, accepted them as her own, both emotionally and legally. Her affection and good nature, however, did the boy much harm. By the time he was eighteen, he was thoroughly spoiled, so lazy he refused to attend school, so full of self-esteem he thought life owed him a living. In despair, Captain Audubon sent him to the United States, thinking he would learn English and also avoid conscription into Napoleon's army.

For a short time Audubon visited a friend of his father, and then he insisted he be permitted to live on a farm outside Philadelphia that his father had purchased earlier as an investment. Arrangements were made with his father's tenant to take care of the boy, who moved to Mill Grove, as the place was called.

In this fashion he began the happiest period of his life. All day long he hunted, walked in the woods, or in wintertime skated on the Perkiomen Creek, which flowed through the property. Among his neighbors was the Bakewell family, who had come from England a short while before. Audubon quickly fell in love with one of the daughters, Lucy, and this affair added zest to his utterly purposeless life. Aside from painting bird pictures, which were not particularly good, and spending hours observing birds, he did nothing of consequence. Even his English remained poor, since he would not make the effort to learn to speak and write the language properly.

This existence might have gone on as long as Captain Audubon continued to pay the bills, except for an unfortunate decision to reopen an old lead mine near the house. During the Revolution, when lead was sorely needed for bullets, the mine had proved profitable, and Audubon, along with the tenant and Captain Audubon's business representative in America, thought it could be operated on the same basis again. But the expense of getting it working proved far greater than they expected, and the returns from the sale of ore much less.

Instead of abandoning their project, which would have been the wise course, they appealed to Captain Audubon for additional capital. The captain, who was now getting on in years, had lost his former astuteness and instead of saying a firm no, agreed to find the money. Because his own fortune had vanished during the Negro uprising in San Domingo, he had to mortgage Mill Grove in order to obtain the funds. But the amount he raised failed to be adequate, and as the undertaking turned into a disaster, John James quarreled with the tenant and with his father's business representative. Then, in a fit of petulance, he boarded a ship and sailed back to France.

This act caused the final upset in Captain Audubon's plans, for he now had to get John James back out of the country without being conscripted into Napoleon's army and also to devise some way for him to make a living. He appealed to a wealthy friend, François Rozier, who held a mortgage on the farm, and Rozier agreed to bind his son, Ferdinand, and John James in a partnership and send them both back to America to start a business.

When the two boys reached the United States, they went directly to Mill Grove. Rozier, who was clearheaded and practical, immediately saw that nothing could be done to salvage the investment in the mine, so he surrendered most of the property and suggested that he and John James each join a mercantile firm in order to learn something about business. After a short apprenticeship they set up a store at Louisville, Kentucky, but the competition from the other merchants was too great, and Aubudon failed to concentrate on his work, leaving most of the duties to Rozier. While Rozier stayed behind the counter, Audubon wandered through the woods, hunting, observing birds, fishing, and visiting the cabins of nearby farmers. It was a continuation of his earlier existence at Mill Grove, careless and irresponsible, although he had by now married Lucy Bakewell and was a father.

Finally, even he recognized the firm could not prosper in Louisville. If he were to make his fortune in the West, he had to move to another town, and this time he and Rozier chose Henderson, Kentucky. Few choices could have been worse. Henderson had been laid out on a grand plan but had attracted few settlers, and these few lived in log houses. As Audubon had noted, competition was nonexistent, but, as he had not observed, that was because business was also practically nonexistent, and it soon became obvious to both men that they could not survive without changing their location once more. Rozier suggested they try some town on the Mississippi River in what is now Missouri.

That winter they rented a keelboat and loaded it with supplies, including 300 barrels of Kentucky whiskey, which they purchased for twenty-five cents a barrel. Leaving Lucy to spend the winter in Henderson, Audubon and Rozier began the long journey down the Ohio River. Before they reached its mouth, they learned that the Mississippi was so filled with floating chunks of ice that they would have to make a winter camp and wait for the weather to turn warmer. To Audubon, who always liked a wilderness adventure, this news was good. Rozier, on the other hand, was depressed. He knew that the firm's slender capital was already dwindling and that the delay could only make their situation worse. The attitudes of the two men toward their business had always been in sharp contrast. The days spent tied up on the shores of the Ohio served to sharpen their differences.

When the Mississippi again became navigable, they began ascending it; but the weather once more turned cold, and they were again forced to make camp. This encampment was a repetition of the first. Audubon enjoyed himself immensely, going off on expeditions and visiting the nearby Indians. Rozier sulked, growing more and more fearful about their business. When they at last reached Ste. Genevieve, the differences between them had become unresolvable. After a bitter discussion they decided to dissolve their partnership. Audubon then set off overland for Henderson, happy to be free of his critical partner, but not realizing how sorely he would need Rozier's business judgment.

I X

In 1811, when Audubon returned alone from Ste. Genevieve to Henderson, he had no plans for the future except to continue doing what he had always done, which was practically nothing. For a time he loafed around Henderson. Then he received word that Lucy's brother, Thomas Bakewell, had made a connection with some businessmen in Liverpool and was setting up a firm in New Orleans to trade with them. Audubon proposed they go into partnership, and Thomas Bakewell agreed. Before they could establish themselves at New Orleans, the War of 1812 broke out, rendering their Liverpool connections worthless. As an alternative to their proposed office in New Orleans, Audubon suggested they try opening another store in Henderson. As the town had scarcely grown since his first arrival, Audubon's suggestion was not realistic, but the two young partners could think of nothing else to do.

Somehow the firm survived the next few years until Audubon suddenly had a burst of energy. He and Bakewell took in another partner, who had some capital to invest, and engaged an engineer named David Prentice. Audubon planned to construct and operate a steam mill to grind grain and saw wood for the people of Henderson. Since the community could barely support their store, it should have been apparent to the firm of Audubon & Bakewell that their new venture was doomed to failure. But Audubon was now in a state of complete self-delusion.

Work on the mill commenced. The stone foundations were four and a half feet thick; the millstones were the finest obtainable, the engine the best. Altogether it cost the partners $5,000 more than they had expected, and business was bad everywhere, not just in Henderson. Audubon was now heavily in debt. Lucy's money was already gone; Captain Audubon had died, leaving only a remnant of his fortune, and that went to his widow; and Thomas Bakewell wanted his money back. Yet Audubon was not the least daunted. He had charming manners and an engaging personality. Everyone in Louisville and Henderson, men and women, too, were fond of the charming millowner, and moreover, they trusted him. As steamboats were making money, Audubon decided to purchase one. Not having sufficient funds, he borrowed additional money from his friends, bought one, and resold it at a profit, but without checking the purchasers' credit. He accepted their notes, which were without value, and the papers also seem to have been drawn up improperly. In a skiff with two Negro rowers, he pursued the boat to New Orleans and instituted legal proceedings. These proved unsuccessful, and he returned to Henderson a defeated man. His creditors demanded their money, and when he could not pay, they haled him into court in Louisville, where he declared himself a bankrupt. The humiliation was overwhelming, but what was even worse was the reaction of his friends and neighbors. They felt Audubon had failed them with his optimistic talk and his happy ways. In Henderson the bitterness was so acute he realized he must move out of the town. He took refuge in Louisville but soon discovered that, although his acquaintances there were not as angry with him, they had no confidence in him. Not one of them would give him a job of any kind.

A friend, however, knowing about Audubon's drawing, asked him to do a portrait for which he was willing to pay. Audubon accepted the commission, and in 1819 he became a professional artist, professional in the sense of being paid for his work, if not in the sense of exercising a high degree of skill. This commission was followed by others, and he soon was making a living doing portraits in black chalk. This, of course, could not last, so Audubon, at the suggestion of some friends, applied for a position at the newly founded Western Museum in Cincinnati. Although he had no standing as a scientist, the museum gave him a job as a taxidermist to stuff fish for its collection.

The experience was valuable to Audubon. Until then he had hardly talked to any professional scientists, but at the museum Audubon began to think for the first time that possibly he could make a living as a scientist, in particular as an ornithologist. For he saw the passage of one of the government's Western expeditions down the river, staffed by men who were on the government's payroll, and he heard Wilson's name constantly mentioned as the authority on American birds.

Ambitiously planned, the Western Museum soon ran into financial difficulties, and although Audubon was entitled to a salary of $125 a month, the museum could not meet its payroll. Dr. Daniel Drake, a physician who had founded the museum, noticed that Audubon had in his collection of bird drawings several species that could not be found in Wilson's, and he correctly surmised that Wilson must have missed many birds on his single trip down the Ohio River. Here, Audubon thought, was an opportunity to write a better bird book, and unaware of Wilson's financial difficulties, he decided to seize it.

X

In October, 1820, Audubon stood on the banks of the Ohio River at Cincinnati prepared to board a flatboat bound for New Orleans. He was starting on what was perhaps the worst-conceived scientific expedition in the history of the United States. He had hardly any money or any idea what he was doing, just a vague plan that during the trip down the rivers he would find new birds and draw them.

The first few days everything went moderately well. Whenever he could, he walked along the banks of the river, following the flatboat on foot and shooting birds as he moved along. In the process he obtained several specimens he wanted and also helped provide the crew and passengers with food. But after the boat passed Louisville and began approaching Henderson, he became subject to profound depression. His memories of his disgrace and the hatred of his neighbors were more than he could bear.

After they had passed the village and seen the steam mill still standing on the banks of the river, Audubon's spirits began to revive, but before the boat reached the Mississippi, they were again dashed. Judging from his journal, he had reached an arrangement with the boat's captain not to pay the full fare, and the captain made some joke at the expense of Audubon's poverty. A day later he was sitting despondently on the deck looking at a picture he had drawn of Lucy. Suddenly it seemed to change before his eyes. He thought the expression altered and became more sorrowful. Actually he was on the verge of insanity after the strain of the last years.

His depression was heightened by his experiences on arriving at New Orleans. He had no means of making a living there except by drawing more black chalk portraits (he had done a few on the way down the river and thus earned some cash), but he found that commissions were difficult to obtain. After wandering through the streets of New Orleans, picking up a few dollars here and a few there, he accepted an offer to serve as a tutor on a plantation up the river. Living in the country, he had an opportunity to collect more birds, but he soon quarreled with the family and had to return to New Orleans. His second attempt to make a living in the city was no more successful than the first. Nobody had any particular interest in either him, his pictures, or his proposed book, and Audubon, now grown sensitive from the many rebuffs he had received, imagined insults where none existed and became a difficult person to help.

Even Lucy, whom he loved so dearly, failed him. She had married him as a young woman, adored him during their days in Kentucky, and moved with him to Cincinnati. But her faith was now shaken. She had believed every word he had uttered in Henderson and had been horrified by the collapse of their fortunes. When the Western Museum had been unable to pay his salary, she had agreed to the trip down the rivers, but nothing had come of that either. By this time she clung to the slight security she had obtained in Cincinnati, where she had a job with a family, and refused to rejoin him in New Orleans. In fact, his journals indicate that she had no real interest in ever seeing him again. In despair, he kept pleading with her in heart-rending letters. Finally, after a fourteen-month separation, she relented and came to New Orleans.

Her arrival temporarily did much to raise his spirits. He continued to give art lessons and do portraits and returned with renewed enthusiasm to the pictures for his projected book. Lucy obtained a position as governess with a New Orleans family, but their happiness did not last long. As the months wore on, both husband and wife could see their work was leading them nowhere.

Audubon could not remain in New Orleans, and having no better plan, he decided to go to Natchez, where he made a meager living by teaching in schools and painting portraits, but he had almost completely abandoned any hope of producing his book. He was, at this point, willing to take any job that might be offered him and considered several opportunities, none of which materialized. Lucy, meanwhile, had found a position as tutor on a plantation in Louisiana, and after an abortive attempt at being an itinerant portrait painter—he had learned to use oils from a painter he had met in Natchez—Audubon joined her. He could have stayed there indefinitely, helping Lucy with her teaching and doing work around the plantation, but once more his pride got in his way. He was commissioned to do portraits of the owner's daughters, but when their mother asked him to make a slight change in the picture, he refused to do so and stalked out of the house in anger.

In company with his son Victor he went up the river to Shippingport, Kentucky, where he hoped that some of his former friends might now have forgiven him. Although they quickly found work for Victor, no one offered Audubon a job except one painting a steamboat. He was in a desperate situation, despised and poor and with only the bleakest of futures ahead of him. On his way to Shippingport, he had written his former partner, Rozier, that he was wearied of the world, having been too much of it, and his lot had not improved.

In the spring of 1824 he set out for Philadelphia. He had no clear plan in mind, merely a general intention of seeking a publisher and finding what Philadelphia might have to offer him. Being still personable in spite of the many rebuffs he had received, he quickly made a number of acquaintances in Philadelphia and was introduced to people like Charles Lucien Bonaparte, a nephew of the emperor and an ornithologist, and Thomas Sully, the artist. These invited him to attend a meeting of the Academy of Natural Sciences and to show his pictures. For Audubon, this was a great opportunity, but he failed to profit by it. For three and a half years he had been competing in his mind with Alexander Wilson, looking for errors in Wilson's book and searching for birds that Wilson had not identified. No minutes of the meeting exist, but what transpired can be deduced from Audubon's later comments and from the events that followed. Forgetting completely that he was among Wilson's friends, Audubon took an arrogant attitude toward the work of the dead ornithologist, comparing it unfavorably with his own. As George Ord, Wilson's executor, was present, the result was a debacle for Audubon. Ord gave him a tongue-lashing and rallied his friends to the attack. In response Audubon lost his temper and began talking in an exaggerated fashion, and by the time the meeting drew to a close, he had hardly a friend left in Philadelphia and no chance whatsoever of obtaining a publisher.

During the days that followed, instead of attempting to placate the men he had offended, he criticized them even more sharply, reacting just as he had done in New Orleans. No one could help him. When he at last realized the futility of remaining in Philadelphia, his reputation had preceded him to New York, his next destination. Try as he could, he found no supporters there either, gave up hope of obtaining a publisher even in Boston, and took a pleasure trip to Niagara Falls.

It was probably the best step. After the disastrous visit to Philadelphia and the frustrating stay in New York, he needed time to think. Obviously his pictures were not sufficiently better than Wilson's to attract an American publisher, and his aggressive personality made it impossible for him to expect to gain a patron. As he watched the waters pour over the great ledge of rock and pound into the abyss below, he began for the first time to appraise his situation realistically. He understood now that his single chance for fame lay in the eventual publication of his book and that this event would never take place unless he adopted a more professional attitude toward his work.

His new resolution was sudden, but it was permanent. From Niagara Falls he went to Pittsburgh, painting portraits as he traveled, and from there continued down the rivers to rejoin Lucy. She must have been amazed at his transformation, for he immediately sought work giving lessons in French, dancing, and fencing, all of which proved so successful that he began earning a regular living. Instead of splurging his funds on new business enterprises as he would have done a few years earlier, he started saving his money. And between 1824 and 1826 he and Lucy between them set aside enough for him to go to England and look for a publisher there.

In view of his past experiences, the venture seemed hopeless. If he had had difficulties in Philadelphia, what could he expect in England, where he was completely unknown? But Audubon was now a truly different person, more earnest and a far better artist, and on May 17, 1826, at the age of forty-one, he boarded a ship at New Orleans and set out for Europe.

XI

When Audubon's ship dropped anchor in the Mersey River at Liverpool, he had few assets aside from his drawings, his knowledge of birds, and a few letters of introduction. These he presented to a family named Rathbone, who took an immediate liking to him and introduced him to a number of Liverpool's leading citizens. Audubon quickly sensed England's interest in the frontier and began assuming a role as the "American woodsman," regaling the Rathbones' guests with stories of his adventures along the Ohio and Mississippi. Word quickly spread about this amazing frontiersman, who wore his hair in curls that hung down to his shoulders and who possessed those fine pictures of American birds, and the Royal Institution of Liverpool invited him to hold a one-man exhibit. This was such a success that Audubon decided to exhibit other pictures in Manchester and charge for admission.

But Manchester was not as hospitable as Liverpool. Instead of making money in Manchester, he did not even cover his expenses, and he returned to Liverpool, discouraged and disheartened. At the end of several weeks it became increasingly apparent that Liverpool could do nothing more for him and that if he wanted to find a publisher, he had to go elsewhere. London, of course, was the obvious place, but Audubon did not have the courage to test himself against the possible indifference of the sophisticated capital. Edinburgh, which was also a leading intellectual center, seemed to present a better opportunity.

He had collected more letters of introduction, which he started delivering as soon as he had found rooms in the city, but the letters were like so many stones thrown into a deep well. No one responded to them, no visitors came to see his pictures, and it seemed that his appearance in Edinburgh would, like his visits to New York, Philadelphia, and Manchester, end in utter failure.

As he was giving up hope, the first visitors started to call, some of them friendly, but none of them possessed the connections he needed. After several days Patrick Neill, a naturalist who also operated a printing shop, came. As soon as he saw the pictures, he insisted that Audubon should meet W. H. Lizars, a noted Scottish engraver. It was a tense moment when Audubon laid his portfolio on the floor, untied the strap that bound it together, and held up the first picture for Lizars to look at. But he should not have worried. Lizars was delighted with it and also with all the others, and his enthusiasm led to action. He introduced Audubon to the appropriate people in Edinburgh, he arranged an exhibit for him, and best of all, he offered to engrave and print five pictures to determine whether they could be sold. Unlike Wilson's plates, these were to be magnificent creations with the birds reproduced life-size in all the beauty of Audubon's pictures. For Audubon was now incomparably the better artist. Wilson's pictures, in contrast, were two-dimensional and stiff, useful for identification, but not art in themselves. Audubon's, as he had intended them to be, were bird, background, and sky blended into a whole scene, each one a work of art in itself. Five pictures, Audubon and Lizars agreed, would sell for two guineas, and when he made each sale, Audubon was to attempt to secure the purchaser as a subscriber for the whole set. (Later Audubon was to produce a text describing the birds, but this was to appear separately.) Furthermore, Lizars was willing to delay payment for his work until the pictures were sold.

The offer was a handsome one, and Audubon seized it avidly. In March, 1827, the first five engravings were ready, and he started out on a canvassing trip like those that Alexander Wilson had had to endure.

XII

Whereas Wilson's book had been small enough to carry with him comfortably, Audubon's was enormous, and the portfolio containing his engravings and other pictures weighed approximately 100 pounds. He could not, therefore, carry it from door to door as Wilson had done with copies of his books, so he evolved a new technique, one he followed throughout the succeeding years. He would visit a city and engage rooms. Then he would go out with all the letters of introduction he had obtained, leave them with an invitation to see his pictures, and return to his rooms to wait. When the visitors arrived, he would show his pictures and attempt to secure subscribers. The process was slow and grueling. Sometimes almost no one came. Sometimes those who arrived were insulting and condescending. But slowly the names in his subscription book began to increase, as he progressed from town to town until he reached London.

There disaster almost overtook him. He had begun to meet some of the important people who could help him and to sell a few subscriptions, when he received word from Lizars that the colorists had gone on strike. Consequently, even if he sold some subscriptions, he could not fill his orders promptly. Audubon was frantic. Without admitting his predicament to his new acquaintances, he searched for another engraver who would be willing to color the black-and-white prints that Lizars was still able to supply. After discussing the problem with several booksellers, he selected an engraver named Robert Havell. Havell not only agreed to handle the coloring, but also suggested that he take over the entire work at a price considerably less than Lizars'. Audubon, who had been becoming impatient with Lizars, agreed to this new arrangement, and Havell did all the remaining plates.

With this crisis handled, Audubon returned to the endless task of making new friends, preparing new pictures, supervising their reproduction (like Wilson, he was plagued with the problem of ensuring that the colorists followed his guides carefully), selling new subscriptions, and handling the business problems connected with the publication. These in themselves were considerable. Audubon had to maintain lists of his subscribers, see to it that each one received the newest set of pictures as they came from the engraver, inspect the quality of each print, answer complaints, and send out the bills. What was truly extraordinary was that he did all this well. Lazy and impractical as a younger man, he now worked long hours, starting early in the morning and continuing until there was no more light.

During the years from 1827 to 1829 he made many more canvassing trips. (On one of them he went to Paris; it was then he met Georges Cuvier.) But his two great desires in life failed to materialize. Although he kept adding new names to his subscription list, the total failed to show much increase. The book was so expensive at two guineas for every five pictures that many subscribers, after receiving a few sets, dropped out. His other frustration was his inability to convince Lucy of the extent of his transformation. He wanted her to come to Great Britain and live with him, but she refused to give up her position on the plantation in Louisiana.

Although he was really too busy to leave Great Britain, Audubon decided in 1829 that he either had to go to the United States and persuade Lucy to come back with him or give up hope of seeing her again. From New York he went to Philadelphia, where he hunted the surrounding countryside for new birds, going as far away as the New Jersey coast. He had had an initial advantage over Wilson by being more familiar with the Mississippi flyway. Now he had to make up for Wilson's advantage in knowing the Northeast as well as he did.

From this point of view, his trip was successful, but he was unable to settle his family affairs. Carefully he explained to Lucy how he hoped to avoid going to Louisiana. His time was limited, and he wanted to devote it to areas where he might find new birds and not use it visiting places he had already thoroughly explored. But Lucy would not heed him, nor would his two boys, Victor and John, to whom he appealed. They all were unable to believe he had changed. In order to convince them, he at last felt forced to make the long journey to Louisiana after all. It was a considerable sacrifice, because he already had more than he could do, but on seeing him and talking to him, Lucy realized he was more changed than she had thought. Overcoming her fears, she consented to return to England with him.

In March, 1830, they boarded a ship at New York, and as soon as they reached Liverpool, Audubon set off on a new canvassing trip, another in the endless rounds of delivering letters of introduction and waiting in his rooms until the visitors came. He was better known now and had friends in most of the cities he visited, but the routine was just as wearing as it had always been, and he was getting older. He also had a new problem. From the first he had intended to write a text to accompany his pictures, but he learned now that he could no longer delay it, because he was again in competition with Alexander Wilson. Wilson's book was popular in Europe, and two new editions were now in the process of preparation. Unless Audubon hurried with his text, he might find the market for it absorbed by Wilson.

He correctly believed that he should not attempt to write it by himself. No one in the world knew the birds of America as well as he did, but he wanted his book to describe not only their habits and appearances, but also the technical aspects of their anatomies. To do this, he needed help. After discussing the problem with several naturalists, he selected William MacGillivray, a young scientist who lived in Edinburgh, to be his collaborator. Working at feverish pace, he finally completed the first volume by April, 1831, and was ready to return to the United States and engage in more collecting expeditions.

As soon as he reached the United States, he started south, stopping for a short time at Philadelphia, where one of his old creditors attempted to have him jailed. From Philadelphia he went on to Charleston, South Carolina. He had not been able to employ assistants on his earlier trips, but he now had two—a taxidermist to help prepare the specimens he collected and an artist to assist him with the backgrounds in his pictures. Unfortunately, he had timed his journey wrong, and the birds he most wanted had migrated, so he left Charleston and went to St. Augustine, where he obtained transportation on a revenue cutter that was bound for the Florida Keys. The weeks that followed were among the happiest Audubon ever spent. The schooner offered enough comforts, so he did not have to exhaust himself, and it cruised slowly and gave him time to explore the islands. Many of his days were spent hunting with one of the Revenue Service's pilots, a man who knew Florida's wildlife well. Under his guidance, Audubon's piles of specimens mounted. Nevertheless, when he returned from the Dry Tortugas, which represented the outward limit of the cutter's patrol, he still did not have all the birds he needed.

He decided, therefore, not to go back to England, as he had originally planned, but to stay another season in the United States and make an expedition northward. In August he was in Maine, but, as he wrote to a friend in Boston, "*Birds* are very, very few and far between." This led him to spend the winter in the United States, and early in the following spring he returned to Maine, where he chartered a schooner and made a voyage up the coast of Nova Scotia and into the Gulf of St. Lawrence. This, however, was not a repetition of his Florida voyage. Although he collected many birds and observed the depredations of the Labrador eggers (they stripped the seabirds' nests of eggs and sold them commercially), the strain of the trip told on him. For the first time he began to complain about the hardships of an outdoor life, noting in his journal that he was often too weary even to draw. He later wrote of his Canadian journey, "At times I felt as if my physical powers would abandon me; my neck, my shoulders, and, more than all, my fingers, were almost useless through actual fatigue at drawing. Who would believe this? Yet nothing is more true. When at the return of dawn my spirits called me out of my berth, my body seemed to beg my mind to suffer it to rest a while longer; and as dark forced me to lay aside my brushes, I immediately went to rest as if I had walked sixty-five miles that day, as I have done *a few times* in my stronger days."

In the spring of 1834 he returned to England with his specimens and until the early fall of 1836 followed his old routine of producing more pictures, selling more subscriptions, and writing more of the text. But once again he realized that he did not have enough birds, and in 1836 he returned to the United States. Although he added to his collection and went as far as Houston, where he had a brief interview with Sam Houston, then president of the newly formed Republic of Texas, he suffered the same fatigue he had felt during his voyage in Canada. Instead of rejoicing in the challenge of each day and the opportunity to exert his once-great physical energy, he complained of his weariness and wrote a friend that he had lost fifteen pounds during the journey. Yet he could not cease working. If his book were to have value, it had to be as nearly complete as he could make it. Consequently, he had no alternative except to return once more to England and work with the new specimens he had obtained.

He was tired now of the whole business, and so were his subscribers.

The seemingly endless stream of plates at two guineas for each set of five was greater than many of them wished to purchase. More and more of them began either to drop their subscriptions or to threaten to do so, and Audubon could see that since the book would not support him indefinitely, he had to bring it to a conclusion as quickly as possible. By dint of combining several species in single plates and by laboring as frantically as he ever had, he finally produced the last plate and the final volume of the text (as well as a synopsis) in 1839.

Yet the end came to him as an anticlimax. Not only was he tired of his work, but he had not earned much money. In 1827, when he left Edinburgh to commence his first canvassing trip, he had written Lucy that he hoped to sell at least 200 subscriptions and perhaps as many as 500. The latter figure would have made him wealthy, but he never even reached the minimum he had set for his goal. His subscribers were so erratic that he was not certain how many complete subscriptions he had sold, but he thought the number must be around 175. This had been enough to support him and his family in modest comfort, but not enough to provide for their future needs. So when he returned to the United States in 1839, his first thought was about how to earn his living in the future.

XIII

When he had begun to realize that *The Birds of America* would never make him rich, Audubon had started thinking about two other endeavors he might undertake. One was a smaller, less expensive edition of his original book with the plates lithographed rather than engraved. The other was a new work on the viviparous quadrupeds of North America.

Tired as he was, as soon as he reached the United States in 1839, he began making the arrangements for the two new publications. Ever since his bankruptcy, he had developed a strong sense of family unity, believing no one outside the family could be trusted to remain faithful to him. He, therefore, hoped that he could turn his new projects into a family business. For some time he had been training his older son, Victor, in business, teaching him how to record and bill for each subscription and to supervise the delivery of the plates as they came out. To his younger son, John, he had entrusted part of the artwork, obtaining his help in the preparation of some of the pictures. With this assistance, he thought he could undertake his two new enterprises in spite of his age.

He first turned his attention to the smaller edition of *The Birds of America,* believing that this was surer of success. In December, 1839, the year he returned to the United States, he started out again on one of his interminable canvassing trips, this time to Boston, and the results met his expectations. *The Birds of America* had made him famous, and he discovered that many of the people who could not afford to buy it were anxious to subscribe to the smaller edition. By December 12 he had sold 31, and when he returned to New York, where he was living, he could report to his family that in a canvassing trip of a little less than three weeks, he had obtained a total of 96 subscribers. By February he had more than 300 names on his list.

In spite of his fears, bred during the days when no man wanted or respected him, he continued to gain subscribers, although only at the cost of much work and long journeys. As the number of names on his list increased, his worries lessened, and in October, 1841, he decided he could give Lucy what she had always wanted, a house of her own. He purchased thirty or forty acres in New York City on the banks of the Hudson River and began constructing the place that the family called Minnie's Land, named after the Scottish term of endearment they called Lucy.

Yet Audubon still could not rest. He had started production of *The Viviparous Quadrupeds of North America,* so he also had this book to sell. (John, however, was assigned to do many of the pictures, and John Bachman, Audubon's friend in Charleston, undertook to prepare the text.) Until early 1843 he labored hard, for he hoped to have both projects well under way so that he could be free to take another expedition, one up the Missouri River as far as the Yellowstone. He had traveled widely in the United States, but he had never seen the Far West, and he wanted to before he died. Although he did some collecting along the way, the journey was more a vacation than a true scientific expedition. Aside from a few more canvassing trips, it was his last journey.

In 1846 his eyes started to fail him, and the blow was as great psychologically as it was physically. Unable to continue with the *Quadrupeds* himself, he turned over all the responsibility for producing the pictures to John. "At that moment," Lucy later wrote, "he drooped. Silent, patient sorrow filled his broken heart." Nothing, not even the affection of his family, could fill the place occupied by the work of his later years. He could not find rest in inactivity.

His friends were horrified at the change that quickly came over him. He lost interest in his book, then in the world around him. Lucy took him for walks around Minnie's Land and every night sang to him the same song, one in Spanish that he much enjoyed. But his powers of concentration could grasp little else. The months turned into years, as time dragged slowly on, while Audubon continued to live in the twilight between life and death, a great figure of a man, but with the mind and comprehension of a child.

At last, in January, 1851, he mercifully suffered a stroke, and the end came only a few days later. As his last act, he opened his eyes and looked wistfully at his wife and two sons, the family he had first treated so badly and then labored so hard to serve. In this fashion, one of his sons wrote later, "his farewell glance fell upon those he has loved so well."

XIV

Few men could have been more dissimilar in their backgrounds and personalities than John James Audubon and Alexander Wilson—one born rich, the other poor; one at first a wastrel who spent half his life in idle pursuits, the other a man who never knew a moment's rest in his industrious search for a meager living.

Yet the two men had much in common, not only with each other, but also with the many other collectors who amassed the material so needed by the biological scientists. Both were willing to endure the hardships of travel, and both, too, had the boundless patience needed in the continual search for additional specimens. A desire for completeness and the willingness to seek it form the hallmark of the important collector.

Intellectually their contributions may seem insignificant compared to those of men like Buffon and Lamarck and Cuvier, who grasped whole truths or developed new and fundamental techniques. But the collectors provided the foundation on which the others could build, and so it is no wonder that Cuvier, although pressed for time, told his servant on September 4, 1828, to admit the former bankrupt from Henderson, Kentucky, the man who could tell him at firsthand about some of the wonders of the life of the New World.

8

A Noble Privilege

ALEXANDER VON HUMBOLDT: 1769–1859

I

The two young foreigners, who were visiting the Spanish port of La Coruña in June, 1799, were restlessly waiting for the packet boat *Pizarro* to leave for Venezuela and Cuba.

Although the Spanish government jealously guarded the secrets of its Latin American colonies, it had made an exception in their case, and in their pockets, they had letters of introduction to the governing officials and documents permitting them to do scientific research. Spain and Great Britain were at war, however, and the high seas were no longer safe for travel. At that very moment a British man-of-war and two frigates lurked outside La Coruña. Until a storm, a change of orders, or a shortage of supplies drove the squadron away, the captain of the *Pizarro* did not dare leave.

Unlike either Wilson or Audubon when they had set off on their travels, these two men were already trained scientists, thoroughly familiar with their respective fields. The younger, Aimé Jacques Alexandre Bonpland, was a French botanist, a quiet, unaggressive man, but a good companion for a long journey. The other, Alexander von Humboldt, was only twenty-nine years old but had already earned a reputation as a competent scientist. Born in Berlin on September 14, 1769, he and his brother, Wilhelm, had been given the best possible education by their parents. As boys, they had been tutored at home by the same man who had taught the sons of Moses Mendelssohn, grandfather of the composer. When they were old enough, they went to the university at Frankfurt. Their father had died by then, but their mother was well-off and had carefully planned their careers. Alexander, she was determined, would enter the civil service. He, therefore, took the course called economics, a purely practical curriculum that dealt with manufacturing and agricultural processes, but not with economic theory. Although it was taken by most students who were candidates for the civil service, it had such little intellectual content that Alexander was bored and finally left the university to spend a year in Berlin. While living again with his mother, he met a young botanist who had written a book on the plants found around Berlin. The two became friends, and the botanist stimulated Humboldt's interest in science by offering to help him classify any plants he collected.

The following year, 1789, Humboldt transferred to the university at Göttingen. In place of economics, Humboldt this time took up physics, chemistry, geology, and mineralogy, subjects that were far better suited to his temperament. He also became a friend of Johann Georg Adam Forster, who had accompanied Captain Cook on his second voyage and whose tales of adventure fired Humboldt with the wish to travel himself.

Humboldt's intellectualism was now thoroughly aroused, and as he had become especially interested in geology and mineralogy, he decided to attend the school of mines in Freiberg. After completing his courses in 1792, he received from the Prussian government an appointment with the department of mining at some mines in the Fichtel Mountains, and he threw himself into his new work so vigorously that after six months he became inspector of three mining districts. The mines he supervised were badly neglected and partially deserted, but he quickly reorganized them, riding from mine to mine, spending much of his time in the pits, and conducting analyses of their ores. He also studied the dangers of firedamp and experimented with safety lamps he had designed. (In one of his experiments, he became unconscious and might have died if some passing workers had not noticed his feet sticking out of the unused opening where he was carrying on his tests.) He also read Luigi Galvani's descriptions of the effect of electricity on frogs' muscles, duplicated what Galvani had done, and then improved his techniques. These experiments led him to investigate the effects of various gases and liquids on life and to study the air in the mines. In 1796 he also made a discovery in the field of magnetism. While traveling through the mountains, carrying his compass as he often did, he came across a vein of rock whose magnetism was directly opposed to that of the earth, a fact that startled him and increased his interest in the subject of terrestrial magnetism.

Nothing in his work, however, realized his true ambition. Remembering his talks with Forster, he desperately wanted to go to some remote area of the world on a scientific expedition. But his respect for his mother held him back. As long as she lived, he thought he should remain in the Prussian civil service, but her death in 1796 freed him, and within a few months he had resigned.

Having received a considerable inheritance, he and his brother, Wilhelm, moved for a short time to Dresden, where Alexander practiced using a sextant and studied the collections of minerals at the Royal Library. They then went to Vienna with the idea of going on to Italy, but when Napoleon's campaign made that trip an impossibility, Alexander joined a friend who was a geologist and spent the winter of 1797 at Salzburg. Humboldt experimented with a new sextant he had purchased, and the two men together conducted systematic meteorological investigations with daily readings of the barometric pressure, the temperature, the oxygen in the air, and the humidity.

He had undertaken all this self-study to equip himself to accompany an expedition if he was asked to do so. Finally, such an invitation came from a wealthy Englishman who was preparing a private expedition to Egypt. But Napoleon's invasion of that country cut his plan short. Humboldt thereupon applied to be a member of a French expedition that was going to visit Mexico and California, study the Pacific Ocean, and finally go to Madagascar and New Guinea. His application was accepted, and Jean Charles de Borda, the French mathematician, advised him to concentrate on measuring the earth's magnetism. But once again Napoleon's Egyptian campaign interfered with his plans; the cost of the invasion was so great that Napoleon withdrew the government's support of the expedition.

Still determined to make a trip somewhere, Humboldt invited Aimé Bonpland, who had also been assigned to the French expedition, to join him on a private voyage to Egypt. They went to Marseilles but, unable to get passage across the Mediterranean, wandered on to Spain.

At Madrid, Humboldt met the chargé d'affaires of Saxony, a man who had many scientific interests. Humboldt poured out his frustrations; the chargé d'affaires listened and made a suggestion: Although the Spanish discouraged foreigners from traveling in their colonies, possibly an exception would be made in Humboldt's case. In an audience with the king, Humboldt explained his desires and all the training he had given himself. After consulting with his ministers, the king, in a surprising gesture, granted permission.

Even though he had to pay his own and Bonpland's expenses, Humboldt could have asked for little better than this chance to explore the mysterious lands owned by Spain. Without further delay, he and Bonpland rushed to catch the packet boat *Pizarro* at La Coruña—only to find the port blockaded by the British.

II

The days passed into weeks as the *Pizarro* lay trapped in the harbor, while the British squadron kept watch along the coast. Never willing to waste a moment, Humboldt checked the accuracy of his "timekeeper," studied the geology of the area, and measured the temperatures of the bay to test a theory that water was colder near sandbanks. Suddenly his investigations were cut short by a violent storm that blew up from the northwest and made it impossible to navigate the bay in a small boat. In the open ocean the waves became so large that the blockading squadron was forced to withdraw, and the captain of the *Pizarro,* thinking he might be able to escape before its return, ordered his passengers to put their luggage aboard. This was no small task, as Humboldt had with him some forty instruments, including thermometers, barometers, sextants, a telescope, a quadrant, various devices for determining the magnetism of the earth, two hygrometers, a microscope, and a rain gauge.

After all this had been safely stowed, Humboldt returned to shore, where he waited for the storm to abate. Since it was impossible for him to do any scientific work, he wrote numerous letters. One of them was to the leader of the French expedition, promising to join him in the Spanish colonies if the French government decided to change its mind. On the second day a heavy bank of fog indicated that the weather was changing, and the wind veered to the northeast. Although the British squadron had been sighted again and the citizens of La Coruña prophesied that the *Pizarro* would be captured if it sailed, the captain weighed anchor during the afternoon of June 5, 1799, and started beating down the narrow channel against a stiff head wind. For four and a half hours the ship tacked close-hauled. Three times the current threw it back to its starting point and once nearly dashed it against the rocks, but by six thirty in the evening it had cleared the harbor mouth.

Because many British ships sailed along the Portuguese coast, the *Pizarro* was not out of danger even after leaving Spain. Just at sunset on the eighth, the lookout called from the masthead that a British convoy was inshore from the *Pizarro* on a course to the southeast. The captain held his own course until darkness, then switched direction. "From this moment," Humboldt wrote, "no light was permitted in the great cabin, to prevent our being seen at a distance. This precaution, used on board all merchant vessels, and prescribed in the regulations of the packet boats of the royal navy, was extremely irksome to us during the passages we made in the course of the five following years" because of the amount of work he wanted to get done during his journey.

Men like Wilson and Audubon, in their travels, limited themselves to a single subject—in their case, birds. Humboldt was far more comprehensive in his interests. Among the many subjects he intended to investigate were the precise location of geographic points, the weather, the distribution of plants, ocean currents, the geology of the areas he passed through, the temperatures and boundaries of the ocean currents, and—a reflection of his economics courses—the industries of the countries he visited, as well as their histories and their social customs. On board ship, for example, even though he found it difficult to work at night, he made astronomical observations, collected jellyfish and other sea life, and speculated on the fall of meteors. He also followed the advice given him earlier by the mathematician Borda and kept detailed records of the magnetic dip, measuring it with a dipping needle. (A magnetic needle not only points in a horizontal direction toward the magnetic pole, but also, if suspended the other way, dips toward the earth at varying angles.)

He was also interested in determining the exact positions of geographic locations and, while at sea, took his own sights, which he compared with the ship's. Before leaving Spain, the captain had been ordered to land first on the island of Lanzarote and determine whether the British were blockading Santa Cruz de Tenerife before proceeding to that port. Soon he and Humboldt were arguing over the course the *Pizarro* should set to reach Lanzarote. In those days, because of the unreliability of the chronometers, navigators had difficulty finding their longitude with any degree of accuracy. Their usual practice, therefore, was to engage in parallel sailing—to sail to the latitude of their destination and then head either east or west. Humboldt had been regularly plotting the *Pizarro*'s position, using his own excellent "timekeeper." Being certain of its accuracy, he tried to persuade the captain to set a more southeasterly course toward Lanzarote, thus following one side of a triangle instead of two. But the captain had no faith in his passenger's calculations. If Humboldt's longitude proved wrong, he ran the risk of missing the island entirely, passing it either to the north or to the south. At last, when he changed his course and bore eastward, Humboldt was delighted to find the island exactly where he had predicted it would be.

The ship drew close enough to the coast for the passengers to see the southern island of Fuerteventura and then turned north to pass between Alegranza and Lanzarote, a dangerous and inaccurately charted passage. After learning from a fisherman that no British ships had been seen in the vicinity for weeks, the captain set sail for Tenerife, which they sighted on the nineteenth.

A heavy fog lay along the shore, and as they drew close to the island, the wind blew stronger. "We anchored after several soundings," Humboldt wrote, "for the mist was so thick that we could scarcely distinguish objects at a few cables' distance; but at the moment that we began to salute the place, the fog was instantly dispelled. The Peak of Teide appeared in a break over the clouds, and the first rays of the sun, which had not yet risen on us, illuminated the summit of the volcano. We hastened toward the bow of the vessel to enjoy the mangificent spectacle, when at the same instant we saw four English ships of the royal navy lying to very near the poop. We had passed without being perceived; and the same mist, which had hidden the peak from our view, had saved us from the danger of being carried back to Europe." Before the English ships could swing into action, the captain of the *Pizarro* had raised anchor and moved inshore under the protection of the fort.

Although the captain of the *Pizarro* had been ordered to stay at Tenerife long enough for Humboldt and Bonpland to climb the peak at their leisure, the presence of the British ships changed this. At the most, the captain would remain only four or five days; this meant Humboldt and Bonpland had no time to lose. Traveling overland, they reached the town of La Orotava, where they spent the night before starting their ascent. The next day, accompanied by guides, they began the long climb, and nightfall found them at a point called the English Halt, the highest part of the mountain that could be reached on ordinary mules. Although they were close to Africa, the thermometer hovered just above freezing, and in order to stay warm, they built a screen by tying together bits of cloth.

At three o'clock the next morning they started on their way by torchlight and after more than five hours reached the Piton, the cone that formed the summit. It was covered with ashes and fragments of pumice stone and was so steep they could gain the top only by following the bed of a former lava current. This channel was sufficiently rough to provide them with handholds, and for half an hour they crawled up it. Arriving at the summit of the Piton, they found themselves on a ledge, which was barely broad enough to sit on, and blocked from the edge of the crater by a small wall of lava. "The west wind blew with such violence that we could scarcely stand," Humboldt wrote. "It was eight in the morning, and we were frozen with the cold, though the thermometer kept a little above the freezing point. For a long time we had been accustomed to a very high temperature, and the dry wind increased the feeling of cold." Working their way along the ledge to the eastern side, they discovered a break in the wall, caused by an old lava flow and, climbing through this, entered the crater. "We descended to the bottom," Humboldt wrote, "on a train of broken lava from the eastern breach of the enclosure. The heat was perceptible only in a few crevices, which gave vent to aqueous vapors with a peculiar buzzing sound." He put his thermometer into several of these and measured the heat. He also obtained samples of the air, which he intended to analyze later, and made a sketch of the volcano. After carefully examining the interior, Humboldt and Bonpland returned to the outer ledge, where they remained awhile, enjoying the view and hoping the clouds would clear away so that they could see even farther. Then they began their descent, taking notes on the distribution of plant life along the slopes and looking for insects. Toward the close of day they arrived back at La Orotava, where they learned that the departure of the *Pizarro* had been delayed, news that irritated Humboldt slightly, because he would have liked to have stayed at the volcano longer. Instead, he contented himself with learning as much as he could about the island generally, and it is indicative of his thoroughness that when he set sail on June 25, he had collected by this stage of his journey enough information to write a book almost 300 pages long.

Their departure from Santa Cruz was uneventful, and as the *Pizarro* moved across the Atlantic, Humboldt continued to make numerous observations of every sort, speculating on the formation of the weather, noting the magnetic dip, dissecting flying fish, and studying the seaweeds they were able to pick up. All went well until the last few days of the voyage, when sickness broke out. Two sailors, several passengers, and two Negroes fell ill, and Humboldt, thinking the disease might be epidemic, was disturbed by the captain's seeming unconcern. "The indifference which prevails on board packet boats for everything that does not regard the working of the ship and the quickness of the passage, prevented the captain from employing the ordinary means of diminishing the danger which threatened us."

Just as he had done on the voyage from La Coruña to the Canary Islands, he had plotted the ship's position each day, and again he and the captain disagreed. (Humboldt later remarked that he was "surer of the position of the vessel than of the land to which we directed our course and which was so differently placed in the French, Spanish, and English charts.") Once again, Humboldt determined their longitude more accurately than the captain.

On approaching the coast of South America, the weather became warmer, and the sick passengers grew worse. One of them, a young Spaniard, died, and Humboldt, as well as many of the other passengers, made up his mind to leave the ship at the first opportunity rather than continue the voyage to Havana. Consequently, when they landed at the port of Cumaná in Venezuela, Humboldt presented his papers to the governor and, in preparation for a prolonged stay, rented a large house to use as his headquarters.

For several weeks he and Bonpland checked their various instruments and collected plants in the neighborhood of Cumaná. Although the city and its surroundings contained much that interested him, he had always been a humanist and a liberal and was, therefore, revolted by the slave trade. "The mildness of the Spanish legislation compared with the Black Code of the greater part of other nations . . . ," he wrote, "cannot be denied. But such is the state of the Negroes, dispersed in places scarcely begun to be cultivated, that justice, far from efficaciously protecting them during their lives, cannot even punish acts of barbarity that have caused their death. If an inquiry be attempted, the death of the slave is attributed to the bad state of his health, to the influence of a warm and humid climate, to the wounds which he has received, but which, it is asserted, were neither deep nor dangerous. The civil authority is power-less with respect to whatever constitutes domestic slavery; and nothing is more illusory than the effect so much vaunted of those laws, which pre-scribe the form of the whip, and the number of lashes which it is permit-ted to give *at a time*. Persons who have not lived in the colonies, or have inhabited only the West India islands, believe in general that the interest of the master in the preservation of his slaves must render their condi-tion so much the milder as their number is less considerable. Neverthe-less, even at Cariaco, a few weeks before my arrival in the province, a planter, who had only eight Negroes, killed six by beating them in the most barbarous manner."

After thoroughly exploring the environs of Cumaná, Humboldt and Bonpland began making preparations for a long journey up the Orinoco River. This trip would give them a chance to observe the llanos, the great plains of Venezuela, and to study the river itself. Humboldt also wanted to determine the exact location of the point where some of the waters of the Orinoco branch into the Casiquiare, follow it to the Negro, and eventually into the Amazon. This unusual phenomenon, whereby the waters of a single stream supply two great river systems, was ru-mored to exist, but its position was not accurately placed.

In order to make this journey, Humboldt wrote, "We had to choose the instruments that could be most easily transported in narrow boats and to furnish ourselves with guides for an inland journey of ten months, across a country that is without communication with the coasts. The as-tronomical determination of places being the most important object of this undertaking, I felt greatly interested in not missing the observation of an eclipse of the sun, which was to be visible at the end of October; and in consequence I preferred remaining till that period at Cumaná, where the sky is generally clear and serene. . . . In fixing with preci-sion the longitude of Cumaná, I had a point of departure for the chrono-metrical determination of longitudes. . . ."

The day before the eclipse, Humboldt and Bonpland went to the coast, where they were studying the rise of the tide. (There was no end to Humboldt's curiosity.) It was about eight o'clock in the evening. The sky was cloudy, and the weather excessively hot. As they walked along the beach, Humboldt heard footsteps behind him. Turning around, he saw a half-naked Indian standing behind him and holding a large palm tree club over his head. Ducking to the left, Humboldt escaped the blow, but Bonpland was not as quick. The Indian's club caught him above the temple, and he fell prostrate on the sand. But instead of attacking Humboldt again, the Indian moved off slowly to pick up Bonpland's hat, which had rolled a short distance away. Humboldt helped Bonpland to his feet—he had been unconscious for a few seconds—and they both started to chase the Indian, who dashed off to a small thicket. Before he reached it, he tripped, and Bonpland leaped on him, whereupon the Indian drew a long knife. The struggle would have been unequal, but some merchants, who were also strolling along the beach, noticed what was happening and came to their rescue. They finally captured the Indian in a cowpen, where he had taken refuge, and led him to the prison.

Astonished at the man's apparent stupidity in chasing after Bonpland's hat, Humboldt inquired into his past and learned that he had served on board a privateer from San Domingo. Because he had quarreled with the captain, he had been abandoned at Cumaná. As a result, he had taken a thorough dislike to the French and, hearing Humboldt and Bonpland speaking in that language, had decided to attack them. Humbolt, humane even to those who tried to injure him, wrote, "Justice being so slow in this country that the prisoners, of which the jail is full, remain seven or eight years without being able to obtain a trial, we learnt with some satisfaction that a few days after our departure from Cumaná, the Zambo [the Indian] had succeeded in breaking out of the Castle of St. Antonio."

The two travelers remained at Cumaná for a few weeks after the eclipse, making observations of the weather and, on November 4, were caught by an earthquake. Clouds had gathered over the mountains and then moved overhead. A thunderstorm broke, and suddenly "there were two shocks of an earthquake, which followed at fifteen seconds distance from each other. The people in the streets filled the air with their cries. Mr. Bonpland, who was leaning over a table examining plants, was almost thrown on the floor. I felt the shock very strongly, though I was lying in a hammock." But not even an earthquake could deter Humboldt from his scientific studies. He immediately looked at his chronometer, noticed the time, and the interval between shocks, measured the magnetic dip, and took barometric readings, continuing his studies on the earthquake's effects until November 16, when he and Bonpland sailed from Cumaná to the port of La Guaira and from there went by land to Caracas.

By February, Humboldt had exhausted the possibility of learning more at Caracas and was ready to start for the Orinoco, but instead of heading directly for the river, he followed a rambling route that took him to the country west of Caracas, visiting La Victoria, Maracay, and Villa de Cura, where he spent considerable time studying Lake Valencia. Over the years, the level of the lake had been dropping, and since there was no visible outlet, the inhabitants were certain that the water must be flowing into a subterranean river or grotto. Humboldt, however, immediately solved the riddle. "The changes, which the destruction of forests, the clearing of plains, and the cultivation of indigo have produced within half a century in the quantity of water flowing in, on the one hand, and, on the other, the evaporation of the soil and the dryness of the atmosphere are sufficiently powerful to explain the successive diminution of the lake of Valencia. I am not of the opinion of a traveler, who has visited these countries since me, that 'to set the mind at rest, and for the honor of science,' a subterranean issue must be admitted. By felling the trees that cover the tops and sides of the mountains, men in every climate prepare at once two calamities for future generations: the want of fuel and a scarcity of water. . . . When forests are destroyed, as they are everywhere in America by the European planters with an imprudent precipitation, the springs are entirely dried up or become less abundant. The beds of the rivers, remaining dry during a part of the year, are converted into torrents whenever great rains fall on the heights. The sward and moss disappearing with the brushwood from the sides of the mountains, the waters falling in rain are no longer impeded in their course: and instead of slowly augmenting the level of the rivers by progressive filtrations, they furrow during heavy showers the sides of the hills, bear down the loosened soil, and form those sudden inundations that devastate the country. Hence it results that the destruction of the forests, the want of permanent springs, and the existence of torrents are three phenomena closely connected together."

After this modern analysis of a conservation problem, Humboldt went north to the coast again, visiting Puerto Cabello, and then turned south and entered the broad plains of Venezuela. "The chief characteristic of the savannahs or steppes of South America," he later wrote, "is the absolute want of hills and inequalities, the perfect level of every part of the soil. Accordingly the Spanish conquerors, who first penetrated from Coro to the banks of the Apure, did not call them deserts, or savannahs, or meadows, but plains, *Llanos*. Often in a space of thirty square leagues there is not an eminence of a foot high. This resemblance to the surface of the sea strikes the imagination most powerfully, where the plains are altogether destitute of palm trees; and where the mountains of the shore and of the Orinoco are so distant that they cannot be seen. . . . A person would be tempted there to take the altitude of the sun with the quadrant, if the *horizon of the land* were not constantly misty, on account of the variable display of refraction. . . ."

After two days of travel by horseback, they came to a typical ranch on the llanos, "a solitary house in the steppes, surrounded by a few small huts, covered with reeds and skins. The cattle, oxen, horses, and mules are not penned, but wander freely over an extent of several square leagues. There is nowhere any enclosure; men, naked to the waist and armed with a lance, ride over the savannahs to inspect the animals, bring back those that wander too far from the pastures of the farm, and mark with a hot iron all that do not already bear the mark of the proprietor. These Mulattoes, who are known by the name of *Peones Llaneros,* are partly freed men and partly slaves. There does not exist a race more constantly exposed to the devouring heat of the tropical sun. Their food is meat dried in the air and a little salted; and of this even their horses sometimes eat. Always in the saddle, they fancy they cannot make the slightest excursion on foot. We found an old Negro slave, who governed the farm in the absence of his master. He told us of herds composed of several hundred cows, that were grazing in the steppes; yet we asked in vain for a bowl of milk." Even the water was almost undrinkable. "The old Negro advised us," Humboldt wrote, "to cover the cup with a linen cloth, and drink as through a filter, that we might not be incommoded by the smell, and swallow less of the fine yellowish clay suspended in the water. We did not think that we should afterward be forced during whole months to have recourse to this expedient. The waters of the Orinoco are alike loaded with earthy particles; they are even fetid, where dead bodies of alligators are found in the creeks lying on banks of sand or half-buried in the mud."

The next day, to avoid the heat, they were off at two in the morning, hoping to arrive at the town of Calabozo by noon. This was a cattle center, and Humboldt immediately set about gathering figures on the industry. One of the citizens of Calabozo was interested in electricity and, after reading the writings of Franklin and other scientists, had built his own equipment and conducted experiments. He, of course, was delighted to meet Humboldt and Bonpland and readily agreed to help them procure some electric eels. The natives, on the other hand, were not so enthusiastic, even though Humboldt offered them a good price for each one brought in. After several unsuccessful attempts to capture specimens —the natives were thoroughly afraid of them—they proposed fishing with horses. Humboldt had no idea what they meant, but they soon returned with thirty wild mules and horses, which they drove into a basin of muddy water.

"The extraordinary noise caused by the horses' hoofs," Humboldt later explained, "makes the fish issue from the mud and excites them to combat. These yellowish and livid eels, resembling large aquatic serpents, swim on the surface of the water and crowd under the bellies of the horses and the mules. A contest between animals of such different organization furnishes a very striking spectacle. The Indians, provided with harpoons and long slender reeds, surround the pool closely; and some climb upon the trees, the branches of which extend horizontally over the surface of the water. By their wild cries, and the length of their reeds, they prevent the horses from running away and reaching the bank of the pool. The eels, stirred by the noise, defend themselves by repeated discharges of their electric batteries. During a long time they seem to prove victorious. Several horses sink beneath the violence of the invisible strokes, which they receive from all sides in organs the most essential to life, and, stunned by the force and frequency of the shocks, disappear under the water. Others, panting, with mane erect and haggard eyes expressing anguish, raise themselves and endeavor to flee from the storm by which they are overtaken. They are driven back by the Indians into the middle of the water. . . . In less than five minutes two horses were drowned. The eel, being five feet long, and pressing itself against the belly of the horses, makes a discharge along the whole extent of its electric organ. . . . The horses are probably not killed, but only stunned. They are drowned from the impossibility of rising amid the prolonged struggle between the other horses and the eels.

"We had little doubt that the fishing would terminate by killing successively all the animals engaged; but by degrees the impetuosity of this unequal combat diminished, and the wearied gymnoti [the eels] dispersed. They require a long rest and abundant nourishment to repair what they have lost of galvanic force. The mules and horses appear less frightened; their manes are no longer bristled, and their eyes express less dread. The gymnoti approach timidly the edge of the marsh, where they are taken by means of small harpoons fastened to long cords. When the cords are very dry, the Indians feel no shock in raising the fish into the air. In a few minutes we had five large eels, the greater part of which were but slightly wounded. Some were taken by the same means in the evening." Humboldt was naturally delighted with his catch, and for the next few days he and Bonpland spent their time experimenting with their specimens, attempting to find out when and how the eels produced the shock, and in the process were shocked themselves many times. As Humboldt wryly commented, "If by chance you receive a stroke before the fish is wounded or wearied by a long pursuit, the pain and numbness are so violent that it is impossible to describe the nature of the feeling they excite."

By March 27, in their long and rambling journey, Humboldt and Bonpland had finally reached San Fernando de Apure on the Apure River. Although the rainy season was starting, the inhabitants advised Humboldt to go south by land to the Meta River where it joins the Orinoco. Humboldt rejected this suggestion and instead hired a boat, called a lancha, to make the journey by water westward to the juncture of the Apure and Orinoco.

Describing nighttime on the river, Humboldt wrote it "was calm and serene, and there was a beautiful moonlight. The crocodiles were stretched along the shore. They placed themselves in such a manner as to be able to see the fire. We thought we observed that its splendour attracted them, as it attracts fishes, crayfish, and other inhabitants of the water. The Indians showed us the traces of three tigers in the sand, two of which were very young. A female had no doubt conducted her little ones to drink at the river. Finding no tree on the strand, we stuck our oars in the ground, and to these we fastened our hammocks. Everything passed tranquilly until eleven at night; and then a noise so terrific arose in the neighboring forest that it was almost impossible to close our eyes. Amid the cries of so many wild beasts howling at once, the Indians discriminated such only as were heard separately. . . . When the jaguars approached the skirt of the forest, our dog, which till then had never ceased barking, began to howl and seek for shelter beneath our hammocks. Sometimes, after a long silence, the cry of the tiger came from the tops of the trees; and in this case it was followed by the sharp and long whistling of the monkeys, which appeared to flee from the danger that threatened them.

"I notice every circumstance of these nocturnal scenes," Humboldt added, "because, being recently embarked on the Río Apure, we were not yet accustomed to them. We heard the same noises repeated, during the course of whole months, whenever the forest approached the bed of the rivers."

On April 5 the party reached the mouth of the Apure and, after towing their boat across several shoals, entered the Orinoco. ". . . we found ourselves in a country of a totally different aspect," Humboldt wrote. "An immense plain of water stretched before us like a lake, as far as we could see. White-topped waves rose to the height of several feet from the conflict of the breeze and the current. The air resounded no longer with the piercing cries of the herons, the flamingoes, the spoonbills, crossing in long files from one shore to the other. . . . All nature appears less animated. Scarcely could we discover in the hollows of the waves a few large crocodiles, cutting obliquely by the help of their long tails the surface of the agitated waters. The horizon was bounded by a zone of forests, but these forests nowhere reached so far as the bed of the river. A vast beach, constantly parched by the heat of the sun, desert and bare as the shores of the sea, resembled at a distance, from the effects of the mirage, pools of stagnant water. These sandy shores, far from fixing the limits of the river, rendered them uncertain by approaching or withdrawing them alternately, according to the variable action of the inflected rays. In these scattered features of the landscape, in this character of solitude and greatness, we recognized the course of the Orinoco, one of the most majestic rivers of the New World."

As they moved up the river against the current, Bonpland collected plants, and Humboldt continued his diverse studies. He took observations, noticed the geology of the country, watched the Indians collect turtle eggs, and remarked on the influence of the missionaries. Sometimes the travelers slept in the open at night, sometimes they enjoyed the hospitality of a mission, and once their boat almost overturned, when the sail they sometimes used was caught in a sudden puff of wind.

On April 9 they had passed the mouth of the Suapure and were at the foot of the rapids of the Orinoco. As their boat was too large to go farther and their pilot was unacquainted with the river beyond this point, they purchased a canoe from some missionaries and hired a new crew. "To gain something in breadth," Humboldt wrote, "a sort of lattice-work had been constructed on the after part of the boat with branches of trees that on each side reached beyond the gunwale. Unfortunately the roof of leaves that covered this lattice-work was so low that you were obliged to lie down without seeing anything, or, if seated, to sit nearly double. The necessity of carrying the canoe across the rapids, and even from one river to another, and the fear of giving too much hold to the wind by making the roof higher, render this construction necessary for vessels that go up toward the Río Negro. The shed was intended for four persons, lying on the deck, or lattice-work, of brushwood; but our legs reached far beyond it, and when it rained, the body was wetted. We lay upon hides or skins of tigers; and the branches of the trees, over which they are thrown, are painfully felt through so thin a covering. The fore part of the boat was filled with Indian rowers, furnished with paddles three feet long in the form of spoons. They are naked, seated two by two, and row in cadence with a surprising uniformity. Their songs are sad and monotonous. The small cages containing our birds and our monkeys, the number of which we augmented as we advanced, were hung some to the leaf roof and others to the bow of the boat. This was our travelling menagerie. . . .

"In a canoe not three feet wide and so encumbered, there remained no other place for the dried plants, trunks, a sextant, a dipping needle, and the meteorological instruments than the space below the lattice-work of branches, on which we were compelled to remain stretched the greater part of the day. To take the least object out of a trunk, or to use an instrument, it was necessary to gain the shore and disembark. To these inconveniences were joined the torment of the mosquitoes that abounded under this low roof and the heat that radiated from the leaves of the palm trees, the upper surfaces of which were constantly exposed to the solar rays. We attempted every instant, and always without success, to amend our situation. While one of us hid himself under a sheet to ward off the insects, the other insisted on having green wood lighted beneath the roof in order to drive off the mosquitoes by the smoke. The painful sensations of the eyes and the increase of the heat, already stifling, rendered both these means alike impracticable."

In these uncomfortable circumstances and continually bothered by insects, Humboldt and Bonpland worked their way up the river, until at last they arrived at San Fernando de Atabapo, where the Orinoco turns abruptly east and then moves southeast. By continuing on the tributary that flows into it from the south, Humboldt planned to reach the portage to the Río Negro. He then intended to descend the Negro to the mouth of the Casiquiare, ascend the Casiquiare to the point just below Esmeralda where it runs directly out of the Orinoco, and then follow the Orinoco back to San Fernando de Atabapo.

After they arrived at the portage, twenty-three Indians worked for more than four days dragging the canoe across on rollers, and it was not until May 4 that Humboldt and Bonpland reached the water again. "The morning was cool and beautiful," Humboldt wrote. "We had been confined thirty-six days in a narrow boat, so unstable that it would have been overset by any person rising imprudently from his seat without warning the rowers to preserve her trim by leaning on the opposite side. We had suffered severely from the sting of insects, but we had withstood the insalubrity of the climate; we had passed without accident the great number of falls of water and bars that impede the navigation of the rivers and often render it more dangerous than long voyages by sea. After all we had endured, I may be permitted, perhaps, to speak of the satisfaction we felt in having reached the tributary streams of the Amazon, having passed the isthmus that separates two great systems of rivers, and in being sure of having fulfilled the most important object of our voyage, determining astronomically the course of that arm of the Orinoco, which falls into the Río Negro and of which the existence has been alternately proved and denied during half a century. . . .

"In that interior part of the New Continent," he continued, "we almost accustomed ourselves to regard men as not being essential to the order of nature. The earth is loaded with plants, and nothing impedes their free development. An immense layer of mould manifests the uninterrupted action of organic powers. The crocodiles and the boas are masters of the river; the jaguar, the peccary, the tapir, and the monkeys traverse the forest without fear and without danger; there they dwell as in an ancient inheritance. This aspect of animated nature, in which man is nothing, has something in it strange and sad. . . . Here in a fertile country adorned with eternal verdure, we seek in vain the traces of the power of man; we seem to be transported into a world different from that which gave us birth."

As they prepared to ascend the Casiquiare, Humboldt was discouraged by the damp weather. It was damaging Bonpland's collection of plants, and if it continued, the clouds would prevent Humboldt from making his observations. Fortunately the weather began to clear as they started up the Casiquiare, working their way against currents which ran, according to Humboldt's measurements, as fast as seven or eight miles an hour. Occasionally they came across a mission where they could spend the night, but more often they slept outdoors. Approaching the Orinoco, Humboldt wrote, "It was impossible to pass the night in the canoe; the *moschettoes,* which tormented us during the day, accumulated toward evening beneath the toldo, that is, the roof covered with palm leaves, which served to shelter us from the rain. Our hands and faces had never before been more swelled. Father Zea [a priest accompanying them], who till then boasted of having in his missions on the cataracts the largest and most valiant mosquitoes (*las más feroces*), at length gradually acknowledged that the sting of the insects of the Casiquiare was the most painful he had ever felt."

On May 21 the expedition at last reached the juncture of the Casiquiare and the Orinoco and headed upstream to the small village of Esmeralda. "There is no missionary at Esmeralda," Humboldt wrote. "The monk appointed to celebrate mass in that hamlet is settled at Santa Barbara, more than fifty leagues distant. It requires four days to go up the river, and he therefore visits this spot but five or six times a year. We were cordially received by an old officer, who took us for Catalonian shopkeepers, whom our little trade had led to the missions. On seeing packages of paper for the purpose of drying our plants, he smiled at our simple ignorance. 'You come,' said he, 'to a country, where this kind of merchandise has no sale; we write little here; and the dried leaves of maize . . . serve us, like paper in Europe, to wrap up needles, fish hooks, and other little articles that we have to treat with care.' This old officer united in his person the civil and the ecclesiastical authority. He taught the children, I will not say the Catechism, but the Rosary; he rang the bells to amuse himself; and impelled by an ardent zeal for the service of the Church, sometimes used his chorister's wand in a manner not very agreeable to the natives."

Humboldt wanted to follow the Orinoco to its source, but this was impossible, because the way was barred by hostile Indians. He, therefore, had to content himself with making observations around Esmeralda, talking to the inhabitants, and helping Bonpland collect plants, and after a little more than a week he was ready to begin the return journey. Now, instead of having to hug the banks to avoid the current, they could follow the center of the riverbed. This greatly reduced the number of insects hovering about the boat and increased the speed and ease of their travel. Within a few hours they were back at the fork of the Casiquiare and a few days later had arrived at San Fernando de Atabapo. They stayed only one night and were off once more, past the cataracts and into the lower reaches of the Orinoco. Occasionally they spent the night at a mission by the river; often they slept in the boat, while the pilot continued to guide them downstream through the darkness. Humboldt still made observations and collected information about the country whenever he could, but he no longer lingered in one place. The expedition had already been sufficiently difficult and time-consuming, and he had no desire to protract it. By early June they were at the mouth of Apure, which they had descended weeks before and, remaining on the Orinoco, arrived at Ciudad Bolívar, then called Angostura, on June 15, 1800, having completed a journey of more than 1,500 miles.

They had not planned on spending much time in Ciudad Bolívar, but shortly after their arrival, they both became ill. Humboldt recovered quickly, but Bonpland was seriously sick for several weeks. Humboldt reproached himself for endangering his friend's life. "It was I," he wrote, "who had chosen the path of the rivers; and the danger of my fellow traveller presented itself to my mind as the fatal consequence of this imprudent choice."

Gradually, however, Bonpland regained his strength, and in the middle of July they left Ciudad Bolívar and went to Cumaná, where they took passage on a ship going, as they had originally planned so long before, to Cuba.

III

Humboldt liked Havana so well he remained in its vicinity during his entire visit to Cuba, wandering through its botanical garden, talking to its citizens, reading the reports filed in the government offices, and, as usual, examining every aspect of the island and its way of life. He studied its geography, finances, industries, climate, plants, and population, to mention only a few of the topics that he discussed in his later writings. All his observations were moderate except for those on one aspect of Cuban society—slavery.

"Slavery," he wrote, "is no doubt the greatest of all the evils that afflict humanity, whether we consider the slave torn from his family in his native country, and thrown into the hold of a slave-ship, or as making part of a flock of black men, parked on the soil of the West Indies." Cuba, he thought, should continue to encourage the emancipation of slaves, and as for the United States, "Let us hope that the generous principles which have so long animated the legislatures in the northern parts of the United States, will extend by degrees towards the south, and towards those western regions, where, by the effects of an imprudent and fatal law, slavery and its inequities have passed the chain of the Alleghenies and the banks of the Mississippi. . . ."

As soon as he had finished his Cuban studies, Humboldt intended to sail to Veracruz, cross Mexico, and go to the Philippines, and he had already arranged for passage with a Spanish squadron. But he read in the newspapers that the French expedition had now been released by Napoleon and was planning to visit Chile and Peru. Remembering the promise he had sent in the letter he had written at La Coruña, Humboldt thought he should attempt to join the expedition at Lima. His Cuban friends tried to dissuade him by telling him that touching at a few islands here and there would not be comparable to observing the Spanish possessions more thoroughly, but Humboldt wanted to investigate the earth's magnetism on a broader scale and also to make more observations on the ocean's currents.

Before leaving Cuba, he provided for the disposition of his collections and notes. During the time he had been in Latin America, he had not received a single letter from Europe, demonstrating to him the uncertainty of the mails. He, therefore, asked Bonpland to divide their collections into three parts. One part he sent to France by way of Spain, one to Germany by way of England, and the other he left with friends in Cuba. He also shipped off his manuscripts, although he did not have the time or patience to make duplicates of all of them, as he would have liked.

Being unable to secure passage on a commercial vessel bound either to Cartagena, Colombia, or to Portobelo, Panama, he chartered a sloop, which was lying in the harbor at Batabanó. The ship was so small it contained no cabin, only a tiny, unventilated hold in which they could barely fit their instruments; nevertheless, on March 9, 1801, they sailed into the Gulf of Batabanó, turned eastward, and, after running aground several times, reached Trinidad. Toward evening Humboldt went on land to take some sights, but his work was interrupted by some traders, who had been to dinner on a foreign ship, and who insisted that he and Bonpland visit the city. The night was hot, and the ground shone with the reddish light of phosphorescent insects, which covered the grass and the leaves of the trees. As Humboldt learned, about fifteen of these insects gave off enough light to make it possible to look for an object on the darkest night. The poor people of the area would capture this number, place them in a calabash pierced with tiny holes, and, when they wanted to see something, would simply shake the calabash and arouse the insects. As the insects could live on sugar cane, their feeding presented no problem, and the calabash lights were both practical and inexpensive.

The evening following their arrival in Trinidad, the residents of the city drove Humboldt and Bonpland back to their ship in a carriage, and after a local priest had recited a poem he had written celebrating their trip up the Orinoco, the captain of the sloop ordered the sails hoisted, and the two scientists began their voyage to Colombia.

For approximately two weeks, they sailed across the Caribbean, sighting land only when they neared the Lesser Cayman Islands, until on March 25 they reached their first port in Colombia, the mouth of the Sinú River, which runs into the Caribbean south of Cartagena. From the Sinú the sloop sailed northeast along the coast to Cartagena, battling against heavy winds that dashed waves across its deck, and finally reached Barú Island. Humboldt took one of the sloop's small boats and attempted to land. As the boat moved toward the shore in the moonlight, he suddenly noticed a young Negro emerge from the bushes. He was completely naked, loaded with chains, and held a large knife in his hand. In an ingratiating manner, he told them where to land their boat so it would be protected from the surf and invited them to tour the island. All he wanted in exchange for his services was some clothing. Humboldt might have accepted his offer, but he heard the one Negro talking to others hidden among the moonlit trees. Certain that he had come across a band of escaped slaves, Humboldt returned to the sloop. Commenting later on his experience, he wrote, "The aspect of a naked man, wandering on an uninhabited beach, without being able to unrivet the chains fastened around his neck and the upper part of his arm, left us the most painful impressions. They could have only been augmented by the ferocious regrets of our mariners, who wanted to return to the shore and seize the fugitives, to sell them secretly at Cartagena. In climates where slavery exists, the mind is familiarized with suffering, and that instinct of pity is stifled which characterizes and enobles our nature."

When they reached Cartagena, the weather was so excessively hot that Humboldt and Bonpland immediately moved from the coastal city to a small Indian village, Turbaco, which was not far away. Originally Humboldt had planned to go from Cartagena to the Isthmus of Panama by ship and take a boat on the Pacific side to Lima, but the citizens of Cartagena offered an alternative. Instead of risking a long delay while seeking a passage at Panama and facing a tedious sea voyage against contrary winds, why not go over the mountains by way of Quito? They said the trip would take less time, and the weather in the Andes would be much cooler than on the Isthmus. Since Humboldt wanted to see the Andes and also disliked the heat, he took their advice.

The first part of their journey brought them up the Magdalena River, which enters the Caribbean at Barranquilla. As usual, Bonpland collected plants as they went along, while Humboldt engaged in map-making. The mosquitoes were bad, but otherwise the trip was reasonably comfortable, the skies overcast, and the nights somewhat cool. The river, however, was full, which slowed their progress, since they had to push their way against the strong current.

After having traveled for thirty-five days, they came to the town of Honda, where they hired pack mules for the trip to Bogotá. News of their coming preceded them, so when they left the narrow trail and entered the city, they discovered the archbishop had sent his carriage to meet them, and one of Bogotá's citizens, who was a botanist and a former friend of Linnaeus, placed his library and his extensive collections at their disposal.

When it came time to leave Bogotá, they had a choice of two routes. By taking one of them, the traveler could pass over the crest of the mountains in a single day and always be in inhabited country. The other, which Humboldt selected, was wilder and, in his mind, more interesting. Describing this route, he later wrote, "The mountain of Quindiu [Nevado Quindió] . . . is considered as the most laborious passage presented by the Cordillera of the Andes. It is a thick forest, entirely uninhabited, which, in the best season, can only be crossed in ten or twelve days. It contains no cabin, no means of subsistence; at every time of year, the travelers take enough provisions for a month, because often the melting of the snows and the sudden flooding of the mountain streams isolates them, so they cannot descend either the side toward Cartago or the side toward Ibagué. . . . The trail by which the traveler crosses the Cordillera is so narrow that its ordinary width is only four or five decimeters [a decimeter is approximately 3.9 inches]; it resembles for much of the way a gallery open to the sky. In this part of the Andes, as in many others, the rock is covered by a thick layer of clay. Streams of water descending from the mountains have dug out ravines that are six or seven meters deep. The traveler walks in these crevices which are filled with mud, and whose darkness is increased by the thick vegetation that covers the opening above. The bodies of the oxen, which are the beasts of burden commonly used in this country, have trouble passing through these galleries, which are sometimes two thousand meters long. If a traveler has the misfortune of meeting these beasts of burden, he has no other way of evading them except by retracing his steps or by climbing up the wall of earth which borders the crevice and keeping himself suspended by hanging on to the roots that have penetrated into the soil."

Humboldt and Bonpland traveled on foot, although in this part of Colombia, as well as in some other areas in the Andes, the wealthier travelers usually hired *cargueros*—mulattoes and sometimes whites, who made their living by carrying riders on their backs. The phrase "riding a man's back," Humboldt said, was just as common as the word "horseback" elsewhere in the world. Describing this employment, Humboldt wrote that "among . . . the *cargueros,* people distinguish and recommend to travelers those who have a sure foot and a gentle and even step. It is painful to hear people speak of the qualities of a man in the terms generally used to describe the gaits of horses and mules."

Neither Humboldt nor Bonpland would travel this way. They thought it so degrading they preferred to walk, followed by a train of twelve oxen carrying their instruments and supplies. The walking was often difficult, for the passage of many oxen had cut ridges in the mud that covered the trails, and when it rained, the water made the surface seem flat. The two travelers, therefore, often slipped as they worked their way up one side of the mountains and down the other. To add to their problems, they passed through areas covered by bamboo, which tore their shoes so badly they walked barefoot part of the way. At night they slept in huts, built out of a framework of tree branches covered by a mat of leaves the guides had collected before setting out.

Under these conditions, the journey was so long and tiring that by the time Humboldt and Bonpland reached Popayañ, Colombia, they could go no farther until they had some rest. But even their weariness did not prevent them from exploring the countryside near the town, visiting the Indian village of Puracé, and looking at the spectacular falls of the Vinegar River, a river naturally so acid that fish could not live in its waters.

After recovering their strength, the two Europeans again began moving south through the steep mountains and arrived at Quito, Ecuador, on January 6, 1802. There they learned that the French expedition had sailed by way of the Cape of Good Hope and did not plan to stop at any South American port. This news meant they no longer had to hurry to Lima, and they remained at Quito for several months. Bonpland needed time to sort the plants he had collected during their journey, and Humboldt wanted to organize his notes and explore the volcanoes near the city. On May 26 he began the ascent to the crater of Pichincha. As far as Humboldt knew, only one man had climbed the mountain before. This climber had spent five or six days trying to find the way but, once at the top, had suffered so severely from the cold that he had been forced to leave after only fifteen minutes. Humboldt, accompanied by an Indian, took the route the previous explorer had finally discovered, thus completing the trip in one day. As he and the Indian neared the edge of the crater, they advanced across an ice field. Suddenly the Indian sank in the snow to his waist. Humboldt hurried toward him and helped him regain his footing. Moving cautiously forward again, they noticed in the surface several holes through which daylight was shining. To their horror, they discovered that they were not standing on solid ground. Instead, they had been walking on a fragile shelf of ice that arched over the mouth of the crater. Anxiously retracing their steps, they reconsidered their approach.

Earlier in the day Humboldt had noticed three rocky peaks rising from the edge of the crater. Because the heat from the volcano had cleared them of snow, Humboldt decided they offered a practical base from which to look into the crater. Climbing to the top of one, he discovered a stone that, as he said, formed a sort of balcony from which he could make his observations. The circumference of the crater, he estimated, was about a mile, large enough to contain several mountains. The peaks of these, he believed, lay about 1,900 feet below, and he thought that the floor of the volcano itself probably was at the same elevation as Quito. The early explorer who had reached the top had found the volcano quiescent and covered with snow, but Humboldt was nearly suffocated by the fumes rising from it and, looking down, saw bluish flames playing in the half-darkness. Every minute or so, the rock on which he crouched shook with tremors caused by the explosions underneath him. Nevertheless, he stayed long enough to complete his observations before going back to Quito, where he warned the citizens that their volcano was active again.

He also attempted the ascent of Chimborazo in the company of Bonpland and a young Spanish naturalist. After having spent the night at the foot of the mountain, they rose early and began climbing the southwestern slope. At one point they halted, while Humboldt tried to measure its height, but the clouds drifted down and obscured the peak before he could do so. Traveling awhile longer, they came to a small lake, which was the highest anyone had gone before. According to Humboldt's barometer, they were at an altitude of more than 14,000 feet. After tethering their mules, they started walking over a belt of grass and reached an area where great columns of rock, some 50 feet high, jutted from the surface. By then they had come to the snow line, and the going became more difficult. One by one, the Indians refused to go on, and the three Europeans were left to find their own route. Since the snow was too soft to walk on, they followed a wind-cleared knife edge that seemed to lead directly to the summit. On one side was a steep downward slope covered with ice, and on the other a cliff that dropped about 1,000 feet. In places, the ridge was only 8 or 10 inches wide. Although they feared falling over the cliff, they were even more afraid of slipping on the icy side and sliding into the valley below.

The rock was crumbly, and often what had seemed to offer solid footing turned out to be a loose stone lying on the ridge. As they moved ahead in single file, the lead man probed the ground ahead with a pole. Finally, when the ridge became too narrow to walk, they crawled on their hands and knees, cutting their palms and fingers on the sharp rock. To their relief, the way gradually became less steep, but the mists through which they had been climbing grew heavier and heavier. They were now so high that they had difficulty breathing, each of the three men felt like vomiting, their eyes were bloodshot, and blood poured from their lips and gums.

On they went, almost exhausted and not knowing exactly where the summit lay in the midst of the mists ahead. Suddenly the clouds broke; the peak of Chimborazo was directly in front of them, white in the afternoon sunshine. It seemed easily within their reach, and to favor them further, the ridge became broader. Excitedly they hurried forward but all at once came to a halt. Before them was a chasm, some 60 feet wide and 400 feet deep. On the other side, the ridge kept climbing directly to the summit, which was only a short distance off, but there was no way around or over the chasm. It formed an absolutely impassable obstacle, blocking them from their goal. Frustrated after all their efforts and the dangers they had risked, they reluctantly turned back. The mists swirled around them again and shut off their view of the inaccessible summit, which a few minutes before had appeared so close. Hailstones clattered on the rocks around them and turned into snow, but the travelers safely rejoined their Indian guides, mounted their mules, and arrived back at the village that night. It had been a disappointing climb, but they had reached an altitude of more than 19,000 feet, the highest any man had ever climbed and a record that stood for some thirty years.

Although he could no longer hope to meet the French expedition, Humboldt decided, on leaving Quito, to continue with his plan of following the Andes to Lima, Peru. Part of the way between Quito and Cuenca, Ecuador, the route he took was that formerly used by the Incas, and Humboldt observed with interest the remains of the great Incan highway. No Roman road he had seen in Italy surpassed it. He also stopped to examine Incan remains like the Fortress of Cañar, which formed an oval 120 feet long. Presumed to be a resting place for the Incas on their travels, it contained two large rooms and was surrounded by the remains of many smaller buildings, enough to house the army the Incas usually took with them for protection.

At Loja the travelers rested from their long, weary journey through the mountains. They had now come well over 1,000 miles since leaving Cartagena, moving by boat, muleback, and foot through some of the most rigorous country in the world, clambering up mountains and down deep valleys, reaching the greatest height that any man had ever climbed, sitting on the lips of volcanoes, and gazing into the craters. Even at Loja, Humboldt's restless activity did not cease. Although his principal purpose was to regain his strength, he studied the groves of cinchona trees and the manufacture of quinine.

Moving southward after their rest, they sometimes traveled with as many as eighteen or twenty mules loaded with their instruments and collections, or they sometimes went by raft. They spent seventeen days in the warmer climate of the valley of the upper Amazon, while Humboldt drew new maps based on his observations and information that he obtained from other people. They then entered the Andes again and stopped near Chota, Peru, long enough to look at the rich silver mines. Although the area was still near the equator, pans of water froze at night throughout a large part of the year, and the land was so desolate that the food eaten by the miners had to be brought in from the warmer valleys. The wealthy people were bored by their lonely lives and gambled incessantly, reminding Humboldt of Pizarro's soldiers in their craze for money. The miners, on the other hand, were condemned to a bitter, grueling existence, carrying the ore from the galleries in large baskets on their backs.

Leaving this depressing place, he and Bonpland went over the mountains on a path that was so rough and narrow even the mules had difficulty following it. The wind that blew around them was cold and cutting, and they were stung by the hail that slapped against their faces. Finally, they could see below them the fertile valley of Cajamarca.

Here the Inca Atahualpa had had a residence that he used when he came to take the natural warm baths, but most of the buildings had been destroyed by the conquistadors in their search for gold. Humboldt visited the room in which Atahualpa had been held prisoner for nine months in 1532 and 1533 and which he had been forced to fill with gold as a ransom. Although the treasure brought in from many temples amounted to millions of dollars, the Spanish executed the Inca anyway.

To guide him through these bloody ruins, where the Incas had suffered the full force of the Spaniards' greed and bigotry, Humboldt used a descendant of Atahualpa. The seventeen-year-old boy had lived so long with the legends of his family that he once seriously assured Humboldt that a golden tree lay under the ground near where they were standing. Such trees and other plants had been described by early travelers, but the boy's believing one was within his grasp struck Humboldt as painful. He saw it as a delusion cherished only because of his poverty. Hoping to bring him back to reality, Humboldt asked him why he did not dig it up. The answer was simple. Each year the family had a small crop of wheat; it was enough to live on happily; if they owned the golden tree, their neighbors would destroy them out of hatred and jealousy. The descendants of Atahualpa, hundreds of years after his death, had not forgotten the lesson of his tragic experience.

From Cajamarca, Humboldt and Bonpland turned westward toward the Pacific, crossing the magnetic equator, where the dipping needle remains level. As they reached a high point on their descent from the ridges, a sharp west wind blew up and swept away the mists that had lain over the foothills before them. They could see the slopes tumbling downward toward the shore, the coastline extending in either direction, and beyond it the great mass of the Pacific, shining in the sun. For Humboldt, the moment was especially emotional, because he had been interested in the Pacific ever since he had talked with Forster. Now for the first time he saw it.

The remainder of their stay in Peru was uneventful. They reached the coast at Trujillo and went down to Lima, where Bonpland searched for more plants and Humboldt studied the climate and made astronomical observations. (He also computed the city's latitude.) Near the end of 1802 they sailed from Lima to Guayaquil on their way to Acapulco. On the voyage, Humboldt measured the temperature of the current that now bears his name, but he never claimed it as his own. Knowing that the fishermen had been familiar with it for hundreds of years, he always called it the Peruvian Current and so designated it on his own maps.

Finding little to interest them in Acapulco, Humboldt and Bonpland stayed only a few days before visiting the pyramid at Cuernavaca and going on to Mexico City. Humboldt was feeling pressed for funds. So far, he calculated, his trip had cost him about 4,000 pounds, a rather large proportion of his inheritance and as much as he thought he could afford. He decided, therefore, to spend only a short time in Mexico. This decision was reinforced by the poor condition of his instruments, which needed repairing after the buffeting they had received in the Andes. The director of the school of mines, on learning this, offered to lend Humboldt a set, and this act of generosity induced him to forget his financial concerns and stay on.

Mexico, of course, had been far better explored and mapped than the wild country of the Andes, where so few scientists had traveled, so Humboldt's studies took a somewhat different turn. "I was necessarily struck," he wrote later, "by the contrast between the civilization of New Spain and the little culture existing in the parts of meridional America through which I had just traveled. This contrast immediately stimulated me into studying the statistical information of Mexico and doing research into the causes that have most influenced the progress of the population and the national industry. My individual situation offered me every means of reaching the goal I had set for myself."

Once more he devoted much of his time to observing the ancient remnants of the earlier civilizations, and in the spring of that year he traveled to Moran and Mineral del Monte to study the Mexicans' methods of mining silver. As he had expected, he found them crude. Although the workers were well paid by Mexican standards, the conditions in which they labored were intolerable. They were practically naked—this made it more difficult for them to hide pieces of ore from their employers—and were required to carry bags weighing sometimes as much as 300 pounds up steps cut at a 45-degree angle and through a wide range of temperatures. At the bottom of the mine, the air might be extremely hot. At the top, perhaps more than 1,000 feet up, it might, in winter, be just above freezing. This was arduous labor for men in their prime, but old men and young children also worked in the mines.

Traveling south from the mines, Humboldt continued his usual practice of taking notes and making observations. (He stopped, for example, at Salamanca to establish its longitude and latitude.) One of his objectives was to observe at firsthand the recent volcano of Jorullo, which had thrust itself upward in 1759. Until that year the site had been covered largely with fields of indigo and sugarcane. In June the inhabitants were alarmed by loud rumblings under the earth. These were followed by frequent earthquakes, which continued for fifty or sixty days, after which, much to the relief of the people, they died out. On the night of September 28, however, the noises recurred, and over an area of 3 or 4 square miles the earth began to rise. Terrified, the Indians fled to the mountains and watched their fields explode in eruptions of mud and gases. Thousands of small cones appeared, and several of these grew in height as they continued to erupt. The largest was the volcano of Jorullo, which rose several thousand feet above the plain before it quieted in February, 1760.

Humboldt stayed at a nearby Indian village while he examined the area closely. The gases still coming from the many cones made the air oppressively hot, but undaunted, Humboldt approached the central volcano, which was still on fire. Layers of ashes covered its lava slopes, and the heat grew almost unbearable as he approached the mouth of the crater. Not satisfied with merely looking into the volcano, he climbed down into it for 250 feet.

After their journeying, Humboldt and Bonpland remained in Mexico City from September, 1803, until January, 1804, once more rearranging their collections and notes. These had now grown to massive proportions, for the two men had investigated so many subjects and traveled so far. Humboldt's exploration of the Orinoco and the Casiquiare rivers had solved an important geographical question, and his maps and observations had added greatly to man's knowledge of the geography of South America. He had collected countless meteorological data, developed new information on the distribution of plants, accumulated figures on the earth's magnetism, measured the temperatures and velocities of ocean currents, gained new understanding of the role of volcanoes in shaping the earth's surface, and had studied the ancient and modern cultures of the countries through which he had passed. No other scientist knew so much about Latin America, and the Mexican government, hoping to induce him to stay on, offered him an official post. But true scientist that he was, Humboldt turned the offer down. He wanted to report his findings freely, unhampered by an obligation to the government of one of the countries he wanted to write about.

The time had come, therefore, when he should return to Europe and begin working with the masses of information he had gathered. Some of it, of course, he had safely with him, but he had heard nothing about the shipments he had sent earlier from Cuba. If they were lost, much of the time he had spent in Venezuela would prove wasted. With this worry nagging at his mind, he said good-bye to his friends in Mexico City and sailed from Veracruz to Cuba, where he and Bonpland took passage to the United States for a short visit on their way to France. In Philadelphia he visited the public library and, while examining the table of contents of a scientific magazine, saw the words: "Arrival of M. de Humboldt's manuscripts at his brother's house in Paris, by way of Spain."

"I could scarcely suppress an exclamation of joy," he wrote. "Never did a table of contents appear to me to be better made."

Humboldt could not afford to stay in the United States as long as he would have liked. So, on July 9, 1804, after a short visit to Washington to see President Jefferson, he and Bonpland boarded a ship for the last time on this incredible journey that had taken them through so much of the New World. They had seen the valleys of the Orinoco, the volcanoes of Quito, and ridden over the long windswept ridges of the Andes. They had observed the ruins of the Incan and Aztec empires and had traveled by sea over two oceans. They had been in the pits of the mines of Moran, surrounded by naked Indians carrying their heavy sacks of ore, and had stood with President Jefferson in the Executive Mansion. It had been a journey of great extremes and enormous length, and although they had enjoyed it, they must have felt a sense of relief that their next destination was not another strange land, but at last—Europe.

I V

When Humboldt disembarked at Bordeaux on August 3, 1804, he had a prodigious amount of luggage. In addition to all his instruments, his journals, and his record books, he carried with him "forty-two boxes, containing an herbal of six thousand equinoctial plants, seeds, shells, insects, and, what had hitherto never been brought to Europe, geological specimens from the Chimborazo, New Grenada [Columbia], and the banks of the river of the Amazons."

Describing the problem of traveling through the Americas with his collections, Humboldt wrote, "The conveyance of these objects, and the minute care they required, occasioned us such embarrassments as would scarcely be conceived, even by those who have traversed the most un-cultivated parts of Europe. Our progress was often retarded by the three-fold necessity of dragging after us, during expeditions of five or six months, twelve, fifteen, and sometimes more than twenty loaded mules, exchanging these animals every eight or ten days, and superintending the Indians who were employed in leading so numerous a caravan. Often, in order to add to our collections of new mineral substances, we found ourselves obliged to throw away others, which we had collected a consid-erable time before. These sacrifices were not less painful than the losses which we accidentally made. Sad experience taught us, but too late, that from the sultry humidity of the climate, and the frequent falls of the beasts of burden, we could preserve neither the skins of animals too hast-ily preserved, nor the fishes and reptiles placed in phials." But in spite of the lack of these, Humboldt had enough material to keep himself busy for the remainder of his life.

From Bordeaux he went to Paris. Much of the old spirit of liberty was vanishing under Napoleon—he was proclaimed emperor by the Senate and the Tribunate only a few weeks after Humboldt's arrival in France—but he did encourage the arts and letters and science. One of the scientists who enjoyed the emperor's favor was the chemist Claude Louis Berthollet, who used to give regular parties at his house in Arcueil, near Paris. Humboldt was one of those invited frequently, and there he met Joseph Louis Gay-Lussac, a physician and chemist. Gay-Lussac had severely criticized some of Humboldt's earlier work on the composition of the air, but the two men, largely because of Humboldt's frankness and amiability, soon became firm friends. Unable to climb the high Andes like Humboldt, Gay-Lussac had been making balloon ascents over France in an effort to measure the effect of altitude on the earth's magnetism and also to take samples of the air, which he then analyzed. He and Hum-boldt started performing experiments together, gathering specimens of the atmosphere during storms and in wet and dry weather. (They even collected it at the Théâtre Française during a performance.) The basis of their analysis was Henry Cavendish's discovery that oxygen and hydrogen combine to form water under the stimulus of an electric spark. By knowing the amount of hydrogen they had added to their sample, they could measure the decrease in the gas caused by the removal of the oxygen. In the course of these experiments they discovered that under all circumstances (at least those they could observe), two units of hydrogen combined with one unit of oxygen. Humboldt gave complete credit for the discovery to Gay-Lussac, saying that he himself was only a collaborator.

They also began reviewing Humboldt's records of the magnetism of the earth. He had taken almost 125 readings of the magnetic dip, in each case carefully observing the latitude and longitude of the location, its height above sea level, and the nature of any nearby rocks. Needing more data, they crossed the Alps on foot in the spring of 1805 and entered Italy, taking additional readings as they went. Then at long last Humboldt returned home to Berlin.

By now he had sufficient information to demonstrate that the intensity of the earth's magnetism increased as the observer approached the poles (a fact that had been noticed by others before but never published), so he decided to study the daily deviation of the magnetic compass. For this purpose, he rented a small cottage outside Berlin and between May, 1806, and June, 1807, took more than 6,000 readings, some of them at half-hour intervals over a seven-day period, and learned that the needle swung slightly to the east during the day and returned to the west at night. During the winter a display of northern lights occurred, and Humboldt noticed that the needles of his equipment were fluctuating wildly. This event led him to study "magnetic storms," a term that he coined.

While Humboldt was busy pursuing his interests in science, Napoleon was in the field again fighting against the forces of the Third Coalition, and Prussia was one of his principal victims. Its lands were partitioned, its army limited to 42,000 men, and its territory occupied by French forces. Under these humiliating conditions, the morale of Berlin collapsed. It was no longer a center capable of attracting intellectuals like Humboldt, and he gladly accepted a position accompanying Prince Wilhelm on a trip to Paris in an attempt to obtain a reduction in the reparations to be paid by Prussia. Because Napoleon had no intention of moderating the severity of the conditions he had imposed, the negotiations came to nothing, but when Prince Wilhelm returned to Prussia in 1808, Humboldt asked, and received, permission to remain in Paris, while retaining his position on the Prussian payroll.

At first he had some financial difficulties. He had spent a sizable part of his inheritance on his travels, so his income was considerably less than it would otherwise have been. Furthermore, much of what remained had been invested in Poland, and this portion was seized as enemy property, although eventually Humboldt regained it. In addition to his own means, he had the modest salary paid by the Prussian government, and this gave him what he needed for the simple and regular routine he followed. Rising at six o'clock in the morning, he went to a laboratory that he shared with Gay-Lussac and stayed there until lunch. In the afternoons he worked on the books he was writing about his experiences and observations in America. In the evenings he visited the leading salons—he liked people and was also quite a gossip—and after midnight returned to his rooms for a few hours' sleep.

During his visits to the Paris salons, Humboldt heard the romantic story of Dominique François Jean Arago. A physicist and secretary of the Paris Observatory, Arago had gone on a surveying trip for the French government and, in order to complete his assignment, visited Majorca. The islanders, fearful of the French, thought he was a spy preparing the way for an invasion by Napoleon, so they arrested him and threw him into prison. He escaped, secured passage on a fishing boat to Algiers, and after many vicissitudes arrived back in France. All through his struggles, he had clung to his records and notes, even hiding them under his clothing when he was a prisoner. This devotion to science captured Humboldt's imagination, and he immediately wrote Arago a congratulatory letter, the first Arago received on his return. Out of this act sprang a lifelong friendship.

As Humboldt worked with the material he had collected, he found that his projected publications were an enormous undertaking and that he needed the help of other scientists in dealing with some of the technical aspects. Obviously he looked to Bonpland for assistance and, to provide him with a livelihood, secured a position for him as superintendent of the garden of the Empress Josephine. But Bonpland's heart was not in his work. He shared responsibility for the publications on botany and zoology, but in 1816 he accepted a professorship of natural history at Buenos Aires and remained in South America for the rest of his life.

To finish the work that Bonpland never got around to doing, Humboldt employed a nephew of his former tutor and also used whatever other assistance he could obtain. He had a young astronomer do the calculations from the astronomical and geographical data he had collected; he had artists draw pictures under his guidance from the sketches that he had made in the field; even Cuvier, busy as he was, helped in the preparation of Humboldt's information on zoology and comparative anatomy. It was an almost inexhaustible store of material that Humboldt had brought back with him, enough for a corps of scientists to work with, and indeed, Humboldt never finished his writing, although the books came off the presses in a stream.

They dealt with every aspect of Humboldt's observations and thus greatly enlarged man's understanding of the world around him. Humboldt did not merely provide statistics. In many cases, he introduced fresh concepts of the natural world. In botany, he dealt not only with the plants he had seen and collected, but also with their distribution according to the climate in which they were found. In geography, he analyzed the character of mountain ranges and their effects on the societies that they divided, pointing out that it was not the height of the peaks, but the height of the passes, that determined their social importance. His studies of volcanoes led to a new understanding of the differences between sedimentary and igneous rocks and the role of faults in molding the earth's surface. (Goethe, as well as many others, disliked a theory that proposed such a disorderly and violent process.) He presented new facts about meteorology. In his maps, he connected points having the same temperatures and coined the term "isothermal line," which is still used. Moreover, he added knowledge about the currents of the oceans and determined the location of many cities and other points, thus increasing the geographical knowledge of Latin America. His measurements of the earth's magnetism were invaluable, and his reading for the magnetic equator, made during his trip down the Andes, provided a standard on which measurements of terrestrial magnetism were based for many years. He also wrote *Political Essay on the Kingdom of New Spain,* in which he discussed its politics, its population, and the economics of its mining industry. (This book was widely read by French and British investors, and Humboldt was offered the chairmanship of a large French-Mexican investment company. Although his recompense would have been magnificent, he refused, wanting to be free to pursue his scientific work without outside obligations.) And to the Incas and the Aztecs, who had so intrigued him, he devoted many pages, describing the manuscripts he had studied and the buildings and art he had examined.

So the years passed while Humboldt, still living in modest circumstances, turned out sheet after sheet of manuscript and sadly watched the political liberalism he had always admired fade from the Continent. After Napoleon's defeat, Prince Metternich, the foreign minister of Austria, had imposed his conservative philosophy on Europe, and in spite of sporadic outbreaks of liberalism, most governments leaned heavily to the right. Both Humboldt and Arago suffered emotionally, as the French government under Charles X tightened the controls of the central authority. In Prussia, for whose government Humboldt still nominally worked, the situation was not much better. Frederick William III, who had once promised to introduce a constitution, had gone back on that pledge and instead had willingly subscribed to the Carlsbad Decrees, instituted by Metternich to establish severe censorship of the press and to restrict academic freedom.

Yet Humboldt could not free himself of his need for his government salary. The cost of publishing his work was far greater than he had anticipated. Prussia helped him with a grant, and he decided he would have to forgo his royalties. (Once he had dreamed he would earn back the cost of the expedition with his books.) But even this sacrifice was not enough, and he had to use more and more of his capital to make up the deficit, until eventually his government salary became his principal source of income.

His duties so far had been nominal—the salary amounted almost to a pension—but in 1826, the government ordered him to return to Berlin. Humboldt protested as vigorously as he dared, even writing personally to the king, but to no avail. In 1827, having exhausted every avenue of appeal, he left Arago and the city he loved so well, paid a short visit to England, and returned to Berlin, a dependent of a government with which he found it increasingly difficult to agree.

V

Hating slavery and admiring liberals like Thomas Jefferson, Humboldt played a unique role in the Prussia of Frederick William III. Instead of advising the government on political matters, he spoke out only on science and the arts, and by restricting himself in this way, he was able to serve his country well.

One of his first acts was to give a series of lectures on physical geography, in which he propounded many of his new ideas. These proved so popular with both the students and the faculties at Berlin that he later gave a simplified version of them to the general public. As many as 1,000 persons came to hear him, and the audiences, much to the amazement of Berlin, included many women. These lectures accomplished two significant purposes: They helped stem the romanticism with which the Germans were approaching science, and they gave science a social respectability that it had not previously enjoyed.

Because the Carlsbad Decrees prohibited large meetings of scholars, they became a target for Humboldt. A few years previously a scientific meeting had been held at Leipzig, but the scientists were compelled to convene in a cellar and suffered continually from police surveillance. Humboldt thought this attitude nonsense, and using his persuasive powers and his influence with the king, he secured permission to hold a scientific congress at Berlin in 1828. This was no paltry affair. Six hundred scientists attended from all over Europe, the Duke of Cumberland and Frederick William III were present at the opening meeting, and the international gathering helped set a pattern that has been followed for many years since.

One of those attending was Karl Friedrich Gauss, a German mathematician and director of the observatory at Göttingen. (He was so devoted to his work he even slept in the observatory and is said never to have left it except on this one occasion.) He had not yet published his first work on magnetism, but he and Humboldt apparently discussed the subject, for shortly after the congress Humboldt's interest in magnetism revived. He went to his friend, Abraham Mendelssohn-Bartholdy, the father of Felix, and asked permission to erect a building in his garden. It was constructed completely of nonmagnetic materials and was free of drafts, so no extraneous force could move the bar magnet hanging in the middle. Each end of the magnet had scales, mounted in ivory, which could be read through two microscopes. With this instrument and the help of a number of assistants, Humboldt began to measure changes in the earth's magnetism. As he had demonstrated during his Latin American trip, he believed in accumulating quantities of data before attempting to draw conclusions. Consequently, he knew that readings taken only at Berlin would have less significance than readings taken simultaneously in several areas. He arranged, therefore, to have similar instruments installed at Paris and also underground in a mine in Freiberg, each to be read at the same time every day. Not only were the measurements helpful in determining daily variations, but they also provided an instance of the international scientific collaboration in which Humboldt was a pioneer.

While he was engaged in all these activities, Humboldt was also trying to arrange another trip, for he had not satisfied his desire to travel. He had, however, no personal funds left—his inheritance was now entirely gone—and he saved nothing from his salary, not because he lived luxuriously, but because he was constantly helping needy students. Wherever he traveled, therefore, he would have to have a patron, and he thought that he might find one in Czar Alexander I of Russia. Quantities of platinum had been discovered in Russia, and the finance minister wanted Humboldt's opinion on establishing a platinum currency. (The Spanish government had asked him the same question after his return from Mexico, and he had advised against it.) He told the finance minister that the world market for platinum was too unstable to provide a basis for an international currency and that Russia was too great a country to have a currency that was limited solely to domestic use. In his correspondence, Humboldt took the opportunity to hint that he would like to make an inspection tour of the mines in the Urals. Although he was embarrassed to ask for his expenses, he carefully explained that all his money had gone to science. The minister replied that the czar was perfectly willing to grant him the allowance he asked.

In April, 1829, Humboldt left Berlin for St. Petersburg, taking with him two companions who were to observe the zoology, geology, and botany of the regions through which they passed. Humboldt was to concentrate on the climate, meteorology, and magnetism and, for this purpose, took with him a number of thermometers and a nonmagnetic tent in which he could set up his magnetometer.

The hospitality of St. Petersburg was so great that he was glad when the time came to leave and he could go southwestward across the Russian plains to Gorki. Several senior officials of the mining department went along to serve as guides, and since they were often joined by local provincial dignitaries, they sometimes needed as many as thirty or forty horses. At Gorki they embarked on a sailing boat large enough to carry their carriages, as well as their luggage, and for three days, they followed the course of the Volga River to Kazan, where they disembarked and headed westward toward the Urals.

By July, Humboldt had reached Sverdlovsk, which he made his headquarters while examining the mines and geology of the Urals. For one month he traveled through the mountains, usually on foot and often working until late at night. As July came to a close, he moved eastward and entered Siberia. After a short visit at Tobolsk, he turned southward through the grasslands of Siberia. An epidemic of typhus was raging, so the party avoided the towns and traveled day and night, often covering 160 or 180 miles in a twenty-four-hour period. The insects were numerous and almost as irritating as on the Orinoco, and the men suffered also from the temperature, which, although not as warm in the daytime as on the river, contrasted sharply with the cold of the nights. By August 1 they had gone as far as Barnaul, approximately 1,000 miles deep into Asia, and finally, after a journey of thousands of miles at the age of sixty, Humboldt arrived back in St. Petersburg in November, 1829.

Once more the city's notables turned out to honor him, and Humboldt took advantage of one meeting to advance a cherished plan. Russia was geographically so large, he said, that its government could establish a worthwhile series of posts, ranging from west to east, to observe changes in the earth's magnetism and to collect meteorological data. All the observations should be made with similar instruments, and the information should be sent to a central institute in St. Petersburg, where it could be collated and published. Although the bureaucracy of Russia was renowned for its inefficiency, Humboldt's prestige and persuasiveness were sufficient to launch the project. Within five years the government had established the network he had suggested.

Leaving St. Petersburg, Humboldt went back to Berlin to resume his old routine. That July the people of Paris, weary of Charles X's despotism, once more barricaded the streets and revolted against their government. Charles X was forced into exile, and Louis Philippe ascended the throne. At first, the Prussian government, fearful that the revolution might spread, regarded the new king with deep suspicion but in the fall of 1830 decided to recognize him. As an envoy to perform this official duty, Frederick William III chose Humboldt, who in this way had a chance to see again his old friend Arago, from whom he had been separated so long.

Although he was now sixty-one years old and had not yet completed all the publications on his Latin American journey (he never succeeded in bringing them to a finish), Humboldt had plans for new projects, including a book on his travels in Russia. When this came out in 1843, it contained a number of faults, as well as virtues. Not limiting himself to what he had actually seen, Humboldt described the geography of areas that he had not visited and knew only by hearsay. As a consequence, he made several errors, including the listing of two volcanoes that did not exist. Nevertheless, the book had much merit, for Humboldt advanced a number of unusual ideas. Earlier, while traveling through the Andes, he had become interested in making profile drawings of the lands he visited and determining the geographic and social effect of mountains. He now became particularly interested in their relation to the mean altitude of landmasses and discovered that they were of far less significance than previously supposed. What counted, he showed, was not the spectacular mountain peaks but the broad plateaus, which covered larger extents of land. He also realized, after visiting Russia, that his previous ideas on climatology had been inadequate; the mean temperatures of a country did not give a clear picture of its climate. Instead, a meteorologist should present the temperatures for the various seasons. In his new maps, he drew lines connecting points that had the same temperatures in summer and also lines between those having equal temperatures in winter.

While he worked on his book on Russia, he continued to play an active role in many scientific and political affairs. In the service of the Prussian king, he undertook numerous missions throughout Europe, traveling around Europe and accompanying his monarch to the spas. He also, whenever he could, helped other scientists, sometimes using his influence at court on their behalf and often assisting them out of his own slender finances. When the young Swiss scientist Louis Agassiz came to Paris to do research on his book about fish, he found himself without a publisher or the money necessary to continue. Deeply discouraged, he was on the verge of giving up when Humboldt, learning of his situation, advanced the money to keep on. And when Gauss prepared a paper proposing a method of describing magnetic intensities that would supplant Humboldt's, Humboldt himself translated the paper into French and sent it off to Arago for the consideration of the French Institute.

Nor with all this activity did he lose his enthusiasm for helping political liberals. In 1837, on the death of William IV of England and Hanover, the throne of Hanover went to a despot, Ernest Augustus, the Duke of Cumberland. He immediately suspended the constitution that William had granted and instituted one of his own that reduced the legislature to nothing and proclaimed that the state's lands were the king's private holdings. The opposition to this centered in the university at Göttingen, several of whose professors were consequently dismissed. Once again, Humboldt used his influence with the king, finally obtaining permission for the professors to apply for posts in Prussia. In the end, three of them found refuge through Humboldt's intervention. Two of them were Jacob and Wilhelm Grimm, authors of the famous fairy tales. Ernest Augustus was furious with Humboldt for what he had done, and when the two men met, which they did several times in Prussia, the new king denounced the scientist, much to Humboldt's positive delight.

In spite of these distractions, his duties at court, and his increasing age, Humboldt's work never ceased. He kept up his voluminous correspondence, attempting to answer every letter; he remembered the birthdays of his friends and their children; he entertained Balzac when he came to Berlin; he nominated foreign associates to the French Institute; and he presided over a new honorary order established by Frederick William IV, who had succeeded to the Prussian throne in 1840. At first, the public had hoped for many reforms, but although Frederick William IV released a number of intellectuals from prison and relaxed the censorship of the press, he soon became concerned about the discontent that was voiced under the looser rules and turned reactionary. For Humboldt, these were unhappy days. He still had good relations with the court, but he was disturbed to see the Prussia that he loved so well and had served so long drifting back into the tyranny he hated. But in spite of his occasional discouragement, Humboldt was busy with one more book, entitled *Cosmos,* which he had planned to write at least twenty-five years before.

VI

In 1845, the year in which the first volume of *Cosmos* appeared, Humboldt celebrated his seventy-sixth birthday. Like many old men, he was lonely. Yet unlike most people his age, his mind was still active, and he was still capable of productive work.

The scope of his labors had been enormous, so he was honored, not for a single, brilliant discovery, but for a wide variety of new ideas. Some of these were already scientifically outdated before his death, and some had been accepted for so long that they were taken for granted. But the total was such that he enjoyed prestige in every intellectual circle.

Aside from his spectacular travels in Latin America and his less satisfactory journey in Russia, both of which gave him a reputation as an explorer, he had conducted penetrating studies of the Aztec and Incan civilizations, collected unusual data on the earth's magnetic field, including acute observations on its regular and irregular changes, had pioneered in systematic meteorology, and had related climatology to the distribution of plant life, thus developing plant geography. He had contributed to geology by recognizing the significance of volcanoes in shaping the earth and to physical geography by the manner in which he saw the importance of gathering and presenting all the facts—climate, economics, plant life, natural resources, altitudes, and physiography. He had also had a less direct, but not less important, influence on his times by his encouragement of international scientific cooperation and the assistance he had given so many individual scientists.

In *Cosmos,* Humboldt tried to put down everything he knew. He wrote, not solely for the professional or for the common layman, but for the educated intellectual, who, he believed, should be more informed about the natural world. Nations, he argued, that drop behind other countries in technology, industry, and science are doomed to be unprosperous. But he also believed that science should not predominate at the expense of the humanities. Both were equally important to the welfare of mankind. In his book, therefore, he discussed history and art, as well as science, attempting to show their interrelationships.

The book was enormously popular. The first volume—there were five volumes in all—was sold out within a few months, and by 1851, six years later, 80,000 copies had been purchased by interested readers. The reviewers, too, were enthusiastic. In part, Humboldt's reputation protected him from attack, and since he had always tried to avoid disputes, he had few enemies and many friends. But the book itself was enough to draw their praise, for Humboldt had written well, developing the theme of the popular lectures he had first given at Berlin into a masterpiece of its kind.

Although he kept on working regularly during his last years, his life became increasingly unhappy. He was still beset by financial problems and would have been in serious trouble except for occasional grants from the king, the willingness of Abraham Mendelssohn-Bartholdy to lend him money, and the faithfulness of his old servant Johann Seifert, who had been with him for many years and who often went without the salary due him in order to keep the household functioning. Under such circumstances, Humboldt could not afford to resign his position at the court, although he would have liked to.

Politically he was in difficulties, too. He had welcomed the uprising in France in 1848, hoping it would bring the French the liberty that had so often seemed in their grasp and then eluded them. When riots broke out in Berlin that March, he had not minded having his house entered four times during a single night. He thought the disorder was merely a disagreeable step on the way toward something better and greater for Prussia, and he later marched at the head of the procession carrying the bodies of the revolutionaries killed in the street fighting.

By the summer of that year the liberalism that Humboldt loved seemed in full flood in the German states. Uprisings had followed uprisings, and the rulers, to retain any power at all, had had to make concessions. In Prussia, for example, Frederick William IV called an assembly and empowered it to write a constitution. But suddenly the reactionary forces rallied, and by the end of the year the revolution was dead.

Humboldt still maintained cordial relations with the king, but other members of the court looked on him more suspiciously than ever. His voluminous correspondence was opened and read by the censor; he was placed under police surveillance. In France, Louis Napoleon, after a skillful political campaign, won the presidency of the new republic and, a few years later, had proclaimed a temporary dictatorship, during which Arago was arrested because of his political views.

As Humboldt watched European liberalism deteriorate, his own life at court became less pleasant. One of his tasks had been to read out loud to the king, and as he usually selected newspaper articles and scientific treatises, he was gradually replaced by an actor with more lively tastes. Humboldt became the man whose stories everybody had heard before, the person whose ideas on every topic are already known—in a word, a bit of a bore tolerated for old times' sake.

In 1853 he finally gave up his position at the court, and in 1857, Frederick William IV, having become insane, was replaced by his brother. William I attempted to institute some reforms but soon virtually abandoned the government to Otto von Bismarck. Fortunately Humboldt did not live to see Bismarck's policies put in effect. The supremacy of the Junkers in German politics would have broken his heart. He had a slight stroke in 1857, the year the king was held insane. Otherwise his health, although gradually declining, was not dramatically impaired. Visitors kept coming to his house, and his correspondence continued on a large scale, but he no longer found enjoyment in his work. In March, 1859, he wrote a letter to the newspapers, begging people not to bother him anymore. He had so little time left. In April, he suddenly grew weaker, and on May 6, 1859, he quietly died at the age of eighty-nine.

Immediately a scandal broke. When his family arrived to seal his rooms, Seifert, the servant, announced that Humboldt had already given him almost everything he owned. The relatives, thinking that Seifert had unduly influenced the old man, were horrified and regretted having left him in such bad care. The affair soon became known to the newspapers, and the gossipmongers of Berlin picked it up, much to the family's despair. Actually Humboldt was practically penniless at the time of his death, with few assets and several debts. The king generously paid off the loans from Mendelssohn-Bartholdy, and Seifert was able to sell the library to a Berlin bookseller, thus gaining some recompense for his years of service. A new scandal broke a few years later. One of Humboldt's closest friends had died only a few months before him, and his widow published his papers, which included many letters from Humboldt, as well as records of Humboldt's conversations. The social world of the court was shocked to read them. Humboldt's apparent courtesy at court and his avoidance of quarrels had been the result of restraint, not inclination. Writing or talking to his friend, he had been both frank and sharp, and the targets of his comments were not pleased to learn what he had really thought.

In time the scandals died. Seifert, with the little money left him by his employer, drifted into obscurity, those who had been wounded by Humboldt's private remarks either died or forgot their injuries, and with the passing of the notoriety following his death came a decline in Humboldt's reputation. He had studied so many fields, done so many things, and lived so long that the world had come to take him and his contributions to science for granted. For almost fifty years before his death the observations that he had made in Latin America had served as the basis for the best maps; his recordings of magnetic deviations had not only been accepted, but been improved; his approach to systematic meteorology had been commonly adopted; the distribution of plants was a standard subject of study; and his ideas on geology and physical geography were regarded as routine. He was an innovator who later had difficulty keeping up with his own innovations, and as a result, the world began to forget what it owed him and remembered him largely for the current that he constantly denied discovering.

But Humboldt would not have minded. He had once written that "one of the noblest privileges, which distinguishes modern civilization from that of remoter times, is our having enlarged the mass of our conceptions, rendering us more capable of perceiving the connection between the physical and intellectual world, and our having aroused a more general interest in subjects that hitherto occupied only a small number of scientific men. . . ." At his death he could feel assured that he was one of the mighty contributors to this "noble privilege." And that, after all, had been the purpose of his life.

9

Reading the Earth's Story

CHARLES LYELL: 1797–1875

I

When, as a young man, Alexander von Humboldt selected the mining school at Freiberg in Saxony as the place to study geology, he was influenced by the reputation of its brilliant professor, Abraham Gottlob Werner, who was known throughout Europe as the man who had raised the school from a minor provincial institution to a major scientific center.

Born in 1750, Werner came from a family that for several hundred years had engaged in various aspects of the mining industry. His father was an inspector of ironworks and, wanting young Werner to follow the family tradition, encouraged his interest in rocks and minerals. After attending school in Silesia, Werner returned home and became his father's apprentice. When he was nineteen, his family decided he would benefit from the courses offered at Freiberg, although the school was only a few years old and had not yet attained the eminence he himself would later bring to it. Because of his knowledge and industry, he stood out among the other students and was a favorite of his instructors, and after two more years of law and mineralogy at the university at Leipzig, he returned to Freiberg as a professor.

Seldom has a teacher been more popular or influential with his students. Unlike Lamarck, who could brook no interruptions during his lectures, Werner was prepared to talk on any subject. If his classes wanted him to, he would discuss the history of mining, its laws and financing, or tell how to construct tunnels and what sort of machinery to use—all this in addition to lectures on mineralogy. Although the topics were heavy, the manner in which he presented them was not. He had a fine sense of humor, adding just the right touch at the right moment, he had enthusiasm for his field and interest in his students, and he also had the quality enjoyed by many great teachers—an ability to be a showman. In the classroom he gave demonstrations that ʾroke up the tedium of the day, and he constantly took his classes on field trips into the mines, so they could see what was actually being done.

He could never bring himself, however, to put his ideas into writing. He published one small book and a few papers, but the masterwork that he promised to give the world never appeared, although he did print and issue its table of contents a few years before he died. (Apparently he was trying to discourage imitators, who might present his ideas under their names.) But lack of publication did not prevent the wide dissemination of his theories, which were known as Wernerism or Neptunism. Everybody who wanted to learn geology went to Freiberg, everybody at Freiberg studied under Werner, and no one who ever listened to Werner's lectures forgot what he said. In Europe, Werner and geology were practically synonymous.

But most of his ideas were utter nonsense.

Buffon had carried geology a long step forward by devising his theory of epochs and by greatly expanding the length of time during which man thought the earth had existed, Lamarck had contributed to the science by his studies of the development of life, and Cuvier had given geologists the tool of paleontology. But Werner had little use for the teachings of any of these men. Instead, he adopted a theory advocated by a professor at Berlin, revising and changing it over the years until it became his own. Many aspects of his final theory were quite simple. Every rock could be forced into four universal formations, which were based on what he had observed near Freiberg. (He never traveled to check his observations elsewhere.) Most of these rocks, even the basalts, were of aqueous origin, having been laid down by a primeval sea. (How this sea was eventually drained off was a point that Werner disdained to explain.) And volcanoes, although they occurred, were abnormal phenomena and of little significance. (He should have stared with Humboldt into the great crater of Pichincha. That might have changed his views.)

As time went on, a few courageous scientists challenged Werner's authority on several points, but that did not daunt him. Convinced he was absolutely right, he refused to read any critical articles and would not allow anyone except his adoring students into his house, thus effectively isolating himself from new ideas. It was an extraordinary situation: an outstanding and prestigious teacher, one who had done much good work in mineralogy and practical mining and had popularized his subject among serious scientists, now blocking his mind like a medievalist to any corrections and continuing to spread his fallacious ideas. Even on his death in 1817, he clung to his beliefs, and much of the world clung to them with him.

One who did not was a Scotsman, James Hutton, who was born in 1726. After being graduated from the university at Edinburgh, he became apprenticed to a lawyer. Legal work, however, proved utterly uncongenial to him, so his articles were canceled, and he took up instead the study of medicine at Edinburgh, Paris, and Leiden. On his return to Edinburgh in 1749, he reconsidered his future and decided that the prospects were not appealing. The medical practice of Edinburgh was dominated by a number of older men, and it would be years before he could succeed them. Casting around for some other career to follow, he thought of a small and rather unprofitable farm that he had inherited from his father. Perhaps he could improve it by applying scientific techniques to its management.

For approximately five years he studied farming in Norfolk, which was reputed to have some of the best-managed farms in Great Britain, and also in France, Holland, and Belgium. He then settled on his own place, where he remained for fourteen years. By that time the farm was earning a good income and no longer required Hutton's personal supervision. So he rented it and moved to Edinburgh, where he lived in the household of his three maiden sisters. Much of his time he spent with a small circle of intellectual friends, which included the Scottish mathematician and physicist John Playfair. When he was not with them, he experimented with chemistry and studied geology, a science that had attracted his attention when he had first tried to determine which soils were best for farming.

In pursuit of his hobby, he took field trips around Edinburgh and to other parts of Great Britain, and as he observed the rock formations, he came up with a geological theory that was completely different from Werner's. He recognized that many of the rocks were formed from the waste of older ones, the sediments having been laid down under the sea and then raised up again out of the water. He also recognized the existence and importance of rocks that had once been molten and saw that these had sometimes cut through sedimentary strata and, therefore, in certain instances, must be younger. Necessarily Hutton made several errors. One of them was attributing too much influence to an imaginary subterranean heat that both hardened the sediments and later raised them. But in regard to his theory as a whole, he laid down the foundations of modern geology and turned it from the direction into which Werner had deflected it.

Except for his close friends, however, no one knew what Hutton was thinking He discussed his ideas with his associates like John Playfair, but he could not bring himself to publish them, and unlike Werner, he had no students to lecture to. Finally, in 1785, he presented a paper to the Royal Society of Edinburgh, which he had just helped establish. The title he chose was "Theory of the Earth, or an Investigation of the Laws Observable in the Composition, Dissolution and Restoration of Land upon the Globe." In spite of its clumsiness, the title outlined the basic elements of his theory—that the land was both being dissolved and restored.

Although the society printed the paper—it appeared in the first volume of its proceedings—it was not widely read. But a professor in Dublin took sharp exception to it and wrote a highly critical attack. This made Hutton decide to prepare a fuller exposition, an undertaking that required the rest of his life. The first two volumes appeared in 1795, and the last one came out after his death in 1797. But the brilliant, quiet bachelor, although an outstanding geologist, was no writer. His style was awkward, heavy, and confused, and his ideas ran the risk of remaining unread, because few people cared to labor through Hutton's prose. John Playfair, Hutton's good friend, realized this, and five years after Hutton's death he published a book entitled *Illustrations of the Huttonian Theory of the Earth.* In this, he set forth Hutton's ideas in a lucid manner and provided additional illustrations that proved their merit. Through this book, Hutton's theory became widely known. As Buffon had said, style was important.

The year before Hutton published the first two volumes of his *Theory of the Earth,* the British Parliament authorized the construction of the Somerset Coal Canal, an action that had an indirect, but important, effect on the study of geology. The engineer and surveyor for the canal was William Smith, who was then twenty-five years old. He had been brought up by his uncle, a bachelor farmer, who could foresee no other trade for his nephew except farming. In spite of his uncle's resistance, Smith bought books on surveying and, at eighteen, became an apprentice surveyor. As he worked, he became interested in soils and rocks, and after he had completed his apprenticeship, he began conducting some independent experiments that demonstrated to him that certain rocks always stood in the same order no matter where he found them. His job for the canal permitted him to carry these observations further, because before construction actually began, he had to make an inspection trip to look at other waterways. This gave him an opportunity to study rock formations in many parts of Great Britain.

When work on the canal commenced, his assignment proved perfect for the continuance of his studies. As each cut was dug, he noticed the character of the rocks and their sequence and soon could predict the type of formation that might be encountered when the workmen started digging.

By 1796, the year after Hutton's first two volumes had appeared, Smith began to think about writing a book based on his new ideas; but the canal left him little free time, and he was further discouraged, because no one showed any interest in what he had to say. He was living in Bath at that time and there fortunately met a minister who was also a collector of fossils. The collection was not in itself significant—it had been gathered in a casual manner around Bath—but the minister was amazed to learn that Smith could tell him in which stratum each fossil had been found. This led him to question Smith further, and the two men agreed to try an experiment. They would go out in the field together, and Smith would describe to the minister what fossils he would discover by looking in a particular area. He proved to be correct.

In 1799, Smith gave up his job with the canal company, but he still did not get around to writing his book. He did not have enough money to publish it himself, and no one else had any interest in it except the minister and a few people in Bath. One day at dinner, however, these friends persuaded him to dictate a table of strata, which the minister took down. They called it the "Order of the Strata, and Their Imbedded Organic Remains, in the Neighborhood of Bath; Examined and Proved Prior to 1799." Copies of this were widely distributed both in England and on the Continent, passing from hand to hand as other geologists made corrections and additions. But Smith still could not bring himself to write his book. Although he was successful as a consulting engineer, his work took up much of his time, and he saved only a little money. Aside from purchasing some land and a house near Bath, he spent practically everything he had on his studies and his fossil collections. In 1801 he issued a prospectus for his book, but the patron who would have supported the project died, and the prospective publisher failed. Four years later, Smith moved his fossils into a London house he had rented and employed an artist to make illustrations of them for publication. This enterprise, too, came to a halt, when Smith began to realize the enormous expense that was involved.

The years went on, and Smith's ideas were adopted by more and more geologists, largely on the basis of the dictated table of strata, while he continued studying and gathering more data. His observations, of course, had made possible the preparation of a geologic map of Great Britain, and since he apparently had no intention of ever making one himself, the Geological Society of London decided to undertake the task. Before they could do so, however, Smith finally set to work. In 1813 he located a publisher who was willing to produce it, but still the delays went on. He had difficulties thinking of names for the strata, and lacking confidence in himself, he constantly went back into the field to confirm his facts. But in 1814 he had finished enough sheets to exhibit them. These attracted a few patrons, whose contributions enabled him to finish the job in 1815. The map, which covered England, Wales, and part of Scotland, contained fifteen enormous sheets, for they were on a scale of five miles to the inch. Each of the black-and-white engravings had to be colored by hand, an expensive process, but one that permitted Smith to make changes. Altogether, approximately 450 copies were purchased, but the publication was not a commercial success. When it was all over, Smith was financially about as badly off as he had been before.

Because what he wanted was a source of income that did not make any demands on his time, he built a railroad across his property with the idea that it could be used to haul stone to the canal. By an ironic twist of fortune, he, the expert at geologic predictions, calculated wrongly. The stone he intended to haul proved to be of poor quality, and the railroad, therefore, was a complete failure. To get himself out of debt, Smith had to sell almost everything he owned, including his house, his furniture, and his best fossils. For the next seven years he was practically homeless, wandering from one furnished room to another. In 1828 he obtained a position as land steward for a baronet, who apparently tried to leave him time for his work. This arrangement lasted for about six years, until Smith tired of it and resigned. (The baronet allowed him a small annual sum for part-time consultation.)

Smith, meanwhile, had kept up his publications, producing some more maps, a portion of the catalogue of his fossils, and part of a work on the identification of strata by their fossil contents. At one time his friends had feared that the almost universal adoption of his ideas through his first handwritten table of strata would prevent people from remembering who had originated this new approach to geology, but fortunately, it did not. As Smith grew older, more and more scientists recognized his contribution and realized he was the man who had proved the similarities between formations that might be geographically separated by many miles. As a result, honors began to come his way. He received several medals and, from his point of view even more important, a small pension from the government. This enabled him to live in modest comfort until he died in 1839.

Smith's lifetime covered a period of extreme change in the study of geology. He lived to see the downfall of the popular, but fallacious, ideas embodied in Werner's Neptunism and the birth of the new, realistic geology founded by himself and Hutton. And in 1830 he had witnessed the publication of the first volume of the most significant book on geology that had ever been written. It was entitled *Principles of Geology,* and its author was a former lawyer named Charles Lyell.

II

Charles Lyell was born on November 14, 1797, at his family's estate in Scotland, but when he was only a few months old, his father moved to the south of England, near Southampton, and took a fourteen-year lease on a house in the New Forest. There, among idyllic surroundings, Lyell spent his boyhood. The New Forest, a royal preserve, contained some of the finest woodland in England, with towering oaks, beeches, and larches, a perfect place for a young boy interested in the outdoors. The place rented by Mr. Lyell included eighty acres of land, seventy of which were given over to grass for the hunting horses at nearby Lyndhurst. Every year at haying time the Lyell children, equipped with small rakes and forks, were allowed to join the workers, and Lyell afterward commented that "I have always since thought haymaking the most delightful of sights."

When Lyell was eight, he attended school at nearby Ringwood, but Mr. Lyell, realizing that the school was providing no intellectual stimulation for his son, let him remain there only about two years, after which he entered him in a school at Salisbury. Describing his sadness at leaving the countryside, Lyell later wrote, "Instead of a large meadow for a playground, near a river, where we could bathe, and where we were in the country the moment we walked out, . . . we now had a small yard surrounded by walls, and only walked out twice or thrice a week, when it did not rain, and were obliged to keep in ranks along the endless streets and dusty roads of the suburbs of a city. It seemed a kind of prison by comparison, especially to me, accustomed to liberty in such a wild place as the New Forest."

But his life at Salisbury was not entirely unhappy. With his friends, he explored the remnants of the Norman fortifications at Old Sarum, crawling down a subterranean passageway that was famous among the schoolboys. He joined with the others in teasing one of the teachers whom they disliked, balancing books so they would crash down when the teacher opened his door and stretching out strings that he would stumble over in the darkness. Best of all were the bolster fights. Each student would shake his bolster until its contents had all collected at one end, then tie a string or a stocking around it to hold them there. "This," Lyell said, "made a formidable weapon, the empty end being the handle, and the ball at the other would hit a good blow, or coil round a fellow's leg, and by a jerk pull him up so that he fell backwards."

These diversions, however, were not enough to make Lyell fond of the school, and when, in his eleventh year, he came down with an illness, he was perfectly willing to follow the doctor's recommendation and return to the New Forest for three months of rest. Mr. Lyell, whose usual hobbies were botany and Dante, had turned his attention to entomology just long enough to purchase a number of expensive books on the subject. During his convalescence, Lyell began reading these and was soon out in the fields and woods gathering his own collection of insects, which he kept in a piece of mahogany furniture given him by his grandmother.

In spite of the derision of his family and classmates, entomology continued to be one of his major interests. "In the course of each holiday, for three or four years successively," he wrote, "I fell back into my old haunts in the woods, and became so keen before my return to school, that I could seldom resist the temptation of employing my leisure hours there in the same way. I could not see a rare moth without catching it, especially if not exposed to being laughed at by any witnesses of such a queer fancy. When taken, they were put between the leaves of my dictionary, as the only book not taken up with lessons. When I looked up a word, I often found the two pages firmly glued together by some moth, the contents of whose body had been squeezed out between the leaves. The disrepute in which my hobby was held had a considerable effect on my character, for I was very sensitive of the opinion of others, and therefore followed it up almost by stealth; so that although I never confessed to myself that I was wrong, but always reasoned myself into a belief that the generality of people were too stupid to comprehend the interest of such pursuits, yet I got too much in the habit of avoiding being seen, as if I was ashamed of what I did."

After several years at Salisbury, Lyell was brought home, and his father personally undertook his education, teaching him Latin and hiring a French tutor to come twice a week. This lasted for about a year and a half until Mr. Lyell decided to send his son to Winchester. Unfortunately, he had overlooked one of the primary requirements for admission: he should have entered his son at least two years previously in order to gain a place for him. Instead of Winchester, therefore, he was forced to settle on another school at Midhurst in Sussex.

Here the conditions were different from anything he had ever known before. As a new boy, he was not accepted by the others and soon found himself being cuffed and persecuted, because he could not bring himself to fight back. Finally, after a younger, but stronger, boy had struck him and knocked him down, he realized that he had to issue a challenge if his school life were to be even tolerable. Each boy chose his seconds, one classmate held the watch to time the rounds, and the battle started. It lasted for five or six hours on two successive days, and at the end both boys were bloody and bruised. Lyell's enemy went to bed, but Lyell, on the advice of his friends, did not. Although his body ached and he was black and blue, he understood that he would gain standing among his former torturers if he appeared to be indifferent to his injuries.

Looking back on those days later, he wrote, "You cannot imagine the extent to which the stronger and more spirited domineer over the milder and more timid. . . . Some boys quite sink under this roughing, but in general they become more manly and hardier. But," he added, "the recollection of it makes me bless my stars I have not to go through it again."

The school, however, contributed greatly to his development. Until then he had been a rather indifferent student, given to playing pranks and chasing butterflies, instead of studying his lessons, and he continued in this pattern during his first months at Midhurst, where each student was ranked in his class by a rigid marking system in which points were kept for the week's performance, and each boy knew his rank. Whether this unimaginative method stirred Lyell's pride or whether the time had come when his intellectual curiosity would have been awakened anyway is not apparent, but he began to strive for better marks and, at the end of his first year, took one of the prizes. Helped by his liking for English literature (he said that he had a livelier sense than most of the boys of the beauty of English poetry) and assisted by his father, who tutored him when he was at home, his marks began to improve, and in 1816, hopeful that he would eventually "do great things in a literary way," he matriculated at Exeter College, Oxford.

III

Like many students newly arrived at college, Lyell discovered that he was better prepared in some subjects than he had thought, and more poorly in others. But having a quick mind, he soon made up his deficiencies and settled down to a scholastic career, which, although not brilliant, was well above average. He continued to have literary ambitions for a while (he often sent verses he had written home to his father), and he kept on with his study of insects, but gradually these interests were replaced by another: geology. He became familiar with the views of men like Werner and Humboldt, and on his vacation trips to such places as the island of Staffa off the west coast of Scotland, he began to observe the geology of the regions through which he passed.

In 1818 he visited the Continent with his mother, father, and two eldest sisters. After landing at Calais, they went directly to Paris, where Lyell made several visits to the Jardin des Plantes. Because Cuvier was in England at the time, Lyell missed a chance to hear him lecture, which he regretted, but he did examine the anatomical collection, which, he said in his journal, "is very beautiful and might tempt anyone who had the opportunity of staying in Paris to take up ardently the study of anatomy. There are a vast number of exquisite models, colored to the life, descriptive of the anatomical structure of the human frame; besides skeletons of a vast number of quadrupeds, birds, fishes, serpents, &c. &c." These inspired him to go to the library and briefly look at some of Cuvier's works, particularly those describing the geology around Paris.

From Paris the travelers moved to Switzerland. Along the way Lyell made notations in his journal on the rock structures he observed, and in Switzerland he often left the rest of his family for short periods to climb mountains, look at waterfalls, and hike over the glaciers. In his opinion, the most picturesque of these was the glacier at Bossons. "It has advanced further than any of them," he wrote in his journal, "in a direct line across the valley, and particularly in the last three years. A fir wood on the farther side marks the spot to which it used to extend before that time. Marching on with its enormous bulk, it has trodden down the tallest pines with as much ease as an elephant could the herbage of a meadow. Some trunks still are seen projecting from the rock of ice, all the heads being embodied in this mass, which shoots out at the top into tall pyramids and pinnacles of ice, of beautiful shapes and of a very pure white, which is finely set off by a background of dark fir. This lower part of the glacier is urged on by an enormous precipice of ice above, descending from the upper parts of the mountain, and which increases in weight every year. It has pressed on not only through the forest, but over some cultivated fields, which are utterly lost. The poor woman whose land has thus been destroyed, came to present us a petition signed by the minister. They have placed a small wooden cross at the bottom, with the intention, no doubt, of arresting the progress of the evil which threatens to overwhelm many houses immediately before it, and indeed all human power can do nothing else towards saving them.

"The Glacier de Bossons," he continued, "marches almost in a straight line, though inclining a little down the valley. There is a declivity before it, all the way to the opposite side, which I think it must reach in less than twenty years, even if it were to advance at half the pace of the late three extraordinary years. Should it ever do so, it must cause a hundredfold the calamity that has just befallen the Valley of Bagne and Martigny, since it would flood the valley above, by stopping the Arve, and then deluge it below when it broke loose. The mischief it has already caused, and the much greater evils which it threatens, must raise in everyone a feeling of horror, in spite of the admiration excited by contemplating this picturesque phenomenon."

Although he was only an amateur geologist, the notations in Lyell's

journal show that his thinking was more professional than Werner's. Instead of vague speculation, he was, like Humboldt, interested in observing geologic forces in action. Humboldt had sat crouched on the edges of
the volcanoes of Latin America, watching the blue flames play in the
dark exteriors; Lyell noted the movement of the glaciers in the past
few years and predicted the future damage that might be expected from
their flow. Both men, reflecting the development of a more modern approach to the science, were unwilling to do what Werner had done, simply theorize on the basis of undemonstrable assumptions.

During most of his stay in Switzerland, Lyell continued his investigations into the geologic structure of the country. Then he left with his
family for Italy, where he spent more time in the art galleries and in visiting famous buildings than he did on geology. Yet the trip, by giving him
a conception of the variety of rock formations, helped enlarge his ideas
about geology.

The following year he was graduated with a second class in classical
honors and was elected a fellow of the Geological Society of London and
of the Linnaean Society. He did not leave Oxford right away but remained long enough to obtain an MA degree. Then, having given up
further thought of a literary career, he entered Lincoln's Inn and started
the study of law. This went slowly for him. His eyes were poor, and the
doctors advised him not to read too much. In the free time thus given to
him, he made numerous trips, one to Rome with his father and many
around Great Britain. In Italy he had little time for geologic investigations, but they formed the principal purpose of most of his other journeys. He went, for example, to Winchelsea, where he observed the lime-
stone formations and studied the actions of the sea against the coast, and
to the Isle of Wight, where he confirmed the ideas he had previously
held concerning the geology of Sussex. All this while, he was regularly
attending the meetings of the Geological Society and corresponding and
talking with the leading geologists of his country. Although still a law student by vocation, he was becoming more and more truly a geologist,
recognized by the other men in that field.

When he paid a visit to Paris in 1823, he carried with him letters of
introduction to many scientists, including Humboldt and Cuvier. "My
reception at Cuvier's last Saturday," he wrote to his father, "will make me
feel myself at liberty to attend his *soirées* every week, and they are a great
treat. He was very polite, and invited me to attend the Institute on Mon-
day. There he introduced me to several geologists and put me in an
excellent place for hearing."

Humboldt was also cordial to the young Englishman. After asking
Lyell about the reviews his latest work had received in Great Britain, he
presented him with a copy and invited him to go to Arago's observa-

tory. "On our way," Lyell wrote to his father, "Humboldt talked with great vivacity and force, of which I may perhaps give you some idea. 'No, Cuvier gives no lectures, and the reason, I regret to say, is that he is still a Politician—no, you were mistaken, if you imagined that the ministry have reached a pitch of ultraism beyond him. . . . That time is yet to come. You observe that his *soirées* are mostly attended by the English; the truth is, the French *savants* have in general cut him; his continual changing over to each new party that came into power at length disgusted almost all, and you know that it has been long a charge against men of science that they were pliant tools in the hands of princes, ministers, and might be turned which way they pleased. That such a man as Cuvier should have given a sanction to such an accusation was felt by all as a deep wound to the whole body. And what on earth was Cuvier to gain by intermeddling in politics? If his ambition could have reasonably flattered itself with the hope that his talents might one day open to him the heights of power, the attainment of *such an object* would have been an excuse for his having *the weakness to desire it*. But this he full knew was impossible in France. First, because he was a *Protestant,* and, secondly, because he was a man of *low family*. You well know with what contempt the old aristocracy of all countries are apt to regard all new men of whatever abilities. *We* feel that but too much in Germany, but *here* it is a principle now to carry such prejudices to the utmost length. Cuvier's situation was a proud one while he stood in the very foremost rank of men of science in France, but when he betrayed the weakness of coveting ribbons, crosses, titles, and Court favour, he fell down to the lowest among his new competitors.' "

This was the year that Cuvier, apparently without Humboldt's knowing it, turned down the ministry of interior, both because he was a Lutheran and because he did not wish politics to interfere with either his work or his nourishing of the dying liberalism of France. Humboldt's description of his colleague was both ungracious and untrue, but Lyell, in spite of his youthful inexperience, saw through Humboldt's remarks. "After what I have given you concerning Cuvier," he continued to his father, "I ought in justice to add my own opinion, which is that he is more liberal and independent than I believe most Frenchmen are. He dares to speak and often with praise of Napoleon, and before Frenchmen, who might, and no doubt do, turn it against him. We must not forget that Baron Humboldt and he are the two great rivals in science. . . . Humboldt's birth places him on the vantage ground, and Cuvier perhaps tries to compensate for this by a little political power. As for his *ratting* so often, *defendit numerus*. What French politician could throw the first stone at him? Humboldt's family is noble and ancient in Germany. His elder brother is a man now in great power there. His talents entitle him to regard with the contempt which he expresses, and I have no doubt *feels,* for *mere rank,* but we may say of him as Chateaubriand said of our English Peers, that he is well aware that when he gets too liberal, he is in no danger of losing the station and the advantages which his birth ensures for him." Yet it was Humboldt, for all the occasional sharpness of his tongue, who won Lyell's admiration. "There are few heroes," he wrote his father, "who lose so little by being approached as Humboldt. Of Cuvier this cannot be said."

One of Lyell's purposes in making this prolonged visit to France—it lasted for several months—was to learn French better, but he was handicapped in this by his inability to use his eyes much. Nevertheless, he profited greatly from his journey. He attended lectures at the Jardin des Plantes, traveled in the environs of Paris to study their geology, and met many men, in addition to Humboldt and Cuvier, who were important for a young scientist to know.

Although Lyell returned to the study of law when he came back to London, he did not neglect geology, which was becoming more and more his consuming interest, and he spent as much time as possible in the field, making trips to Bristol and through much of Scotland. Under these circumstances, his legal studies suffered, but he was finally admitted to the bar in 1825 and began active practice.

Whenever he could, he continued to attend meetings of scientific societies, corresponded with other geologists, and wrote several papers. One of these, published in the *Edinburgh Journal of Science,* dealt with a dike of serpentine cutting through a bed of sandstone. Another was on the clays and certain freshwater strata in the south of England. In 1827 he wrote a review of a work on the geology of central France. In this, he showed that, although he had slight respect for what he had called "cabinet geologists," he was fully aware that geology could not be learned entirely in the field, that much of the knowledge he wanted must come from books. His review also showed that by then he not only was thoroughly familiar with the work of Hutton and Playfair, but had checked their findings against his experience in the field and found them correct. In doing so, he had become convinced that the geology of the past could be interpreted by watching the geologic forces of the present in action, just as he had watched the glacier in Switzerland.

That year he also became familiar with the writings of Lamarck. In replying to a friend who had sent him a copy of the Frenchman's work, he described both his difficulty in finding time to carry on the studies that most interested him and the pleasure he had in reading Lamarck. "On my return from the circuit yesterday," he wrote, "I found your second letter, having received the first with Lamarck at Dorchester. You know that half my time is now spent at Sessions, Circuits, &c., and must not therefore be surprised when you receive no immediate answers to your correspondence, which I always receive with great pleasure. I devoured Lamarck *en voyage.* . . . His theories delighted me more than any novel I ever read, and much in the same way, for they address themselves to the imagination, at least of geologists who know the mighty inferences that would be deducible were they established by observations. But though I admire even his flights, and feel none of the *odium theologicum* which some modern writers in this country have visited him with, I confess I read him rather as I hear an advocate on the wrong side, to know what can be made of the case in good hands. I am glad that he has been courageous enough and logical enough to admit that his argument, if pushed as far as it must go, if worth anything, would prove that men may have come from the Ourang-Outang! But after all, what changes species may really undergo! How impossible will it be to distinguish and lay down a line, beyond which some of the so-called extinct species have never passed into recent ones. That the earth is quite as old as he supposes, has long been my creed, and I will try before six months are over to convert the readers of the Quarterly [*Quarterly Review*] to that heterodox opinion. I should like to discuss these matters with you . . . , but between law excursions and town studies, I have never a moment to spare."

Although Lyell, like others of his generation, could not accept the preposterous conclusion that men might have been descended from some form of primate, he had absorbed completely the other advanced ideas of his time. He agreed with Hutton and Playfair that the world was subject to continuous geologic action, thus dispensing with the catastrophes that Buffon had had to invent, and he believed with Lamarck that the earth must be much, much older than had previously been supposed. Lamarck had needed this longer time to account for the developments he thought had taken place in the species; Lyell needed it if geological change had been gradual, not abrupt.

The letter Lyell wrote to his friend thanking him for Lamarck's book also revealed the difficulty he was having pursuing on an equal basis both a vocation and an avocation. "I have never a moment to spare," he had told his friend. To his father, he wrote more explicitly about this problem and about his finances and future plans. "It is wonderful," he wrote, "how little mercy one's friends have on one's time, if one has no excuse deemed valid for declining unprofitable parties, or refereeships of papers, or secretaryships, &c. The circuit costs under 50 pounds, everything included. My purse would not have required replenishing for some time, but I am much obliged to you for anticipating my wants as usual. I find they diminish monthly, in proportion as I am more agreeably employed, and if with the willingness to work and industry that I now have, I had any chance of earning what I require by my own exertions, I should be without a care, as far as I am myself concerned. But to be willing without avail to work hard, and almost for nothing, is now the fate of many hundreds of barristers, and many millions of our labouring classes, and we must congratulate ourselves at not being among the latter. I am quite clear, from all that I have yet seen of the world, that there is most real independence in that class of society who, possessing moderate means, are engaged in literary or scientific hobbies; and that in ascending from them upwards, the feeling of independence decreases pretty nearly in the same ratio as the fortunes increase."

Lyell's future course was becoming clear in his mind. He would have liked to have become financially independent through the law, but the law was not sufficiently lucrative, unless he were to spend all his time at his practice. On the other hand, the Lyell family was among those fortunate enough to possess "moderate means" and therefore free to engage in "literary or scientific hobbies." Within a short time of writing this, he took the step that had been inevitable for several years: He abandoned the law and gave himself wholly to geology.

To prepare himself more thoroughly for the geology book that he hoped eventually to write, he toured the Continent in 1828 with Sir Roderick Impey Murchison. The son of a wealthy Scottish family, Murchison had entered the army and, at the age of sixteen, had fought in Spain. The end of the Napoleonic Wars made an army career unattractive to him, and he returned to England, where he spent most of his time fox hunting, becoming well known for his excellence at the sport. The idleness of this life, however, began to wear on him, and at the urging of a friend and of his wife, he decided in his early thirties to take up science. All the energy that he had previously poured into his play was now centered on his work, and in a surprisingly short time, he became a competent geologist and eventually an outstanding one. In 1828 he was thirty-six years old, able to afford the cost of travel, and anxious to learn more about geology. The idea that he and Lyell, together with Mrs. Murchison, should make a serious study of the geology of the Continent suited him perfectly.

The spring of 1828 found them in Paris, where Lyell's wide acquaintanceship opened many doors to them. After visiting people like Cuvier, they started south toward Marseilles. On his other trips, Lyell had been a tourist with an interest in geology; on this one, he was a geologist with a slight interest in tourism. Using Clermont-Ferrand, a city in Auvergne, as their headquarters, he and Murchison started an intensive investigation of the geology of that part of France. By six o'clock each morning they were hard at work, and they kept going all day. Murchison proved to be a fast and capable worker (he was also excellent at driving a bargain, and Lyell, with relief, left the business arrangements up to him), and Mrs. Murchison labeled their specimens and made sketches. It would have been impossible, Lyell wrote home, to have formed a better party.

Although they had been told before leaving Paris that the geology of Auvergne had already been well studied, this was not so, as they discovered when they began examining it at firsthand. Both men had agreed to concentrate on places where there was work to be done, rather than dash all over the Continent, so they remained in Auvergne for several weeks, studying in particular the freshwater formations and the volcanic rocks. Writing about their work and about Murchison, Lyell said, "He has much talent for original observation in geology, and is indefatigable, so that we make much way, and are thrown so much in the way of people, high and low, by means of our letters of introduction and our pursuits, that I am getting large materials, which I hope I shall find means of applying. Indeed, I think I am most profitably employed on this tour, and as long as things go on as well as they do now, I should be very sorry to leave off; particularly as, from our plan of operation, which is that of comparison of the structure of different parts of the country, we work on with continually increasing power, and in the last week have with the same exertion done at least twice as much in the way of discovery, and in enlarging our knowledge of what others had done, as in any preceding. I expect it will be at least three weeks before we can have done with Central France, and then we hope to work south towards Nice. . . ."

By the time they reached Nice, the expedition was running into difficulties. Although Murchison was an extraordinarily energetic person, he was dependent on medications and refused to take care of himself. He had already expressed some doubts about braving the heat of an Italian summer and had thought he might drop out before they had gone that far. Because he positively refused to rest (they were on a schedule that permitted only five hours of sleep a night), he finally broke down and was unable to go out into the field. The time was not, however, wasted. He and Lyell, using the information they had already collected, prepared a paper on the geology of central France, which they later presented to the Geological Society and subsequently published.

Lyell also took time to write his father about his future plans and about the way in which the trip had confirmed his ideas on geology. "Before we cross the Alps," he said, "and enter as it were upon a new expedition, I will send a few words on the fruits and adventures of our past tour, and the plans I wish still to realize before I return. . . . The whole tour has been rich, as I had anticipated (and in a manner which Murchison had not), in those analogies between existing nature and the effects of causes in remote eras which it will be the great object of my work to point out. I scarcely despair now, so much do these evidences of modern action increase upon us as we go south (towards the more recent seat of volcanic action), of *proving* the positive identity of causes now operating with those of former times. . . .

"But I feel, as Murchison says, that if I wish to get out, by November a year, such a book as will decidedly do me credit, and probably be a source of profit, it is to the south of the Po I should hasten, and before Christmas everything might be done. He said yesterday, 'At Milan or Verona, in three or four weeks or thereabouts, the operations connected with our paper will be over, but Sicily is for your views the great end: there are the most modern analogies, volcanic, marine, elevatory, subsiding, &c. I know the island as a soldier, and if you make straight for Etna, you will just time it right for work, for the season will be exactly suitable.' . . . I feel so decidedly that three months' more steady work will carry me through all, and tell greatly both to the despatch of finishing my work, as well as to the power I shall have in writing it, that I shall greatly repent if I do not do all in my power to accomplish it now."

As soon as Murchison had recovered, he and Lyell went to northern Italy, where they continued their studies until the end of September. At Verona they separated. Murchison and his wife planned to go to the Tyrol, while Lyell headed south toward Sicily. Although still working at a feverish pace, Lyell occasionally took time off to enjoy himself. At Padua he delighted in a religious satire painted by Giotto, showing a Pope, and a naked cardinal in hell, and at Parma he enjoyed the perplexity of the customs official who wished to tax his fossils. The official could not decide whether they were minerals or "vegetating things," and Lyell led him on. He wanted a receipt calling them "vegetating things" that he could show to his friends as a joke, but the soldiers and clerks in the office started laughing so hard that the official, after long consideration, labeled them minerals.

At Naples he expected to take a boat directly to Palermo, but the government had sent it off on a special mission. While he waited for its return, he climbed Vesuvius but found, to his regret, that a small, sputtering cone prevented him from descending into the crater to examine it more closely. He also visited the island of Ischia and collected a large quantity of fossils. After he had had them identified by a local geologist, he was ready to state categorically that the island had risen 2,600 feet during the period in which contemporary shellfish had lived in the Mediterranean. As he wrote to his sister, "My wish was to find this peninsula get younger and younger as I traveled towards the active volcanoes, and it has hitherto been all I could wish. . . ."

As soon as he reached Sicily, he prepared to climb Mount Aetna. "Old

G. [a geologist with whom he was staying] started me in the middle of a coolish night, by moonlight, so that we reached by daybreak the highest part of the woody region. There a fire was made of boughs from the old chestnuts and oaks, which, though one or two thousand years old, stand on *modern* lavas of the volcano. I had taken my tea kettle, and, as a preservative against the cold, made a breakfast of hot tea. . . . We did not cross much snow before Casa Inglese (9,000 feet high): then we ascended the cone. I had determined to think with Ferrara, who has published the best guidebook of Sicily, that the sickness felt from the rarity of air on the summit of Etna was all nonsense, but I had no sooner ascended 200 feet from the hut called 'Casa Inglese,' than my head ached, and I felt squeamish. My guide said, 'We must go slower; I have known many to vomit violently during this part of the ascent.' The fact is, you go up gradually to the foot of the cone, your lungs get pretty well weaned of breathing more condensed air; but when you rise almost perpendicularly from 9,000 to 10,000 feet, the air within you is so condensed, compared to the atmosphere you enter, that you are ready to burst. . . . Inside the crater, near the lip, were huge masses of ice, between which and the . . . lava of the crater issued hot sulphurous vapours, which I breathed in copiously, and for six hours after I could not, even after eating and drinking, get the horrid taste out of my mouth, for my lungs had got full of it. The wind was so high, that the guide held my hat while I drew; but though the head was cold, my feet got so hot in the cinders, that I was often alarmed that my boots would be burnt." On his descent, Lyell's friends told him that, because it was so late in the year, he was fortunate in having been able to complete the climb, and the very next morning his muleteer woke him with cries to look at the mountain. It was one mass of snow.

Except for its geology, Lyell found Sicily depressing. Only a short time before, highwaymen had been so numerous the government had moved in with a strong force of military policemen and executed bandits without trial. (Lyell's muleteer had seen twenty-six shot in one day.) Such measures were needed to impose order, Lyell thought, but because of the extreme poverty and misery of the people, they had every reason to turn into robbers. At least two-thirds of the land, which belonged to the church and to the nobility, was badly cultivated, the taxes were exorbitant, and the roads were terrible, either laid through bogs or so filled with rocks that the horses' hooves often became wedged between them. To add to Lyell's discomfort, the inns were unbelievably bad, and he often searched for some private citizen who might put him up. Even this was not satisfactory. In one town, when the innkeeper wanted him to sleep in the dirty barn, Lyell walked out into the street and asked the first peasant he met to give him a room. But he later wrote his sister, "I will employ a few minutes, if but to tell you that in the honest peasant's bed above mentioned I slept not, though tired, ten minutes in the whole night. They had added, at my asking for a covering, an old blanket, in which were more fleas than all the insects in our collection, and I suppose they had starved since last winter, for the next morning I was marked all over from head to foot with red spots like one of the Ancient Britons with his body painted. I never passed such a night since I had the measles at Sarum [Salisbury, where he had gone to school], yet the host and Rosario [his muleteer] thought it a capital joke, and I heard them laughing about the 'pulce' having found a piece of 'carne fresca,' and they gave me pretty clearly to understand that they thought one who could not stand a flea-bite was unfit to travel. Rosario must needs pull out the blanket to show where they were sleeping next day, and they were in the thousands, yet the owner and his wife use this blanket without inconvenience when it is cold." Lyell's only consolations were the two lessons he finally taught his muleteer: "First, not to bring in the salt in his hands, often none of the cleanest; and secondly, not to stuff the meat remaining after dinner, and intended cold for next morning, into my slippers, without at least some paper around it."

It was a relief, therefore, to reach the relatively civilized town of Palermo, where he took a boat back to Naples. Uncomfortable as it had been, however, the five-week journey through Sicily had been successful in terms of the knowledge he had gained. From Naples he wrote to Murchison, assessing this part of his journey and outlining his future plans, "The results of my Sicilian expedition exceed my warmest expectations in the way of modern analogies. I will tell fairly that it is at present of no small consequence to me to get a respectable sum for my volume,—not only to cover extra expenses for present and future projected campaigns, but because my making my hobby pay its additional costs, which it entails, will alone justify my pursuing it with a mind sufficiently satisfied with itself, and so as to feel independent, and free to indulge in the enthusiasm necessary for success. . . . My work is in part written, and all planned," he continued. "It will not pretend to give even an abstract of all that is known in geology, but it will endeavour to establish the *principle of reasoning* in the science; and all my geology will come in as an illustration of my views of those principles, and as evidence strengthening the system necessarily arising out of the admission of such principles, which, as you know, are neither more nor less than that *no causes whatever* have from the earliest time to which we can look back, to the present, ever acted, but those *now acting;* and that they never acted with different degrees of energy from that which they now exert." If he could accomplish his plan, he would revolutionize geology.

I V

He remained for a while in Rome, studying various formations and talking to other geologists, then visited Siena and Genoa, which had suffered from an earthquake only six months before. From there, in the bitter cold of February, he crossed the Alps by diligence. Two days previously an avalanche had blocked the road; but fifty workmen cleared it, making the final breakthrough just as Lyell arrived. He stayed for a short time at Geneva to consult with other scientists, after which he moved to Paris and saw some of his old friends, including Cuvier once again. By the end of February, 1830, he was back in London.

The Geological Society took up much of his time. Although more scientists were beginning to think, as Lyell did, that geology was a continuous process, many still did not. At one meeting, a member proposed that there were three deluges before the one in which Noah figured. This, he said, explained everything. And Lyell's former professor of geology at Oxford clung tenaciously to a series of "catastrophes," although greatly enlarging the number that Buffon had admitted. But others were slowly becoming converts. Adam Sedgwick, one of the more noted contemporary geologists, returned from an expedition with Murchison to the basin of the Danube. He "throws overboard all the diluvian hypothesis," Lyell wrote delightedly, "is vexed he ever lost two years time about such a complete humbug; says he lost two years by having also started a Wernerian."

But Lyell did not permit the discussions and arguments at the society to divert him from his principal work. Interested as he was in gaining converts for his new geology, he knew this could best be done, not by debating with individuals, but by publishing his book. As the months passed, he remained for the most part in London, rewriting and correcting the draft about which he had told Murchison. Even when he went that October to the family place in Scotland—Lyell's father had returned there— his thoughts were constantly on geology, and by early December, 1829, he was able to report to a friend that, although he was "bound hand and foot" and obviously weary of the pace he had kept, Volume I would be completed by the end of the year and that Volume II was "in a manner written, but will require great recasting."

To his pleasure, his eyes held up under the strain. He used an amanuensis and, with this assistance, had not strained his eyes and could see as well as when he had first gone to school. By early February, 1830, he wrote a friend that "I have only corrected the press to page 80, and get on slowly, but with satisfaction to myself. How much more difficult it is to write for general readers than for the scientific world, yet half our

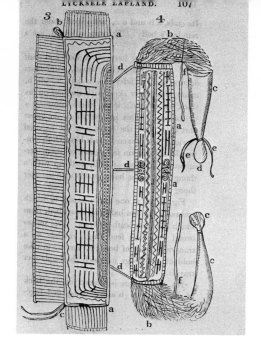

Carl Linnaeus. As explorers pushed further into strange lands and scientists brought back more and more specimens to Europe, the older methods of classifying the material proved inadequate. Linnaeus developed a system of classification that has since been replaced but that served to restore order at a critical period. He also invented the binomial nomenclature that is still in use.

Drawing by Linnaeus. One of Linnaeus' first attempts to win fame as a scientist was to undertake a one-man expedition through Lapland. As he traveled, he made notes and sketches of the fauna, flora, geology, and native customs. This drawing of his shows a saddlecloth and harness for a reindeer.

Uppsala Garden. 1749. When Linnaeus first went to the university at Uppsala, Sweden, its famous botanical garden had fallen into disrepair. Nevertheless, it served him in developing his system of classification. Later, when he returned to the university as a professor, the garden was put under his care, and he restored it.

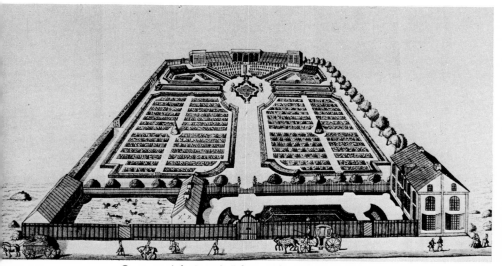

Courtesy of the Burndy Library (Photos by J. P. Holmes)

Georges Buffon. A competent man of affairs, as well as a scientist, Buffon used his skills to enlarge the Jardin du Roi at Paris and to popularize the study of science. He recognized the significance of fossils, and his views on the history of the earth were so advanced that they brought him into conflict with the church.

The confusion of the early attempts at classification is illustrated by this chart of Buffon's in which he tried to arrange breeds of dogs. He divided them into two principal classes: sheep dogs and running dogs. His approach broke down completely when he tried to apply it to larger groups of animals.

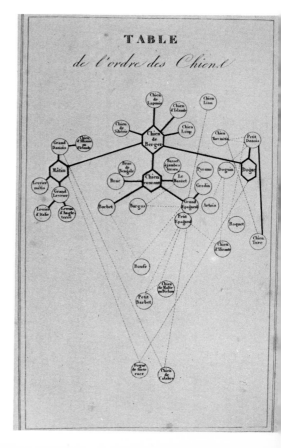

Buffon believed that the expression of an idea was almost as important as the idea itself and that although the idea could be borrowed, the style could not. Style, he pointed out, was integral to the writer. The numerous corrections in this manuscript of Buffon's illustrate the care with which he wrote.

At first Buffon was derisive of Linnaeus' system of classification, calling it unnecessarily complicated. The simpler method, he believed, was to start with the more familiar birds and animals, then to advance to the less familiar. Thus, in this illustration he had the artist group together a horse, an ass, and a bull. He soon found that this approach to classification was impractical.

Buffon intended to cover the whole of natural history in a single book, but his views on the formation of the earth were so important that eventually they were printed separately. This is the title page from the first edition. Buffon denied that the Creation and the Deluge had alone shaped the earth and insisted that other events must also have occurred.

LES ÉPOQUES

DE

LA NATURE,

PAR MONSIEUR

LE COMTE DE BUFFON,

Intendant du Jardin & du Cabinet du Roi, de l'Académie Françoise, de celle des Sciences, &c.

TOME PREMIER.

A PARIS,

DE L'IMPRIMERIE ROYALE.

M. DCC. LXXX.

Courtesy of the Burndy Library (Photos by J. P. Holmes)

Jean Lamarck. After an undistinguished career in the French army and long efforts to become a professional botanist, Lamarck finally secured an appointment at the Jardin des Plantes as professor of invertebrates, a subject about which little was known. As a result of his studies, he developed a theory of evolution. Because it contained numerous mistakes, such as the belief that acquired characteristics could be inherited, it was widely ridiculed. Nevertheless, it was a pioneering effort.

Linnaeus' system of classification was a great improvement over every system devised previously, but he failed with the invertebrates, which he lumped into one group that he called "insects and worms." Lamarck finally developed a more effective classification, which he set forth in *Système des Animaux sans Vertèbres*. The copy from which this title page was reproduced was one of the author's presentation copies.

SYSTÊME

DES

ANIMAUX SANS VERTÈBRES,

O U

TABLEAU général des classes, des ordres et des genres de ces animaux;

Présentant leurs caractères essentiels et leur distribution, d'après la considération de leurs rapports naturels et de leur organisation, et suivant l'arrangement établi dans les galeries du Muséum d'Hist. Naturelle, parmi leurs dépouilles conservées;

Précédé du discours d'ouverture du Cours de Zoologie, donné dans le Muséum National d'Histoire Naturelle l'an 8 de la République.

PAR J. B. LAMARCK,

De l'Institut National de France, l'un des Professeurs-Administrateurs du Muséum d'Hist. Naturelle, des Sociétés d'Histoire Naturelle, des Pharmaciens et Philomatique de Paris, de celle d'Agriculture de Seine et Oise, etc.

A PARIS,

Chez { L'AUTEUR, au Muséum d'Hist. Naturelle; DETERVILLE, Libraire, rue du Battoir, n° 16, quartier de l'Odéon.

AN IX — 1801.

Courtesy of the Burndy Library (Photos by J. P. Holmes)

Georges Cuvier. Working with the collections at the Jardin des Plantes in Paris, Cuvier developed his theory of the correlation of the parts—that each part of the body supplemented the others to form a whole. Using this theory, he was able to reconstruct a whole body even when he had only a few fragmentary bones. This work laid the basis for modern paleontology.

This plate, showing fossil remains found near Paris, was used by Cuvier to illustrate his work in paleontology. Although he had large collections at his disposal, he could find in them no evidence that evolution had occurred. Consequently he became a leading opponent of Lamarck.

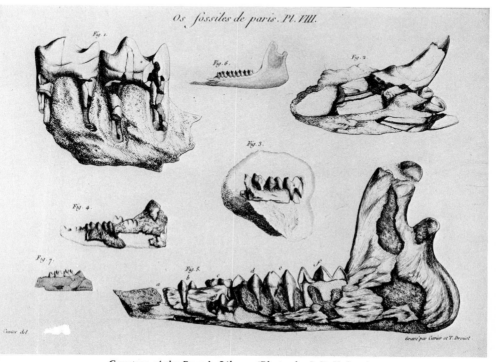

Courtesy of the Burndy Library (Photos by J. P. Holmes)

John James Audubon. One of the best-known figures in American ornithology, Audubon first attempted to become a businessman on the frontier. Only after an unsuccessful career did he turn to the study of birds on a professional basis. After years of work, he finally finished *The Birds of America,* which remains a classic. This photograph is by Brady.

Courtesy of the
New-York Historical Society,
New York City

Although Alexander Wilson was the pioneer in American ornithology, Audubon's name is more widely known. Both men were self-taught artists, but of the two, Audubon was incomparably the better. Wilson's pictures remained two-dimensional, but Audubon achieved his ambition of creating paintings in which the birds, background, and sky blended into an artistic whole.

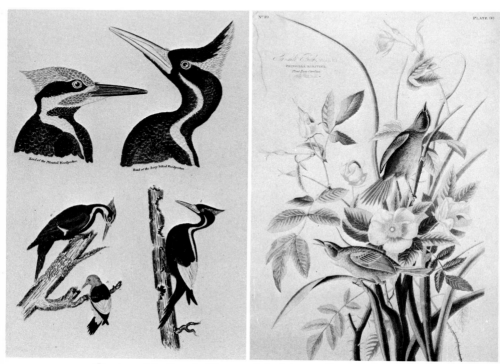

Courtesy of the Burndy Library and the Princeton University Library

As a surveyor, William Smith noticed that strata were repeated in the various places that he worked and that he could predict the fossils they contained. This discovery created the foundation for modern stratigraphy. In the book whose title page is reproduced here, Smith illustrated the characteristic fossils by which certain strata could be identified.

Charles Lyell. As a geologist, Lyell realized that the forces shaping the earth today must be the same as those that had shaped it in the past. He stressed this theory of continuity in his book *Principles of Geology*. Although he had difficulty accepting Darwin's theory of evolution, his work inspired much of Darwin's thinking.

Lyell's subtitle, "An Attempt to Explain the Former Changes of the Earth's Surface by Reference to Causes Now in Action," contains the essence of his geologic theory. His book, *Principles of Geology*, went through many editions during his lifetime. This is the title page of the first edition of the first volume.

Courtesy of the Burndy Library (Photos by J. P. Holmes)

Charles Darwin. One of the world's foremost scientists, Darwin's early career showed so little promise that his father despaired of his future. But once on board H.M.S. *Beagle,* his intellectual curiosity was aroused, and he began to think about the origin of species. Out of these thoughts came his theory of evolution, which revolutionized man's attitude toward his place in nature.

Plan of H.M.S. *Beagle.* The *Beagle* was a small vessel with confined quarters. Because it often remained on the same coast for weeks at a time while conducting its surveying, Darwin was able to go ashore. It was during these periods that he did the studying and collecting that provided him with the basic ideas for his theory of evolution.

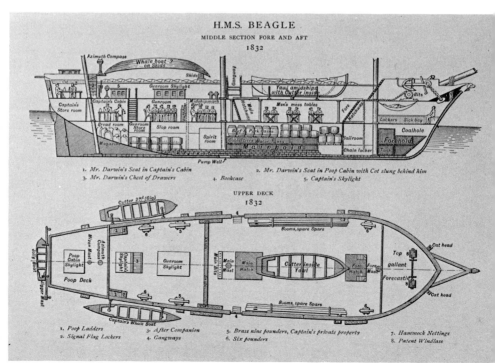

No provision had been made for H.M.S. *Beagle* to study natural history, but the captain decided to take along an unsalaried naturalist. Darwin accepted the appointment, and from this voyage came the basic ideas that later enabled him to develop his theory of evolution. In this picture, the *Beagle* is in the Strait of Magellan.

During its cruise off the coast of South America, H.M.S. *Beagle* often stopped, permitting the captain and Darwin to go ashore. This is an encampment of Patagonian Indians they visited. The picture appears in the captain's account of the voyage.

THE ORIGIN OF SPECIES

BY MEANS OF NATURAL SELECTION,

OR THE

PRESERVATION OF FAVOURED RACES IN THE STRUGGLE FOR LIFE.

By CHARLES DARWIN, M.A.,

FELLOW OF THE ROYAL, GEOLOGICAL, LINNÆAN, ETC., SOCIETIES;
AUTHOR OF 'JOURNAL OF RESEARCHES DURING H. M. S. BEAGLE'S VOYAGE
ROUND THE WORLD.'

LONDON:
JOHN MURRAY, ALBEMARLE STREET.
1859.

John Murray, Darwin's publisher, looked forward to only a modest sale for Darwin's book, but the first edition, published in 1859, sold out immediately. In spite of Murray's slight expectations, it quickly gained recognition as one of the great scientific works of all time.

Courtesy of the Burndy Library (Photos by J. P. Holmes)

Alfred Wallace. While Darwin was writing his theory of evolution, he received a paper from Wallace, who had come to the same general conclusions about the origin of species. Troubled by the ethics of what to do, Darwin finally published Wallace's paper simultaneously with one of his own, thus recognizing Wallace as the co-discoverer of evolution.

The financial success of Wallace's expeditions depended on the quantity and the rarity of the specimens he obtained for sale in Europe. He therefore often employed native hunters to help him. This picture, drawn under his direction, shows natives collecting birds of paradise on the islands of Aru.

Courtesy of the Burndy Library
(Photos by J. P. Holmes)

While in the Moluccas, Wallace unknowingly slept within a few feet of a python that had coiled up in his house. One of the workers on the plantation agreed to remove it. The struggle that followed was described by Wallace, and an artist drew this picture to illustrate it.

VESTIGES

OF

THE NATURAL HISTORY

OF

CREATION.

LONDON:

JOHN CHURCHILL, PRINCES STREET, SOHO.

M DCCC XLIV.

A Chambers title page. Because he was afraid of retaliations against his printing business, Robert Chambers preferred to remain anonymous when he published this book about evolution in 1844. Although scientifically unsound, it stimulated Wallace's thinking on the origin of species.

Thomas Huxley. The publication of *Origin of Species* brought forth vehement protests from both scientists and laymen, many of them bitter against Darwin personally for upsetting the established order. One of Darwin's ablest defenders was Thomas Huxley, a noted zoologist and skillful writer. His rebuttal of the attacks against Darwin helped gain relatively early acceptance for evolution.

Gregor Mendel. Mendel's laws are today taught in every elementary biology course, because they form the basis of modern genetics. At the time of his death, however, both he and his work were unknown. Many years elapsed between the time when his short, but revolutionary, paper was published and when it was discovered simultaneously by three research scientists.

Versuche über Pflanzen-Hybriden.

Von

Gregor Mendel.

(Vorgelegt in den Sitzungen vom 8. Februar und 8. März 1865.)

Einleitende Bemerkungen.

Künstliche Befruchtungen, welche an Zierpflanzen desshalb vorgenommen wurden, um neue Farben-Varianten zu erzielen, waren die Veranlassung zu den Versuchen, die her besprochen werden sollen. Die auffallende Regelmässigkeit, mit welcher dieselben Hybridformen immer wiederkehrten, so oft die Befruchtung zwischen gleichen Arten geschah, gab die Anregung zu weiteren Experimenten, deren Aufgabe es war, die Entwicklung der Hybriden in ihren Nachkommen zu verfolgen.

Dieser Aufgabe haben sorgfältige Beobachter, wie Kölreuter, Gärtner, Herbert, Lecocq, Wichura u. a. einen Theil ihres Lebens mit unermüdlicher Ausdauer geopfert. Namentlich hat Gärtner in seinem Werke „die Bastarderzeugung im Pflanzenreiche" sehr schätzbare Beobachtungen niedergelegt, und in neuester Zeit wurden von Wichura gründliche Untersuchungen über die Bastarde der Weiden veröffentlicht. Wenn es noch nicht gelungen ist, ein allgemein giltiges Gesetz für die Bildung und Entwicklung der Hybriden aufzustellen, so kann das Niemanden Wunder nehmen, der den Umfang der Aufgabe kennt und die Schwierigkeiten zu würdigen weiss, mit denen Versuche dieser Art zu kämpfen haben. Eine endgiltige Entscheidung kann erst dann erfolgen, bis Detail-Versuche aus den verschiedensten Pflanzen-Familien vorliegen. Wer die Ar-

1*

After he had completed his experiments in breeding peas, Mendel reported his findings to his local natural history society, which printed this paper in its proceedings. Although it contained the key to variation in species for which the evolutionists were looking, it remained unnoticed for many years.

Courtesy of the Burndy Library (Photos by J. P. Holmes)

savants think that to write *popularly* would be a condescension to which they might bend if they would.

"I daresay I shall not keep my resolution," he continued in much the spirit of Linnaeus and Newton, "but I will try to do it firmly, that when my book is attacked . . . I will not go to the expense of time of pamphleteering. I shall work steadily on at Vol. II., and afterwards, if the work succeeds, at edition 2, and I have sworn to myself that I will not go to the expense of giving time to combat in controversy. It is interminable work."

Yet he was not quite so self-assured and self-controlled as he pretended to be. In June he wrote to a friend who had been asked to prepare an article on the book for the *Quarterly Review* and revealed that he was just as nervous as any author. He did not want to influence the reviewer—indeed, he praised him as a "disinterested umpire"—but he could not resist pointing out what was his original work, what he had borrowed from other scientists, whose thinking had helped him, and just how much. Then dropping some of the reticence with which he had begun, he stated his fundamental philosophy. "Probably," he wrote, "there was a beginning—it is a metaphysical question, worthy a theologian—probably there will be an end. Species, as you say, have begun and ended—but the analogy is faint and distant. Perhaps it is an analogy, but all I say is, there are, as Hutton said, 'no signs of a beginning, no prospect of an end.' . . . All I ask is, that at any given period of the past, don't stop inquiry when puzzled by refuge to a 'beginning,' which is all one with 'another state of nature,' as it appears to me. But there is no harm in your attacking me, provided you point out that it is the proof I deny, not the probability of a beginning. Mark, too, my argument, that we are called upon to say in each case, 'which is now most probable, my ignorance of all possible effects of existing causes,' or that 'the beginning' is the cause of this puzzling phenomenon? It is not the beginning I look for, but proofs of a *progressive* state of existence in the globe. . . ."

Instead of waiting for the publication date, Lyell left England and went to the south of France, visited the Pyrenees, and traveled in Spain. The mountains so fascinated him that in July he wrote his sister that he cared less about the "birth of my book" than he had, but he was still far from indifferent and was anxious to know whether it had yet come out, and on his return to France, he was still worrying about the reviews he might receive.

He stayed in Paris for five weeks, during which he employed an expert to help him learn to identify shells. They worked with a collection of 35,000, representing 8,500 species, and Lyell was amazed at how much he could learn in so short a time, following the system of classification devised by Lamarck. While he was engaged in this work, he began to receive encouraging reports from John Murray, his publisher. During the first three months, 650 copies of the book had been sold, and Murray thought that a truly good article, such as the one written for the *Quarterly Review,* would greatly accelerate the sales. "It seems that, for the first three months," Lyell wrote, "they sold fifty copies a week, and since that I have heard no bulletin, except that the demand is constant. Murray declared, that if I would give him vol. ii in six months, before half the purchasers of the first had either forgotten it, lost it, or gone abroad, died, &c., he was convinced that in twelve months from the present time not a single copy of either volume would be unsold. With this encouragement I shall be glad to persevere. . . ." And a few days later, he wrote his sister, "I have pretty good news to tell you about my volumes. . . . The booksellers assure me that if the latter part of my work is as popular and readable as the first, it will prove an annuity to me."

Even Lyell could not have dared hope for the success that his book enjoyed, for it went through edition after edition during his lifetime. Summarizing its contents, he later wrote, "In the 'Principles' a systematic account is given of the operations of inorganic causes, such as rivers, springs, tides, currents, volcanoes, and earthquakes; the effects of all being particularly considered, with a view to illustrate geological phenomena." By showing that the geologic past could be read by studying the geologic present, Lyell had dispensed with the hypothetical theories of the past and placed the science on a realistic basis. The geologic process was continuous. The forces acting in Lyell's day, and before his eyes, were the forces that had acted in the past. The waves were wasting away some shores and building others with fresh deposits. Streams were eroding mountains and creating deltas. Volcanoes were exploding as they had always done. There was no longer any need to create imaginary catastrophes to explain the past. This could be done simply by using observable forces, provided, of course, there was sufficient time for them to act. Time had bothered Buffon. He knew that the amount permitted by the church for the history of the earth was clearly inadequate, but even he had not envisioned the length of time needed, if Lyell's theories were correct. An enormous amount was required for the normal geologic forces to do their vast work.

Many of the reviewers recognized the importance of the book. To advertise later editions, Lyell could quote comments like the *Quarterly Review*'s: "We hail with the greatest satisfaction the appearance of Mr. Lyell's work, which henceforward, we can hardly doubt, will mark the beginning of a new era in Geology. The title of the book shows that it is an attempt to place the study of the science on its true basis—to explain the former changes of the earth's surface by reference to causes now in operation." And it received similar praise in the United States, where *The Transactions of the Geological Society of Pennsylvania,* for example, said in part: "Its appearance will always form an epoch in the history of Geology. Up to that time the doctrine which assumed the causes of changes, whether of a destroying or productive character, actually in progress on the surface of the globe, to be utterly inadequate to explain, scarcely even to illustrate, the earlier changes of which that surface exhibits such striking traces, held almost undisputed sway in the geological circles. Mr. Lyell, applying himself to the elucidation of the existing causes of change, and their probable influence on the older geological formations, with an industry and research which are joined to the happiest powers of description and command of language, has produced a Work not only of the highest interest to the scientific world, but of the most popular and fascinating nature to the general reader."

Not everyone was so enthusiastic. That year, when Lyell was being considered as professor of geology at King's College, London, an appointment that was to be decided by three clergymen and two laymen, the clergymen were dubious. Lyell said that "the prelates declared 'that they considered some of my doctrines startling enough, but could not find that they were come by otherwise than in a straightforward manner, and (as *I* appeared to think) logically deducible from the facts, so that whether the facts were true or not, or my conclusions logical or otherwise, there was no reason to infer that I had made my theory from any hostile feeling toward revelation.' " And an American geologist wrote Murchison "that in the United States he should hardly dare in a review to approve of my doctrines, such a storm would the orthodox raise against him!"

He had some misgivings about accepting the appointment at King's College for fear its duties would interrupt his independent work but thought he would at least try a teaching career. Although the book showed every sign of doing well financially, he was not yet sure enough of it, particularly since he was planning to be married. During the year 1831 he followed a busy schedule, lecturing to his classes, making more trips to seek additional evidence in support of his theory, attending meetings of the Geological Society, and attempting to finish the *Principles.* Those who read the manuscript of the second volume were excited by it, and Lyell, instead of completing it at once, decided to divide it and make two volumes of it, so that it could come out sooner. But as he had feared, the extra load of his teaching was proving too much. On New Year's Eve, 1831, he wrote in the journal that he had started keeping for the woman to whom he had become engaged: "If I could secure a handsome profit in my work, I should feel more free from all responsibility in cutting my cables at King's College. Do not think that my views in regard to science are taking a money-making, mercantile turn. What I want is, to secure the power of commanding *time* to advance my knowledge and fame, and at the same time to feel that in so doing I am not abandoning the interests of my family, and earning something more substantial than fame. I am never so happy as when at the end of a week I feel I have employed every day in a manner that will tell to the rest of my life. . . ." This latter wish, always to be constructively employed, was being fulfilled by his energetic character. His other, to earn enough from his book to gain independence, looked as though it might come true also. For in January, 1832, when the second volume of the *Principles* appeared, it was accompanied by a new edition of the first. The original edition was already sold out.

V

In 1830, the year the first volume of the *Principles* appeared, Lyell turned thirty-three. For so young a man, his career had been exceptionally distinguished and successful. He had finished his university education, become a practicing lawyer, abandoned that profession for geology, mastered his new subject, and produced an outstanding book. This achievement could be attributed in part, to his clear and excellent intellect, in part to his willingness to work hard (he could not keep from working), and in part to his even temperament. He was one of those people who are rarely flustered, always know what they are doing, and never exhaust themselves emotionally. Linnaeus, in his later years, gave himself up to the bitter thoughts contained in *Nemesis divina*; Humboldt, a romantic, continually sought political liberalism; Cuvier gave much of his time to politics, so much that he was criticized for it. But Lyell had only one basic interest: geology. When he traveled, it was in pursuit of geologic knowledge; when he worked, it was on geology. He had only a gentleman's interest in politics, he would visit an art gallery or a castle if he had time, and he had a wide circle of friends, all of whom seemed to enjoy his company. But geology was his consuming passion.

His lectures went well, and he wrote enthusiastically that "they were splendidly attended. I have shown the public, and made the discovery myself, that I can do the thing, and it may yet provide traveling money. But I shall not give much time to it, at least for several years. When the course was over, I received from some of the class whom I never saw, most enthusiastic letters, expressive of their admiration and gratitude. This is worth much," and then he added with upper-class British reticence, "especially as they had the good taste not to applaud in the theatre."

In 1833, Lyell married Mary Horner, daughter of a Scottish geologist

and a member of the commission appointed to study child labor. Together they traveled on the Continent on another of Lyell's endless geologic explorations, but on his return he found the pressure was telling
on him. In the spring of 1833 he wrote to a friend, "Like all the world, I
have had the influenza, which went through my house, servants, visitor
and all, save Mrs. Lyell, who remained well to nurse us. This *embarras,*
and getting *out* vol. iii. and *up* two courses of lectures, must be my excuse for not having written to you or anyone. My introductory lecture at
the Royal Institution last Thursday was attended by 250 persons. This
morning, the first King's College lecture by 200 persons, or, as some
compute, 250. Nevertheless, I doubt whether I shall have any class, scarce
any having as yet entered; and Jones, the Professor of Political Economy,
a very eloquent man, having had an audience of 200 the first day, had
on the third not *one individual,* and now he goes on lecturing to five,
which I would not." His worries were not completely justified. The enrollment proved to be somewhat larger than he had anticipated, but the
college forbade women to attend, for fear they would distract the other
students. This reduced the total to 15 students, not enough, in Lyell's
opinion, to justify the time. The series of seven lectures that he gave
at the Royal Institution fared better. He rarely had an audience of
fewer than 250, more than half of which were women. "But," he wrote,
"I do not fancy this want of concentration of my lecturing labors, and
shall either settle upon some one theatre, or stick to writing, which I believe is most improving and profitable in every way."

The *Principles* continued to sell well, and he was pleased that summer, when he was in Paris, to find that the French were also reading it.
The first two volumes, he was told, had been more than they could understand, but the last volume was proving popular. Lyell hoped that a
French translation could be published, but he discovered that in
France "everyone writes, and no one reads or buys." Most French scientists depended on their book sales not in France, but in Germany and
England. Yet even without a French edition, Lyell was financially able to
concentrate more and more on his studies and writing and spend less
time on diversionary activities.

In 1834 he was, therefore, free to travel in Scandinavia, for he thought
that he "was not justified in writing any more until I had done all in my
power to ascertain the truth in regard to 'the great northern phenomenon,' as the gradual rise of part of Sweden has been very naturally
called." He did not take his wife with him, because he considered the
trip too rough for her to make, particularly since he expected to spend
most of his time in the field. He visited Lund, where Linnaeus had first
studied, a fact he noted in his journal, as well as Uppsala. Linnaeus'

gardens were well kept up, his daughters delighted in showing their father's house to visitors, and the lecture room where he had given his courses was displayed to those who wanted to see it.

Both the geology and the countryside of Sweden appealed to Lyell, and his only frustration lay in the conduct of his interpreter, a man named Johnson, who did not understand Lyell's habit of getting things done quickly. "Johnson, who gets on in many respects very well," Lyell wrote, "is so slow at getting up in the morning, that I have taken up the thing in earnest, having lost on the whole journey several days by want of method in posting. I have ordered the carriage to be greased overnight, and have got up some phrases in Swedish, to order the man myself. He is astonished to see already the difference; but I will show him yet, when I have a few more words, that we can do a stage at least more in the same day's work, for when the horses come he has a number of things to do, and the bill is never paid." Lyell, always thrifty with time, would not allow anyone to waste a moment.

Back in England again, he continued his now normal routine, working on revised editions of his book (it was proving enormously popular, and he was continually occupied with bringing it up to date as he gathered new knowledge), and taking trips throughout Europe to learn more about its geology. But all the while he was bothered by a question that was concerning other scientists, too—the origin of new species. Pondering this problem, which still deeply puzzled the nineteenth century, he wrote to a friend at some length, "In regard to the origination of new species, I am very glad to find that you think it probable that it may be carried on through the intervention of intermediate causes. I left this rather to be inferred, not thinking it worthwhile to offend a certain class of persons by embodying in words what would only be speculation. But the German critics have attacked me vigorously, saying that by the impugning of the doctrine of spontaneous generation, and substituting nothing in its place, I have left them nothing but the direct and miraculous intervention of the First Cause, as often as a new species is introduced, and hence I have overthrown my own doctrine. . . . I have not wasted time in any controversy with them or others, except so far as modifying in new editions some opinions or expressions, and fortifying others, and by this means I have spared a great deal of ink-shed, and have upon the whole been very fairly treated by the critics. When first I came to the notion, which I never saw expressed elsewhere, though I have no doubt it had all been thought out before, of a succession of extinction of species, of creation of new ones, going on perpetually now, and through an indefinite period of the past, and to continue for ages to come, all in accommodation to the changes which must continue in the inanimate and inhabitable earth, the idea struck me as the grandest which I had ever conceived, so far as regards the attributes of the Presiding Mind. For one can in imagination summon before us a small part at least of the circumstances that must be contemplated and fore-known, before it can be decided what powers and qualities a new spe-cies must have in order to enable it to endure for a given time, and play its part in due relation to all other beings destined to coexist with it, before it dies out. . . . But I cannot do justice to this train of specula-tion in a letter, and will only say that it seems to me to offer a more beau-tiful subject for reasoning and reflecting on, than the notion of great batches of new species all coming in, and afterwards going out at once." Like other significant thinkers of his time, Lyell was overwhelmed by the problem. He could not accept the Creation and the Deluge described in the Bible, he could not believe in spontaneous generation, but having eliminated these, he could also find no substitute. One thing he did know, however: the subject was dangerous. To become directly involved, to do more than infer his thoughts, would arouse the critics and take time and energy from his real work—geology.

He continued to follow a pattern of traveling abroad, returning to Great Britain to revise his book, and exchanging ideas with other scien-tists. One whom he particularly favored was Charles Darwin, whose work on coral reefs especially interested him. Darwin shared Lyell's basic be-lief that the geologic forces that had acted in the past were those that were acting in modern times, and the two men often came to the sup-port of each other during public discussions.

As he revised the *Principles,* Lyell decided to add a new section, then thought he would bring it out as a separate book, *Elements of Geology.* It was intended, he said in his preface, to enable his readers "to follow more easily the meaning of that part of the 'Principles' in which an at-tempt is made to point the bearing on geology of the modern changes of the earth. . . ." This book, which became a standard handbook on paleontology and strata, proved immediately popular and went through six editions in Lyell's lifetime. He had now realized his ambition to support his work through his writing. Therefore, in 1841, when he re-ceived an invitation to give twelve lectures at the Lowell Institute in Bos-ton, he was in a position, not only to accept, but to use the occasion for an extensive tour of the United States and Canada.

After landing at Halifax, he went to Boston for a short visit and then by way of New Haven to New York City, which he found amazingly clean compared to some of the cities of England. (He attributed this to the only fuels available—anthracite coal and wood.) The Hudson River earned high praise from him for its beauty, and he was amused by Al-bany's reaction to the state's natural history survey. Because so many Pennsylvanians had grown rich mining coal, the New Yorkers thought they could, too, and many of them had been investing heavily in buying land and digging exploratory holes. These people were furious when the state's geologists reported that no coal was likely to be found.

The newness of the nation especially interested Lyell. Proceeding from Albany to Niagara Falls by railroad at a speed of sixteen miles an hour, he commented, "The traveller views with surprise, in the midst of so much unoccupied land, one flourishing town after another, such as Utica, Syracuse, and Auburn. At Rochester he admires the streets of large houses, inhabited by 20,000 souls, where the first settler built his log cabin in the wilderness only twenty-five years ago. At one point our train stopped at a handsome new built station-house, and, looking out at one window, we saw a group of Indians of the Oneida tribe, lately the owners of the broad lands around, but now humbly offering for sale a few trinkets, such as baskets ornamented with porcupine quills, moccasins of moose-deerskin, and boxes of birchbark. At the other window stood a well-dressed waiter handling ices and confectionary. When we reflect that some single towns, of which the foundations were laid by persons still living, can already number a population, equal to all the aboriginal hunter tribes who possessed the forests for hundreds of miles around, we soon cease to repine at the extraordinary revolution, however much we may commiserate the unhappy fate of the disinherited race." Yet he realized that the vast optimism of America, its desire for education, its unwillingness to dwell on the past, and its hopes for the unoccupied lands to the west all contained the seeds of future disillusionment and that "where the success has been so brilliant and where large fortunes have been hastily realized, there will be rash speculations and bitter disappointments."

When John James Audubon, after his abortive attempt to find a publisher in Philadelphia, had made his trip from New York to Niagara Falls, he had traveled in poverty and despair. But he had been stimulated by the magnificence of the falls. Lyell, famous and well-off, did not need the same emotional inspiration, but he found the falls no less stirring. Describing his first sight of them, he wrote, "The sun was shining full upon them—no building in view—nothing but the green wood, the falling water, and the white foam. At that moment they appeared to me more beautiful than I had expected, and less grand; but after several days, when I had enjoyed a nearer view of the two cataracts, had listened to their thundering sound, and gazed on them for hours from above and below, and had watched the water foaming over the rapids, then plunging headlong into the dark pool,—and when I had explored the delightful island which divides the falls, where the solitude of the ancient forest is still unbroken, I at last learned by degrees to comprehend the wonders of the scene, and to feel its full magnificence."

He spent some time studying the geology of the falls and then returned to New York, marveling at the Americans as he traveled through
the country. He had been warned that the stagecoaches would be both
slow and rough, but one in particular seemed especially bad. Lyell complained at an inn that "our coachman seemed to take pleasure in driving
rapidly over deep ruts and the roughest ground" and was told that "this
was the first time in his life he had ever attempted to drive any vehicle,
whether two or four-wheeled." This startled Lyell, who wrote, "The
coolness and confidence with which everyone here is ready to try his
hand at any craft is truly amusing." He was also somewhat disturbed
by the use of the words "gentleman" and "lady." At one farm, the owner
referred to Mrs. Lyell as "the woman" and to his own daughers as "the
ladies." It was Lyell's conclusion that "the spirit of social equality has left
no other signification to the terms 'gentleman' and 'lady' but that of 'male
and female individual.' "

Nevertheless, he liked Americans, and although their democratic ways
sometimes surprised him, he appreciated their unfailing courtesy to
women—in this respect, he thought them far ahead of the British and
French—and believed the English were much too critical of the people
of the United States.

In Philadelphia, to which he traveled next, he was kept awake every
night by the noise of the firemen. There was always an alarm—usually
a false one. "At the head of the procession came a runner blowing a horn
with a deep unearthly sound, next a long team of men (for no horses
are employed) drawing a strong rope to which the ponderous engine
was attached with a large bell at the top, ringing all the way; next followed a mob, some with torches, others shouting loudly; and before they
were half out of hearing, another engine follows with like escort. . . ."
He had no question about the firemen's gallantry—they were not sham-
ming—but he did comment that "they manage these matters as effectively at Boston without turmoil."

In October he returned to Boston to give his lectures, which proved
so popular—usually 3,000 people attended—that he had to give each
one twice in order to accommodate the audience. He was so busy with
his lectures and with reports to the Geological Society about his findings
in America that he had almost no social life, going to only one ball (he
wanted to see if American women were as beautiful as they were reported to be) and making a few side excursions to nearby points of geologic interest.

As soon as the lectures were finished, he started south and visited
Washington and the Dismal Swamp, wasting as little time as he usually
did and taking copious notes of everything that he saw. He stopped
shortly at Charleston, then swung through Georgia, always hurrying in

his quiet way, and returned to Charleston. There he met John Bachman, who was working on Audubon's book describing the quadrupeds of North America. With his usual courtesy, Bachman took time to review the animal geography of the continent with Lyell, explaining that the animals were limited in their range, not so much by physical barriers as by climate.

He did not find slavery as depressing as Humboldt had. The Negroes, he observed, seemed happy and contented, although he admitted that most of those he saw closely were servants. Nevertheless, he was quick to understand that "the effect of the institution on the progress of the whites is most injurious, and, after travelling in the northern States, and admiring their rapid advance, it is most depressing to the spirits. There appears to be no place in society for poor whites. If they are rich, their slaves multiply, and from motives of kindly feeling towards retainers, and often from false pride, they are very unwilling to sell them. Hence they are constantly tempted to maintain a larger establishment than is warranted by the amount of their capital, and they often become involved in their circumstances, and finally bankrupt." Lyell hoped that slavery could eventually be abolished, but he was not impassioned like Humboldt—instead, in everything but science, inclined to remain aloof from current problems so he could concentrate on his work.

Considering the difficulties of travel in those days, Lyell covered much of the United States. From Charleston he returned to New York, where he stayed several weeks, and then went back to Boston before starting out for the South again. On leaving the city, Lyell was urged to avoid Rhode Island, where Dorr's Rebellion was taking place. The railway, according to rumors, was commanded by the cannon of the insurgents. But he passed through Providence without incident, noting favorably the prevalent respect for law and order at a time of such tension. On this trip he went farther west than before, visiting Pittsburgh, whose coal deposits amazed him, and followed the Ohio River to Cincinnati. There he turned north to Cleveland, back to Niagara Falls, where he again studied its geology, on to Toronto, Montreal, Quebec, and back to Boston.

After a short stay he took the boat for Halifax and remained a month in Nova Scotia before returning to England. He had endured none of the hardships of Humboldt on the Orinoco or even of Wilson on the Ohio and Mississippi, because he was traveling through civilized country and could afford the best transportation and accommodations. Nevertheless, the journey had been wearisome. He had covered many miles, noting every geologic feature of the country and carefully recording his observations, and during the thirteen months he had taken hardly any time off for a normal social life or even for relaxation.

He was weary, and describing his arrival in England, he wrote, "as we flew along in the railway carriage between Liverpool and London, my eye, so long accustomed to the American landscape, was struck with the dressy and garden-like appearance of all the fields. . . . Eight hours conveyed us from sea to sea, from the estuary of the Mersey to that stream which Pope has styled 'The Father of British Floods.' Whatever new standard for measuring the comparative size of rivers I had acquired in my late wanderings, I certainly never beheld 'the swelling waters and alternate tides' of Father Thames with greater admiration than after this long absence, or was ever more delighted to find myself once more in the midst of the flourishing settlement which has grown up upon his banks."

VI

In the early fall of 1842, just as soon as he had arrived home from America, Lyell set to work to write his experiences. At first he intended to produce a book that would contain both his geologic findings and his personal impressions of the United States and Canada, but he soon realized that the result would please neither scientists nor general readers and that it would be better to divide some of his material. He, therefore, wrote twelve scientific papers, which were published in various journals, and a two-volume book entitled *Travels in North America,* which appeared in 1845.

That year he returned to the United States for another visit. Although he did not remain as long—only nine months this time—he traveled even more extensively, landing at Halifax, touring through the New England states and going south as far as New Orleans. As usual, he kept copious notes of his geologic observations and even began writing scientific articles while he was still in the country. In addition, he started a popular travel book. (His experience with *Travels in North America* led him to believe that such a book might sell well.) *A Second Visit to the United States of North America,* another two-volume book, was presented in journal form. In his first travel book, he had included considerable information about the geology of the United States. In the second, he did not but, instead, devoted more pages to American politics, the people he had met, the appearance of the countryside, the customs of the inhabitants, as well as his personal experiences. The result was a delightful book about life in the United States in 1845, and it proved sufficiently popular to go through several editions.

His earlier hopes had now come true. His books provided him with the independence that he had wanted, and he was famous. He served two terms as president of the Geological Society. He published more papers, served as a royal commissioner of the Great Exhibition, and personally knew the consort, Prince Albert. In 1852 he returned to the United States for a third time to lecture again at the Lowell Institute and made another trip to New York the following year as one of the British representatives to the International Exhibit. The attitude that he took toward this appointment was typical. When it was offered to him, he told the government that "I must take time, at least a day or two, to consider; for unless I could calculate by great exertion to get out my ninth edition of 'Principles,' now eight months out of print, I could not go. I must also, I said, see the instructions, and I stipulated that if I went, I would not undertake any share, much less a superintendence, of the Report. . . . I also bargained that I might return as soon as the New York business is over, as my scientific work, to be cleared off before sailing for the Canaries [which he planned to visit] in the autumn, will be much interrupted by this affair." He was fifty-five when he wrote this, an age when he might have felt free to relax, but his old habits persisted. Geology came before everything else.

In spite of all the conditions Lyell laid down, his role as a representative was more active than he had planned, because the person in charge became ill, and most of his duties fell on Lyell. Nevertheless, Lyell was off to the Canaries on schedule and examined the volcano at Tenerife, the same volcano that Humboldt had climbed more than fifty years earlier after his adventurous entry into the harbor at Santa Cruz de Tenerife. During the next few years he made regular, two-month trips to the Continent to enlarge his knowledge of its geology, for he wanted to continue an active career, and to do so, he had to keep up with the new developments in his field. He had almost turned sixty when he wrote to a friend, "I am glad that you have been thinking of the future as well as of the present of the Geological Society. . . . My taking the office [of president] a third time is out of the question. I have done a fair share of that duty, and hope to continue for years travelling, making original observations, and above all learning from the younger, but not, for all that, young geologists whom I meet everywhere, so far ahead of us old stagers, that they are familiar with branches of the science that are fast rising in importance which were not thought of when I began." Much of his time was now spent on the study of glaciers in Switzerland and volcanoes in Italy and Sicily.

Lyell's continual traveling and research were necessary, because by now the *Principles* was more than a book; it was practically an institution. At first Lyell had limited it primarily to a discussion of the changes in the earth's surface, but with each new edition he expanded it by including his latest discoveries and ideas and those of other scientists. Thus it became the standard up-to-date reference work, embracing almost the whole of contemporary geologic knowledge. No student of geology could afford to be without it.

His interests, however, were not restricted to geology proper. Earlier he had joined with other scientists in speculating on the origin of species, and although he had been careful to avoid controversy, his interest in the subject remained. In the first edition of the *Principles* he had carefully stated his thinking, which he later summarized by saying, "I pointed out in 1832, as the two great flaws in Lamarck's attempt to explain the origin of the species, first, that he had failed to adduce a single instance of the initiation of a new organ in any species of animal or plant; and secondly, that variation, whether taking place in the course of nature or assisted artificially by the breeder and horticulturist, had never yet gone so far as to produce two races sufficiently remote from each other in physiological constitution as to be sterile when intermarried, or, if fertile, only capable of producing sterile hybrids, &c.

"To this objection Lamarck would, no doubt, have answered that there had not been time for bringing about so great an amount of variation; for when Cuvier and some other of his contemporaries appealed to the embalmed animals and plants taken from the Egyptian tombs, some of them 3,000 years old, which had not experienced in that long period the slightest modification in their specific characters, he replied that the climate and soil of the Nile valley had not varied in the interval, and that there was therefore no reason for expecting that we should be able to detect any change in the fauna and flora. . . .

"Although I cited this answer of Lamarck, in my account of his theory, I did not, at the time, fully appreciate the deep conviction it displays of the slow manner in which geological changes have taken place, and the insignificance of thirty or forty centuries in the history of a species, and that, too, at a period when very narrow views were entertained of the extent of past time by most of the ablest geologists, and when great revolutions of the earth's crust, and its inhabitants, were generally attributed to sudden and violent catastrophes.

"While in 1832," he continued, "I argued against Lamarck's doctrine of gradual transmutation of one species into another, I agreed with him in believing that the system of changes now in progress in the organic world would afford, when fully understood, a complete key to the interpretation of all the vicissitudes of the living creation in past ages. I contended against the doctrine, then very popular, of the sudden destruction of vast multitudes of species, and the abrupt ushering into the world of new batches of plants and animals."

After briefly reviewing his attempt to sketch "the laws of extinction," he went on: "But while rejecting transmutation, I was equally opposed to the popular theory that the creative power had diminished in energy, or that it had been in abeyance ever since Man had entered upon the scene. That that renovating force [which was supposed to give sudden rise to new species], which had been in full operation for millions of years, should cease to act while the causes of extinction were still in full activity, or even intensified by the accession of Man's destroying power, seemed to me in the highest degree improbable. The only point on which I doubted was, whether the force might not be intermittent instead of being, as Lamarck supposed, in ceaseless operation. Might not the births of new species, like the deaths of old ones, be sudden? Might they not still escape our observation? If the coming in of one new species, and the loss of one other which had endured for ages, should take place annually, still, assuming that there are a million of animals and plants living on the globe, it would require, I observed, a million of years to bring about a complete revolution in the fauna and flora. In that case, I imagined that, although the first appearance of a new form might be as abrupt as the disappearance of an old one, yet naturalists might never yet have witnessed the first entrance on the stage of a large and conspicuous animal or plant, and as to the smaller kinds, many of them may be conceived to have stolen in unseen, and to have spread gradually over a wide area, like species migrating into new provinces."

In this statement, Lyell summarized not only his own thinking, but that of many other important scientists. They had long since denied the Creation and the Deluge as depicted literally in the Bible, but they could find no substitute. A succession of revolutions and catastrophes no matter how long, failed to provide a reasonable answer. Lamarck's theories did not stand up under scrutiny. Nor did the idea of a creative force capable of suddenly bringing a series of new species into existence. The problem was there, and even men of the intelligence of Lyell did not know how to cope with it. Yet a few were working toward a solution, and one of these was Lyell's friend, Charles Darwin.

Originally Lyell had mostly talked about geology with Darwin, but in time, as Darwin developed his theory of evolution, Lyell discussed this new work with him and was one of those who kept encouraging him to publish the *Origin of Species*. On October 3, 1859, he had just finished reading the published book and sat down to write Darwin enthusiastically. "It is a splendid case of close reasoning," he said, "and long sustained argument throughout so many pages, the condensation immense, too great perhaps for the uninitiated, but an effective and important preliminary statement. . . . " And to another friend, he wrote early the following January, "I have been so absorbed in preparation for a new edition of my 'Geology' that I have really had no ideas to exchange, except on those matters which the initiated are discussing, or that question which my friend Charles Darwin's book has brought before the British reading public, both scientific, literary, and theological. . . ."

The following year Lyell was offered a seat in the House of Commons. This greatly tempted him, for he would have represented the University of London and thus the scientific and literary circles of Great Britain. But he decided to refuse. His happiness, he said, lay in the pursuit of geology, and he still had on hand the notes from years of travels. Also the latest edition of the *Principles* was almost out of stock, which meant preparing another. Furthermore, he had undertaken a new effort, writing a book about the great length of time man must have existed, a question that interested him after reading Darwin. For three years he visited Belgium, England, and France, trying to determine whether man had been coexistent with certain of the extinct mammals. The book, *The Geological Evidences of the Antiquity of Man,* which came out in 1863, contained his findings and also his thoughts on evolution. "Darwin," he wrote to a friend, "seems much disappointed that I do not go farther with him, or do not speak out more. I can only say that I have spoken out to the full extent of my present convictions, and even beyond my state of *feeling* as to man's unbroken descent from the brutes, and I find that I am half converting not a few who were in arms against Darwin. . . . I plead guilty to going farther in my reasoning towards transmutation than in my sentiments and imagination, and perhaps for that very reason I shall lead more people on to Darwin . . . than one who, being born later . . . has comparatively little to abandon of old and long cherished ideas, which constituted the charm to me of the theoretical part of the science in my earlier days. . . ." To Darwin himself, he said, "My feelings, however, more than any thought about policy or expediency, prevent me from dogmatizing as to the descent of man from the brutes, which, though I am prepared to accept it, takes away much of the charm from my speculations on the past relating to such matters. . . . I cannot go [Thomas] Huxley's [the noted zoologist] length in thinking that natural selection and variation account for so much, and not so far as you, if I take some passages of your book separately. I think the old 'creation' is almost as much required as ever, but of course it takes a new form if Lamarck's views improved by yours are adopted.

"What I am anxious to effect is to avoid positive inconsistencies in different parts of my book, owing probably to the old trains of thought, the old ruts, interfering with the new course.

"But you ought to be satisfied, as I shall bring hundreds towards you, who if I treated the matter more dogmatically would have rebelled.

"I have spoken out to the utmost extent of my tether, so far as my reason goes, and further than my imagination and sentiment can follow. . . ." Lyell was now sixty-five. He had led a long career, during which he had carried the science of geology far, but like many older men, he could not, for all his brilliance, accept the entirely new without some conditions. But in time he let his reason prevail over his sentiment and imagination and brought himself to abandon his "old and long cherished ideas."

VII

The world continued to honor Lyell in his later years. Great Britain made him a baronet; Queen Victoria received him in private and talked to him about Prince Albert, who had recently died, and about science (Lyell reported to his sister that "she has a clear understanding, and thinks quite fearlessly for herself and yet very modestly"); Prussia conferred on him the order of merit that had once been headed by Humboldt; France elected him a corresponding member of the French Institute; and scientists from many countries wrote to and conferred with him.

His books still sold well. Before his death, four editions of the *Antiquity of Man* appeared, six of the *Elements of Geology,* and eleven of the *Principles of Geology.* The latter, however, needed much revision. As Lyell explained in a letter to a friend, "I am now re-editing the 'Principles of Geology,' . . . which my publisher says ought without delay to be reprinted; a more arduous task than he is aware of, since already eleven years have elapsed since the last version saw light, and Darwin, among others, has done much to shake our old opinions since that time." Just as Humboldt had been, he was troubled by the difficulty of keeping up with the science that he himself had fostered. So many concepts were changing—and changing so fast.

His eminence was secure. Everyone, even the younger men, regarded him as an outstanding geologist, but all were beginning to forget his original contributions. Almost pathetically, when he was seventy-one years old, he wrote to another author, thanking him for "sending me a copy of your important work on the 'History of Creation,' and especially for the chapter entitled 'On Lyell and Darwin.' Most of the zoologists forget that anything was written between the time of Lamarck and the publication of our friend's 'Origin of the Species.'

"I am therefore obliged to you for pointing out how clearly I advocated a law of continuity even in the organic world, so far as possible without adopting Lamarck's theory of transmutation. I believe that mine was the first work (published in January, 1832) in which any attempt had been made to prove that while causes now in action continue to produce unceasing variations in the climate and physical geography of the globe, and endless migration of species, there must be a perpetual dying out of animals and plants, not suddenly and by whole groups at once, but one after another. . . .

"But while I taught that as often as certain forms of animals and plants disappeared, for reasons quite intelligible to us, others took their place by virtue of a causation which was beyond our comprehension; it remained for Darwin to accumulate proof that there is no break between the incoming and the outgoing species, that they are the work of evolution, and not of special creation."

Although he was having a problem keeping up with science and although he knew that many had forgotten what he had accomplished, particularly the pioneering aspects of his work, he had no intention of stopping. Even in his seventies, he continued to travel throughout Great Britain and the Continent. At seventy-five, his eyes, which had always been weak, made it impossible for him to read or write, but he overcame this difficulty by having others perform these functions for him. Otherwise, physically he was able to get around and to enjoy life. Then, that year, his wife died. The loss struck him hard. He thought, at his age, that "the separation cannot be very long," but because she was twelve years younger than he, he had never contemplated his surviving her. As always in his life, he had one means of escaping "the shock which this has given me. I endeavour by daily work at my favorite science to forget as far as possible the dreadful change which this has made in my existence." That summer he worked on a new edition of one of his books. Then he left for the Continent.

Such a pace could not go on forever. Even his intense dedication to his work could not postpone death. A year and a half later, on February 22, 1875, at the age of seventy-seven, Lyell's long career ended.

Immediately the fellows of the Royal, the Geological, and the Linnaean societies addressed a memorial to the Dean of Westminster, requesting that he be buried in the abbey. "For upwards of half a century," they said, "he has exercised a most important influence on the progress of geological science, and for the last twenty-five years he has been the most preeminent geologist in the world. . . ." His reputation, of course, justified their statement, and the request was granted.

Lyell's long lifetime had covered a revolution in man's thinking, a revolution to which he had been one of the principal contributors. Through his investigations and his books he had destroyed the last of the mythology that had surrounded geology and laid the basis of a modern science. But in turn, he had been forced by others to go beyond his sentiment and his imagination and to abandon many of the ideas he had formerly cherished. This process had been painful to him, but he had accepted the pain as the cost of truth.

The facts of his science were known through the many pages of his books. The philosophy that made those pages possible was contained in a paragraph of a letter he wrote when he was seventy-five, shortly after his wife's death and just before he set out on another journey. "I am told by some," he wrote, "that if any of our traditionary beliefs make us happier, and lead us to estimate humanity more highly, we ought to be careful not to endeavour to establish any scientific truths which would lessen and lower our estimate of man's place in nature; in short, we should do nothing to disturb any man's faith, if it be a delusion which increases his happiness. But I hope and believe," he continued, "that the discovery and propagation of every truth, and the dispelling of every error, tends to improve and better the condition of man, though the act of reforming old opinions and institutions causes so much bitter pain and misery."

10

The Teacher from Switzerland

LOUIS AGASSIZ: 1807–1873

I

To Louis Agassiz, the young Swiss scientist whom Humboldt helped support in Paris, financial problems were nothing new. His father had been the clergyman at Motiers, drawing a small salary that in good years was supplemented by the income from the parsonage's vineyard. There was money enough for all the basic requirements of a respectable life, but at the end of the year nothing was ever left over. Luxuries such as travel or extensive education for the children had to be kept to a minimum if the family were to survive.

Louis (he was christened Jean Louis Rodolphe but was always called simply Louis) was born on May 20, 1807, and led a quiet country boyhood, spending much of his time outdoors with his younger brother, Auguste. Together they collected mice and rabbits for pets, and both were avid fishermen, pursuing a sport that subsequently played an important part in shaping Louis' scientific career. Until he was ten years old, his father tutored him at home. Then he went to school at Bienne, twenty miles from Motiers.

His mother and father expected to give him a few years of education, after which they wanted him to go into business at Neuchâtel, the home of his mother's family. But Louis had entirely different ideas. Writing in one of the many notebooks that he kept as a boy, he stated that he would like to spend a year and a half as an apprentice in Neuchâtel, then study in Germany and Paris, and, finally, at the age of twenty-five become a man of letters, writing on scientific subjects. This program, in the opinion of Agassiz's father, was utterly impractical; the boy should start thinking about a career that would make him financially independent of his family. But Agassiz, who had a charming and persuasive way about him even then, rallied numerous allies to his cause. Under pressure from his son's teachers and an uncle, who was a physician, Agassiz's father agreed to a compromise: Louis could study for a few years at Lausanne before learning a business.

Agassiz later wrote, "The first course of lectures on zoology I attended was given in Lausanne in 1823. It consisted chiefly of extracts from Cuvier's 'Animal Kingdom' and from Lamarck's 'Invertebrate Animals.' I now became aware, for the first time, that the learned differ in their classifications. With this discovery, an immense field of study opened before me, and I longed for some knowledge of anatomy, that I might see for myself where the truth was." But to study science further, he still had to gain his father's consent. Once more he found an ally in his uncle, and between them, they somehow managed to persuade Agassiz's father that the boy should give up all thought of business and become a physician.

Agassiz and his brother, Auguste, enrolled at the university at Zurich in 1824. (The family apparently did not want to favor one of their sons over the other.) For the two years he remained there, he devoted himself exclusively to anatomy, zoology, and physiology, while he and his family worried about the necessary money. Later on, however, he thought that he might have gained an advantage by being poor. "My inability to buy books," he wrote, "was, perhaps, not so great a misfortune as it might have seemed to me; at least, it saved me from too great dependence on written authority. I spent all my time dissecting animals and in studying human anatomy, not forgetting my favorite amusements of fishing and collecting. I was always surrounded with pets and had at this time some forty birds flying about my study, with no other home than a large pine tree in the corner." Commenting further on his lack of funds, he said that he carefully studied the bird collection of one of his professors and "described every bird it contained, as I could not afford to buy even a textbook of ornithology. I also copied with my own hand, having no means of purchasing the work, two volumes of Lamarck's 'Invertebrate Animals,' and my dear brother copied another half volume for me. I finally learned that the study of the things themselves was far more attractive than the books I so much coveted; and when, at last, large libraries became accessible to me, I usually contented myself with turning over the leaves of the volumes on natural history, looking at the illustrations, and recording the titles of the works, that I might readily consult them for identification of such objects as I should have an opportunity of examining in nature." Somewhat as Linnaeus had done, Agassiz was finding that circumstances forced him to make his own observations, rather than rely on the words of authorities.

Before he had passed two years at Zurich, Agassiz once again turned his extraordinary charm on his family, for he now wanted to leave Zurich and attend a better university. His family could not withstand him, and in 1826 he enrolled at Heidelberg. This time his brother, Auguste, did not accompany him. The family could not afford such expensive educations for both boys.

At Heidelberg, Agassiz quickly made two good friends, Alexander Braun and Karl Friedrich Schimper, both of whom remained close to him throughout his university years. He also became something of a hero among the other students, for he upheld the honor of the Swiss club by defeating the four best German duelers. These social activities, however, did not interfere with his studies. Once again, he proved to be a hardworking, brilliant scholar. But money problems continued to plague him. "As soon as I know," he wrote his father from Heidelberg, "for I cannot as yet make an exact estimate, I will write you as nearly as possible what my expenses will be. Sometimes there may be unlooked-for expenses, as, for instance, six crowns for a matriculation paper. But be assured that at all events I shall restrict myself to what is absolutely necessary, and do my best to economize." And during the Christmas vacation that year he wrote again: "My happiness would be perfect were it not for the painful thought which pursues me everywhere, that I live on your privations; yet it is impossible for me to diminish my expenses farther."

In the spring of 1827 an epidemic of typhus swept the university, and Agassiz was one of its victims. For many days the doctors feared for his life. Then they gave orders to move him to the home of the Braun family in Karlsruhe, where Alexander's sister, Cecile, nursed him until he was well enough to rejoin his own family at Orbe, where they had moved. During his convalescence he continued to study and to enlarge his collections, but he was extremely restless. Orbe was too provincial, and he could not stand the thought of practicing medicine there after his graduation. While he was considering what to do, he received a letter from Braun saying that he and Schimper were transferring to the university at Munich. Would Agassiz join them?

Once more his parents reluctantly agreed to a change in his plans, and in November, 1827, Agassiz and Braun arrived at Munich, which, in every respect, measured up to their expectations.

They took rooms in a house belonging to Ignaz Döllinger, professor of embryology, and, with Schimper, soon created a combination of living quarters, museum, and laboratory. A friend later described Agassiz's life at Munich by saying that "he never lost his temper, though often under great trial; he remained self-possessed and did everything calmly, having a friendly smile for every one and a helping hand for those who were in need. He was at that time scarcely twenty years old, and was already the most prominent among the students at Munich. They loved him, and had a high consideration for him. I had seen him at the Swiss students' club several times, and had observed him among the *jolly* students; he liked merry society, but he himself was in general reserved and never noisy. He picked out the gifted and highly learned students, and would not waste his time in ordinary conversation."

He quickly came to know the best faculty members, who respected both his brilliance and his industry. Under Döllinger, he studied embryology and became expert at using the microscope. (Out of his small allowance, he was able to save enough money to buy a good one for himself.) Finding that no one in Munich was an ichthyologist, he himself wisely specialized in fish, a field in which he would have no competition. He spent hours at the Munich market (his searches there resulted in his discovering an entirely new species) and wrote Auguste to catch him more specimens. In a short time he made himself one of the university's experts.

His financial problems continued to trouble him, and he experienced growing difficulties with his parents. Having persuaded them to let him enter Munich to become a doctor of medicine, he soon confessed to them his true ambition—to be a man of science, not a doctor. In January, 1828, a few months after his arrival, his mother wrote him in great concern. "You left us a few months ago with the assurance that two years would more than suffice to complete your medical studies. You chose the university which offered, as you thought, the most ample means to reach your end; and now, how is it that you look forward only with distaste to the practice of medicine? Have you reflected seriously before setting aside this profession? Indeed, we cannot consent to this step."

Agassiz was in a difficult position. Ever since his schoolboy days he had been maneuvering his parents toward his point of view, but he now realized that he had overstepped himself by openly avowing his true aims. Quickly he wrote a retraction. "It seems that you have misunderstood me," he said, "for your answer grants me after all just what I ask. You think that I wish to renounce entirely the study of medicine? On the contrary, the idea has never occurred to me, and according to my promise, you shall have one of these days a doctor of medicine as a son. What repels me is the thought of practicing medicine for a livelihood."

Agassiz's letter was a diplomatic retreat from a badly taken position, but it did not fool his father.

The clergyman, who had already made more concessions than he had ever intended, let his son know in reply that "our gratification lacks something; it would be more complete had you not a mania for rushing full gallop into the future. I have often reproved you for this, and you would fare better did you pay more attention to my reproof.

Agassiz now decided to try a new approach. "Your letter," he wrote to his father, "made me feel so keenly the anxiety I had caused you by my passion for travel [in the interests of natural history], that I will not return to it; but as my object was to make in that way a name that would win for me a professorship, I venture upon another proposition. If during the course of my studies I succeed in making myself known by a work of distinction, will you not then consent that I study, at least during one year, the natural sciences alone, and then accept a professorship of natural history with the understanding that in the first place, and in the time agreed upon, I shall take my Doctor's degree." Agassiz had not told his father that one of the professors at Munich had been to Brazil collecting fish and had asked Agassiz to catalogue the specimens and publish the results. Because of this opportunity, there was no doubt he would shortly produce a work of sufficient "distinction" to fulfill the terms that he had proposed.

His father, however, was not persuaded. He had already made many financial sacrifices on behalf of his son's education, and he wanted results that he could understand. Rather sharply, he replied that "the natural sciences, however sublime and attractive, offer nothing certain in the future. They may, no doubt, be your golden bridge, or you may, thanks to them, soar very high, but—modern Icarus—may not also some adverse fortune, an unexpected loss of popularity, or, perhaps, some revolution fatal to your philosophy, bring you down with a somersault, and then you would not be sorry to find in your quiver the means of gaining your bread. Agreed that you have now an invincible repugnance to the practice of medicine, it is evident from your last two letters that you would have no less objection to any other profession by which money is to be made. . . ."

Like a wise general, Agassiz realized that he could not win this battle with a frontal attack, so he quietly bided his time. His book *Brazilian Fishes* appeared in May, 1829, and although it was not an outstanding work of science, it represented a considerable accomplishment for a young student. To Agassiz, it was the first step down the long road he had charted for himself years ago, and he also saw it as a means of currying favor with Cuvier. By dedicating it to the French scientist, he hoped to call attention to himself. Cuvier received the book at the Jardin des

Plantes, liked it, and wrote Agassiz that he planned to use some of the material in his own books.

Excited by this success with such a great figure, Agassiz next undertook to make friends with Humboldt, who was planning his expedition through Russia. Although he had never met him, he wrote and offered himself as one of Humboldt's assistants on the journey. The offer came to nothing, because Humboldt had already made his selection, but Agassiz was showing himself adept at getting his name before the prominent men of the time.

He had also, contrary to the plan he had agreed to with his parents, secured his doctorate in the natural sciences before his doctorate in medicine. One of his professors had suggested that a degree would lend prestige to his authorship of *Brazilian Fishes*, and since he had completed the requirements and had only to take the examination, the suggestion seemed logical. He passed brilliantly, and the appearance of the book (it was reviewed in the Lausanne *Gazette*) helped improve his relations with his parents, although they still insisted that he obtain his doctorate in medicine. In spite of his sometimes underhanded way of circumventing them, Agassiz had no thought of directly rebelling against them. He stayed at Munich and, during 1829 and 1830, took the required courses, announced the publication of a book on European fishes, found a prospective publisher for it, and tacitly became engaged to Cecile Braun. It was a whirlwind finish to his university career, and in April, 1830, he received his doctorate in medicine—with, of course, absolutely no intention of ever using it professionally.

II

Although his family had worried about his future, few people have pursued more direct routes to their chosen careers than Agassiz. Except for obtaining his medical degree and thus fulfilling his promise to his mother and father, he had not lost any time in becoming a man of letters writing on scientific subjects. Every act, including the judicious dedication of *Brazilian Fishes*, had been designed for only one purpose—to help him realize his ambition.

On leaving the university, he knew exactly the steps that he proposed to take. He would go home and prepare his next book on fish. To his long-suffering parents, he wrote, "According to your wish, I shall not bring any friend with me. . . . I shall, however, be accompanied by one person, for whom I should like to make suitable arrangements. He is the artist who makes all my drawings. . . . My affairs are all in order with [Johann Friedrich] Cotta [the publisher of his new book], and I have concluded the arrangement more advantageously than I had dared to hope,—a thousand louis, six hundred payable on the publication of the first number, and four hundred in installments, as the publication goes on. If I had not been in haste to close the matter in order to secure myself against all doubt, I might have done even better. But I hope that I have reconciled you thereby to Natural History."

His enthusiasm was not reciprocated by his father. After commenting on the many friends and relatives that Agassiz would probably visit on his way from Munich, he said, "And during all these indispensable excursions, for which, to be within bounds, I allow a month at least, it is as clear as daylight that regular work must be set aside, if, indeed, the time be not wholly lost. Now, for Heaven's sake, what will you do, or rather what will *we* do, with your painter, in this interval employed by you elsewhere."

In the past, Agassiz had always had his way, and he did this time, too. He explained to his father that his publisher was paying the artist, thus settling his father's fears about the expense, and agreed to have him work in separate lodgings. Otherwise, he still planned to use the family's house at Concise, where they now lived, as his headquarters. And since that was his intention, that was what he did.

Until September, 1831, he worked at Concise on his studies of freshwater and fossil fish, but the small Swiss town seemed dull to him after the intellectual excitement of Munich, and it did not contain the research facilities he needed. If his publication was to be successful, he should visit more of Europe's museums and particularly the Jardin des Plantes. Once again, though, he was faced with the problem of money. By telling his parents that he would further his knowledge of medicine and by appealing to a relative and to a family friend, he finally obtained sufficient funds. In the fall of 1831 he started for Paris.

The ultimate success of his trip depended largely on Cuvier's reaction to his efforts. In February, 1832, he described his fears to his parents. "I think I told you when I left for Paris," he wrote, "that my chief anxiety was lest I might not be allowed to examine, and still less to describe, the fossil fishes and their skeletons in the Museum. Knowing that Cuvier intended to write a book on this subject, I supposed that he would reserve these specimens for himself. I half thought he might, on seeing my work so far advanced, propose to me to finish it jointly with him—but even this I hardly dared to hope. It was on this account, with the view of increasing my materials and having thereby a better chance of success with M. Cuvier, that I desired so earnestly to stop at Strasbourg and Karlsruhe, where I knew specimens were to be seen which would have a direct bearing on my aim. The result has far surpassed my expectation. I hastened to show my material to M. Cuvier the very day after my arrival. He received me with great politeness, though with a certain reserve, and immediately gave me permission to see everything in the galleries of the Museum. But as I knew that he had put together in private collections all that could be of use to himself in writing his book, and as he had never said a word to me of his plan of publication, I remained in a painful state of doubt, since the completion of his work would have destroyed all chance for the sale of mine.

"Last Saturday I was passing the evening there, and we were talking of science, when he desired his secretary to bring him a certain portfolio of drawings. He showed me the contents; they were drawings of fossil fishes and notes which he had taken in the British Museum and elsewhere. After looking it through with me, he said that he had seen with satisfaction the manner in which I had treated this subject; that I had indeed anticipated him, since he had intended at some future time to do the same thing; but that as I had given it so much attention, and had done my work so well, he had decided to renounce his project, and to place at my disposition all the materials that he had collected and the preliminary notes that he had taken."

With the same generosity he had shown to many other men, Cuvier gave up his own plans in favor of the young Swiss. To Agassiz, it was the greatest possible opportunity. To take full advantage of it, he regularly worked at least fifteen hours a day during the next months, attempting to get the publication finished and out as quickly as possible, for his lack of means was still troubling him. When his brother, Auguste, wrote and asked him to send a book, he delayed for weeks, not so much because he had difficulty finding it in the bookstores, but because he did not have the eighteen francs with which to purchase it. When he explained this to his brother, his mother immediately responded by saying that "I want to talk to you, my dear Louis, of your future, which has often made me anxious. . . . With much knowledge, acquired by assiduous industry, you are still at twenty-five years of age living on brilliant hopes, in relation, it is true, with great people, and known as having distinguished talent. Now, all this would seem to me delightful if you had an income of fifty thousand francs; but, in your position, you must absolutely have an occupation which will enable you to live, and free you from the insupportable weight of dependence on others."

Such arguments, however sensible, could not prevail against Agassiz's determination. He did not like a life of poverty, and he did not like being dependent on others. But these dislikes were not as abhorrent as the thought of giving up the career he had set for himself so many years ago. He, therefore, kept working at his fish, working so hard that he dreamed about them at night. One in particular, of which there was only a faint impression on a stone slab, haunted him. In his sleep one night, he thought he had seen it with all its missing features restored, but when he woke up, he could not recall the image. Nevertheless, he hastened to the Jardin des Plantes early in the morning, hoping that the sight of the stone might help him remember what he had dreamed. It was of no use. The next night he underwent the same experience—the vision of the perfect fish and the inability to remember it the following day. On the third night he placed paper and a pencil beside his bed. Once more the complete fish appeared before him, and half-awake, half-asleep, he took his pencil and, in the darkness, drew what he thought he had seen. When he looked at his drawing by daybreak, he discovered he had included features he believed were zoologically impossible. Back at the Jardin des Plantes, he took up his chisel and gently cut away pieces of the slab in accordance with his nighttime drawing. To his surprise, the fish was revealed to be what his dream had shown him. He often spoke of this experience later as an example of the brain's ability to work while the body rested.

In March of that year, in the hope of gaining his understanding, he tried to explain to his father what it was he was doing. "The aim of our researches upon fossil animals is to ascertain what beings have lived at each one of these (geological) epochs of creation, and to trace their characters and their relations with those now living; in one word, to make them live again in our thought. It is especially the fishes that I try to restore for the eyes of the curious, by showing them which ones have lived in each epoch, what were their forms, and, if possible, by drawing some conclusions as to their probable modes of life. You will better understand the difficulty of my work when I tell you that in many species I have only a single tooth, a scale, a spine, as my guide in the reconstruction of all these characters, although sometimes we are fortunate enough to find species with the fins and the skeletons complete." This was the work in which Cuvier had been the pioneer and still reigned as master. To be near him and to study his collections were worth any sacrifice, even the dependency of which Agassiz's mother was so critical.

Although his studies occupied practically every working hour, he had time to listen to the debates raging between the adherents of Cuvier and those of Geoffroy Saint-Hilaire, who were arguing bitterly over Lamarckism. German science at this period was influenced by a romantic attitude, and Lamarck's theories were naturally more appealing to someone with a German background like Agassiz's. But Cuvier was Agassiz's god, and he fell completely under his influence. For the most part, this was excellent. He learned from Cuvier the techniques of reconstructing bodies by the correlation of the parts, but more than that, he absorbed Cuvier's empiricism and exactitude. Cuvier's refusal to indulge in broad speculation without what he considered an adequate factual basis became a part of Agassiz's philosophy, too. Unfortunately, he also sided with Cuvier in refusing to recognize any relationship between the fossils of different periods and became, in this respect, just as rigid as Cuvier.

The relationship between the two men grew closer and closer during the first half of 1832. Agassiz was frequently at Cuvier's house (it was one of the few places he found time to go), and they saw each other regularly at the Jardin des Plantes. One Sunday morning he was working at a task that Cuvier had given him, saying to him, "You are young; you have time enough for it; I have none to spare." Eleven o'clock came, and Cuvier asked Agassiz to stay for breakfast. After they had finished eating, they returned to work again, each at his own job. The day went by so quickly that Agassiz was surprised to hear the clock strike five, the hour for his dinner. He excused himself to Cuvier by remarking that he ate with the students, and therefore, his meal would not be kept for him. In fatherly fashion, Cuvier commended him on his interest in his studies but advised him that he was wise not to neglect regular meals. "Be careful," Cuvier said, "and remember that *work kills*." It was the last advice he ever gave. The next day was the date of Cuvier's fatal illness.

The loss was serious for Agassiz, but he had one other influential friend—Alexander von Humboldt. Of those to whom Agassiz had introduced himself when he had first arrived in Paris, Humboldt was perhaps the most sympathetic. In March, Agassiz wrote his parents that he had called on Humboldt the day before. "In former visits I had spoken to him about my position, and told him that I did not know what course to take with my publisher. He offered to write to him, and did so more than two months ago. Thus far, neither he nor I have had any answer. This morning, just as I was going out, a letter came from M. de Humboldt, who writes me that he is very uneasy at receiving no reply from Cotta [the publisher], that he fears lest the uncertainty and anxiety of mind resulting from this might be injurious to my work, and begs me to accept the enclosed credit of a thousand francs." Once again, as he had done so many times, Humboldt had drawn on his limited means to aid a needy student.

Humboldt's gift (he called it a loan to spare Agassiz embarrassment) came at a time when Agassiz was almost prepared to give up his research on the fossil fish, discharge his artist, and at last follow his parents' bidding and obtain a job. It would have meant, he knew, a long delay in his career, if not the end of it, but he had reached the point where he could carry on no longer. Agassiz never forgot the help he received and always had the warmest recollections of Humboldt. Years later, on the hundredth anniversary of Humboldt's birth, he gave an intimate picture of Humboldt at this time and of his relations with him. "The life which Humboldt now led," he said, "was less exclusively that of a student than it had been during his former Paris life. He was the ambassador of a foreign court. His official position and his rank in society, as well as his great celebrity, made him everywhere a cherished guest, and Humboldt had the gift of making himself ubiquitous. He was as familiar with the gossip of the fashionable and dramatic world as with the higher walks of life and the abstruse researches of science. He had at this time two residences in Paris—his lodgings at the Hôtel des Princes, where he saw the great world, and his working-room in the Rue de la Harpe, where he received with less formality his scientific friends. It is with the latter place I associate him: for there it was my privilege to visit him frequently. There he gave me leave to come to talk to him about my work and consult him in my difficulties. I am unwilling to speak of myself on this occasion, and yet I do not know how else I can do justice to one of the most beautiful sides of Humboldt's character. His sympathy for all young students of nature was one of the noblest traits of his long life. It may be truly said that toward the close of his career there was hardly one prominent or aspiring scientific man in the world who was not under some obligation to him. His sympathy touched not only the work of those in whom he was interested, but also extended to their material wants and embarrassments."

But even with such assistance as Humboldt could offer, Agassiz could not remain indefinitely in Paris. Whether he wanted to or not, he had to find some means of earning his living. His mother, always practical, had a suggestion. Neuchâtel was forming a secondary school and a public museum and would need someone to lecture both to the students and to adults. Perhaps Agassiz could obtain the appointment. Two groups had to be satisfied: the local aristocracy, who were providing most of the money, and the King of Prussia, who retained political control. The Agassiz family used their influence with the first, and Humboldt with the second. As a result of their efforts, Agassiz, in September, 1832, returned to Switzerland at the age of twenty-five to take up the first job he had ever held.

III

The reception given Agassiz by the community was, he wrote Humboldt, even more cordial than he had expected. His first lectures—he spoke before both the general public and the classes of the school—proved extremely popular, and the young professor found himself welcome everywhere. In a short time, he was asked to form the Neuchâtel Society of Natural Sciences and had, with Humboldt's assistance, arranged for the sale of part of his collection to the new museum. This provided him with the funds to continue paying his artist. His position at Neuchâtel was further fortified by an offer to teach at Heidelberg. Agassiz knew that at the large university he would not, as a young faculty member, receive the attention and support that he could gain at Neuchâtel, so he had no intention of accepting the offer. He nevertheless told everyone about it, appeared to hesitate about staying, and finally let himself be persuaded to.

During those early months his only difficulties were caused by his eyes, which were strained from overwork, and by the death of Cotta, his publisher. But in January, 1833, he wrote Humboldt that he had discovered two lithographers and two printers in Neuchâtel who were capable of handling his book on fish and that he planned to publish it locally. "The problem that remains now," he said, is "in the distribution of the numbers, and in finding a sufficient sale so that they may follow each other with regularity."

Like so many naturalists—Audubon, Wilson, and others—Agassiz was struggling with the economics of publishing, underwriting the expense himself and hoping to make a profit that he could use both to support himself and to continue his work. Humboldt immediately undertook the responsibility for selling the book in Germany. He rejected a letter Agassiz had written to the king, saying, "You have been ill-advised as to forms," and told him exactly how to win the support of the court and which people should be approached first. He also listed for Agassiz the names of the German publishing houses that would be the best distributors, volunteered to sell some copies in Russia, and obtained a considerable number of subscriptions himself in Germany. With assistance like this for his book and with his new job turning out so well, Agassiz at last felt able to support Cecile Braun, to whom he had been engaged so long.

They were married in October, 1833, and set up housekeeping in a small apartment in Neuchâtel. Because of her brother Alexander's scientific work, Cecile was sympathetic to her husband's studies and was soon playing an active part in them, particularly helping him with the illustrations he needed. That year the first number of *Investigations of Fossil Fishes* appeared, and it entirely justified the sacrifices of Agassiz's parents and the hopes of Humboldt. When the book was finally completed, it contained approximately 1,700 species, each illustrated and carefully described. Among them were many new orders, genera, and species, and together they represented the collections of most of the major museums in Europe. To arrange this vast amount of material in an orderly fashion, Agassiz had had to devise a new method of classification. Although eventually this had to be replaced because of its limitations, it still served Agassiz's purpose well and thus performed a useful function for science. In addition, he was able to link ichthyology, paleontology, and geology in a manner that Cuvier would have approved. Agassiz's thinking showed all the clarity and preciseness that Cuvier demanded of science, and the book was a masterpiece of paleontology in every respect except one: Agassiz could not bring himself to consider the possibility of transmutation. He was just as firm on this point as Cuvier had been.

After the complete book had been published, he received a letter from the British geologist Adam Sedgwick which clearly described Agassiz's position among the more conservative scientists. "The opinions of Geoffroy Saint-Hilaire and his dark school," Sedgwick wrote, "seem to be gaining some ground in England. I detest them, because I think them untrue. They shut out all argument from [sic] design and all notion of a Creative Providence, and in so doing they appear to me to deprive physiology of its life and strength, and language of its beauty and meaning. I am as much offended in taste by the turgid mystical bombast of Geoffroy as I am disgusted by his cold and irrational materialism. When men of his school talk of the elective affinity of organic types, I hear a jargon I cannot comprehend, and I turn from it in disgust; and when they talk of spontaneous generation and transmutation of species, they seem to me to try nature by an hypothesis, and not to try their hypothesis by nature. Where are their facts on which to form an inductive truth?"

To these remarks, Agassiz replied with a clear statement of his position: "I find it impossible to attribute biological phenomena, which have been and still are going on upon the surface of our globe, to the simple action of physical forces. I believe they are due, in their entirety, as well as individually, to the direct intervention of a creative power, acting freely and in an autonomic way. . . . I have tried to make this intentional plan in the organization of the animal kingdom evident, by showing that the differences between animals do not constitute a material chain, analogous to a series of physical phenomena, bound together by the same law, but present themselves rather as the phases of a thought, formulated according to a definite aim. I think we know enough of comparative anatomy to abandon forever the idea of the transformation of organs of one type into those of another. . . . The idea of a procreation of new species by preceding ones is a gratuitous supposition opposed to all sound physiological notions."

Continuing with the animals he knew best, he wrote, "Have fishes descended from a primitive type? So far am I from thinking this possible, that I do not believe there is a single specimen of fossil or living fish, whether marine or fresh-water, that has not been created with reference to a special intention and a definite aim, even though we may be able to detect but a portion of these numerous relations and of the essential purpose. . . .

"I know now one hundred and four species of fossil fish from the Old Red [Devonian strata], belonging to forty-four genera, comprised under seven families, between several of which there is but little analogy as to organization. It is therefore impossible to look upon them as coming from one primitive stock. The primitive diversity of these types is quite as remarkable as that of those belonging to later epochs. It is nevertheless true that, regarded as part of the general plan of creation, this fauna presents itself as an inferior type of the vertebrate series, connecting itself directly in the creative thought with the realization of later forms, the last of which (and this seems to me to have been the general end of creation) was to place man at the head of organized beings as the key-stone and the term of the whole series, the final point in the premeditated intention of the primitive plan which has been carried out progressively in the course of time. I would even say that I believe the creation of man has closed creation on this earth, and I draw this conclusion from the fact that the human genus is the first cosmopolite type in Nature."

Agassiz would readily admit that there had been a "development" of various species, but he would not admit that there was any relationship between one and another. Each had been an individual creation, and each had been part of a master plan, predesigned by an intelligent force, that was devised to culminate in the formation of man. That, Agassiz believed, was the purpose of the program. Man was the final objective. Such thinking, of course, did nothing to diminish his standing among the best scientists. He was merely repeating and reinforcing what many of them believed to be true. His reputation, therefore, rested totally on the other aspects of his work, and since these were excellent, he began to receive recognition. Various British societies, such as the Geological Society, with which Lyell was so closely connected, gave him awards and honors; the King of Prussia increased his support of Agassiz's work; the scientists of England several times invited him to visit their country; and other scientists in Europe, having become his ardent admirers, were spreading his fame. Everything he had wished for as a boy seemed to have come true. Yet his restless spirit was not satisfied. He wanted to encompass the whole of natural history.

In 1836 he, therefore, accepted an invitation from Jean de Charpentier, director of the saltworks at Bex, to study the glaciation of the Chamonix, Diablerets, and Rhône valleys. Most scientists, while recognizing the enormous power of glaciers, thought they were purely local phenomena with no relevance to the history of the earth as a whole. (This was the same light in which they had once considered volcanoes.)

Charpentier, who had been carrying on his own investigations, had convinced himself that the boulders covering the part of the country in which he lived had been dropped by glaciers—not by water, as most geologists supposed. Agassiz belonged to this latter school, but Charpentier thought he could make a convert of him. After spending the summer at Bex and walking through the valleys with Charpentier, Agassiz not only agreed with Charpentier's findings, but decided Charpentier had not gone far enough in his thinking. The glaciers had exercised even more influence on the shaping of the earth than Charpentier believed.

With his usual energy, Agassiz decided to pursue this new field further. On his return to Neuchâtel, he began independent studies of the nearby valleys and in 1840 constructed an observation station on the Aar Glacier. At first he and the staff he had been gathering together to help him with his work took shelter under an overhanging boulder. By enclosing one side with a stone wall and placing a blanket over the entrance, they formed a crude shelter where six people could sleep. Using this as their headquarters, Agassiz and his friends were able to keep detailed records of the movement of the glacier, its temperature, the amount of melting that took place each year, and other data. (The boulder, which soon proved unsafe, was replaced by a more permanent wooden hut, which gave better protection both to the men and to their instruments.) The results of this work were sufficiently important to warrant the King of Prussia's making a specific grant to it.

In 1837, Agassiz first publicly discussed his theories of glaciers, and this statement was followed by several publications that expanded his ideas. As Lyell had done, he studied the present-day actions of glaciers and their effects. He then applied these findings broadly to areas that were not now glaciated and gained an understanding of many phenomena —boulders, polished rocks, gravel ridges, and what we now know to be glacial moraine. Until then, these had been generally attributed to the catastrophes, particularly large floods, in which so many geologists believed. Agassiz now showed that the continent of Europe had been covered by vast sheets of ice, and this concept of an Ice Age explained much about the surface of the earth and also the geographic distribution of animals and fossils. One more barrier to the understanding of nature had been broken. The effect on other geologists was described by one in a letter to Agassiz: "Lyell has adopted your theory *in toto*!!! On my showing him a beautiful cluster of moraines, within two miles of his father's house, he instantly accepted it, as solving a host of difficulties that have all his life embarrassed him. And not these only, but similar moraines and detritus of moraines, that cover half of the adjoining counties are explicable by your theory, and he has consented to my proposal that he should immediately lay them down on a map of the county and describe them in a paper to be read the day after yours at the Geological Society."

During those years at Neuchâtel, Agassiz made outstanding contributions to science with his studies of fossil fishes and the development of his Ice Age theory, but these did not represent the limits of his work. He also produced publications on freshwater fish and mollusks (he was as interested in the animals that inhabited the shells as he was in the shells) and an enormous bibliography on natural history, as well as several monographs. To accomplish all this, he had gathered around him numerous paid assistants and even ran his own publishing house. Scientifically, the results were immensely significant; personally, they were damaging.

As early as 1837, Humboldt wrote to him, "The charming letter (again without a date) which preceded your package impressed me painfully. I see you are ill again; you complain of congestion of the head and eyes. For mercy's take care of your health which is so dear to us. I am afraid that you work too much, and (shall I say it frankly?) that you spread your intellect over too many subjects at once."

Even the hardworking Humboldt, always occupied with so many projects, was concerned about the effect of so much activity on Agassiz's scientific studies. And Cecile was just as concerned about the effect on their marriage. When she had first came to Neuchâtel, she had shared Agassiz's enthusiasm for his future, but his driving ambition had created for her a world that was alien and uncomfortable. Money was never lacking for Agassiz's science, but there was little to spare for the household. Practically every franc he earned went into additional travel and hiring more assistants or vanished in the accounts of the publishing house. These expenditures added to the luster of her husband's name but did nothing for her. He moved around Neuchâtel as one of its distinguished citizens, received everywhere. She was the young housewife who had to remain home, trying to keep her expenses within an inadequate income. Agassiz's mother, a wise woman, attempted to intervene and to persuade Agassiz to give up his expensive publishing house, but he would not consider doing so.

With unrest growing at home and financial problems increasing at the publishing business, Agassiz also began to have differences with some of his staff. His ambition and his impulse to try to do everything at once amused other scientists, but his assistants either succumbed to his magnetic personality and his enthusiasm or quarreled with him. One of the first to break away was Karl Schimper, his old university friend, who had come to work for him. Schimper believed that he had not been given the credit due him for his collaboration on the Ice Age theory and also for his descriptions of some of the fossil fish. Then followed a quarrel with Charpentier, the director of the saltworks at Bex. Charpentier, too, thought that Agassiz had not given him sufficient recognition for his contributions. Another geologist soon joined the growing chorus of complaints, and then came a sharp and especially bitter break with one of his closest helpers. Again the accusation was the same: insufficient acknowledgment of the efforts of others. Whatever the merits of each case—and there was something to be said on both sides—the resulting controversy did nothing to help Agassiz. Unlike Humboldt, who had carefully preserved so many friendships over the years, Agassiz had developed personal enemies among other scientists, people who were glad to take any opportunity to speak out against him.

By 1845 Agassiz's personal life had reached a point of crisis. Cecile, weary of the existence she was leading at Neuchâtel and convinced that Agassiz would never change, agreed to leave one child in school in Neuchâtel, but she took the other two and returned home to her family. The publishing house was now in such deep financial trouble that even Agassiz realized he must abandon it. And those whom he had offended were talking against him. His star had risen brilliantly and fast, but in 1845, just thirteen years after he had come to Neuchâtel, it was falling.

For several years Agassiz had been talking about going to America. As a scientist, the trip was necessary to him. Now it also offered him an escape from his personal problems, but as usual, he could not find the money. He talked to various people about his situation. For a while it looked as though one wealthy naturalist might pay part of the expense, but this possibility came to nothing. Then the Lowell Institute in Boston, before which Lyell had lectured, invited Agassiz at Lyell's urging to give a series of talks for a fee of $1,500. Since this did not provide Agassiz with as much money as he thought he needed (he wanted this to be a well-staffed expedition, not just a visit), he turned again to the faithful Humboldt. Once more the aging scientist came to Agassiz's aid. From the Prussian king, he obtained a grant of 15,000 francs to help defray the cost of an American trip.

Everyone, including Agassiz himself, pretended that it was a foregone conclusion that he would return to Switzerland, but underneath the pretense ran the suspicion that he well might not. He delayed his departure for several months while he put his affairs in the best possible order. He paid a good-bye visit to Cecile and the children at her family's home. He stopped for a while at Paris to visit his friends and arranged for the publication of another of his books. In England, his next stopping place, he saw his old acquaintances. Then on September 19, 1846, he boarded his ship at Liverpool, bound for Halifax and Boston.

Among the last letters he received before leaving Europe was one from Humboldt. It said, "Be happy in this new undertaking, and preserve for me the first place under the head of friendship in your heart. When you return I shall be here no more, but the king and queen will receive you . . . with the affection which, for so many reasons, you merit. . . . Your illegible but much attached friend, A. Humboldt."

IV

When Agassiz arrived in the United States, he was generally regarded as one of Europe's finest scientists, especially for his work in paleontology and glaciation, and he was, therefore, a figure of authority whom Americans wanted to meet. He stopped in Boston long enough to introduce himself to John Amory Lowell, the patron of the Lowell Institute. Then, since he had a few weeks before his lectures were scheduled to begin, he made a whirlwind tour through part of the eastern United States, accompanied some of the way by Asa Gray, the Harvard botanist. During this journey he talked with many of America's leading scientists, men like James Dwight Dana, the geologist.

In November he addressed his Boston audience, delivering the first in the series of lectures that he had spent months in preparing. His fears that he might be a failure quickly disappeared. He was everything the people of Boston wanted, cultivated, urbane, given to making small and appropriate jokes, and speaking in a delightful foreign accent. The subject he had chosen, "The Plan of Creation in the Animal Kingdom," was a comfortable one for Boston to accept, and it permitted Agassiz to expound his theories of creation. Each living thing, he pointed out, was a special creation brought into being according to an intelligent plan that had man as its final goal. What could be more reassuring than to hear this statement from a renowned scientist, who backed his conclusions with the weight of his vast scientific knowledge? The crowds flocked to listen to him in such numbers that, like Lyell, he had to repeat each lecture twice. But even Lyell had not stimulated the interest that Agassiz aroused. The man was a born public speaker and teacher. He could command his audiences as no other scientist in the United States could.

His fame as a lecturer quickly spread, and other cities wanted the opportunity to hear him. Soon he was writing to a friend, "Never did the future look brighter to me than now. If I could for a moment forget that I have a scientific mission to fulfill, to which I will never prove recreant, I could easily make more than enough by lectures which would be admirably paid and are urged upon me, to put me completely at my ease hereafter. But I will limit myself to what I need in order to repay those who have helped me through a difficult crisis, and that I can do without even turning aside from my researches. Beyond that all must go again to science,—there lies my true mission. . . . If only I have time to finish what I have begun! You know my plans are not wont to be too closely restricted."

In February, 1847, the members of Agassiz's staff began to arrive. These were financed from the king's grant and established themselves in a house provided by John Amory Lowell. Soon Agassiz had set up the same sort of workshop that he had had at Neuchâtel, with artists and assistants to help him with his research on the North American continent. One of the men Agassiz brought over was Edward Desor, who had always been close to him. He had left Desor in Europe for a time to handle his finances and to supervise the publication of his latest European book. But his choice of a confidant was a curious one, because Desor had already proved himself disloyal. Cecile had never liked him: indeed, he was one of the causes of her differences with Agassiz. And Desor had written bitter letters to Agassiz's mother, complaining about his employer's character and his treatment of his wife. But Agassiz had always overlooked Desor's faults and welcomed him as eagerly as any of his helpers.

As Agassiz's establishment began to expand, he considered the possibility of remaining longer in the United States than he had originally planned. Never had he imagined the reception he had been given, the enthusiasm with which he was received everywhere. And he liked Americans. "Naturalist as I am," he wrote to a friend, "I cannot but put the people first,—the people who have opened this part of the American continent to European civilization. What a people! But to understand them you must live among them. Our education, the principles of our society, the motives of our actions, differ so greatly from what I see here, that I should try in vain to give you an idea of this great nation, passing from childhood to maturity with the faults of spoiled children, and yet with the nobility of character and the enthusiasm of youth. Their look is wholly turned toward the future; their social life is not yet irrevocably bound to exacting antecedents, and thus nothing holds them back, unless, perhaps, a consideration for the opinion in which they may be held in Europe. This deference toward England (unhappily, to them, Europe means almost exclusively England) is a curious fact in the life of the American people. . . . But since these men are so worthy to soar on their own wings, why not help them to take flight?" And who could better do that than Louis Agassiz himself?

In November, 1846, while Agassiz had been delivering the Lowell lectures, Harvard had been considering the establishment of a scientific school. In February of the following year it formally announced plans to create a "School of Instruction in Theoretical and Practical Science" and started to raise the funds to support it. Abbott Lawrence, a cotton manufacturer and a friend of Lowell, agreed to donate $50,000 and to underwrite the salaries of two professors, one of whom was to be a geologist. Although there were numerous men in the United States qualified to fill this new professorship, Lawrence had Agassiz in mind and made his preference known to the president of the university.

Agassiz had few doubts about accepting the appointment. The funds granted him by Prussia were beginning to run out, and if he wished to remain in the United States, he would have to support himself. Although Cecile was seriously ill with tuberculosis and could not have joined him, even if she had wanted to, this was no deterrent. Their disagreement was irreconcilable. His only hesitation arose over some of the terms. Harvard, for example, suggested the title of Professor of Geology. This was not quite broad enough for Agassiz, who thought it did not reflect the depth of his knowledge. Professor of Natural History was out; that title already belonged to Asa Gray. During the summer, which Agassiz spent largely on a United States Coast Survey ship, the negotiations between him and the university continued. In September the Harvard Corporation elected him Professor of Geology and Zoology, and in October, on the anniversary of his arrival in the United States, Agassiz accepted the position.

In the fall he made a triumphal lecture tour, entertaining and instructing audiences in New York and Charleston, South Carolina. Back in Cambridge in January, Agassiz delivered a new series of Lowell lectures and laid his plans for the future. First and foremost, he wanted a museum in which he could house his collections and the additions that he hoped to secure, for without a research museum he could not teach effectively. In Lawrence's original gift to the scientific school, no provision had been made for such a museum, but Agassiz persuaded the university's treasurer to provide $400 for the purchase of a bathhouse on the Charles River, which would serve until he could obtain something better.

He was now well established at Cambridge, with a house on Oxford Street, a staff, a museum, and classes to instruct. He was also popular socially, invited regularly to the best homes and a friend of many wealthy Bostonians. His only immediate problem was his assistant, Desor. Agassiz had committed an unfortunate mistake in inviting Desor to the United States, and he soon began to realize it. As the spring wore on, he learned that Desor had not been honest in handling Agassiz's finances and that he had put his name on the title page as coauthor of a book whose publication he had supervised. Furthermore, he had published under his own name the results of some research that Agassiz had conducted on starfish. Infuriated by these disclosures, Agassiz dismissed Desor, who thereupon promised to take revenge by telling Boston what Agassiz was really like. Gradually rumors, all directly traceable to Desor, spread. Agassiz had maltreated his wife; Agassiz was sleeping with a Boston servant named Jane; Agassiz had borrowed money from Desor and never repaid it; Agassiz had stolen work done by Desor and published it under his own name. In June, Agassiz's first American work appeared, a textbook entitled the *Principles of Zoology*, written in collaboration with another author. (It was immensely popular and went through sixteen editions during Agassiz's lifetime.) Desor now complained that Agassiz had never paid him for the work he had done on the book.

Ignoring these wild charges, Agassiz led an expedition of nine students, two doctors, two businessmen, and two European naturalists to Lake Superior, where they studied the zoology and geology of the region, and Agassiz, ever the teacher, lectured to them on what they saw. When he returned to Cambridge in August, he found word that Cecile had died and discovered that Desor was telling more falsehoods. Everyone who cared to listen heard that her death had been entirely due to Agassiz's neglect. The scandal grew to such proportions that Agassiz's friends advised him to resort to a typically Bostonian device for settling at least one of the difficulties between himself and Desor. Two outstanding citizens were chosen to act as a private, but formal, tribunal. Desor and Agassiz appeared before them and presented their cases concerning some of the research material of Agassiz's that Desor claimed as his own. When the tribunal ruled against him, Desor was furious and refused to accept its findings. Another was formed to consider the authorship of the *Principles of Zoology*. Once again Desor lost, although the tribunal ordered Agassiz to pay him $100 for the assistance he had given. Refusing to keep quiet, Desor launched new attacks on Agassiz, and one more tribunal was formed. The first two had limited themselves to a few of Desor's charges. The third looked into every accusation, even interviewing the servant girl named Jane and obtaining letters from Agassiz's mother and from friends in Neuchâtel. By mail, they questioned Agassiz's bankers in Europe, and they directed the members of Agassiz's American staff to appear before them. The investigation was so intensive it lasted approximately four months. When it was finished, the word was passed in Boston society that Agassiz was completely exonerated and Desor was branded a scoundrel.

With Desor's slanders thoroughly refuted, Agassiz's place in Boston —and in the United States—was secure. He continued to be invited into the best circles, to draw large audiences wherever he lectured, and to exercise a national influence on American science. Earlier he had remarked on the Americans' dependence on European approval of their efforts. In the position that he had now attained, he almost stood for Europe and was consulted by scientists, government officials, university staffs, and philanthropists. His endorsement of a project or an individual carried weight.

In June, 1849, he brought his son, Alexander, to the United States, for although he never said so, America was obviously becoming his permanent home. During the remainder of the summer he worked on his science and, when he was not busy in the laboratory or in the field, spent his hours courting Elizabeth Cary, a girl fifteen years younger than himself and the daughter of a prosperous family. Her father was uncertain whether he should give his approval. Marriage to a Harvard professor was, of course, perfectly acceptable, but this one was a foreigner who was reputed to have unpaid debts in Europe. Once more Agassiz underwent an intensive investigation. Worried about his future, he talked to Lawrence, who was about to leave the country as ambassador to England. Lawrence agreed to extend the period of time during which he would underwrite Agassiz's salary. This gave him financial security for the next five years and enabled him to continue his courtship, while Elizabeth's father continued his investigation. At last, in April, 1850, the couple was married.

Elizabeth was of a different character from Cecile, and she immediately took charge of the household. The various assistants who lived with Agassiz were either dismissed or told to do their work at the university, and although she put up with the collections for a time and even with live specimens of snakes, she made it clear that these must eventually go, too. She also took hold of Agassiz's finances. There had to be money set aside, she insisted, for the family. Pressed by his wife's demands (there is no evidence that she was unpleasant about this, merely business-like), Agassiz secured from Harvard the use of the upper floor of the new Engineer Hall for his collections and a grant that was matched by Lowell for his research. With the arrival of Agassiz's daughters in August, 1850, the family was well settled.

Alexander Dallas Bache, head of the United States Coast Survey, asked Agassiz to make a study of the Florida reefs during the winter of 1850–1851, placing a ship at his disposal and providing the funds. Agassiz undertook the assignment but had returned by March, 1851, to defend himself against a suit for libel. The case reflected his deep interest in improving the standards of American science and education. An Albany schoolteacher, two years before, had published a grossly inaccurate chart of American geologic formations for the use of the public schools. James Hall, an outstanding New York geologist, showed it to Agassiz, who immediately agreed that education had no place for such quackery and joined Hall in violently denouncing the chart in writing. The publishers replied by filing suits for libel against the two men. Agassiz was bewildered by this turn of events and could not understand how a lay jury in a court of law could determine a scientific truth. Nevertheless, he had no thought of publishing a retraction. He had assumed a role of influence in the nation's science, and he was determined to use it responsibly. After discussions with Hall and with their lawyers, he agreed to let the case against himself be tried first. This was not a light matter; the plaintiffs were asking damages of $20,000. Many of the country's leading geologists agreed to testify in Agassiz's behalf, but their offers proved unnecessary. The brilliant lecturer, the skillful teacher, needed no help in convincing the jury. With the same charm and lucidness that he had shown on the platform and in the classroom, Agassiz single-handedly destroyed the case. The plaintiffs moved for dismissal and dropped the suit against Hall. Agassiz, of course, emerged a national hero among scientists for his willingness to risk his personal fortune in defense of honesty and accuracy.

But the esteem in which Agassiz was held did not relieve his finances. No matter how much money he had or was given, he always needed a little more, because he was unable to resist the purchase of another collection or the employment of another assistant. Lecture engagements always offered him a means of augmenting his income, but they were tiring work. Therefore, he gladly accepted an invitation to teach during part of each winter, when his Harvard schedule permitted, at Charleston, South Carolina. This brought him the funds he wanted without his having to endure the discomfort of a tour, but it also nearly cost him his life. While in Charleston during the winter of 1852–1853, he became seriously ill with typhoid fever. On his recovery, even he realized that he could not go back to his teaching immediately, and he agreed to a convalescent tour through the South. Although he was supposed to be taking a rest, he could not avoid several invitations to give lectures along the way, and the sight of America's great rivers inspired him to undertake a new endeavor, a book on all the freshwater fish in the United States. As he obviously could not collect the necessary specimens himself, he enlisted the help of others. In the next few years, he sent out 6,000 circulars, many of them accompanied by personal letters, that described his needs, and he interested Spencer Fullerton Baird, assistant secretary of the Smithsonian, in what he was doing. Although Baird was sometimes reluctant to lend specimens—Agassiz did not have a good reputation for returning those he borrowed; somehow they seemed to slip into his own collection—he was able to be of great assistance because of his official standing with government expeditions.

This new venture cost additional money. Most of the specimens were provided free, but the collectors wished to be reimbursed for their out-of-pocket costs for barrels and freightage. By then the treasurer of Harvard probably shuddered every time he saw Agassiz. Nothing seemed to satiate his need for money. He appealed to Lawrence for help, but although Lawrence guaranteed Agassiz's salary for an additional term of five years, that was the limit of what he would do. The treasurer then began to raise money to purchase Agassiz's private collections, thus providing him some financial relief. He finally obtained $10,500, to which the university added another $1,800 and the purchase was completed. Although the amount of money involved was considerable, the price Agassiz asked was probably below what he could have obtained elsewhere. He was not entirely motivated by disinterest. Above almost everything else, he wanted Harvard to have a museum comparable to the great institutions of Europe. Now that it had invested heavily in collections it would have to house them, and in 1855, the university gave up the entire Engineer Hall to him, not just the top floor.

Engaged as he was in so many different activities, Agassiz had as yet failed to produce in America any scientific work comparable to his studies of fossil fish or of glaciers. He was busy arranging his museum, collecting fish, studying his notes on the Florida reefs, doing research in embryology, and trying to raise the general level of science in the United States. But he seemed unable to finish anything he started. He was worried about this and wrote to a friend, "I have now been eight years in America, have learned to understand the advantages of my position here, and have begun undertakings which are not yet brought to a conclusion. I am also aware how wide an influence I already exert upon this land of the future,—an influence which gains in extent and intensity with every year,—so that it becomes very difficult for me to discern clearly where I can be most useful to science."

In such circumstances, most men would have consolidated some of their projects or delegated them to assistants, but Agassiz was not an ordinary man. Instead of reducing his activity, he announced his largest endeavor yet: the publication of a book that would cover the entire natural history of the United States. In the preface to the first volume, he stated his aims. "I must beg my European members," he wrote, "to remember that this work is written in America, and more especially for Americans; and that the community to which it is particularly addressed has very different wants from those of the reading public in Europe. There is not a class of learned men here distinct from the other cultivated members of the community. On the contrary, so general is the desire for knowledge, that I expect to see my book read by operatives, by fishermen, by farmers, quite extensively as by the students in our colleges or by the learned professions, and it is but proper that I should endeavor to make myself understood by all." With this book, he intended to increase scientific understanding in America and thus repay the debt he thought he owed the United States.

Once more Agassiz faced the problem of money. A wealthy Bostonian, Francis Calley Gray, secured the agreement of Little, Brown and Company to print the book, if Agassiz could obtain a sufficient number of subscribers. Agassiz had done a magnificent job of publicizing his need for fish; he did an even better one for his proposed book. Approximately 10,000 people received circulars advertising *Contributions to the Natural History of the United States*. Originally Agassiz and Gray had figures showing that 450 subscriptions would make the book a success. In the end, Agassiz obtained 2,500.

As Agassiz dashed from one project to another, Elizabeth looked for some means of relieving the financial pressure on the household. It was obvious to her that another source of income should be found, because Agassiz was too weary to start a fresh round of lectures. Discussing the problem with the two older children (she and Agassiz never had any of their own), she decided the best course would be to start a school for young ladies. Because she was uncertain about Agassiz's reaction, she said nothing to him about her plans until they were well advanced. When she finally talked to him, she found to her surprise that he was very enthusiastic and wanted to play a major role. The printed circular announcing the establishment of the school appeared under his name and contained this statement: "I shall myself supervise the methods of instruction and tuition, and while maintaining that regularity and precision in the studies so important to mental training shall endeavor to prevent the necessary discipline from falling into a lifeless routine, alike deadening to the spirit of teacher and pupil. It is further my intention to take the immediate charge of the instruction in Physical Geography, Natural History, and Botany, giving a lecture daily, Saturdays excepted, on one or the other of these subjects, illustrated by specimens, models, maps, and drawings." This was a large assignment for someone about to write the definitive work on the natural history of the United States, but Agassiz's active participation added to the appeal of the school. In no time the faculty had been hired (several Harvard professors were members), and the enrollment was filled. As he had promised, Agassiz was a regular lecturer, and years later his students recalled the excellent training they had received from him. Mrs. Agassiz taught no classes, but she was in charge of general discipline and management and also attended her husband's lectures. (Later, after Agassiz's death, when she was president of Radcliffe College, she said that her philosophy of education had been formed while working for the school.)

Neither the plans for his new book nor the school distracted Agassiz from his intention of getting a better museum in which to work and teach. Lawrence, the philanthropist who had guaranteed Agassiz's salary, died in 1855, and although he left $50,000 to ensure Agassiz's continued employment, he made no provision for the museum, which was a bitter disappointment. Agassiz, having lost one friend, turned to another, Francis Gray, the man who was helping him with the *Contributions*. Gray was unable to resist Agassiz and in 1856 told him he was making a provision in his will for the museum. A number of details had to be worked out, and he wanted Agassiz's guidance. The final terms of his bequest became known shortly, because Gray died in December, 1856. He had provided that two years after his death his nephew, William Gray, as executor, was to offer Harvard—or any other institution, as he saw fit—$50,000 under these conditions: The museum must be called the Museum of Comparative Zoology, the name chosen by Agassiz; the income from the gift was to be spent solely on scientific research, not on a building or faculty salaries; and the museum must be maintained as a separate institution, independent of any other department. Agassiz had maneuvered well. Harvard had either to provide a building and assume the cost of the faculty or lose $50,000—and probably Agassiz as well. For he would go to the institution that accepted both the gift and its conditions.

Previously he had received several offers of important positions in Europe, and in the fall of 1857 the French government asked him to become professor of paleontology at the Jardin des Plantes with a higher salary and more privileges than he enjoyed at Harvard. Agassiz had no interest in moving to France. As he wrote a friend, "The work I have undertaken here, and the confidence shown in me by those who have at heart the intellectual development of this country, make my return to Europe impossible for the present; and, as you have well understood, I prefer to build anew here rather than to fight my way in the midst of the coteries of Paris. Were I offered absolute power for the reorganization of the Jardin des Plantes, with a revenue of fifty thousand francs, I should not accept it. I like my independence better." To the general public, he was somewhat less frank. He let the word spread that by rejecting the French offer, he was purposely sacrificing himself in the cause of American science. This further strengthened his hold over Harvard. When he rejected a second and even more liberal offer from the French government, his position was more enhanced.

Agassiz had delayed the publication of *Contributions*, because of his insistence on better illustrations (they also entailed more expense), but the first two volumes came out in 1857. The work he had included on American turtles—he had been studying turtles, too, along with everything else—was significant in itself as being the best of its kind until that time. But the important part of the book, to which Agassiz had given much publicity, was the "Essay on Classification." In this, he had promised to lay a new basis for studying nature. In actuality, he did nothing of the kind. After reviewing many systems of classification, he reverted to Cuvier's and tried to force everything that had been learned since Cuvier's day into the framework devised by Cuvier. What Agassiz wrote may have been an act of loyalty to his old master, but it was not an act of science. For all his brilliance, he had remained at a dead standstill as far as his basic attitude was concerned. The public received the books avidly, but some of the better scientists, like Asa Gray and James Dwight Dana, were concerned. They had expected a fresh approach to some of the new questions of the age, like the distribution of animals. Instead, all they found was an expanded version of the beliefs that Agassiz had uttered years ago from the lecture platform and printed in the *Principles of Zoology*.

Agassiz lost further prestige at this time by letting a foolish quarrel develop between himself and Dana. A Frenchman had produced a publication on American geology, which contained a number of errors and disparaging remarks about several competent American geologists. Dana wrote a harsh review. Agassiz promptly replied in defense of the Frenchman but admitted in print that he had never read the work. He did not need to, he illogically said, and threatened to resign as an editor of the *American Journal of Science* unless his reply was published.

He also came under attack from Asa Gray, who had been studying the botany of Japan and had decided the similarities between certain Japanese plants and those found elsewhere could not be explained by any ideas as simple as Agassiz's. Speaking before the American Academy of Arts and Sciences, he stated that something more than a bland reference to divine will was needed to understand the phenomena he had observed. Because Agassiz had just reaffirmed his ideas by publishing a separate edition of the *Essay on Classification* in England, no one was in any doubt about the object of Gray's criticism. Although these incidents made some scientists start to question Agassiz's authority, they in no way interfered with his plans for the museum.

Harvard accepted the provisions of Gray's bequest and some additional restrictions laid down by Gray's nephew, one of which was that Agassiz was to be appointed director. In his annual report to the Massachusetts legislature, the governor asked for an appropriation for the museum, and a group of important businessmen, headed by the son of Agassiz's original benefactor, Lawrence, met to raise additional funds. In the spring of 1859 the legislature passed a bill that provided up to $100,000 to the museum—the amount was contingent on the sale of some lands owned by the commonwealth—and private sources had contributed more than $71,000. Agassiz then turned his attention to the organization of the museum and assumed the titles of both curator and director. By June he was in a state of exhaustion and took a trip to Europe, but he was back in the fall in time to supervise the installation of some of the collections on the already completed first floor of the new building.

These were wonderful days for Agassiz. He had a group of devoted assistants and students, who formed the Agassiz Zoological Society. They would do anything for this stimulating teacher, who brought to the classroom the same excitement he could create in the lecture hall. He knew how to talk to young men, to arouse their enthusiasm, and he had that gift of the rare teacher: He could be intimate with his students and not lose their respect. During his career at Harvard he had always shown these qualities, but now that he at last had his museum, he reached new heights as a teacher. One former student said he had never in his life met a man with a more engaging presence and recalled an event that he considered illustrative of Agassiz's ability to influence people. At a time when Agassiz was interested in comparing the skeletons of ordinary horses with thoroughbreds, flames broke out at a nearby racing stable. The student ran to the fire to persuade the jockeys and owners to let him have the skeletons of the horses that died, but the men were profanely angry and flatly rebuked him. On his way back to the museum, he met Agassiz starting out on the same mission. He told Agassiz that his cause was hopeless, but Agassiz went to the burning building, quietly took command, helped the men with the injured horses, and, when everything was over, obtained all the skeletons he wanted. He could deal with almost anybody, students, faculty, audiences, the philanthropists of Boston, and even irate stablemen.

But there was one thing that he could not cope with. That was Darwin's theory of evolution. Ever since his days with Cuvier, Agassiz had been convinced that each species was a special creation, and he held to that belief in spite of the evidence before his eyes. Nothing could shake him. In his books, in his classroom, and on his lecture tours he had preached his theories over and over again, and they had been accepted, particularly by the general public. Even when Darwin published his *Origin of Species* in 1859, Agassiz was unwilling to retract.

The result was a tragedy. Agassiz considered the book nonsense; it struck at the roots of his faith. Therefore, he became its principal critic in the United States, defending a worn-out creed before the onslaught of more vigorous and modern minds. The battle was one-sided. Only Agassiz's enormous knowledge gave it dignity and meaning. Like Cuvier arguing with Geoffroy Saint-Hilaire, he had a great stock of information on which to draw, and he used it as best he could, pointing to the fallacies in Darwin's statements, underlining their weaknesses, and especially stressing the inadequacy of the geologic record. No one else in the United States could have done it so well; no one else could have carried such weight with the public, who tended to side with Agassiz even when the scientists did not. But the struggle was hopeless.

Turning, dodging, and refusing to give an inch, Agassiz fought his way through the scientific debates that marked the first half of 1860, the year following the publication of Darwin's book. By the time spring had reached Cambridge, it was clear to some that his brilliant reputation was now tarnished.

V

Nothing, not even his stubborn opposition to Darwinism, could eclipse Agassiz's wide popularity. Some of the better scientists might question him, but the public did not. To them, he was the supreme arbiter, and he decided to use his influence to launch a wholesale attack against Darwinism, not at scientific meetings, but in the nation's lecture halls. From now on, he intended to carry his case to the people. In a new series of lectures he repeated all his old ideas, almost as though the mere reiteration would give them validity. The theory of transmutation, he stated flatly, ran contrary to the processes of nature. Once again, supported by his reputation and by the many facts at his command, he presented as good an argument as could be made; and the public flocked to hear him. Many prominent citizens—particularly ministers—were persuaded by what he said and regarded him as the principal defender of their orthodox ideas. When he finished the lectures, he published them in the *Atlantic Monthly*, whose editor was extremely friendly to him, and then brought them out as a book, *Methods of Study in Natural History*. This volume attracted so many readers that it eventually went through nineteen editions.

In 1862 he accepted an invitation from the Brooklyn Institute to give the Graham Lectures, which had been established to show the "Power, Wisdom, and Goodness of God" by examining natural history. Agassiz opened his first lecture by saying, "You are aware that in conformity with the foundation of this course of lectures, of which mine are to form a part, a special object is assigned to them; and considering the position in which I have been reported to stand with reference to my opinions in matters of science, I feel bound in frankness to explain to you, before I proceed to my subject, in what light I view the study of nature, and in what way it may promote the object that these lectures are especially intended to further.

"The study of nature has one great object which fairly comes within the scope of the foundation of this course of lectures; it is to trace the connection between all created beings, to discover, if possible, the plan according to which they have been created, and to search out their relation to the great Author. . . .

"At this moment," he continued, "natural history can show not only that there is a plan in the creation of the animal kingdom, but that the plan has been preconceived, has been laid out in the course of time, and executed with the definite object of introducing man upon the earth. . . . The moment this suggested itself it became self-evident that the work of naturalists, instead of consisting of ingenious devices for classification, was henceforth to consist only in an attempt to read more and more accurately a work in which they had no part, a work which displayed the thought of a mind more comprehensive than their own, which called into existence the various beings that we see around us, and established their classification. It is now, therefore, the task of the naturalist to read the thoughts of that mind as expressed in the living realities that surround us. . . . I shall endeavor to show that there is really a plan —a thoughtful plan—a plan which may be read—in the relations which you and I, and all living beings scattered over the surface of the earth, hold to one another . . . and I shall endeavor to . . . show you what has been the thought running through the succession of creations, from the beginning, down to the time when, as the crowning act of the Creator, man was placed on the earth at the head of creation.

"It was Cuvier," Agassiz went on, "who first recognized the fact that the animal kingdom is constructed upon a plan, though that plan did not necessarily imply, according to Cuvier, a conception by an intelligent author. Cuvier only recognized certain structural complications among animals, which brought them together in accordance with the resemblance of their combinations. He recognized four such plans, and showed that all animals, however diversified, are built upon these four plans; and all investigation since that time has only confirmed his discovery." Agassiz was still back at the Jardin des Plantes, listening to the debates between Cuvier and Geoffroy Saint-Hilaire, completely a captive of the ideas he had absorbed then. No matter what evidence was presented to the contrary, he could not free himself.

Several factors may have accounted for his intellectual obstinacy. By nature, he liked personal authority, and to accept Darwinism, even to examine it critically, meant repudiating everything he had said in the past about creation. He had spoken too strongly, too definitively, too widely to retreat with grace and without sacrificing the position he thought he had established for himself in American science. He had also, in his efforts to popularize science in America, spent more of his time and effort with the public than with his colleagues. Somewhat like Werner, although not nearly to the same degree, he had isolated himself from the critical thinking of his age. But perhaps more than anything else he was guilty of human blindness. At the Museum of Comparative Zoology, he had all the material he needed to evaluate Darwin's ideas, but instead of using them for that purpose, he employed them only to support his own. He could not bring himself, as Lyell had done, to discard long cherished ideas in favor of new ones, to reexamine his work in the light of fresh facts and theories.

Even Agassiz's devoted students began to desert him. The Agassiz Zoological Society, in which he had taken such pride, had given way to a secret Society for the Protection of American Students from Foreign Professors. Many of its members complained of his dictatorial supervision of their activities, and he responded only by tightening the rules. No one could publish the results of his research without Agassiz's permission; no one could keep a private collection at the museum for study purposes. His staff began accepting appointments elsewhere—without even bothering to ask Agassiz for recommendations. More and more, Agassiz filled the resulting vacancies with Europeans, who, he thought, were more susceptible to discipline. They proved themselves faithful, but their coming marked the end of the enthusiastic spirit that had once pervaded Agassiz's workrooms.

The museum was further disrupted by an acrimonious quarrel between Agassiz and the man he had chosen as his principal assistant and future successor, an assistant professor named Henry Clark. They had worked together on *Contributions*, and with the appearance of the fourth volume, Clark complained that Agassiz had not given him sufficient credit. He announced that from then on, he would publish the results of all his research under his own name. The argument became so bitter that Agassiz demanded that Clark surrender his set of keys to the museum. Clark considered this as a request for his resignation, which Agassiz did not have the authority to ask for. The difference between the two men was widely publicized—Clark circulated a folder setting forth his claims—and the Harvard Corporation had to step in and work out an unsatisfactory compromise.

But everything was not bad. In 1863, Agassiz's income had become sufficient to make him independent of his school, which he closed. He embarked on a new project, collecting fish from all over the world, not merely the United States. By using his still great influence, he was once more able to enlist wide support, and barrels of specimens arrived at Cambridge. As for the museum, it was prospering. The Commonwealth of Massachusetts had sold its lands, paid the promised $100,000, and voted new appropriations. Other funds came in, but never enough to satisfy Agassiz. This was to be the greatest museum in the United States and at least equal to, if not better than, the finest in Europe. To reach that goal, he needed money and more money. And because he could never afford to purchase all the specimens he wanted, he enlisted as many volunteer collectors as he could all over the world. Even the American consulates were pressed into service.

In the midst of this success, the struggle with Asa Gray continued to smoulder and then broke out at a meeting of the National Academy of Sciences, an organization that Agassiz had helped establish. Baird, the assistant secretary of the Smithsonian, was proposed for membership. Although Agassiz had had Baird's help in building up the museum's collections, he did not regard Baird highly as a scientist and, therefore, opposed his election. When the returns were in, however, Baird had been elected anyway. Agassiz interpreted this, and probably rightly, as a direct, personal challenge from scientists like Gray and Dana. In retaliation, he threatened again to resign as an editor of the *American Journal of Science* and berated several of his friends, who he thought had deserted him.

Part of these deepening troubles were certainly caused by overwork. His health was beginning to fail; he lost his temper easily; he wearied quickly. Noticing his condition, a Boston businessman offered to finance an expedition to Brazil. This would give Agassiz a deserved rest and at the same time permit him to do research in an important area. A steamship company provided free passage to Rio de Janiero, and the government of Brazil promised its fullest cooperation. Agassiz, accompanied by his wife and a number of assistants, left New York in April, 1865. Humboldt would have been amazed at the style in which the formerly penniless student traveled. Instead of voyaging in a cramped native boat the way Humboldt and Bonpland had done, Agassiz rode on a Brazilian gunboat. "Here I am," Agassiz wrote home, "sailing on the Rio Negro, . . . provided with all the facilities which modern improvements, the extraordinary liberality of the Brazilian government, and the kindness of our commander can bestow, and pursuing my scientific investigations with as much ease as if I were in my study, or in the museum at Cambridge." When Agassiz and his staff came back to the United States in August of the following year, they brought with them some 80,000 specimens as evidence of the work they had put in.

On his return, he gave lectures about Brazil and, with Mrs. Agassiz as coauthor, published a book, *A Journey in Brazil*. In both his speeches and his book, he stated that Brazil had once been covered by a glacier, but although this ran contrary to the conclusions of other observers, Agassiz cited little evidence to support his statement. In his criticism of Darwin, he wanted to point to a mass of ice large enough to destroy all life in order to prove that there had been a genetic break between all previous forms and those existing today. Wanting the ice, he simply created it, much to the scorn of other scientists like Lyell. This was no longer the careful student of glaciers who had spent years observing and studying before he published his remarkable conclusions. This was a sixty-year-old man, sadly inventing assumptions to support his tattered and outmoded theories.

In 1868 he led an expedition of businessmen and Congressmen along the route of the Union Pacific Railroad as far as Wyoming and on the way back stopped at Ithaca, New York, where he stayed for two months advising the founders of Cornell. When he returned to Cambridge, he found that all was going well with his museum. The Massachusetts legislature had appropriated funds for an addition to the building, and private donors were trying to double the amount. After a trip to Florida, Cuba, and the Bahamas on a Coast Survey ship, he returned to Cambridge to oppose fiercely the selection of Charles Eliot as president of Harvard. Because Eliot was chosen anyway, his opposition cost him most of his influence in the administration of the university. But he put aside his quarrels long enough to be, on November 14, 1869, the principal speaker at the celebration of the hundredth anniversary of Humboldt's birth. In touching terms, he told of his relationship with the great scientist and ended his remarks with words that expressed his own philosophy and what he himself had successfully attempted to do in America. "We all have a great task to perform," he said. "It should be our effort, as far as it lies in our power, to raise the standard of culture of our people, as Humboldt has elevated that of the world. May the community at large feel with equal keenness the importance of each step now taken for the expansion, in every direction, of all the means of the highest culture." On his return home from the lecture, he suffered a cerebral hemorrhage.

For months, he lay in bed, fretting at his own inactivity. Then he was allowed to go to Deerfield, Massachusetts, for a period of convalescence. After that, in November, 1870, the doctors permitted him to resume his usual schedule, and in 1871 he accepted an invitation of the Coast Survey to travel on one of their ships from New York to San Francisco by way of the Strait of Magellan. On the journey, he received word that he had been elected a foreign member of the French Institute, a final honor in a long career. But he was growing old and wrote, "The distinction pleased me the more because so unexpected. Unhappily it is usually a brevet of infirmity, or at least of old age, and in my case it is to a house in ruins that the diploma is addressed. I regret it the more because I have never felt more disposed for work, and yet never so fatigued by it."

With his increasing age, he was becoming less severe in his attitude toward Darwinism. He realized that other scientists thought he was letting his criticism degenerate into a personal quarrel. He therefore made an intellectual attempt to reexamine Darwinism and, at the beginning of his trip around South America, thought he might find some evidence supporting evolution. But he did not do so even at the Galápagos Islands. "Our visit to the Galápagos has been full of geological and zoological interest," he wrote. "It is most impressive to see an extensive archipelago, *of most recent origin*, inhabited by creatures so different from any known in other parts of the world. Here we have a positive limit to the time that may have been granted for the transformation of these animals, if indeed they are in any way derived from others dwelling in different parts of the world. If descended from some other type, belonging to any neighboring land, then it does not require such unspeakably long periods for the transformation of species as the modern advocates of transmutation claim. . . ." He could even turn Darwin's own evidence against him and, given the knowledge of genetics at the time, make a telling point.

In October, 1872, Agassiz returned to Cambridge and, although he was weary from his journey, almost immediately launched into a new project. He had always been especially interested in the education of teachers, welcoming them to the museum and eagerly accepting them as students. He thought a summer school should be established for them on the Massachusetts coast. Along with some new gifts for the museum, he succeeded in obtaining the donation of Penikese Island in Buzzards Bay and enough money to erect the necessary buildings and gather a staff. When Agassiz went out to inspect the school a few days before it was scheduled to open, he found that the dormitory was still unfinished, and neither the architect nor the workmen believed it could be completed in time. That was on a Saturday. Undaunted, Agassiz called the carpenters together. This was not a profit-making enterprise, he explained to them. This was for the betterment of American education. He had charmed thousands of people from the lecture platforms, had talked the philanthropists of America and the Massachusetts legislature into donating money for science, and had calmed the irate jockeys at the burning stable. He had equal success with the carpenters. After listening to him speak, they gave up their Sunday, worked hard, and finished the building in time.

That fall he again took up the discussion of Darwinism. He planned to express his views again in his coming lectures and, to gain a wider audience for them, fashion them into articles for the *Atlantic Monthly*. The first was entitled "Evolution and Permanence of Type." In it, he carefully analyzed Darwin's ideas once more. But once more he saw faults in Darwin's theory—real faults, too—and failed to be convinced by its truths. "Whatever be the means of preserving and transmitting properties," he wrote, "the primitive types have remained permanent and unchanged,—in the long succession of ages, amid all the appearance and disappearance of kinds, the fading away of one species and the coming in of another,—from the earliest geological periods to the present day. How these types were first introduced, how the species which have successively represented them have replaced one another—these are the vital questions to which no answer has been given. We are as far from any satisfactory solution of this problem as if development theories had never been discussed."

Although he was sixty-six years old, he worked as hard that fall as he had encouraged others to do for so many years. He developed a plan for attempting to persuade the federal government to give the museum a million acres that it could sell; he gave a lecture on the "structural growth of domesticated animals" for the Massachusetts Board of Agriculture; he conducted his classes at the museum. On December 6, 1873, he complained of being more tired than usual. He went to the museum but in a short time returned and fell asleep. Although he occasionally regained consciousness, he never spoke again, and on December 14, he died.

On the day of his funeral, all classes at Harvard were suspended. The president of Harvard and the Vice-President of the United States attended it; so did students, scholars, professors, scientists, and the public whom he had tried to educate in the ways of science. Students carried the bier, and as they passed, one professor remarked that Agassiz was still younger than his pallbearers. So general was the sadness that the Boston papers reported the event in editions edged with black. A few months after his death, his friends placed over his grave a massive boulder brought from the Aar Glacier, and on it they placed his name and the one word he had chosen as an epitaph: "teacher." Better yet, as far as the spirit of Agassiz was concerned, they subscribed generously to a new fund-raising campaign for his beloved museum as a tribute to this contradictory, but influential, man.

In his lifetime he had done so much, and he had done so little. He had been so great and, at times, so small. In his loyalty to Cuvier and his own obstinate, intellectual blindness, he had tried to impede science and, to an extent, had succeeded. In his desire for personal authority, he had sometimes stooped to foolish quarrels, both with his students and with his colleagues. These were faults, but they were human faults, and if he had not been Agassiz, they would have hardly mattered. Laid against them were his great achievements: the studies of glaciers; the Ice Age theory; the stimulation of science in the United States; the brilliant work in paleontology; the popularization of intellectualism in America; the courses that no one ever forgot; the encouragement of better teaching; and the museum he had made a reality. These were the truths of his existence, the heritage he left, the reasons for which he is remembered.

But even above them there was something else. Thirteen years after his death, it was put into words by his former antagonist, Asa Gray. "Those who knew the man during the twenty-seven years of his American life," Gray wrote, "can quite understand the contagious enthusiasm and confidence which he evoked."

11

The Great Discovery

CHARLES DARWIN: 1809-1882

I

Dr. Robert Darwin of Shrewsbury, England, was not especially satisfied with his young son, Charles Robert Darwin. He himself was an eminently practical man, sure of his opinions and highly successful. His own father, Erasmus Darwin, who had had a considerable reputation as a doctor, naturalist, and man of letters, had given him 20 pounds before he was twenty-one and told him to make his own way in the world. Considering the wealth of Erasmus Darwin, the gift was insignificant, but Robert Darwin never asked for more. With this sum and another 20 pounds he received from an uncle, he set up practice and, at the end of the first year, was able to support two horses and a servant. Although he had little interest in science, he seemed to be instinctive in his diagnoses of diseases and had a charming manner with his patients. His practice rapidly grew, until it was rumored that he earned more than any provincial doctor in England. His financial security was further increased by his marriage to one of the daughters of Josiah Wedgwood, the manufacturer of chinaware, and by an inheritance of 25,000 pounds when Erasmus died. Worldly, ambitious, and dictatorial in his own family, he was in many respects the antithesis of the son who was born to him on February 12, 1809.

Charles, in the opinion of his father, was careless, indolent, and perhaps not too bright. During his mother's long and final illness—she died when he was only eight—he was brought up almost entirely by his domineering older sister, Caroline, who taught him at home, and Caroline believed that he was not as intelligent as his younger sister, Catherine, whom she also instructed. This opinion, of course, became the family's. "You care for nothing but shooting, dogs, and rat-catching," Dr. Darwin once told him, "and you will be a disgrace to yourself and all your family."

The criticism to which he was subjected did not apparently affect Darwin deeply, although in later years, whenever he saw Caroline, he always wondered what she was going to reprove him for. His childhood was happy. He revered his father, loved his sisters, and enjoyed the Shrewsbury countryside, taking life as it was and adopting the self-defense of indifference that is one of the protections of the weaker members in strong-willed families.

At the age of eight he was sent to a day school, which apparently had no effect on him at all. He remembered only two incidents during the year he attended. In one, he beat a puppy too severely, an action that was utterly uncharacteristic and weighed heavily on his conscience. In the other, he watched a dragoon receive a military burial, a sight that stirred him deeply. But he learned nothing that influenced him.

Dr. Darwin next arranged for him to enter the Shrewsbury School, where he remained for seven years as a boarder, although being only a mile from home, he could, and did, return frequently. This was hardly an improvement for someone of Darwin's interests and temperament. He summed up his experience by saying, "Nothing could have been worse for the development of my mind than Dr. Butler's school, as it was strictly classical, nothing else being taught, except a little ancient geography and history. The school as a means of education to me was simply a blank. During my whole life I have been singularly incapable of mastering any language. Especial attention was paid to verse-making, and this I could never do well. . . . Much attention was paid to learning by heart the lessons of the previous day; this I could effect with great facility, learning forty or fifty lines of Virgil or Homer, whilst I was in morning chapel; but this exercise was utterly useless, for every verse was forgotten in forty-eight hours." When, at the age of sixteen, he left the school, he was certainly not at the top of his class, but he was not at the bottom. Nevertheless, he said that "I believe I was considered by all my masters and by my father as a very ordinary boy, rather below the common standard in intellect."

Dr. Darwin next sent him to the University of Edinburgh, where Darwin's older brother, Erasmus, was studying medicine. Convinced that his son was not bright, Dr. Darwin nevertheless believed he would make a good doctor, meaning by that one who would attract many patients.

Darwin found Edinburgh as unstimulating as Shrewsbury. All the courses were taught by lectures, most of which Darwin found "intolerably dull." Even anatomy, which he later wished he had learned, was given by a professor who made Darwin regard the subject with disgust. On two occasions he watched operations being performed at the Edinburgh hospital. The clumsiness of the surgeons and the pain endured by the patients—this was long before the use of anesthetics—revolted him, and Darwin left the room before either of them was completed. After the second one, he vowed he would never go back and quietly made up his mind that medicine was a profession he had no intention of following. He was helped in this decision by hearing various remarks that led him to believe he would inherit enough from his father to live comfortably. With this knowledge, he saw no reason for doing something he disliked.

He returned to Edinburgh for one more year. Because Erasmus had left, he was thrown more on his own resources and found this a great advantage. He attended a professor's lectures in zoology and geology but said of them that "the sole effect they produced on me was the determination never as long as I lived to read a book on geology, or in any way to study the science." This was a subject that had interested him, but his professor was incapable of capitalizing on his latent enthusiasm.

The two years, however, were not entirely wasted. He became friends with the curator of the museum and discussed natural history with him; he went to the meetings of several scientific societies; and he found among his acquaintances a number with interests like his own. One of them was an admirer of Lamarck, and Darwin later thought a conversation with him had perhaps first aroused his curiosity about the origin of the species. (His grandfather, Erasmus Darwin, had written a book, *Zoonomia*, in which he had advanced a theory of evolution, but although Darwin had, of course, read and admired it, he later decided that it contained far too much speculation and far too few facts.)

Two of his friends were marine biologists, and they often went on collecting expeditions to the tidal pools near Edinburgh. And Darwin became sufficiently friendly with the local fishermen to accompany them on their trawling expeditions. In this way, he obtained a considerable number of specimens, which he tried to dissect. He had only a poor microscope and extremely little skill, so the results of this work, aside from showing where his real bent lay, were not significant. The autumn always found him out shooting birds. He was an excellent shot, for this was what he most enjoyed doing. (At night he placed his shooting boots ready by his bedside so that he would not lose even a minute in the morning.) Aside from the excellence of his aim, the only unusual feature of his participation in this sport was his insistence on keeping an exact record of every bird he brought down. This was the instinct of a future collector.

Pleasant as it was, this life was leading nowhere, and whereas Darwin had no objection to becoming an "idle sporting man," Dr. Darwin definitely did not want him to be one. Casting about for a different career for his son, he thought of the clergy. Amazingly enough, Darwin received this suggestion seriously, saying that if he entered the church, he wanted to be a country minister—no city parish for him. He only doubted his ability to accept all the dogmas of the Church of England. But after reading a few theological books, he set these scruples aside, for although he believed literally in the Bible, he could find no contradictions in the Anglican Creed.

A degree from an English university was a requirement for admission as a minister in the Church of England. Darwin, therefore, left the University of Edinburgh and entered Christ's College, Cambridge—but not without some difficulty. "As I had never opened a classical book since leaving school," he wrote, "I found to my dismay, that in the two intervening years, I had actually forgotten, incredible as it may appear, almost everything which I had learnt, even to some few of the Greek letters." Dr. Darwin probably threw up his hands when he heard this, but he brought Darwin home to Shrewsbury and employed a private tutor, who soon helped him recover his "school standard of knowledge."

In 1828 he moved to Cambridge, and of his education there he wrote, "During the three years which I spent at Cambridge my time was wasted, as far as the academical studies were concerned, as completely as at Edinburgh and at school." Several professors at Cambridge gave public lectures in subjects that should have appealed to Darwin, but he was so weary of lectures after his experience in Edinburgh that he failed to attend them. He quietly did his required work and, not being as unintelligent as his father thought, succeeded in passing the necessary courses with modest marks. Intellectually, however, he gained little from his formal courses.

The values he received from Cambridge came almost entirely from his extracurricular activities. He had a cousin who liked to collect beetles, and soon Darwin became an ardent beetle collector. He could even remember years later the exact posts and trees on which he had found certain specimens. The science faculty also treated him considerately, and he was invited regularly to the houses of the three leading professors and sometimes went with them on field trips. Because of his delay in entering Cambridge, caused by his failure to remember his classics, he had to stay at Cambridge for two extra terms. One of the professors encouraged him to use the time to study geology under Adam Sedgwick and persuaded Sedgwick to let him go on a field trip with him.

On the way to their destination, they stopped for the night at the Darwin house at Shrewsbury. Here an incident occurred that made a deep impression on Darwin and revealed the quality of mind with which so many innovators have had to contend. In recounting the event, Darwin wrote, "Whilst examining an old gravel-pit near Shrewsbury, a labourer told me that he had found in it a large worn tropical Volute shell, such as may be seen on the chimney-pieces of cottages; and as he would not sell the shell, I was convinced that he had really found it in the pit. I told Sedgwick of the fact, and he at once said (no doubt truly) that it must have been thrown away by some one into the pit; but then added, if really embedded there it would be the greatest misfortune to geology, as it would overthrow all that we know about the superficial deposits of the Midland Counties. These gravel-beds belong in fact to the glacial period, and in after years I found in them broken arctic shells. But I was then utterly astonished at Sedgwick not being delighted at so wonderful a fact as a tropical shell being found near the surface in the middle of England. Nothing before had ever made me thoroughly realize, though I had read various scientific books, that science consists of grouping facts so that general laws or conclusions may be drawn from them." This was a valuable lesson for Darwin to learn and one that he applied to his great scientific works. But ironically, Sedgwick did not know that he was teaching it to the man who would overthrow far more than "all we know about the superficial deposits of the Midland Counties." As it was, he taught Darwin as much geology as he believed he could absorb, knowledge that was later helpful to him. But as soon as the hunting season started, Darwin left for home. "At that time I should have thought myself mad," he wrote, "to give up the first days of partridge-shooting for geology or any other science."

Two other events that influenced him greatly occurred during those years at Cambridge. One was reading a *Preliminary Discourse on the Study of Natural Philosophy* by Sir John Herschel, the astronomer. In this book, Herschel tried to raise the esteem in which science was generally held. He argued that science played a useful role in the advancement of society and that its future achievements would be great, this at a time when many thought the pursuit of science should be regarded as a gentleman's hobby. The other event was reading Humboldt's account of his travels in Latin America. Darwin was so taken by Humboldt's description of Tenerife that he copied out the pages to read to his friends and became determined that he would visit the Canary Islands himself. He even started to learn Spanish and inquired about merchant ships that might be stopping there.

His plans were changed, however, by two letters he received right after he had left Sedgwick and returned home for the shooting. From them, he learned that H.M.S. *Beagle* was leaving for a two-year scientific trip around the world. Its captain, Robert Fitz-Roy had conceived the idea of taking along a naturalist, who would share his cabin. Both of Darwin's correspondents had recommended him. This was better than any trip merely to Tenerife, but there were several obstacles to Darwin's acceptance. First of all, the naturalist was to receive no salary, just his passage. And second, there was Dr. Darwin. His reaction was inevitable. He shrewdly guessed that the position must have been offered to more competent naturalists, who had turned it down. (He was right.) Therefore, there must be something wrong. The ship might be unsafe, for example. Furthermore, he did not think that wandering around the world was a fitting occupation for a future clergyman and would do nothing but damage Darwin's reputation. Besides, of what practical use could such a journey be? The next day Darwin wrote his refusal.

But Dr. Darwin had left one possible opening. "If you can find any man of commonsense who advises you to go," he said, "I will give my consent." Since Darwin knew that university professors or scientists would fail to qualify as "men of commonsense" by the standards Dr. Darwin applied, Darwin thought the question was closed. To his surprise, help came from an unexpected source. His uncle, Josiah Wedgwood, heard about the offer and thought it too good to pass by. He sent for Darwin, who was out shooting, drove him home to see his father, and, because of the high opinion in which Dr. Darwin held him, in no time at all had won the doctor's consent.

Other problems now presented themselves. Not only was Darwin to receive no salary, but he had to provide his own equipment and pay for his meals. That was more expense for Dr. Darwin. Then it appeared that the *Beagle* might not go around the world, just to South America. Then there was the *Beagle* itself. It had come back from its last voyage with some of its planks so rotten it had to be almost entirely rebuilt. Then twice, when it did set out, it was immediately blown back into port by gales. Finally, after all these trials, it raised anchor once more and on December 27, 1831, set out on what proved to be one of the most important scientific cruises in history—with its amateur, inexperienced naturalist on board.

I I

The *Beagle* was a small vessel, but it carried seventy-four persons, including the crew, officers, several supernumeraries, some marines, a surgeon and assistant surgeon, and three natives of Tierra del Fuego. On his last voyage, Fitz-Roy had taken some hostages as punishment for the theft of a whaleboat at Tierra del Fuego. The hostages had eaten the meal he gave them, then jumped overboard, leaving behind their eight-year-old girl and three babies. Fitz-Roy forced some natives to take the babies and kept the girl. Later two young men joined the ship, and Fitz-Roy also acquired a young boy. When he finally arrived in England with them, he had had some vague idea of having the government civilize them and return them to Terra del Fuego. One had died, but Fitz-Roy was now completing his self-assigned mission.

With such a large number on board, space was limited. Dr. Darwin had warned his son that his accommodations might not be comfortable, but even he had not foreseen the actuality. Fitz-Roy had promised to share his cabin with the naturalist, but unfortunately his cabin was so filled with equipment that he could not sleep in it himself. Darwin, therefore, was to have a corner of the chart table as his working area, and when he wanted to sleep, he was to swing his hammock over it. But before stretching out, he always had to remove a nearby cabinet drawer so as to have a place in which to put his feet. These conditions were so intolerable that Fitz-Roy eventually let him have the use of a small cabin located under the forecastle. Although roomier, it was hardly more comfortable, for Darwin was easily made seasick, and the location of the cabin caught the full motion of the ship.

Fitz-Roy also turned out to be somewhat less charming than he had at first appeared. His character, Darwin wrote, had "many noble features; he was devoted to his duty, generous to a fault, bold, determined, and indomitably energetic, and an ardent friend to all under his sway. He would undertake any sort of trouble to assist those whom he thought deserved assistance." On the other hand, his "temper was a most unfortunate one. It was usually worse in the early morning, and with his eagle eye he could generally detect something amiss about the ship, and then was unsparing in his blame. He was very kind to me, but was a man very difficult to live with on the intimate terms which necessarily followed our messing by ourselves in the same cabin." He and Darwin had several violent quarrels on the voyage, particularly on the subject of slavery. Fitz-Roy saw nothing wrong with the institution; Darwin was utterly opposed to it.

But these problems, while troublesome, did not detract from Darwin's enthusiasm for the voyage. Even when they discovered they could not land at Tenerife—his original goal after reading Humboldt—because of an outbreak of cholera, he was not discouraged, and the sight of St. Jago, one of the Cape Verde Islands, almost in itself made the trip worthwhile. The only science Darwin had really studied while he was at Cambridge was geology, and the island was an exhibition of geologic forces at work. Darwin had with him a copy of Lyell's book, and here he saw Lyell's principles confirmed. "The geology of this island," he wrote, "is the most interesting part of its natural history. On entering the harbor, a perfectly horizontal band in the face of the sea cliff, may be seen for some miles running along the coast, and at the height of about forty-five feet above the water. Upon examination, this white stratum is found to consist of calcareous matter, with numerous shells embedded, most of all of which now exist on the neighboring coast. It rests on ancient volcanic rocks, and has been covered by a stream of basalt. . . ." Here Darwin could observe at firsthand that the importance Humboldt had attached to volcanoes was not misplaced, but he did not limit his attention to geology. Following the tradition of the foremost naturalists on a trip of this sort, he investigated other aspects of natural history, measuring the humidity, taking samples of the dust that filled the air, and collecting octopuses in the tidal pools.

From St. Jago, the *Beagle* sailed westward to Brazil, touching the mainland at São Salvador, and then worked down the coast to Rio de Janeiro, which it reached on April 4. Darwin spent slightly more than a week traveling with a European landowner to visit an estate, which was some 100 miles from the city. He had always hated slavery and now saw the system in operation. Because of a quarrel and a lawsuit, the European was considering separating the women and children from the men and selling them in the slave market at Rio. To Darwin, this was the height of inhumanity. Yet otherwise, he regarded his host as a cultivated, civilized person. Like Humboldt, he began to realize that slavery had an evil effect on the owners, as well as on the slaves. Another incident increased his aversion to the institution. He called it "trifling," but it struck him forcefully. "I was crossing a ferry with a Negro, who was uncommonly stupid," Darwin wrote. "In endeavoring to make him understand, I talked loud, and made signs, in doing which I passed my hands near his face. He, I suppose, thought I was in a passion, and was going to strike him; for instantly, with a frightened look and half-shut eyes, he dropped his hands. I shall never forget my feelings of surprise, disgust, and shame, at seeing a great powerful man afraid even to ward off a blow, directed, as he thought, at his face. This man had been trained to a degradation lower than the slavery of the most helpless animal." To Darwin, who had worried for years about having whipped a puppy too strenuously, the event was utterly repulsive—first, the belief that he might strike the man; second, the man's inability to defend himself from attack.

He remained near Rio until July 5, 1832, while the *Beagle* returned to São Salvador to recheck the longitudes it had determined. The fundamental purpose of its voyage was navigational—to complete a survey of Patagonia and Tierra del Fuego that had already been started; to survey the shores of Chile, Peru, and some of the Pacific islands; and to take "chronometrical measurements." The study of natural history was only incidental, so the *Beagle* spent more time at sea than Darwin would have liked. Its return to São Salvador, therefore, gave him a welcome chance to stay for three months in one place, and he used the opportunity to make an extensive collection of Brazilian insects.

From Rio, the *Beagle* sailed southward to Montevideo and Buenos Aires. At Buenos Aires, the soldiers fired on the ship to keep it from landing, because the government had heard reports that England was being swept by cholera. After this inhospitable reception, they returned to Montevideo, where the police chief greeted them warmly. The local troops were in mutiny, and the chief wanted Fitz-Roy's help in maintaining order. Abandoning science for a time in the interests of diplomacy, Fitz-Roy briefly lent his marines to the chief.

On December 17, 1832, he brought the *Beagle* through the Le Maire Strait at the southern end of South America and prepared to land at Tierra del Fuego. As they entered the bay he had chosen as an anchorage, several Fuegians stood on a point and waved their tattered blankets and shouted. These were people such as Darwin had never seen before, and he was anxious to meet them and find out what they were like. "In the morning," he wrote, "the captain sent a party to communicate with the Fuegians. When we came within hail, one of the four natives who were present advanced to receive us, and began to shout most vehemently, wishing to direct us where to land. When we were on shore the party looked rather alarmed, but continued talking and making gestures with great rapidity. It was without exception the most curious and interesting spectacle I ever beheld: I could not have believed how wide was the difference between savage and civilized man: it is greater than between a wild and domesticated animal, inasmuch as in man there is a greater power of improvement." At first, the Fuegians were distrustful, but presents of scarlet cloth, which they tied around their necks, soon won them over. As a gesture of friendship, the chief patted "our breasts, . . . making a chuckling kind of noise, as people do when feeding chickens. I walked with the old man, and this demonstration of friendship was repeated several times; it was concluded by three hard slaps, which were given me on the breast and back at the same time. He then bared his bosom for me to return the compliment, which being done, he seemed highly pleased."

They spent a few days in the harbor—Darwin used the time to collect flowers—and on December 21 got under way again and doubled Cape Horn. "The evening was calm and bright," Darwin wrote of this dangerous spot, "and we enjoyed a fine view of the surrounding isles. Cape Horn, however, demanded his tribute, and before night sent us a gale of wind directly in our teeth. We stood out to sea, and on the second day again made the land, when we saw on the weather bow this notorious promontory in its proper form—veiled in a mist, and its dim outline surrounded by a storm of wind and water. Great black clouds were rolling across the heavens, and squalls of rain, with hail, swept by us with such extreme violence, that the captain determined to run into Wigwam Cove. This is a snug little harbor, not far from Cape Horn; and here, on Christmas-eve, we anchored in smooth water. The only thing which reminded us of the gale outside, was every now and then a puff from the mountains, which made the ship surge at her anchors."

Christmas in Tierra del Fuego was a far cry from Christmas in Dr. Darwin's comfortable house at Shrewsbury, but the trip was proving well worth the discomfort and the long absence from home. Not only was Darwin seeing new lands, having romantic encounters with savage peoples, adding to his knowledge of geology, and increasing his collections, but he himself was changing, changing profoundly. When he had left England, he had been the sports-loving son of a wealthy English physician, more interested in shooting and fishing than in anything else in the world. Now he was becoming truly a man of science. In discussing the transformation, he later said of the voyage, "During some part of the day I wrote my Journal, and took much pains in describing carefully and vividly all that I had seen; and this was good practice. My Journal served also, in part, as letters to my home, and portions were sent to England whenever there was an opportunity.

"The above mentioned special studies were, however, of no importance compared with the habit of energetic industry and of concentrated attention to whatever I was engaged in, which I then acquired. Everything about which I thought or read was made to bear directly on what I had seen or was likely to see; and this habit of mind was continued during the five years of the voyage. I feel sure that it was this training which has enabled me to do whatever I have done in science.

"Looking backwards, I can now perceive how my love for science gradually preponderated over every other taste. During the first two years my old passion for shooting survived in nearly full force, and I shot myself all the birds and animals for my collection; but gradually I gave up my gun more and more, and finally altogether, to my servant, as shooting interfered with my work, more especially with making out the geological structure of a country. I discovered, though unconsciously and insensibly, that the pleasure of observing and reasoning was a much higher one than that of skill and sport."

That Christmas Eve, as the *Beagle* lay snug in its remote harbor and the winds whistled down from the mountains, the change in Darwin was far from complete. He still had a year to go before he entirely abandoned his love of shooting, but the process of change was already well started. The cruise on the *Beagle* was doing for him what the professors of Edinburgh and Cambridge had failed to do, and the genius of the man was slowly awakening.

III

For six days the *Beagle* lay in the shelter of Wigwam Cove, while storms continued to rage outside. When the ship finally put to sea again, it turned westward, because Fitz-Roy wanted to land the Fuegians he had brought from England among their people. The heavy gales and strong currents kept pushing them back, but by January 11, 1833, they were close to the point they wanted to reach. The surf was smashing against the coast with enough force to carry the spray over a cliff they estimated to be 200 feet high. The next day the gale was blowing wildly and reached new heights of fury on the thirteenth. "The sea looked ominous," Darwin wrote, "like a dreary waving plain with patches of drifted snow: whilst the ship laboured heavily, the albatross glided with its expanded wings right up the wind. At noon a great sea broke over us, and filled one of the whale-boats, which was obliged to be instantly cut away. The poor *Beagle* trembled at the shock, and for a few minutes would not obey her helm; but soon, like a good ship that she was, she righted and came up to the wind again. Had another sea followed the first, our fate would have been decided soon, and for ever. We had now been twenty-four days trying to get to westward; the men were worn out with fatigue, and they had not for many nights or days a dry thing to put on."

By dropping closer to land and taking the Beagle Channel, Fitz-Roy was eventually able to land at a part of Tierra del Fuego, near where the tribe of Jemmy, one of the three Fuegians he was returning, lived. The Englishmen were soon surrounded by a group of natives, who showed signs of increasing hostility as more and more of them arrived. The Europeans were at a distinct disadvantage, because the Fuegians had no respect for their guns and cutlasses, not knowing what they were. Fitz-Roy, in an effort to frighten away one small party, waved his cutlass; the natives only laughed. He twice fired his pistol close to one of the natives; each time the man looked astounded, but he made no attempt to run away. Darwin realized that even if they killed an animal with one of their guns, the Fuegians would have difficulty understanding that it was the gun that had brought death.

No conflict developed, however, and Fitz-Roy took his passengers down the sound they had entered, closer and closer to where he had originally found Jemmy. At last they came across a member of Jemmy's tribe, who sent word to his mother and brothers. The next morning "the Fuegians began to pour in, and Jemmy's mother and brothers arrived.

Jemmy recognized the stentorian voice of one of his brothers at a prodigious distance." But, Darwin added disappointedly, "the meeting was less interesting than that between a horse, turned out into a field, when he joins an old companion. There was no demonstration of affection; they simply stared for a short time at each other; and the mother immediately went to look after her canoe."

The two other Fuegians, whom Fitz-Roy had brought, came from farther to the west, and Fitz-Roy had originally intended to take them there; but as they expressed a desire to stay where they were, he permitted them to. The goods they had been given in England were unloaded, and Fitz-Roy was prepared to see the start of his experiment at civilizing a wild race. All went well for three days, although the Fuegians asked for everything they saw and stole what they could. Suddenly the women and children disappeared. Neither of Fitz-Roy's two Fuegian boys understood why. Some of the Europeans thought the Fuegians had been frightened by the firing of muskets the evening before; others remembered an ugly incident in which a sentry had warned a Fuegian not to come nearer. The Fuegian had spit in his face and had indicated with graphic gestures that he would like to cut off the sentry's head. In this situation, it seemed wise to camp some distance away, although Matthews, a missionary, who planned to remain with the civilized Fuegians and help them, decided to remain.

The next morning, when Fitz-Roy and Darwin returned to the camp, everything was quiet, and the men were spearing fish. Whatever the crisis had been, it was over, and Fitz-Roy was free to take his men and spend the next several days exploring the Beagle Channel. When he returned on February 6, he learned that his experiment had already dismally failed. Fresh parties of natives had begun arriving almost immediately after his departure and had slowly plundered the civilized Fuegians. Among the thieves had been Jemmy's brother, who would not let his blood ties keep him from acquiring some of those strange and novel goods. Matthews, too, had suffered. Beleaguered on every side, he had passed his nights awake in order to protect his belongings. Even then he had been unsuccessful except with those he had buried. There was clearly no purpose in leaving him there. "Even our three Fuegians," Darwin wrote, "though they had been only three years with civilized men, would, I am sure, have been glad to have retained their new habits; but this was obviously impossible. I fear it is doubtful, whether their visit will have been of any use to them."

For the next months the *Beagle* remained on the eastern coast of South America, a survey of this shore being one of its primary assignments. Sometimes Darwin stayed with the ship; at other times he remained ashore or traveled overland to pick it up at its next destination. All this while his scientific development was continuing, and he was taking pages and pages of notes on the geology and flora and fauna of each place he visited, as well as building up large collections.

In March, 1834, the *Beagle* was back in Tierra del Fuego again and had returned to the place where it had left Jemmy. The men had heard that fighting had broken out and were alarmed by what they might find. But soon, Darwin wrote, "a canoe, with a little flag flying, was seen approaching, with one of the men in it washing the paint off his face. This man was poor Jemmy,—now a thin haggard savage, with long disordered hair, and naked, except a bit of a blanket around his waist. We did not recognize him until he was close to us; for he was ashamed of himself, and turned his back to the ship. We had left him plump, fat, clean, and well dressed;—I never saw so complete and grievous a change. As soon however as he was clothed, and the first flurry was over, things wore a good appearance. He dined with Captain Fitz-Roy, and ate his dinner as tidily as formerly. He told us he had 'too much' (meaning enough) to eat, that he was not cold, that his relations were very good people, and that he did not wish to go back to England." That evening they learned the reason for his happiness, when they met his young and good-looking wife. (She was announced by one of the natives as "Jemmy Button's wife." He had been teaching them random English words.) The other two Fuegians had long since left for their own country, not, however, without first stealing everything that Jemmy had owned. But that was all right with Jemmy. He now considered himself prosperous again, as well as a good friend to all Englishmen. "Every one," Darwin wrote, "must sincerely hope that Captain Fitz-Roy's noble hope may be fulfilled, of being rewarded for the many generous sacrifices which he made for these Fuegians, by some shipwrecked sailor being protected by the descendants of Jemmy Button and his tribe."

At the end of May, 1834, its assignment on the east coast completed, the *Beagle* entered the Strait of Magellan and on June 10 reached the open Pacific. Everyone expected better weather, but the ship sailed up the coast of Chile against heavy gales, the small boat pitching and tossing as the waves struck it, and was forced to take shelter for three days at Chiloé Island. When the *Beagle* at last dropped anchor late at night in Valparaiso Bay on July 23, Fitz-Roy was an exhausted man. High-strung and irritable, he had been working hard and taking his ship through stormy, dangerous waters, and he had almost reached the breaking point. Earlier he had chartered two smaller ships to help him with his surveying, and when their charters ran out, he had purchased a small schooner, paying for it out of his own pocket and hoping that he would be reimbursed. At Valparaiso he learned that the Admiralty would not allow him the money he had spent, and this reversal so upset him that he thought he was becoming insane, put himself on the sick list, and resigned his command. His action threatened the fulfillment of the *Beagle's* mission. As his officers were unwilling to return to England with their work undone, they at last persuaded him to return to his post. This, combined with the work of assembling the data they had collected in Patagonia and Tierra del Fuego, delayed their sailing.

In August, Darwin, having completed everything he could do around Valparaiso, "set out on a riding excursion, for the purpose of geologizing the basal parts of the Andes, which alone at this time of the year are not shut up by the winter snow." He discovered that "the appearance of the mountains was different from that which I had expected. The lower line of the snow was of course horizontal, and to this line the even summits of the range seemed quite parallel. Only at long intervals, a group of points or a single cone, showed where a volcano had existed, or does now exist. Hence the range resembled a great wall, surmounted here and there by a tower, and making a most perfect barrier to the country." As Humboldt had done farther north, he noted the lust for gold and silver that obsessed the people of the Andes, commenting that "the rage for mining has scarcely left a spot of Chile unexamined." On the whole, he liked Argentina much better. "Chile is the more civilized of the two countries," he wrote, "and the inhabitants, in consequence, have lost much individual character. Gradations in rank are much more strongly marked: the Gauso [the Chilean cowboy] does not by any means consider every man his equal. . . . This feeling of inequality is a necessary consequence of the existence of an aristocracy of wealth. It is said that some few of the greater landowners possess from five to ten thousand pounds sterling per annum; an inequality of riches which I believe is not met with, in any of the cattle-breeding countries eastward of the Andes. A traveller does not here meet that unbounded hospitality which refuses all payment, but yet is so kindly offered that no scruples can be raised in accepting it. Almost every house in Chile will receive you for the night, but a trifle is expected to be given in the morning; even a rich man will accept two or three shillings. The Gaucho [the Gauso's Argentine equivalent], although he may be a cut-throat, is a gentleman; the Gauso is in few respects better, but at the same time a vulgar ordinary fellow."

After a pleasant week's stay at Santiago, which he had reached by a circuitous route to the north, he returned to Valparaiso by a similar route to the south. On the way, he stopped at a mining town, and like Humboldt, was appalled at the working conditions—the heavy loads and the steep ascents, the poor pay, the youth of some of the men (he saw no women and children), and their near nakedness. His humanity was especially offended by their enforced diet. "With this very severe labour," he wrote, "they live entirely on boiled beans and bread. They would pre-fer having bread alone; but their masters, finding that they cannot work so hard upon this, treat them like horses, and make them eat the beans."

Toward the end of this journey, which lasted a little more than a month, Darwin became seriously sick. (He thought his illness had been caused by drinking some freshly made Chilean wine.) But this did not make him stop work; he even spent two days searching for marine fos-sils in one formation. When he reached Valparaiso, however, he had to take to his bed in the house of a friend. And there he remained from September 22 until the end of October.

On November 10, the *Beagle* once more weighed anchor. Turning southward, it retraced its course to Chiloé, where it had taken refuge from the gales on its way north. Its next assignment was to make charts of the island's coast and then to survey the coast of the Chonos Archipelago. Much of this shoreline was wild and desolate, and some-times, when he was on land, Darwin could not help wondering whether his feet were the first human's to touch that particular plot of soil. Once, in his wanderings, he came across "a bed made of grass be-neath a ledge of rock. Close by it there had been a fire, and the man had used an axe. The fire, bed, and situation showed the dexterity of an In-dian; but he could scarcely have been an Indian, for the race is in this part extinct. . . . I had at the time some misgivings that the solitary man who had made his bed on this wild spot, must have been some poor shipwrecked sailor, who, in trying to travel up the coast, had here laid himself down for his dreary night." In that part of the world, Darwin's surmise might well prove correct, and it did, for only ten days later, when they had anchored in a small harbor, they saw a man waving his shirt. Fitz-Roy promptly ordered a boat to put in. It shortly returned with two seamen, part of a group of six who had deserted from a New Bedford whaler. They had stolen off one night in a whaleboat, hoping to make their way to Chiloé, but during their first landing they had so badly dam-aged their whaleboat that it was beyond repair. The country was impen-etrable inland, and the coast so rocky it was impassable. (One of the men had died when he had tried to leap across a chasm.) Thus, they were trapped at their landing spot and could make only short excursions in search of food. For some fifteen months they had remained there, living on seal's flesh, shellfish, and wild plants, until the *Beagle* rescued them. As they often separated in search for food, Darwin concluded that one of them must have slept in the grass bed he had seen.

On February 4, having finished this part of their survey, Fitz-Roy turned north from Chiloé and brought the *Beagle* into Valdivia on the night of the eighth. Twelve days later, while they were still there, the town suffered the severest earthquake any inhabitant remembered. In similar circumstances, Humboldt had whipped out his watch, timed the quakes, and made other observations. Darwin regarded the phenomenon more philosophically. "I happened to be on shore, and was lying down in the wood to rest myself," he wrote. "It came on suddenly, and lasted two minutes, but the time appeared much longer. The rocking of the ground was very sensible. . . . There was no difficulty in standing upright, but the motion made me almost giddy: it was something like the movement of a ship in a little cross-ripple, or still more like that felt by a person skating over thin ice, which bends under the weight of his body.

"A bad earthquake," he continued, "at once destroys our oldest associations: the earth, the very emblem of solidity, has moved beneath our feet like a thin crust over a fluid;—one second of time has created in the mind a strange idea of insecurity, which hours of reflection would not have produced."

Fitz-Roy and some of the officers were in the town, and there the effects were more startling. The wooden houses heaved, their boards creaking and rattling. The terrified people rushed out into the streets. And although it was low tide, the water swiftly rose, although not in waves, until it reached the high tide mark. During the evening a few weaker shocks occurred, but although they sent strange currents running in the harbor, they did no damage.

Valdivia was much more fortunate than Concepción, which experienced an earthquake on the same day. When the *Beagle* arrived there early in March, Darwin saw desolation everywhere—rows of houses lying in rubble and along the shore, which had been struck by a tidal wave, chairs, tables, and timbers "as if a thousand ships had been wrecked." On one nearby island, cattle that had been grazing on a steep slope were simply rolled into the sea, and on a low island, near the head of the bay, seventy cattle were washed into the ocean. Among the eyewitnesses to whom Darwin talked, the British consul told his story: ". . . he was at breakfast when the first movement warned him to run out. He had scarcely reached the middle of the courtyard, when one side of his house came thundering down. He retained presence of mind to remember, that if he once got on top of that part which had already fallen, he would be safe. Not being able from the motion of the ground to stand, he crawled up on his hands and knees; and no sooner had he ascended this little eminence, than the other side of the house fell in, the great beams sweeping close in front of his head. With his eyes blinded, and his mouth choked with the cloud of dust which darkened the sky, at last he gained the street. As shock succeeded shock, at the interval of a few minutes, no one dared approach the shattered ruins; and no one knew whether his dearest friends and relations were not perishing from the want of help. Those who had saved any property were obliged to keep constant watch, for thieves prowled about, and at each little trembling of the ground, with one hand they beat their breasts and cried 'Misericordia!' and then with the other filched what they could from the ruins. The thatched roofs fell over the fires, and flames burst forth in all parts. Hundreds knew themselves ruined, and few had the means of providing food for the day."

Darwin studied this earthquake from every aspect. He considered the effect of earthquakes on a country's economy, he thought how different England would be if it were subject to these violent tremblings, he examined some fissures a yard wide that he found on a neighboring island, he observed the direction that the destructive forces had taken, he gathered information about the waves that had appeared, and he compared some of his conclusions with those of Lyell. He later wrote that "I feel it is quite impossible to give the mingled feelings which I experienced. . . . It is a bitter and humiliating thing to see works, which have cost man so much time and labour, overthrown in one minute; yet compassion for the inhabitants was almost instantly banished, by the surprise in seeing a state of things produced in a moment of time, which one was accustomed to attribute to a succession of ages. In my opinion, we have scarcely beheld, since leaving England, any sight so deeply interesting."

From Concepción, they sailed north again to Valparaiso, which they reached on March 11, 1835. Darwin had been spending much of his time aboard ship, which, although it was pleasant when the weather was good, did not enable him to get on with his work. At Valparaiso, when the *Beagle* turned southward again to continue its surveying, he stayed ashore and made an enjoyable overland trip across the cordillera to Mendoza in Argentina. With him he had a Chilean with whom he had traveled before and a muleteer with his ten mules.

The mountain torrents they saw particularly caught Darwin's attention. They were steep and swift, and, he wrote: "Amidst the din of rushing waters, the noise from the stones, as they rattled one over another, was most distinctly audible even from a distance. This rattling noise, night and day, may be heard along the whole course of the torrent. The sound spoke eloquently to the geologist; the thousands and thousands of stones, which, striking against each other, made the one dull uniform sound, were all hurrying in one direction. It was like thinking on time, where the minute that now glides past is irrecoverable. So was it with these stones; the ocean is their eternity, and each note of that wild music told of one more step towards their destiny.

"It is not possible for the mind to comprehend, except by a slow process, any effect which is produced by a cause repeated so often, that the multiplier itself conveys an idea, not more definite than the savage implies when he points to the hairs of his head. As often as I have seen beds of mud, sand, and shingle, accumulated to the thickness of many thousand feet, I have felt inclined to exclaim that causes, such as the present rivers and the present beaches, could never have ground down and have produced such masses. But, on the other hand, when listening to the rattling noise of these torrents, and calling to mind that whole races of animals have passed away from the face of the earth, and that during this whole period, night and day, those stones have gone rattling onwards in their course, I have thought to myself, can any mountains, any continent, withstand such waste?"

Darwin still thought of himself primarily as a geologist, that being the branch of science he had most studied, and in his concentration on this subject, he was already advancing beyond the comparatively conservative scientists like his former professor, Sedgwick. In a few weeks' time he had witnessed the sudden, but profound, changes wrought by an earthquake and the slower, but equally profound, changes brought about by the rivers of the Andes. He did not consider these as isolated phenomena but looked at them in their relationship to time and thought about their effects on the geologic structure of the whole world. This philosophic attitude and this ability to extrapolate from limited data were qualities that the Edinburgh and Cambridge professors had not recognized, but they were qualities that were essential to Darwin's ultimate greatness, and on the *Beagle,* he had an opportunity to develop them. Free from formal instruction and with a multitude of objects to observe on his own, he was rapidly maturing as a scientist.

On his journey across the Andes he noted the effects of the high altitude on his breathing and on the boiling of water—they had difficulty cooking their potatoes—and he remarked on the great strength of the mules, saying of them that "art has here outdone nature." The men carried with them a large, extra supply of food, for fear that they might be caught by a snowstorm in the heights of the mountains, and one night Darwin awoke to see clouds suddenly covering the sky. Throwing off his blankets, he roused the sleeping muleteer, but the muleteer reassured him that snow never fell on that part of the Andes without lightning and thunder, and he went to sleep again. As a weather prophet, the muleteer turned out to be accurate, and they descended the eastern slopes of the ridges in safety.

Here the land was flat and dry, and it reminded him of the pampas near Buenos Aires, for he saw "the disk of the rising sun, intersected by an horizon, level as that of the ocean." After two days of travel that Darwin could only call tedious, they welcomed the sight of Luxan, with its rows of poplars and willows and its flowing river. They did not pass the night comfortably, however, because, Darwin wrote, "I experienced an attack (for it deserves no less a name) of the *Benchuca,* . . . the great black bug of the Pampas. It is almost disgusting to feel soft wingless insects, about an inch long, crawling over one's body. Before sucking they are quite thin, but afterwards they become round and bloated with blood, and in this state are easily crushed." Later, in northern Chile, he caught one of these insects and experimented with it. "When placed on a table, and though surrounded by people, if a finger was presented, the bold insect would protrude its sucker, make a charge, and if allowed, draw blood. No pain was caused by the wound. It was curious to watch its body during the act of sucking, as in less than ten minutes it changed from being as flat as a wafer to a globular form. This one feast, for which the *Benchuca* was indebted to one of the officers, kept it fat during four whole months; but, after the first fortnight, it was quite ready to have another suck." As he tossed during the night, while the *benchucas* crawled over his body and sucked his blood, Darwin regarded them as both a nuisance and a biological curiosity. He had no way of knowing, because the discovery had not yet been made, that these were carriers of Chagas' disease, a serious tropical illness that was common in Mendoza. He thought little of the incident, but it was perhaps the most dangerous night that he spent during his entire cruise on the *Beagle*.

After a few days in the city of Mendoza, Darwin made his way back across the Andes to Valparaiso by a different route, pausing to study the geologic record as told, in part, by a group of petrified tree stumps, some of them three to five feet around. Back in Valparaiso, he awaited the return of the *Beagle* from Concepción. Fitz-Roy planned next to take his ship farther north to Coquimbo, Chile, for refitting before making the trip across the Pacific. Since there was no reason for Darwin to stay with the ship during this operation, he bought four horses and two mules and made the journey by land "in a zigzag line; sometimes stopping a day to geologize." At Coquimbo he experienced another sharp earthquake, although nothing like the one that had struck Concepción, and examined some "step-formed terraces of shingle" in the light of what Lyell had written. Because the *Beagle* was still not ready to leave, he secured Fitz-Roy's permission again to travel north by land and rejoin the ship at Copiapó in Chile. From there they sailed up the coast of Peru, which at that time was in a state of anarchy and, therefore, difficult for Darwin to study even when the ship stayed for a while in one harbor. Then, its survey of the South American coastline finished, the *Beagle* turned westward toward the Galápagos Islands.

On the morning of September 17, 1835, they landed on Chatham (San Cristóbal) Island, the most easterly of the group, which, Darwin wrote, "like the others, rises with a tame and rounded outline, broken here and there by scattered hillocks, the remains of former craters. Nothing could be less inviting than the first appearance. A broken field of black basaltic lava, thrown into the most rugged waves, and crossed by great fissures, is everywhere covered by stunted, sunburnt brushwood, which shows little signs of life. The dried and parched surface, being heated by the noonday sun, gave the air a close sultry feeling, like that from a stove: we fancied that even the bushes smelt unpleasantly."

Although Darwin had been concentrating his attention principally on the geology of the countries he had visited, he had also been collecting plants, birds, fossils, and animals during his travels. That first day on Chatham Island he tried to gather as many plants as possible but "succeeded in getting very few; and such wretched-looking little weeds would have better become an arctic than an equatorial Flora." He had little better luck with animals and birds. With interest, he looked at two large tortoises, one of which was eating a piece of cactus, but he found the birds were few and "dull-coloured."

On September 23 the *Beagle* came to anchor at Charles (Floreano or Santa Maria) Island, where there was a small colony of 200 or 300 people, most of them political exiles from Ecuador. Here the tortoises were so numerous that they formed a staple food for the inhabitants, and the ships that landed there sometimes caught them by the hundreds. (One ship was reported to have captured 200 in a single day, and another sailed off with a total cargo of 700.) As the days turned into weeks, the *Beagle* cruised in between the islands, and as Darwin went ashore and gathered specimens on one after another, his amazement increased. Here was something that he had never before in his life seen or even imagined, and although his scientific education had been sketchy indeed, his mind was quick to grasp that what he observed was significant.

"The natural history of these islands is eminently curious," he said, "and well deserves attention. Most of the organic productions are aboriginal creations, found nowhere else; there is even a difference between the inhabitants of the different islands; yet all show a marked relationship with those of America, though separated from that continent by an open space of ocean, between 500 and 600 miles in width. The archipelago is a little world within itself, or rather a satellite attached to America, whence it has derived a few stray colonists, and has received the general character of its indigenous productions. Considering the small size of these islands, we feel the more astonished at the number of their aboriginal beings, and at their confined range. Seeing every height crowned with its crater, and the boundaries of most of the lava-streams still distinct, we are led to believe that within a period, geologically recent, the unbroken ocean was here spread out. Hence, both in space and time, we seem to be brought somewhere near to that great fact—that mystery of mysteries— the first appearance of new beings on this earth."

In his collecting, he obtained twenty-six kinds of land birds, "all peculiar to the group and found nowhere else, with the exception of one larklike finch from North America. . . ." Turning his attention to the waders and water birds, he was able to secure eleven kinds, "and of these only three (including a rail confined to the damp summits of the islands) are new species. Considering the wandering habits of the gulls, I was surprised to find that the species inhabiting the islands is peculiar, but allied to one from the southern parts of South America." (His extensive studies in South America helped him make these comparisons.) He became fascinated by the tortoises, animals so large that sometimes a single one would provide 200 pounds of meat. On the islands where springs existed, the turtles would walk along the "broad and well-beaten paths" they had created to the water, bury their heads in it, and greedily swallow mouthfuls. "The tortoises," he wrote, "when purposely moving towards any point, travel by night and day, and arrive at their journey's end much sooner than would be expected." The inhabitants told him that they would go about 8 miles in two or three days, and he himself clocked a large one traveling at the rate of 360' yards an hour, or 4 miles a day. "There can be little doubt," he wrote, "that this tortoise is an aboriginal inhabitant of the Galápagos; for it is found on all, or nearly all, the islands, even on some of the smaller ones where there is no water; had it been an imported species, this would have hardly been the case in a group which has been so little frequented."

He collected plants, too, although rather "indiscriminately," taking everything that he saw that was in flower. Fortunately, he kept what he took from each island separate, so when he returned to England, he was able to identify the origin of each group. For as he remarked, "I have not as yet noted by far the most remarkable feature in the natural history of this archipelago; it is, that the different islands to a considerable extent are inhabited by a different set of beings." His attention had been first drawn to this fact by the vice-governor, who claimed that the tortoises from each of the islands were so distinct that, by examining one, he could name the island where it had been captured. Reporting this conversation, Darwin said that "I did not for some time pay sufficient attention to this statement, and I had already partially mingled together some of the collections from two of the islands. I never dreamed that islands, about fifty or sixty miles apart, and most of them in sight of each other, formed of precisely the same rocks, placed under a quite similar climate, rising to a nearly equal height, would have been differently tenanted. . . . It is the fate of most voyagers, no sooner to discover what is most interesting in any locality, than they are hurried from it; but I ought, perhaps, to be thankful that I obtained sufficient material to establish this most remarkable fact in the distribution of organic beings."

Just as his night among the bloodsucking insects of Luxan had been the most dangerous moment in his journey, his visit to the Galápagos was the most fruitful. Here, as he had said, he had been "brought somewhere near to that great fact—that mystery of mysteries—the first appearance of new beings on the earth." He did not, of course, recognize the full significance of what he had seen. He did not even have his collections in workable shape—he would need help later in examining and classifying many of his specimens—but his reflective and open mind understood that he had witnessed the unusual and the unexpected, and he was already considering the questions that it proposed. When, in October, the *Beagle* finished its survey and turned westward again, he had among his belongings the materials for years of study and, in his mind, the beginnings of ideas that would require years of contemplation.

In November the *Beagle* brought Darwin to Tahiti and remained there for more than a month. Darwin liked the Tahitians (he thought the women left something to be desired in spite of their charming use of flowers), and he went on a tour of the interior in the company of some of the men.

He thought rather less of the natives of New Zealand, "Both their persons and houses are filthily dirty and offensive," he wrote. "The idea of washing either their bodies or their clothes never seems to enter their heads. I saw a chief, who was wearing a shirt black and matted with filth, and when asked how it came to be so dirty, he replied, with surprise, 'Do you not see it is an old one?' " Commenting on the *Beagle*'s departure in December, Darwin said that "I believe we were all glad to leave New Zealand. It is not a pleasant place. Amongst the natives, there is absent that charming simplicity which is found in Tahiti; and the greater part of the English are the very refuse of society."

Sydney, Australia, on the other hand, made Darwin proud to be an Englishman. They reached the city on January 12, 1836, and he was immediately struck by its impressive appearance and its prosperity. In a few score years the British had been able to accomplish what the Spanish and Portuguese had not succeeded in doing in South America even after the passage of centuries. Three questions were uppermost in Darwin's mind when he landed on the Australian continent: What was the state of society among the upper classes? How were the convicts faring? And what would induce people to emigrate to the continent? Although the *Beagle* remained there less than a month, Darwin made a quick journey to Bathurst in the interior. On this trip he went kangaroo hunting, watched the natives throw their spears, and observed the geology. In addition, during his stay in Australia, he found tentative answers to his questions. On the whole, he was disappointed with the state of society. He found it "rancorously divided into parties on almost every subject." He criticized its preoccupation with wool and sheep grazing to the exclusion of almost every other subject of conversation. And he felt it suffered from being so dependent on convicts as servants. Of the convict system itself, he said that "as a real system of reform it has failed, as perhaps would every other plan; but as a means of making men outwardly honest,—of converting vagabonds, most useless in one hemisphere, into active citizens of another, and thus giving birth to a new and splendid country—a grand centre of civilization—it has succeeded to a degree perhaps unparalleled in history." In conclusion, he rather liked the country and was impressed by its vigor and the opportunities to make money, but only "sharp necessity" would have compelled him to emigrate.

After briefly touching at Tasmania, the *Beagle* continued its westward course toward the Cocos Islands in the Indian Ocean. Darwin had become interested in coral reefs and atolls, and during the days the *Beagle* spent at the Cocos, he had an excellent opportunity to study them. Fitz-Roy made soundings along the shores, taking samples from the bottom, and Darwin examined the construction of the islands from the land. Although they spent little more than a week at this work, they collected a considerable amount of data, and Darwin said of the islands, "Such formations surely rank high amongst the wonderful objects of the world."

From the Cocos the *Beagle* went to Mauritius, rounded the Cape of Good Hope, and stopped at St. Helena and Ascension before returning to São Salvador, Brazil, to make some more "chronometrical observations." When they tried to sail from there directly to the Cape Verde Islands, they met with head winds and had to put back into Recife and wait for better weather.

At last after short visits to the Cape Verde Islands and the Azores, the *Beagle* reached home in October, 1836, completing a cruise of nearly five years. Afterward Darwin wrote that "it appears to me that nothing can be more improving to a young naturalist, than a journey in distant countries. It both sharpens, and partly allays that want and craving, which . . . a man experiences, although every corporeal sense be fully satisfied. The excitement from the novelty of objects, and the chance of success, stimulate him to increased activity. Moreover, as a number of isolated facts soon become uninteresting, the habit of comparison leads to generalization." In writing down those words, Darwin perfectly described the effects of the *Beagle's* cruise on himself. He had left England a rather indolent amateur in science. He returned "stimulated to increased activity" and had gained a "habit of comparison" that would lead to great generalizations.

IV

During his first weeks back in England, Darwin visited his father and his uncle Josiah Wedgwood and spent a little time in London, before settling down for three months in Cambridge. His first business was to get some of his specimens examined and identified by appropriate experts and to prepare his journal of the cruise for publication. He had originally kept this only for his personal use, but when Fitz-Roy liked it well enough to want to incorporate abstracts in his official account of the voyage, Darwin, on the advice of friends, decided that it should be printed as a separate volume in the official account.

In March, 1837, he moved from Cambridge to London, but his health was not good, and he had occasional fits of the sickness that would remain with him the rest of his life. None of his contemporaries was able to diagnose the trouble, and he has been accused by some of being a hypochondriac. On the other hand, Dr. Darwin, who was certainly familiar with the case and knew his son well, took it seriously. Many of the symptoms were those of Chagas' disease, and because of his experience at Luxan, where he was so badly bitten by its carriers, the possibility exists that this was his illness. In any case, as far as he was concerned, the headaches, nausea, insomnia, and heart palpitations were real enough, and they affected both his personal life and his science. He saw far fewer people than a man of his position ordinarily would, either socially or professionally. This isolation protected him in his work, although it also limited what he could do.

Just as he had aboard the *Beagle,* he still considered himself first and foremost a geologist and attended the meetings of the Geological Society. One of the men whose work he had most admired and who had most influenced his own thinking was Charles Lyell, and he now saw a great deal of him. "One of his chief characteristics," Darwin wrote, "was his sympathy with the works of others, and I was as much astonished as delighted at the interest which he showed when, on my return to England, I explained to him my views on coral reefs. This encouraged me greatly, and his advice and example had much influence on me."

This was especially generous of Lyell, because Darwin, as a result of his observations of coral reefs, had come to a point of view that opposed the one held by Lyell. In his *Principles of Geology,* Lyell had stated that the corals formed atolls on the rims of submerged volcanoes, but Darwin was able to demonstrate that this could not be true. One of the key reasons was that corals could not live at a depth greater than 120 feet. It seemed hardly likely that volcano after volcano would be formed in the ocean within that small tolerance. This unbelievable regularity would not be required if the land were subsiding. It could then sink from any height to any depth, the coral building on the dead organisms below it. While this accounted for the atolls and the barrier reefs, Darwin thought that fringing reefs, which are narrower than barrier reefs, could have been formed on sloping shores that were either stationary or rising. (He did not know about the changes in sea level that were also a factor, but that supplemented, rather than contradicted, his theory.) Instead of being jealous, Lyell immediately recognized the superiority of Darwin's ideas, urged the president of the Geological Society to persuade Darwin to read a paper on the subject and urged Darwin to write a book, *The Structure and Distribution of Coral Reefs,* which remains a classic of scientific writing.

Toward the end of the cruise of the *Beagle* he had begun to puzzle over the species that he had seen during the voyage, their likenesses, their differences, and their geographical distribution. At the beginning of the journey, he had been a believer in individual creation, but as he began to look back over the facts he had collected, he started to think that there must be some other, or at least fuller, explanation. "During the voyage of the *Beagle*," he wrote, "I had been much impressed by discovering in the Pampean formation great fossil animals covered with armour like that on the existing armadillos; secondly, by the manner in which closely allied animals replace one another in proceeding southwards over the Continent; and thirdly, by the South American character of most of the productions of the Galápagos archipelago, and more especially by the manner in which they all differ slightly on each island of the group; none of the islands appearing to be very ancient in the geological sense.

"It was evident [after some reflection] that such facts as these could only be explained on the supposition that species gradually became modified; and the subject haunted me. But it was equally evident that neither the action of the surrounding conditions, nor the will of the organism [as Lamarck had believed] . . . could account for the innumerable cases in which organisms of every kind are beautifully adapted to their habits of life—for instance, a woodpecker or a tree-frog to climb trees, or a seed for dispersal by hooks or plumes. I had always been much struck by such adaptations, and until these could be explained it seemed to me almost useless to endeavour to prove by indirect evidence that species have been modified.

"After my return to England," he went on, "it appeared to me that by following the example of Lyell in Geology, and by collecting all facts which bore in any way on the variation of animals and plants under domestication and nature, some light might perhaps be thrown on the whole subject. . . . I soon perceived that selection was the keystone of man's success in making useful races of animals and plants. But how selection could be applied to organisms living in a state of nature remained for some time a mystery to me." In July, 1837, he started his first notebook on this general subject and thus began the work that would occupy him for years.

In October, 1838, he read for pleasure *An Essay on the Principle of Population as It Affects the Future Improvement of Society,* written by the British economist and clergyman Thomas Malthus. The book had come out of some discussions between Malthus and his father. Malthus, who was a thorough humanist, believed that society was being misled by optimistic—and unrealistic—hopes of a perfect world that could never exist. Since the population will always tend to increase faster than its means of subsistence, he argued, misery will also tend to hinder the formation of ideal social conditions. Realization of this fact, he thought, might produce a more practical approach to society's problems. His father was much impressed with his ideas and urged him to publish them. The first edition of his subsequent book appeared in 1798, and an enlarged edition was published in 1803. Malthus' thoughts were not entirely new— many of them had been recognized for some time—but he presented them more formally and made people aware that many checks existed that prevented the automatic increase of populations.

Later Darwin recalled that "being well prepared to appreciate the struggle for existence which everywhere goes on from long-continued observation of the habits of animals and plants, it at once struck me that under these circumstances favorable variations would tend to be preserved and unfavorable ones to be destroyed. The result of this would be the formation of new species. Here, then, I had at last got a theory by which to work; but," he added, "I was so anxious to avoid prejudice, that I determined not for some time to write even the briefest sketch of it." This was a curious statement for a scientist to make, but it reflected an essential part of Darwin's character. Instead of pursuing his new idea almost immediately and testing it to determine its validity, he set it aside "to avoid prejudice." There are also many other reasons why he delayed. His health could account, in part, for his action; the pursuit of a scientific idea requires energy, and Darwin did not have much energy to spare. He was also perhaps like Newton, glad to work out problems to his own satisfaction but not in a hurry to publish them. And, too, he knew it would take much work to assemble the facts necessary to prove or disprove what he now thought.

In November, 1838, Darwin became engaged to his cousin, Emma Wedgwood, daughter of Josiah Wedgwood, the uncle who had realized the importance of his traveling on the *Beagle*. Darwin had worried about supporting a family, but these worries proved needless. Dr. Darwin gave him 13,000 pounds, and Emma brought with her a dowry of 5,000, plus an additional income of 400 a year. From that point on, Darwin never wanted for money. His tastes were simple—indeed, he practiced many almost foolish household economies—and he inherited more money on the death of his father and invested his capital well. Aside from his royalties, he had at the time of his death an income of 8,000 pounds a year.

Emma was a good wife to him. She had few social aspirations and was perfectly content to lead the quiet life that he liked, nursing him when he was ill and, when he was well, maintaining the kind of household in which he could best work. She met the first test of her abilities at once, for at the time of his marriage, Darwin's sickness became worse. Writing about the period later, Darwin said, "During the three years and eight months whilst we resided in London, I did less scientific work, though I worked as hard as I possibly could, than during other equal length of time in my life. This was owing to frequently recurring unwellness, and to one long and serious illness." What work he did was limited largely to his book on coral reefs. Describing that publication, he wrote that "this book, though a small one, cost me twenty months of hard work, as I had to read every work on the islands of the Pacific and to consult many charts." He was not content to study merely his observations and the data collected by Fitz-Roy; he also felt it necessary to examine everything that anybody else had written or reported. This thoroughness was characteristic of him and illustrates one of the qualities that may have led him to postpone his study of the species, but after correcting the last proof sheets of *Coral Reefs,* Darwin wrote down, in pencil, a brief abstract of the ideas that had occurred to him earlier.

Neither he nor Emma was enjoying life in London, and they decided they should move to some quiet country place. After a search that they found wearying, they finally settled on Down in Kent. "The village stands on solitary upland country," Darwin's son later wrote, "500 to 600 feet above the sea—a country with little natural beauty, but possessing a certain charm in the shaws, or straggling strips of wood, capping the chalky banks and looking down upon the quiet ploughed lands of the valleys. The village, of three or four hundred inhabitants, consists of three small streets of cottages, meeting in front of the little flint-built church. It is a place where new-comers are seldom seen, and the names occurring far back in the old church registers are still known in the village." The house itself was not especially attractive—"a square brick building of three storeys, covered with shabby whitewash, and hanging shabby tiles." But Darwin and Emma made some immediate improvements, building an addition, covering the walls with stucco, and landscaping the grounds.

At Down House, as he called his new establishment, Darwin settled into a routine that was designed to let him accomplish the utmost with the small amount of physical energy he had available. He rose in the morning and went to his study where he worked until nine thirty. He then read his mail and talked with his family. At ten thirty, he worked again for an hour and a half, and often that was as much as he could do. On other days, when he felt especially well, he might add another hour in the afternoon.

His first year at Down House was spent mostly on a new book, *Geological Observations on Two Volcanic Islands,* and he prepared another work, this one on barnacles. Even in remote Down—it was twenty miles from

London by coach—Darwin kept up with his scientific acquaintances like Lyell, making occasional trips to the city and writing to them frequently. With them he discussed his book on barnacles, the study of which taught him much about biology. Yet he was not completely ignoring his ideas about the species. In the summer of 1844 he wrote out a larger version of his original sketch and thought so highly of it that he gave Emma instructions to follow in the event of his sudden death. He wished that she set aside 400 pounds—or even 500—and "that my sketch be given to some competent person, with this sum to induce him to take trouble in its improvement and enlargement." The person he suggested was Charles Lyell.

He was not satisfied with the paper in its present form. As he said later, ". . . at that time I overlooked one problem of great importance; and it is astonishing to me, except on the principle of Columbus and his egg, how I could have overlooked it and its solution. The problem is the tendency in organic beings descended from the same stock to diverge in character as they become modified. That they have diverged greatly is obvious from the manner in which species of all kinds can be classed under genera, genera under families, families under sub-orders, and so forth; and I can remember the very spot in the road, whilst in my carriage, when to my joy the solution occurred to me; and this was long after I had come to Down. The solution, as I believe, is that the modified offspring of all dominant and increasing forms tend to become adapted to many and highly diversified places in the economy of nature." Darwin's book was coming to him, not as a sudden inspiration, but as the result of step-by-step thinking. On the *Beagle,* he had been a devout believer in orthodox creation. Even in the Galápagos, it had taken the vice-governor to point out to him the differences between the plants and animals on the various islands. But gradually he had seen the significance of this and of the distribution of animals and fossils in South America. He had then lost his faith in the immutability of the species. The reading of Malthus had provided another idea, the element of selectivity. Gradually, he was putting his ideas together, and as he did so, he discussed them with Lyell and entered into correspondence with such scientists as Agassiz's opponent, Asa Gray, the American botanist. Another of Darwin's confidants was Joseph Dalton Hooker, the British botanist, who as a young man had gone on an expedition to Antarctica and then on one to India and was now assistant director of Kew Gardens.

So the years passed at Down House, and the quiet routine of Emma's household continued. When he was well, Darwin did his four hours of work each day; when he was sick, he was forced to give up entirely. To his widening circle of acquaintances, he added at this time a naturalist named Alfred Russel Wallace, who was then collecting in the Malay Archipelago. He had written an article entitled "On the Law Which Has

Regulated the Introduction of New Species," which appeared in the fall of 1855 in the *Annals and Magazine of Natural History*. In it, Wallace argued in favor of evolution and said that a chart of the development of life would take the form of a branching tree, not a series of straight lines. Wallace was disappointed that his ideas had attracted so little attention and took the liberty of writing Darwin, whom he had heard of, to ask his opinion of what he had said. Darwin was always generous about answering his mail—although in later years he finally adopted a printed form for cranks—and replied that he agreed with almost everything that Wallace had written, commenting that this was unusual in a hypothetical paper. Darwin's response and encouragement meant much to Wallace, working by himself in some of the most remote parts of the East, and he wrote Darwin occasionally thereafter.

In 1856, Lyell discussed Darwin's evolutionary theories with him and advised him to write out his "views pretty fully." So once more Darwin returned to his endless thinking and revising and came closer and closer to a form that he thought publishable. But as the weeks turned into months and the months became years, Lyell and others of Darwin's friends grew nervous. He had no monopoly on evolution. Lamarck's ideas were still being studied by some scientists. Wallace had published his article. An anonymous publication, *Vestiges of Creation,* had appeared some years before and had evoked considerable discussion about evolution. Granted that most scientists still believed in the old ideas of individual creation, there was an undercurrent running, and Darwin's friends were fearful that, after all his work, somebody might come out with a theory approximating his.

Such worries did not bother Darwin. Nobody could set his pace but himself. He had little time in which to work; he could not spend days and nights in his study as healthier men could do; he wanted to accumulate all the data he could. No matter how hard Lyell pressed him, he would not hurry.

One of his working habits was to read his mail after the hour and a half that he spent in his study every morning. On June 18, 1858, as he went through his letters, he saw one postmarked from Ternate in the Molucca Islands of the Malay Archipelago. Obviously it was from Wallace, with whom he had had a slight correspondence. Slitting it open, he noticed that Wallace had sent him an unpublished paper with a covering letter. Wallace wanted Darwin's opinion of it, and if Darwin thought it worthwhile, perhaps he would be good enough to show it to others. It seemed a routine request, a courtesy exchanged between scientists—until Darwin sat down to read the paper itself.

That same day he wrote Lyell, "Your words have come true with a vengeance—that I should be forestalled. You said this, when I explained to you here very briefly my views of 'Natural Selection' depending on the struggle for existence. I never saw a more striking coincidence; if Wallace had my MS. sketch written out in 1842, he could not have made a better short abstract! Even his terms now stand as heads of my chapters."

Of all the people to whom Wallace might have turned, only to Darwin could he have presented such an enormous moral dilemma. What should Darwin do with Wallace's paper? Should he announce it and let himself be forestalled? Or should he suppress it and perhaps be accused of stealing Wallace's ideas? The quiet of Down House had been shattered.

12

A Coincidental Discovery

ALFRED WALLACE: 1823–1913

I

Two qualities marked the early life of Alfred Russel Wallace, the co-discoverer with Darwin of the principles of evolution. These qualities were restlessness and an inability to make up his mind. Together they led him into a career in science that turned him into one of the foremost men of his century.

He was born on January 8, 1823, in the town of Usk in Monmouthshire. When he was still a young child, his family moved to Hertford about twenty-five miles north of London. Since Mr. Wallace had a large family —Alfred was one of eight—and only limited means, he could not afford expensive tuition bills. When his children were young, he taught them himself and then permitted them a few years at school. But he did encourage them all to read and, being the librarian at a small library, kept the house filled with books.

Wallace passed a quiet—but short—childhood. At the age of fourteen, his education came to an end, and he was expected from then on to earn his own living. The family planned to have him join his brother William, who was a surveyor, but first he paid a short visit to London, where another brother, John, was apprenticed to a master builder. In John's company, he spent many hours at a workingman's club, at which some followers of Robert Owen, the social reformer, usually met either to hear lectures or to discuss Owen's ideas among themselves. From this experience, he gained a certain religious skepticism, a tendency toward social criticism, and learned the proposition stated by Owen that an individual's life was influenced by his inherited qualities and his environment—that everything was not in the hands of either the individual or of God. This was the first of his intellectual awakenings.

The second came when he joined William. He liked surveying and the long days spent in the British countryside and quickly saw that the mathematics he had studied in school had a practical application. He learned that rock structures were not everywhere the same, as he had previously supposed, and William taught him some geology and the names of a few fossils. From this experience, Wallace developed a lifelong love for the outdoors. When the firm that employed William ran out of jobs for him to do, Wallace went to work for a watchmaker, thinking this might be a useful trade to learn. Before a year was over, at which time Wallace would have become formally apprenticed and, therefore, unable to leave, the watchmaker accepted a partnership in London. Wallace later said that "this may be considered the first of several turning-points of my life at which, by circumstances beyond my own control, I have been insensibly directed into the course best adapted to develop my special mental and physical activities." It "prevented me from becoming a mechanical tradesman in a country town, by which my life would almost certainly have been shortened and my mental development stunted by the monotony of my occupation."

As William again had work, Wallace returned to surveying. During his second attempt at this business he became even more interested in the natural world. He made instruments to study the sun and stars and began collecting wild flowers, which especially appealed to him. Through self-study, he was turning himself into a rather competent amateur naturalist. But surveying was uncertain. Once more William was unable to find jobs, and the year Wallace became twenty-one, he found himself unemployed and without a career to pursue.

Taking stock of himself and the little he had to offer the world, he thought he might try to become a schoolteacher. An employment agency told him of two vacancies he might be able to fill. The first school turned him down because of his lack of education, but the second accepted him to teach reading, writing, and mathematics to the younger students and surveying to the older ones. At Leicester, where the school was located, he had both leisure and encouragement to continue his self-education, for the town had a good library, and the headmaster, seeing something in this restless young man that no one else had noticed, urged him to study. Soon he was reading such books as Malthus' work on the control of populations, Humboldt's accounts of his travels in Latin America, and Darwin's published *Journal* describing the voyage of the *Beagle*. The last two particularly made an enormous impression on him, and after finishing them, he decided that he would someday travel in far-off places.

Perhaps an even greater event in his life was his meeting with Henry Walter Bates, the son of a Leicester hosiery manufacturer. Bates, who was about two years younger than Wallace, was also interested in the natural world; his specialty was entomology. He taught Wallace about insects, and Wallace taught him about plants, and the two spent most of their free time together. One of the books that they discussed was the anonymous volume entitled *Vestiges of Creation*, which appeared in 1844 and attacked the old theories of creation, arguing in favor of a "progressive development." Since the author was unable to support his ideas with scientific reasoning, he was quickly dismissed by most of his readers. (One of those who had absolutely no use for him was, of course, Louis Agassiz.) Perhaps if Wallace had had a better education, he would have recognized the book's deficiencies more readily. As it was, he read it carefully, and although he did not completely subscribe to its theory, he thought it deserved study by all naturalists.

At Leicester, Wallace seemed to have found the right life for himself. He appears to have been a satisfactory teacher in spite of a native shyness that may have been a slight barrier between him and his students. He had a library from which he could obtain the books he wanted, time to pursue his studies of natural history, and a friend with whom he could share his interests. But early in 1845, William died, and when Wallace settled his affairs, he discovered that with the construction of railways, surveying was flourishing. Once more he switched jobs. Instead of continuing at Leicester, he took over his brother's business. The change proved financially advantageous. Not only was he able to make a living, but he could even set some money aside. Yet he was still restless.

In 1847 he traveled with some of his family to Paris for a short vacation. While he was there, he visited the Jardin des Plantes, and the sight of the vast collections renewed his interest in the development of species. On his return to England, he went to the insect room at the British Museum. The exhibits there stirred his curiosity further. He was now convinced, after so many restless, purposeless years, that he would like to be a naturalist and travel. But could he support himself at this work? This was the question that was uppermost in his mind when he opened a book describing a voyage up the Amazon. Wallace had known of the wide variety of life in Brazil, and from the book he was reading he now learned that the country was a relatively inexpensive place in which to live. Perhaps he and Bates, with whom he discussed the idea, could collect specimens and sell them for enough money to pay their travel expenses.

The British Museum's curator of butterflies, to whom he wrote, assured him that they could and an enthusiastic collector of insects agreed to serve as their agent. Each time their collection grew large enough to warrant shipment, they would send it to him. He would sell the duplicates and store the remainder until their return. The sale of the duplicates, they hoped, would provide the funds to continue, and yet they would still have a collection of their own on which to work when they came back to England. Having made this arrangement, they mustered their courage— and their slight financial resources—purchased the necessary equipment, and on April 26, 1848, boarded a ship for Brazil.

II

In May, 1848, after an uneventful voyage of twenty-nine days, the ship reached Bélem. The city (it was then called Pará) was the capital of the largest province in Brazil, an area of almost 100,000 square miles, but in spite of its strategic location near the mouth of the Pará River, it was not prosperous. "At the time of our arrival," Bates later wrote, "Pará had not quite recovered from the effects of a series of revolutions, brought about by the hatred which existed between the native Brazilians and the Portuguese; the former, in the end, calling to their aid the Indian and mixed coloured population. . . . The place had the aspect of one that had seen better days; the public buildings, including the palaces of the President and Bishop, the cathedral, the principal churches and convents, all seemed constructed on a scale of grandeur far beyond the present requirements of the city."

Wallace and Bates lived for about two weeks in the house of the ship's consignee, while they looked for a suitable one of their own. At last they found a Portuguese tile manufacturer who was willing to rent them his country place in the village of Nazaré, about a mile and a half from Belém. Once they had unpacked their instruments and other equipment, they began to explore the roads leading from the village and, as Bates expressed it, "settled ourselves for a few months' serious collecting." The regime they followed was so regular that it was almost monotonous. Every morning they rose shortly after dawn and drank a cup of coffee. In the two hours before breakfast they collected birds, while their servant walked back to Belém for the day's provisions. From ten in the morning until two or three in the afternoon, when it became unbearably hot and even the natives lay sleeping in their hammocks, Wallace and Bates worked and then stayed inside during the invariable afternoon thunderstorms that followed a pattern as routine as their own working habits. "First, the cool sea-breeze, which commenced to blow about 10 o'clock, and which had increased with force with the increasing power of the sun, would flag and finally die away. The heat and electric tension of the atmosphere would then become almost insupportable. Languor and uneasiness would seize on every one; even the denizens of the forests betraying it by their motions. White clouds would appear in the east and gather into cumuli, with an increasing blackness along their lower portions. The whole eastern horizon would become almost suddenly black, and this would spread upwards, the sun at length becoming obscured. Then the rush of a mighty wind is heard through the forest, swaying the tree-tops; a vivid flash of lightning bursts forth, then a crash of thunder, and down streams the deluging rain. Such storms soon cease, leaving bluish-black motionless clouds in the sky until night. Meantime all nature is refreshed; but heaps of flowerpetals and fallen leaves are seen under the trees. Towards evening life revives again, and the ringing uproar is resumed from bush and tree. The following morning the sun again rises in a cloudless sky, and so the cycle is completed; spring, summer, autumn, as it were, in one tropical day."

At first both men were discouraged by Brazil, for they had expected too much. Wallace said that "my previous wanderings had been confined to England and a short trip on the Continent, so everything here had the charm of perfect novelty. Nevertheless, on the whole I was disappointed. The weather was not so hot, the people were not so peculiar, the vegetation was not so striking, as the glowing picture I had conjured up in my imagination, and had been brooding over during the tedium of a seavoyage." And Bates wrote that "the number and beauty of the birds and insects did not at first equal our expectations. The majority of the birds we saw were small and obscurely coloured; they were indeed similar, in general appearance, to such as are met with in country places in England." But as time passed and their eyes became more accustomed to looking at tropical life, they saw more and more of interest.

They examined the great mounds, thirty or forty feet long and ten or fifteen wide, built by the sauba ants. These would sometimes strip the entire foliage from a young tree in a single night, and "we often see, hurrying across the pathways, rows of small green leaves; these are the Saübas, each with a piece of leaf cut as smoothly as with scissors, and completely hiding the body from sight. The orange-tree is very subject to their attacks, and in our garden the young trees were each planted in the centre of a ring-shaped earthen vessel, which being filled with water . . . prevented the ants from reaching it. Some places are so infested by them that it is useless planting anything." The two men looked at many different kinds of wasps' nests, and they saw a horse whose blood had been sucked by bats. It "presented a most pitiable appearance, large streams of clotted blood running down from several wounds on its back and sides." They shot monkeys—and ate one. They purchased snakes from the natives, including several poisonous ones and a boa constrictor. "A man who had caught it in the forest left it for our inspection," Wallace wrote. "It was tightly tied around the neck to a good-sized stick, which hindered the freedom of its movements, and appeared nearly to stop respiration. It was about ten feet long, and very large, being as thick as a man's thigh. Here it lay writhing about for two or three days, dragging its clog along with it, sometimes stretching its mouth open with a most suspicious yawn, and twisting up the end of its tail into a very tight curl. At length we agreed with the man to purchase it for two milreis (4s. 6d.), and having fitted up a box with bars at the top, got the seller to put it into the cage. It immediately began to make up for lost time by breathing most violently, the expirations sounding like high-steam pressure escaping from a Great Western locomotive. This it continued for some hours, making about four and a half inspirations per minute, and then settled down into silence, which it afterwards maintained, unless when disturbed or irritated."

Aside from two short expeditions away from Nazaré, they remained in the small village until the end of August, when they accepted an invitation from a millowner to travel up the Tocantins River in search of cedar. Before leaving, they packed their first collection of insects to send to England. According to Wallace, it contained more than 1,300 species, and both men felt justified in taking pleasure over the results of their two months of work.

The preparations for their journey were complicated by the bureaucratic Brazilian government. Although they were not leaving the country, they still had to obtain passports and clear customs and had "as much difficulty and delay as if we had been taking a two hundred ton ship into a foreign country."

By the thirtieth they had reached the main stream of the Tocantins, but although the trip was proving comfortable and successful—they had already collected many new insects—they realized their crew was too small. Instead of being able to employ more men, however, they lost their pilot, who simply disappeared in one of the towns at which they landed. This placed an extra burden on the remaining two men, one of whom grew sullen and lazy and refused to take orders. His attitude left them only one working crew member, and they would have had to drift back to Belém if it had not been for the kindness of a settler, who lent them some of his employees until they could find some additional men.

For a few days on the journey, Wallace and Bates rested at a house just below Baião and, much to the bewilderment of the natives, prepared the specimens they had taken thus far. "While preparing insects or skinning birds in the house, the window which opened into the street was generally crowded with boys and men, who would wait for hours," Wallace said, "watching my operations with the most untiring curiosity. The constantly repeated remark, on seeing a bird skinned, was, 'Oh, the patience of the whites!' Then one would whisper to another, 'Does he take all the meat out?' 'Well, I never!' 'Look, he makes eyes of cotton!' And then would come a little conversation as to what they could possibly be wanted for. 'Para mostrar' (to show) was the general solution; but they seemed to think it rather unsatisfactory, and that the English could hardly be such fools as to want to see a few parrot and pigeon skins. The butterflies they settled much to their own satisfaction, deciding that they were for the purpose of obtaining new patterns for printed calicoes and other goods, while the ugly insects were supposed to be valuable for 'remedios,' or medicine. We found it best quietly to assent to this, as it saved us a deal of questioning, and no other explanation that we could give would be at all intelligible to them."

Wallace and Bates were thoroughly enjoying their journey. Although they did not travel in the luxury Agassiz would enjoy aboard his gunboat almost twenty years later, they were far more comfortable than Humboldt had been when he had pushed up the Orinoco in his crude canoe at the beginning of the century. And the purpose of their trip was being fulfilled; everywhere they stopped, they were able to obtain numerous specimens for shipment back to Europe. But the millowner was not faring so well. Not only was he failing to discover the cedar he wanted, but he was having difficulty finding replacements for his crew members. In town after town, when he tried to hire men, he was met only by refusals and at last decided he should turn back. Wallace and Bates persuaded him to go a little farther than he cared to, but even then the trip was much shorter than they had originally planned. They had expected to be away for three months, but at the end of the fifth week, they were back in Belém, unloading their many boxes of specimens.

The only casualty they had suffered during their travels had occurred to Wallace. He had been badly bitten by wasps and was extremely sick when they returned to Belém. After his recovery, he and Bates went back to work, following much the same routine as before. For many months more, they made their headquarters at Belém, taking an occasional short expedition away from the environs of the city. The country that they had at first thought so barren was proving in actuality far more fruitful than they had hoped, and there was no need for them to undertake an expensive and time-consuming trip farther into the interior. Because the collections grew and their English agent was able to sell the duplicates, Wallace wrote to his younger brother Herbert and asked him to join them. Herbert arrived in Brazil in July, 1849, and it gave great happiness to Wallace to have him there.

Deciding that they could collect more efficiently by separating, he left Bates and the next month set off with Herbert on the longest expedition he had yet taken, this time up the Amazon. In a leaky canoe, redolent with the odor of fish, they followed the course of the Pará, crossed to the Amazon, and, after twenty-eight days of hard travel, reached Santarém, some 500 miles upstream. Although they were cordially received by the inhabitants and had no problem finding a house in which to live, they soon moved to a smaller town a few miles down the river. As Humboldt had done, they were now discovering that the mosquitoes were a true menace. "We were warned that the mosquitoes here were very annoying," Wallace commented, "And we soon found them so, for immediately after sunset they poured in upon us in swarms, so that we found them unbearable, and were obliged to rush into sleeping rooms, which we had kept carefully closed. Here we had some respite for a time, but they soon found their way in at the cracks and keyholes, and they made us very restless and uncomfortable all the rest of the night. After a few days' residence we found them more tormenting than ever, rendering it quite impossible for us to sit down to read or write after supper." The only way to protect themselves was to follow the native practice of burning smoky fires of cow dung at each doorway. If the smoke was heavy enough and if they also kept walking around the room instead of remaining still, they could, Wallace said, "pass an hour pretty comfortably."

They next moved back to Santarém, where they followed almost exactly the same routine as at Belém, arising early each morning and doing their collecting in a businesslike fashion. By November they had obtained as many specimens as they wanted and were ready to go to the Rio Negro, whose headwaters Humboldt had explored more than forty years before. The canoe they were using was rotten, but they repaired its bottom, and the *comandante* of the town secured three Indians to take them as far as Óbidos, about a three-day journey. At one place where they made their usual request to the *comandante* for crew members, the official did nothing in spite of his promises. A week passed, and nobody appeared. Wallace at last turned for help to the priest, who persuaded a trader to lend them three of his employees. "One of the Indians, however, did not choose to come," Wallace wrote, "and was driven to the canoe by severe lashes, and at the point of the bayonet. He was very furious and sullen when he came on board, vowing that he would not go with me, and would take vengeance on those who had forced him on board. He complained bitterly of being treated like a slave, and I could not much blame him, offering him good pay and plenty to eat and drink, but to no purpose; he declared he would go back from the first place we stopped at, and kill the man who had struck him. At the same time he was very civil, assuring me that he felt no ill-will against me, as I had had nothing to do with it." It was afternoon before they started, and at sunset they went ashore to make supper. True to his threat, the Indian politely said good-bye to Wallace and disappeared into the forest, leaving the canoe undermanned and unable to go farther. Keeping his temper, Wallace made camp for the night and the next day took the risk of sending one of his remaining Indians back for assistance. Fortunately, the man proved faithful and returned later with another.

The travel now was extremely uncomfortable. The rains had started, and it seemed to Wallace that they were almost incessant. The mosquitoes became a torture. Night after night, the men were unable to sleep and lay rolling in torment in their bedding. On December 31, 1849, Wallace arrived at Manaus, but he had timed his visit poorly, because the rains made it practically impossible to collect either birds or insects. He learned, however, that the rare umbrella birds could be found at that season on the islands just above Manaus. Since these would be extremely valuable to European collectors, he hired native hunters and during the next month was able to take twenty-five specimens.

On August 31, 1850, he said good-bye to his brother Herbert, who planned to return to England in six more months, and started off to explore the upper reaches of the Negro. The first part of the trip he made with a Portuguese trader in a boat laden with calicoes, bales of coarse cotton cloth, axes, cutlasses, fishhooks, and other goods. Slowly they worked their way up the river, stopping at the small settlements on its banks, until they reached the falls of the Negro on October 19. Because their large boat could not ascend them, they transferred their cargo to two smaller canoes, which were much less comfortable but more easily handled in the swift currents that raced among the rocks. "As we went on," Wallace wrote of the falls, "we constantly encountered fresh difficulties. Sometimes we had to cross into the middle of the stream, to avoid some impassable mass of rocks; at others, the canoe was dragged and pushed in narrow channels, which hardly allowed it to pass. The Indians, all naked, with their trousers tied around their loins, plunged about in the water like fishes. Sometimes a projecting crag had to be reached with the tow-rope. An Indian takes it in his hand, and leaps into the rapid current; he is carried down by its irresistible force. Now he dives to the bottom, and there swims and crawls along where the stream has less power. After two or three trials he reaches the rock, and tries to mount upon it; but it rises high and abruptly out of the water, and after several efforts he falls back exhausted, and floats down again to the canoe amid the mirth and laughter of his comrades. Another now tries, with the same result. Then another plunges in without the rope, and thus unencumbered mounts the rock and gives a helping hand to his companion; and then all go to work, and we are pulled up past the obstacle." They continued to advance in this manner for hour after hour, resting occasionally in the eddies formed behind the rocks. Then, suddenly, they entered a current stronger than any they had encountered so far. Control of the boat slipped away from them, and it began to move backward faster and faster. For several moments they were in serious danger of being dashed against the rocks below them, but at almost the last moment the trader was able to wheel the canoe around and into the shelter of an eddy.

It took them four days of this exhausting work to reach the top of the rapids. There the water was calm, and they proceeded with no more trouble to the small village of Guía, where the trader lived. He had, Wallace said, "informed me during the voyage that he did not patronise marriage, and thought everybody a great fool who did. He had illustrated the advantages of keeping oneself free of such ties by informing me that the mother of his two elder daughters having grown old, and being unable to bring them up properly or teach them Portuguese, he had turned her out of doors and got a younger and more civilized person in her place. The poor woman had since died of jealousy, or 'passion,' as he termed it. When young, she had nursed him during an eighteen months' illness and saved his life; but he seemed to think he had performed a duty in turning her away,—for, said he, 'She was an Indian, and could only speak her own language, and, so long as she was with them, my children would never learn Portuguese.' " Nevertheless, toward Wallace he was cordiality itself, offering him a small house in which to live and inviting him to stay as long as he wanted.

Toward the end of January, 1851, Wallace was ready to continue his trip and left Guía with four Indians and a badly leaking canoe lent to him by the trader. At the end of nine days they had crossed the Venezuelan border and reached the town of San Carlos, one of the many where Humboldt had once stayed, a point carefully noted by Wallace who was glad to be "entering ground gone over fifty years ago by that illustrious traveller." He passed the Casiquiare and then, leaving his canoe, walked overland to the settlement of Javíta. He had now left the watershed of the Amazon and entered that of the Orinoco, reaching the farthest point he had hoped to attain.

Unfortunately, he had misjudged the season. On the very night he arrived, it began to rain after three months of the most splendid summer weather. "I had been wasting all this time in the rain district of the cataracts of the Río Negro," he complained. "No one there could tell me that the seasons, at such a short distance, differed so completely, and the consequence was that I arrived at Javíta on the very last day of summer. . . . Day after day the rain poured down; every afternoon or night was wet, and a little sunshine in the morning was the most we were favoured with." As a result, the insects were scarcer than they would have been if he had arrived earlier, but he nevertheless found many species that he had not seen in Brazil. He was also able to collect birds and fishes that were new to him, but he found his evenings dull—there was no one to talk to—and his Indians were growing restless. Wanting to leave this country where no one spoke their language, they began to use up the supplies as rapidly as possible in order to force Wallace to return. When this ruse did not work, they simply deserted him during the night.

None of the inhabitants would cook for him, so he kept house for himself during his remaining, discouraging weeks at Javíta. "The weather was now terribly wet," he wrote. "For successive days and nights rain was incessant, and a few hours of sunshine was a rarity. Insects were few, and those I procured it was almost impossible to dry. In the drying box they got destroyed by mould, and if placed in the open air and exposed to the sun, minute flies laid eggs upon them, and they were soon eaten by maggots. The only way I could preserve them was to hang them up some time every evening and morning over my fire. . . . Although, considering the season, I had done well, I knew that had I been earlier I might have done much better."

Back at Guía, after a month's rest, he joined the Portuguese trader on another journey, this time up the Uaupés, one of the tributaries of the Negro. The water was high and the current so strong that they could not move against it by paddling but had to pull themselves by tugging at the tree branches and creepers that grew along the banks. Often they ran into wasps' nests, and the boat became filled with biting ants that stung them viciously. At each Indian center they would stop and trade. Often it took some time for the Indians to come in from the outlying districts, because occasionally the Portuguese would force the Indians to work for them. Once their suspicion was overcome, however, they became friendly, and Wallace was able to purchase many specimens from them, which he added to those he collected himself. He decided that no place in the world was as good as the Uaupés for capturing live birds and animals and made up his mind that he would abandon an earlier plan of traveling to the Andes and instead make another trip farther up the river. Before he could do so, however, he had to return to Manaus to obtain more supplies and also to dispose of the collections he had stored there before they were destroyed by the damp and the insects.

On September 1, 1851, he left the Portuguese trader at Guía and began the descent of the Negro to Manaus. Bad news awaited him there. Letters from Belém, dating back three months, told him that his brother Herbert was dangerously ill with yellow fever and that his friends had little hope he would live. Wallace was both concerned and puzzled. If his brother was alive, why had he not written? If he was dead, why had his friends not sent word? But since there was nothing he could do from such a distance, he packed up his collections and made the necessary preparations to return to the Uaupés.

Most of the time he had been in Brazil, his health had been excellent, but on the way back up the river he became sick with fever. Traveling with only Indians for company and with the news of his brother weighing heavily on his mind, he fell into a fit of half-consciousness, from which he aroused himself only to take his medicine. "All this time," he remembered later, "the Indians went on with the canoe as they liked; for during two days and nights I hardly cared if we sank or swam. While in that apathetic state I was constantly half-thinking, half-dreaming, of all my past life and future hopes, and that they were perhaps doomed to end here on the Rio Negro. And then I thought of the dark uncertainty of my brother Herbert. . . . But with returning health these gloomy thoughts passed away. . . ." In this happier state of mind, he ascended the falls of the Negro, maneuvering the canoe between the rocks. Later the fever came back, and for several days he was seriously ill. Then it abated, and he thought he was cured. Then it returned again. Every other night at São Joaquim, the starting point for the next lap of his journey, he was feverish and, on the following day, was depressed and unable to do anything. In this weakened condition, he passed the months until February, when he decided to make his final trip up the Uaupés. "I was still so weak that I had difficulty in getting in and out of the canoe," he wrote, "but I thought that I should be as well there as confined in the house; and as I now longed more than ever to return home, I wished first to make this voyage, and get a few living birds and animals to take with me."

The upper reaches of the Uaupés, he discovered, were far more rocky than the Negro, and he passed through one dangerous rapid after another, swinging into the eddies for short rests and then out into the main stream again to battle the current. Under this battering, the bottom of the canoe became so weak that Wallace thought he had to replace one of the boards, a difficult task to accomplish in the middle of wilderness. His crew spent five days looking for a tree of good wood large enough to make a plank twelve or fourteen inches wide but could not find one. Becoming desperate over the delay, Wallace finally settled for two small boards, "rather clumsily inserted." Throughout the journey he was plagued with problems like these, and although he went up the river farther than any European had ever been and took three months on the trip, he did not obtain any of the "rare and handsome" birds he had expected. The total results he achieved amounted to about a dozen new species of fish and two or three scarce butterflies and birds. "This was entirely owing, however, to my unfortunate and unforeseen illness," he wrote, "for birds in great variety had been very abundant, but the time of the fruit was now over; fish and turtles, too, were in extraordinary plenty at the commencement of the fall of the river, two months back; and during that period, constituting the short summer in these districts, while I lay half dead, . . .

insects were doubtless more numerous." In addition to the specimens he had taken, he returned down the river with four live monkeys, about a dozen parrots, and six or eight small birds that he hoped eventually to sell in England. By the time he left the juncture of the Uaupés and the Negro, he had increased his stock of wild animals and birds to fifty-two, "which, in a small canoe, were no little trouble and annoyance."

Back in Belém, after the long voyage down the river, he found that his brother had indeed died of yellow fever. Except for this one sadness, he could regard his Brazilian expedition as a success. He had not traveled as far as Humboldt, nor had he been an explorer in the same sense. Except for his trip up the Uaupés, most of the places he had visited were by then relatively well known to Europeans. And he had not like Humboldt taken as many observations or recorded such a wide variety of information. Yet he had attained his first objective, one that Humboldt had not been able to accomplish: He had made his trip pay for itself. During this period he had also matured as a scientist. He had continued, for example, to wonder about the variety of the structures of animals. "In all works on Natural History," he wrote, "we constantly find details of the marvellous adaptation of animals to their food, their habits, and the localities in which they are found. But naturalists are now beginning to look beyond this, and to see that there must be some other principles regulating the infinitely varied forms of animal life. It must strike everyone, that the numbers of birds and insects of different groups, having scarcely any resemblance to each other, which yet feed on the same food and inhabit the same localities, cannot have been so differently constructed and adorned for that purpose alone." In these words, he presented a question on which he would ponder during the years to come.

He also made a major scientific contribution by carefully describing the location of each specimen he took. Many naturalists of his day were vague on this point, often merely indicating the country or some other general geographical designation. Wallace was far more particular. He wanted to know exactly where he had found each one, for he had become extremely interested in, and puzzled by, the distribution of animals. Although the surroundings might be the same in two locations, the species living in them could be different. Different species of howler monkeys lived in various parts of Brazil, and on one side of the Amazon, he had found one species of butterfly, while a different species flew among the trees on the other side. What was the reason for this? Did the river form a barrier even for insects? These were among the questions he was asking himself as he prepared to leave Brazil.

He had arrived in Belém on July 2, 1852, and learned that there were still occasional outbreaks of yellow fever, particularly among those persons who had not been in the city for any length of time. This danger, combined with the weakness that resulted from his bouts with fever, kept him indoors most of the time, but he did not have to stay in Belém long. The brig *Helen* was sailing shortly and would accept him as a passenger, along with the specimens and live animals and birds he had collected since his last shipment to England. While Wallace was packing up his possessions, Bates was exploring the Tapajós River, so that Wallace did not see him before leaving. Bates remained in Brazil for eleven years before he returned to England in 1859, and during that time he collected more than 14,000 species, 8,000 of which were previously unknown.

With his animals, birds, and specimens safely on board the *Helen,* Wallace saw the shoreline recede into the distance, and his thoughts, as they had so often recently, turned to home. When they had been at sea only two days, his fever recurred. After that he was so weak and also so seasick that he kept to his cabin most of the time. On August 6, however, some three weeks after their departure, the captain knocked on his cabin door and said the ship was on fire. On deck, Wallace could see smoke pouring from the forecastle, and it grew thicker when they removed the fore hatchway. The crew first tried to carry out the cargo so they could get at the fire. When they were unsuccessful at this, they opened the after hatchway, and the smoke only grew worse. The fire had apparently started in the stern of the hold among some kegs of South American balsam, but they were unable to reach it—the smoke suffocated them—and the captain gave the order to prepare to abandon ship. Describing those last minutes, Wallace said, "The boats, having been so long drying in the tropical sun, were very leaky, and were now half full of water, and books, coats, blankets, shoes, pork, and cheese, in a confused mass, were soaking in them. It was necessary to put two men in each to bail; and everything necessary being now ready, the rest of the crew were called off again to pour water into the hatchways and cabin, from which rose volumes of thick yellow smoke. Now, too, we could hear in the hold the balsam bubbling, like some great boiling cauldron, which took hold of such intense heat, that we knew the flames must soon break out. And so it was, for in less than half an hour the fire burst through the cabin-floor into the berths, and consuming rapidly the dry pine-wood, soon flamed up through the skylight. There was now a scorching heat on the quarter-deck, and we saw that all hope was over, and that we must in a few minutes be driven by the terrible element to take refuge on the scarcely less dangerous one, which heaved and swelled its mighty billows a thousand miles on every side of us."

After taking to the boats, they lay astern of the ship, watching the destruction of the *Helen.* The shrouds and sails caught fire, as the flames leaped upward. Without sails to steady it, the ship rolled heavily from side to side, and one by one, the weakened masts snapped under the strain.

"Many of the parrots, monkeys, and other animals we had on board, were already burnt or suffocated," Wallace wrote, "but several had retreated to the bowsprit out of reach of the flames, appearing to wonder what was going on, and quite unconscious of the fate that awaited them. We tried to get some of them into the boats, by going as near as we could venture; but they did not seem at all aware of the danger they were in, and would not make any attempt to reach us. As the flames caught the base of the bowsprit, some of them ran back and jumped into the midst of the fire. Only one parrot escaped; he was sitting on a rope hanging from the bowsprit, and this burning above him let him fall into the water, where, after floating a little while, we picked him up." This was the last of the birds and animals that Wallace had so laboriously brought with him down the Uaupés, the Negro, and, finally, the Amazon to Belém.

They stayed near the burning ship all night, vainly hoping some other vessel would sight it and come to their rescue. "It was now a magnificent spectacle," Wallace wrote, "for the decks had completely burned away, and as it heaved and rolled with the swell of the sea, presented its interior toward us filled with liquid flame,—a fiery furnace tossing restlessly upon the ocean."

When dawn broke and no help came, they agreed to set their course for Bermuda. For the first two days the sun shone hot and blistered their hands and faces. Then they passed through days of squalls with the wind veering and making it impossible to head for the island. On the thirteenth the weather cleared, but the next two days there was almost no wind at all, and they decided they had better go on short rations. But on the fifteenth, late in the afternoon, they saw a sail. It was the *Jordeson,* bound for London, and its captain welcomed them on board.

In the days that followed, regrets for what he had lost began to overcome him. Except for the collections he had sent to England earlier, everything had vanished in the flaming *Helen.* "With what pleasure had I looked upon every rare and curious insect that I had added to my collection!" Wallace wrote. "How many times, when almost overcome with the ague, had I crawled into the forest and been rewarded by some unknown and beautiful species! How many places, which no European foot but my own had trodden, would have been recalled to my memory by the rare birds and insects they had furnished to my collection! How many weary days and weeks had I passed, upheld only by the fond hope of bringing home many new and beautiful forms from those wild regions; every one of which would be endeared to me by the recollections they would call up,—which should prove that I had not wasted the advantages that I had enjoyed, and would give me occupation and amusement for many years to come! And now everything was gone, and I had not one specimen to illustrate the unknown lands I had trod, or to call back the recollection of the wild scenes I had beheld!" But knowing that such regrets were useless, he tried to put them behind him, as the *Jordeson* held its course for England.

III

In spite of his longings to return home, not much awaited Wallace in London. He collected 200 pounds in insurance for his losses on the *Helen,* and this amount took care of his financial needs. But he received little scientific recognition for what he had done. Many of the specimens he had gathered, although salable, were already known. He published at his own expense a book on the palms of the Negro and Amazon; it sold just enough copies to cover its cost. He wrote *A Narrative of Travels on the Amazon and Rio Negro*; although years later it became popular, at the time it produced no profit for him. He would have liked to have obtained employment as a naturalist, but such jobs were few (the study of natural history was still regarded largely as a hobby), and he was not qualified to fill any of them, because most of them required more formal training than he had received.

He spent his time, therefore, working over the specimens he had retained for himself—he had sold only his duplicates—visiting the British Museum to study its collections of insects, and attending the meetings of the Zoological and Entomological societies. Still shy and still relatively unrecognized as a scientist, he nevertheless met many of the leading men of the day, although none of them seems to have been greatly taken by either his experiences or his ideas. A short visit to Switzerland in 1853 broke his routine but did nothing to answer his basic question: How could he make a living as a naturalist?

He had already demonstrated to himself that he could earn his expenses by collecting and selling specimens, and he thought that he might be able to do so again. To be successful, however, he had to select a region that, like Brazil, was rich in its variety of life and yet still relatively unexplored. From examining the collections of the British Museum, he decided that the Malay Archipelago best met his qualifications. Previous collectors had proved it to be a fertile source of specimens. Yet the collections at the museum were far from complete.

Gathering together what information he could about the area—the few books that had been published and the notes he had taken while at the British Museum—he left England, and on April 20, 1854, he entered Singapore's harbor, which was crowded with the men-of-war and trading vessels of many European nations, praus from the Malay Archipelago, junks from China, and passenger-carrying sampans. Once ashore, he walked through streets lined with Mohammedan mosques, Chinese joss houses, the warehouses of European traders, Chinese bazaars, and long rows of Malay cottages. After finding a place to stay, Wallace immediately began his collecting. The interior of the island consisted of numerous small hills, 300 or 400 feet high, and covered by trees that the Chinese cut for lumber. This area proved to be an excellent collecting ground for insects, but Wallace had to be wary of the tigers, which killed an average of one Chinese a day. As he commented, ". . . it was rather nervous work hunting for insects among the fallen trunks and old sawpits, when one of these savage animals might be lurking close by, waiting an opportunity to spring upon us."

At the end of two months' time he had obtained a large number of insects, including 700 species of beetles. But birds and animals—except for tigers—were scarce at that time of year, so he moved to Malacca, one of Malaya's coastal towns. There he engaged two Portuguese to accompany him on a two-week trip into the interior, where he collected several specimens. A visit to Mount Ophir, in the middle of the Malay Peninsula and about fifty miles from Malacca, completed his preliminary exploration of the mainland. Since this area had already been explored by several naturalists, he would have to go farther afield if he wanted valuable specimens.

On November 1, 1854, he landed at Sarawak on the island of Borneo and received a cordial welcome from Sir James Brooke, an adventurous soldier of fortune. As a young man, Brooke had purchased a large yacht, manned it with twenty sailors whom he spent three years training, and then sailed to the Malay Archipelago. Learning that some of the Dyak tribesmen were in revolt against their government, he offered his services to the sultan. When the rebellion had been put down, the sultan in gratitude named him Raja of Sarawak, and he thereafter occupied a unique position in the Far East, cooperating with the British navy in putting down piracy (a government scandal developed over the vast amount of head money paid him for dead pirates), serving as the British consul to Borneo, and taking an active part in native affairs. His house was always open to Wallace, who used it as his headquarters whenever he was in the city of Kuching.

For the first four months Wallace found the collecting poor. Once again he had misjudged the season, and the rain prevented him from taking many specimens. But the time was not wasted, even though he could not spend much of it in the field. In the evenings and during the rainy days he kept thinking about the origin of species and in February put his ideas on paper, submitting them to the *Annals and Magazine of Natural History* in England under the title "On the Law Which Has Regulated the Introduction of New Species." Like Darwin, he had been much influenced by Lyell's line of reasoning in geology and believed that it could be applied to the development of species. If the changes in the earth's surface had been slowly brought about by forces still in operation today, why could not this be equally true of the species? This led him to think, as Darwin did, that the intermediate changes had been small and not that one large class of animals had developed directly. This, in turn, brought him to the conclusion that the truth might be uncovered by paying attention to the more primitive type rather than to the more advanced. Furthermore, a more primitive type might have given rise to a single species, but it also might have given rise to several. Therefore, a chart of the development of the species would look more like a tree than a straight line. The law he proposed was this: no species has come into existence unless it coexisted, both in time and space, with another closely allied species that was its predecessor.

Sitting in his room with the rain pouring down outside and alone except for the Malay boy who cooked his meals, Wallace had written a remarkable paper. True, he could give no description of the mechanism that brought about the phenomenon, and in this respect his paper was more an affirmation of faith in evolution than an explanation of it. But he had gone far beyond most of the leading scientists of the day, men like Agassiz, for example, who remained trapped by their old ideas. Probably several factors contributed to Wallace's achievement. His absence of a formal education may have been one. In a way, Agassiz had known too much. Like Cuvier, he recognized the paucity of the fossil record, and he was so well trained that he could immediately see the loopholes in the evolutionists' arguments, loopholes that actually existed. Wallace did not suffer from this disadvantage. Knowing as little as he did, he could consider everything.

He also kept himself free of preconceived notions. He had never locked himself into a position, as Agassiz had done. In part, this was because he was not sufficiently well known for it to be important that he take a position. But in even larger measure, it was because he had an open mind, an ability to consider facts in various lights, not just one. Then, too, he grasped the significance of Lyell's discoveries and was able to apply them, as even Lyell was unable to, to a broader range of phenomena. Newton had shown that general laws answered the questions proposed by the universe, that there were no special laws for one time or place. Lyell had done this for geology when he had eliminated the catastrophes and showed that the past of the earth could be revealed by a study of its present. Wallace was gifted with the intellect to carry this principle into biology.

He was further favored by his experiences in both Brazil and the Malay Archipelago, where he had observed the locality of species and how one species might exist on one side of the river, while another, only slightly different, existed on the other. To these circumstances, of course, must be added genius. The former surveyor, watchmaker, and schoolteacher had native genius, although no one, including himself, recognized it at the time.

When his paper had been completed and the rainy season had ended, Wallace moved to a new coal mine that was being opened up some twenty miles inland and to the east of Kuching. There he started collecting in earnest, and the location turned out to be especially favorable. Many of the insects he wanted fed on decaying leaves, bark, and wood, but to find many dead trees in the forest, he would have had to travel for miles. At the coal mines, twenty to fifty Chinese and Dyaks had been employed for several months in clearing the forest and cutting a right-of-way for a railroad to the nearest large river. Because the area was littered with dead wood, conditions were exactly right.

He also collected some butterflies and a frog that he had never seen before, but one of his primary purposes for going to Borneo was to obtain some orangutans, the large apes that live there and in Sumatra. These, he knew, would command a high price in Europe. He saw his first one about a week after his arrival at the mine but lost it when it moved through the trees to a swampy location, where he could not follow. A week later he came across another, a half-grown male, which he shot. In April he saw one more. "It fell at the first shot," he wrote, "but did not seem much hurt, and immediately climbed up the nearest tree, when I fired, and it again fell, with a broken arm and a wound in the body. The two Dyaks now ran up to it, and each seized hold of a hand, telling me to cut a pole, and they would secure it. But although one arm was broken, and it was only a half-grown animal, it was too strong for these young savages, drawing them up towards its mouth notwithstanding all their efforts, so that they were obliged to leave go, or they would have been seriously bitten." Realizing that he could not take his quarry alive and not content to let it escape, Wallace shot the animal through the heart.

He took several more specimens and in May shot a female. He was preparing to take the body home, when he discovered a young orangutan, apparently her child, lying face down in the mud near the tree from which the mother had fallen. "Luckily it did not appear to have been wounded," Wallace wrote, "and after we had cleaned the mud out of its mouth it began to cry out, and seemed quite strong and active. While carrying it home, it got its hands in my beard, and grasped so tightly that I had great difficulty in getting free, for the fingers are habitually bent inwards at the last joint so as to form complete hooks."

Once he had it back at the mines, he had difficulty feeding it. Neither the Malays, the Chinese, nor the Dyaks drank milk, so none was available. In its place, Wallace used rice water. "This was a very meager diet and the little creature did not thrive well on it, although I added sugar and cocoa-nut milk occasionally, to make it more nourishing. When I put my finger in its mouth it sucked with great vigour, drawing in its cheeks with all its might in the vain effort to extract some milk, and only after persevering a long time would it give up in disgust, and set up a scream very like that of a baby in similar circumstances. . . .

"I fitted up a little box for a cradle, with a soft mat for it to lie upon, which was changed and washed every day; and I soon found it necessary to wash the little Mias [the native name for orangutan] as well. After I had done so a few times, it came to like the operation, and as soon as it was dirty would begin crying and not leave off until I took it out and carried it to the spout, when it would immediately become quiet, although it would wince a little at the first rush of the cold water and make ridiculously wry faces while the water was running over its head." Unfortunately, all of Wallace's care was not sufficient to keep the orangutan alive. When it was three months old, it became sick and soon died.

One of Wallace's problems in hunting orangutans was recovering the animals once he had shot them. Several times they failed to fall out of the trees in which they had been killed. Then he would either have to persuade a tribesman to climb the tree and cut the branch or have to chop down the tree itself.

Describing one such occasion, he told how he had taken four shots at an orangutan but, because of the heavy foliage in the trees, was not certain whether they had taken effect. The orangutan then "got on one of the loftiest trees in the forest, and we could see one leg hanging down useless, having been broken by a ball. He now fixed himself in a fork, where he was hidden by thick foliage, and seemed disinclined to move. I was afraid that he would remain and die in this position, and as it was nearly evening I could not have got the tree cut down that day. [It was important to recover the bodies quickly, before the insects destroyed them or decomposition set in.] I therefore fired again, and he then moved off, and going up the hill was obliged to get on to some lower trees, on the branches of one of which he fixed himself in such a position that he could not fall, and lay all in a heap as if dead, or dying.

"I now wanted the Dyaks to go up and cut off the branch he was resting on, but they were afraid, saying he was not dead, and would come and attack them. We then shook the adjoining tree, pulled the hanging creepers, and did all we could to disturb him, but without effect, so I thought it best to send for two Chinamen with axes to cut down the tree. While the messenger was gone, however, one of the Dyaks took courage and climbed towards him, but the Mias did not wait for him to come near, moving off to another tree, where he got on to a dense mass of branches and creepers which almost completely hid him from our view. The tree was luckily a small one, so when the axes came we soon had it cut through; but it was so held up by jungle ropes and climbers to adjoining trees that it only fell into a sloping position. The Mias did not move, and I began to fear that after all we should not get him, as it was near evening, and half a dozen more trees would have to be cut down before the one he was on would fall. As a last resource we all began pulling at the creepers, which shook the tree very much, and, after a few minutes, when we had almost given up all hopes, down he came with a crash and a thud like the fall of a giant. And he was a giant, his head and body being full as large as a man's."

Since he was engaged in vigorous work like this, day in and day out, it was a wonder that Wallace did not have any serious accidents, but in July he slipped while walking among some fallen logs. Carelessly he did nothing to take care of himself and as a result developed a "severe inflamed ulcer" on his ankle, which kept him in the house for several weeks. On his recovery, he went to live for a while among the Land Dyaks, who never went near the sea and whose moral character he found high in spite of their reputation for fierceness. (He generously dismissed their headhunting as being no greater a stain on their innate qualities than the slave trade on the Europeans'.)

But they puzzled him biologically. He had read Malthus at Leicester, and according to Malthus' thinking, conditions for an expansion of the Dyak population were ideal. They had an abundance of food, a healthy climate, the custom of marrying early, and an apparent absence of disease. Yet as far as Wallace could discern, their population was either not increasing at all or increasing extremely slowly. He began to keep figures on the numbers of children and learned that in a village of 150 families, only 1 family had 6 children, and only 6 had 5 children. The majority possessed only 1, 2, or 3. From this he concluded that infertility must be a more important factor in checking population growth than Malthus had believed. These reflections indicated the direction that Wallace's reasoning was taking. His thinking was growing broader and more encompassing. In Brazil he had been interested in the location of populations. He was now thinking of the natural forces that controlled them.

Altogether he stayed in Sarawak for approximately fourteen months, his longest visit at any one island. But by January, 1856, he had exhausted its possibilities and returned to Singapore, which served as his base, to work over his collections and pack some of them for shipment. In May he started looking for transportation to Macassar on the island of Celebes but was unable to find anyone making the passage direct, so he took a schooner that was stopping at Bali and at Lombok, where he hoped to locate a ship that would carry him the rest of the way. (The schooner was named *Kembang Djepoon,* meaning Rose of Japan, and was owned by a Chinese merchant, manned by a Javanese crew, and captained by an Englishman.) Commenting on this part of his journeys through the archipelago, Wallace wrote, "The islands of Bali and Lombok, situated in the east end of Java, are particularly interesting. They are the only islands of the whole Archipelago in which the Hindoo religion still maintains itself— and they form the extreme points of the two great zoological divisions of the Eastern hemisphere; for although so similar in external appearance and in all physical features, they differ greatly in their natural productions. It was after having spent two years in Borneo, Malacca and Singapore, that I made a somewhat involuntary visit to these islands on my way to Macassar. Had I been able to obtain a passage direct to that place from Singapore, I should probably never have gone near them, and should have missed some of the most important discoveries of my whole expedition to the East."

He stayed only two days at Bali, just long enough to realize it was essentially like the other Oriental areas he had visited, and then entered the wild harbor of Lombok, known for its heavy surf which beat against the beaches even when the water offshore was calm. Several traders offered him lodgings and horses, but since the collecting around the town was not as productive as he wished, he moved to the house of a Malay at the southern end of the bay. Here he found numerous birds, but even more important, he saw the difference between Bali and Lombok. For the birds of Bali were Oriental, while many of the birds he collected at Lombok were Australian. The narrow Lombok Strait, approximately twenty miles wide, biologically divided the Orient from the continent of Australia. This was indeed "one of the most important discoveries" of his entire journey.

The house of the Malay was small, and although he was kind to Wallace, he could let the naturalist have only part of the reception room in his bamboo house. "My collecting operations here were carried on under more than usual difficulties," Wallace wrote, describing the problems of a naturalist in the field. "One small room had to serve for eating, sleeping and working, for storehouse and dissecting room; in it were no shelves, cupboards, chairs or tables; ants swarmed in every part of it, and dogs, cats and fowls entered it at pleasure. Besides this it was the parlour and reception-room of my host, and I was obliged to consult his convenience and that of the numerous guests who visited us. My principal piece of furniture was a box, which served me as a dining-table, a seat while skinning birds, and as the receptacle of the birds when skinned and dried. To keep them free from ants we borrowed, with some difficulty, an old bench, the four legs of which being placed in cocoa-nut shells filled with water, kept us tolerably free from these pests.

"The box and the bench were however literally the only places where anything could be put away, and they were generally well occupied by two insect boxes and about a hundred birds' skins in process of drying. It may therefore be easily conceived that when anything bulky or out of the common way was collected, the question 'Where is it to be put?' was rather a difficult one to answer. All animal substances moreover require some time to dry thoroughly, emit a very disagreeable odour while doing so, and are particularly attractive to ants, flies, dogs, rats, cats, and other vermin, calling for especial cautions and constant supervision, which under the circumstances above described were impossible."

He then went on to talk about some of the handicaps of the field naturalist. "My readers may now partially understand why a travelling naturalist of limited means like myself, does so much less than is expected or than he would himself wish to do. It would be interesting to preserve the skeletons of many birds and animals, reptiles and fishes in spirits, skins of large animals, remarkable fruits and woods, and the most curious articles of manufacture and commerce; but it will be seen that under the circumstances I have just described it would have been impossible to add to the collections which were my own more especial favorites. When travelling by boat the difficulties are as great or greater, and they are not diminished when the journey is by land. It was absolutely necessary therefore to limit my collections to certain groups to which I could devote constant personal attention, and thus secure from destruction or decay what had often been obtained by much labour and pains." This might have been Humboldt writing more than fifty years before in the Andes.

One incident occurred, however, that disturbed him greatly while he was on Bali. The men were extremely jealous of their women, who were not allowed to accept any present—even a flower—from another man. The penalty for disobeying this rule was death; the husband or a relative was expected to kill the offending woman immediately with his kris, the native knife worn by every man. The donor of the present seems to have escaped any punishment. In more serious cases, however, the woman and her lover were tied back to back and thrown into the sea, where, Wallace said, "some large crocodiles are always on the watch to devour the bodies." One such execution took place in the town where Wallace was staying. This was too much for the curious scientist. "I took a long walk into the country," he said simply, "to be out of the way until it was all over."

At the end of August he left Bali and reached Macassar in three days. "It was with great satisfaction," he commented, "that I stepped on a shore which I had been vainly trying to reach since February." In the endless effort to secure more and more specimens, he asked for, and received, the rajah's permission to move farther into the interior. Here he was truly in the wilderness. "Not a single person in the village could speak more than a few words of Malay," he wrote, "and hardly any of the people appeared to have seen a European before. One most disagreeable result of this was," he added wryly, "that I excited terror alike in man and beast.

Wherever I went, dogs barked, children screamed, women ran away, and men stared as though I were some strange and terrible cannibal monster. Even the pack-horses on the roads and paths would start aside when I appeared and rush into the jungle; and as to those horrid, ugly brutes, the buffaloes, they could never be approached by me; not for fear of my own, but others' safety. They would first stick out their necks and stare at me, and then on a nearer view break loose from their halters or tethers, and rush away helter skelter as if a demon were after them, without any regard for what might be in their way. Whenever I met buffaloes carrying packs along a pathway, or being driven home to the village, I had to turn aside into the jungle and hide myself until they had passed, to avoid a catastrophe which would increase the dislike with which I was already regarded.

"Every day about noon," he complained, "the buffaloes were brought into the village and were tethered in the shade around the houses; and then I had to creep about like a thief by back ways, for no one could tell what mischief they might do to the children and houses were I to walk among them. If I came suddenly upon a well where women were drawing water or children bathing, a sudden flight was the certain result; which things occurring day after day, were very unpleasant to a person who does not like to be disliked, and who had never been accustomed to be treated as an ogre."

Ever since he had been in Celebes, his health had been poor—he had come down with an intermittent fever—and with the arrival of the rainy season in November, he returned to Macassar. Sick as he was, he could not turn down the unusual opportunity to visit the islands of Kai and Aru, which lie more than 1,000 miles west of Macassar and just to the south of New Guinea. Once a year the native trading ships made the journey, leaving in December or January with the west monsoon and returning in July or August with the east monsoon. Wallace regarded these islands as the " 'Ultima Thule' of the East," and being in Macassar at the proper time of year, he made arrangements with a Javanese half-caste to sail in his prau as a passenger.

The ship was something like a Chinese junk with a mainsail and foresail made of matting and two jibs and a sail in the aft made of cotton canvas. About fifty persons were on board, including Wallace and his three servants. Thirty of these were crew members, men of several tribes and languages. The remainder were agents and petty dealers who were working off debts they owed the owner. In this strange company, and with no compass or other navigational instrument aboard, Wallace sailed from December 16 to December 31, when he approached the islands of Kai. "The sea was calm as a lake," he wrote, "and the glorious sun of the tropics threw a flood of golden light over all. The scene was to me inexpressibly delightful. I was in a new world, and could dream of the productions hid in those rocky forests, and those azure abysses. But few European feet had ever trodden the shores I gazed upon; its plants, and animals, and men were alike almost unknown, and I could not help speculating on what my wanderings there for a few days might bring to light."

After a short stay at the Kai Islands, the prau sailed to the Aru Islands, where Wallace first lived in the principal trading center, Dobo. Although the specimens he secured there were valuable, he was frustrated by the weather and his inability to secure a boat that would take him to the larger islands to the west. He had earlier written the governor, requesting his assistance in gaining the natives' cooperation. The governor had responded by sending out the proper orders and, as an additional courtesy to Wallace, had warned the natives they would be held responsible for his safety. This almost put an end to his collecting. During his first months at Dobo, two praus had been attacked by pirates, and under such circumstances and in view of the governor's warning, no native would put out in a boat with Wallace.

Not until March, therefore, could Wallace make the journey to what he called the mainland of Aru. Here he again followed his usual routine of collecting specimens himself and teaching natives to help him. Many of the ones he obtained, including several birds of paradise, were extremely valuable, but ever since he had left Dobo, he had suffered terribly from the insects, "who," he said, "seemed here bent upon revenging my long-continued persecution of their race." His feet and ankles were particularly affected and soon were covered with red swollen specks, which turned into inflamed ulcers that were so painful he could not walk.

Aside from the hardships he was suffering, his expedition had turned out well, and even on the main island of Aru, although he was confined to the house for three straight weeks—a situation he found almost intolerable—his hunters and the natives were filling his boxes with birds and insects.

Yet he was not content. For months he had been bothered by the chilly reception given the article he had written on the origin of the species. Granted that he was not well known as a scientist and that his opinions, therefore, carried relatively little weight and granted, too, that he had not been able to complete his theory by suggesting a mechanism, nevertheless, he had hoped that his article would generate some comment, even if the comment were negative. But its publication seemed to have gone almost unnoticed, a matter of deep regret to him. That past October, while he was in Celebes, he had written directly to Charles Darwin, whose reputation he knew, asking his opinion, and while he was sitting in the house in Aru with his festering feet, Darwin was writing a reply. The article had not, as Wallace had supposed, gone unnoticed. Few naturalists had paid much attention to it—they were interested only in describing species, Darwin later said—but Darwin himself agreed with almost everything that Wallace had written. And Charles Lyell had thought so highly of the article that he had discussed it with Darwin. Wallace may have had a smaller audience than he had hoped, but although he did not know it yet, it included the two men whose approval he would have valued the most.

In early May he returned to Dobo, where he remained until July 2, 1857. In spite of the weeks of bad weather and the handicap imposed by his feet, he carried back with him to Macassar 9,000 specimens, which, as he had foreseen when he undertook the voyage, were among the most valuable he could have found anywhere; they eventually brought him approximately 1,000 pounds. In addition, he had seen the birds of paradise in their native forests and had explored "a new fauna and flora, one of the most remarkable and most beautiful and least-known in the world." Years later he still regarded those months as "the portion of my travels to which I look back with the most complete satisfaction."

Once back in Celebes, Wallace took what for him was a month's vacation. He spent the time packing his new collections for shipment to Singapore, repairing his guns, and going through the supplies he had recently received from England. At the end of the month, he felt eager for work again and moved about thirty-five miles north of Macassar to a rice plantation.

In the latter part of September a heavy shower of rain warned him that the wet season was approaching and that his time in Celebes was running out. By the middle of October a deluge came down every afternoon. Great numbers of millipedes appeared—large ones, eight or ten inches long and as thick as a man's finger. Snakes became so numerous that when he beat among the dead leaves for insects, he sometimes accidentally caught one in his collecting net. With him, he had two servants, and they came down with fever, dysentery, and swollen feet. After he had nursed them back to health, he became ill. These hardships and a shortage of supplies made him return to Macassar.

Probably he should have taken another rest, a longer one this time; but instead, he boarded the Dutch mail steamer, which first called at Kupang in Timor and then turned northwest to the Banda Islands, where he admired the live volcano, although he did not climb it as Humboldt would have done. Twenty hours from the Bandas brought him to Amboina, the capital of the Molucca Islands and one of the oldest European settlements in the East. There he made arrangements to stay a few weeks in a small hut on a plantation in the interior. One evening about nine o'clock, he heard a curious rustling overhead as though some animal were crawling over the thatch. Since it soon stopped, he thought no more about it and went to bed. The next afternoon he happened to glance up and saw an object that was colored like a tortoiseshell and wedged between the ridgepole and the roof. Suddenly Wallace recognized what he was looking at and knew what had caused the noise the night before. A twelve-foot python had climbed up one of the posts of the house and had been sleeping just a yard away from Wallace's head. His helpers would have nothing to do with it. They simply wanted Wallace to leave the house until the snake departed of its own will. But one of the plantation workers volunteered to dispose of it. "He made a strong noose of rattan," Wallace wrote, "and with a long pole in the other hand began to poke at the snake, which then began slowly to uncoil itself. He then managed to slip the noose over its head, and getting it well on to the body, dragged the animal down. There was a great scuffle as the snake coiled around the chairs and posts to resist its enemy, but at length the man caught hold of its tail, rushed out of the house (running so quickly that the creature seemed quite confounded) and tried to strike its head against a tree. He missed however, and let go, and the snake got under a dead trunk close by. It was again poked out, and again the . . . man caught hold of its tail, and running away quickly dashed its head with a swing against a tree, and it was then easily killed with a hatchet."

Wallace was at the plantation for twenty days, but since his health was still poor, he could not work at times because of attacks of fever. Yet when he returned to Amboina on Christmas Day, 1857, he made plans to go almost immediately to Ternate, an island to the north. He was still pondering the problem of the origin of the species and, before he left Amboina, began a long letter to Bates on the subject. Although he intended to write a book about evolution, buttressing his earlier statements with more illustrations, in his general thinking he had not advanced beyond the point he had reached almost three years before when he had been at Sarawak.

At Ternate, Wallace located a house that was to serve as his headquarters for the next three years, while he made trips through the Molucca Islands and New Guinea. The house was surrounded by gardens and "a wilderness of fruit trees." In one direction, it overlooked the old Portuguese fort and the native town beyond, and in the other, it gave an uninterrupted view of Ternate's mountain. A five-minute walk took Wallace to the marketplace or the beach. Yet he was on the outskirts of the settlement; no European house stood between him and the forest.

In his years of wandering he had never enjoyed anything either so luxurious or so permanent, but after a few weeks at Ternate he came down with recurring bouts of fever. Every day, for several hours, he would have to lie down while he suffered first a severe chill and then the fever, both of which made him unable to work or read. During daily periods he could do nothing but rest on his bed and think of things that interested him. One of these, of course, was the origin of species.

Writing later, he said that "my paper written at Sarawak rendered it certain to my mind that . . . change had taken place by natural succession and descent—one species becoming changed either slowly or rapidly into another. But the exact process of the change and the causes which led to it were absolutely unknown and appeared almost inconceivable. The great difficulty was to understand how, if one species was gradually changed into another, there continued to be so many quite distinct species, so many which differed from their nearest allies by slight yet perfectly definite and constant characters. One would expect that if it was a law of nature that species were continually changing so as to become in time new and distinct species, the world would be full of an inextricable mixture of various slightly different forms, so that the well-defined and constant species we see would not exist. Again, not only are species, as a rule, separated from each other by distinct external characters, but they almost always differ also to some degree in their food, in the places they frequent, in their habits and instincts, and these characters are quite as definite and constant as are the external characters. The problem then was, not only how and why do species change, but how and why do they change into new and well-defined species, distinguished from each other in so many ways; why and how do they become so exactly adapted to distinct modes of life; and why do all the intermediate grades die out (as geology shows they have died out) and leave only clearly defined and well-marked species, genera, and higher groups of animals."

Wallace had arrived in Ternate in January. In early February the fits of fever were still continuing, forcing him to lie down every day. On one of these occasions, he began idly to think once again about Malthus and the *Principle of Population*. Letting his mind wander, it occurred to him that Malthus' checks on the growth of populations must also apply to animals, which usually breed more rapidly than humans and yet "evidently do not increase regularly every year, as otherwise the world would long ago have been densely crowded with those that breed most quickly. Vaguely thinking over the enormous and constant destruction which this implied, it occurred to me to ask the question, Why do some die and some live? And the answer was clearly, that on the whole the best fitted live."

Down in the town, life went on as usual. Chinese merchants stopped to talk to one another as they passed on the streets, Ternate Malays made purchases at the native market, and the Dutch governor and the police magistrate reviewed the reports that daily accumulated on their desks. To any observer, it was a routine day at Ternate, quiet, calm—and, for the Europeans, perhaps a bit dull. But up on the slope the lonely English traveler, wracked by fever, was close to discovering one of the great scientific truths.

Wallace later wrote that as he lay there in his thatched house, "it suddenly flashed upon me that this self-acting process would necessarily *improve the race,* because in every generation the inferior would inevitably be killed off and the superior would remain—that is, *the fittest would survive.* Then at once I seemed to see the whole effect of this. . . ."

He was too weak at the moment even to write and waited anxiously for the fever to pass. As soon as it was gone, he began making notes for a paper and worked at the task throughout the evening. In two more evenings he had finished it and placed it in an envelope addressed to Charles Darwin. When the Dutch mail steamer left Ternate that week, it carried Wallace's remarkable letter in its hold.

13

Champions of the Cause

CHARLES DARWIN: 1809–1882
ALFRED WALLACE: 1823–1913
THOMAS HUXLEY: 1825–1895

I

When Charles Darwin, on June 18, 1858, opened the startling letter from Alfred Wallace, the quietude of Down House was shattered. Darwin faced a moral problem that most men would have found difficult to solve, for the receipt of Wallace's paper laid him open to the suspicion that anything he himself subsequently published had found its roots in the work done by Wallace. Several courses of action lay before him, some of them honorable, some dishonorable. He could ignore Wallace's letter—even deny ever having received it, an assertion which, since it had been mailed from faraway Ternate, would have been believable. Or he could write Wallace and explain that he himself had already made the same discoveries and attempt to allay any doubts Wallace might have that this was untrue. Or he could admit that he had been, to use his own word, "forestalled" and give Wallace credit for being the first with the idea.

Being a man of great honor, he had no hesitation over which choice to make. That very day he sent Wallace's paper to Lyell and wrote him, "Please return the MS., which he does not say he wishes me to publish, but I shall, of course, at once write and offer to send it to any journal."

Then he added sadly, "So all my originality, whatever it may amount to, will be smashed, though my book, if it will ever have any value, will not be deteriorated; as all the labour consists in the application of the theory."

Darwin showed good judgment in announcing his plan to Lyell, because Lyell was as honorable as himself and, at the same time, was more detached. Lyell immediately disapproved of Darwin's first impulse to publish Wallace's account with no mention of his own work. Although this action would leave Darwin untainted by any suspicion of unfairness, it was too great a sacrifice and, Lyell thought, unnecessary. By June 25 he had persuaded Darwin to reconsider his position, and Darwin now wrote him at length, suggesting a plan that he hoped would be honorable and also do justice to both Wallace and himself. "I am very sorry to trouble you, busy as you are, in so merely personal an affair," he wrote, "but if you will give me your deliberate opinion, you will do me as great a service as ever man did, for I have entire confidence in your judgment and honour. . . .

"There is nothing in Wallace's sketch which is not written out much fuller in my sketch, copied out in 1844, and read by Hooker some dozen years ago. [Hooker was his friend, the botanist.] About a year ago I sent a short sketch, of which I have a copy, of my views (owing to correspondence on several points) to Asa Gray, so that I could most truly say and prove that I take nothing from Wallace. I should be extremely glad now to publish a sketch of my general views in about a dozen pages or so; but I cannot persuade myself that I can do so honourably. Wallace says nothing about publication, and I enclose his letter. But as I had not intended to publish any sketch, can I do so honourably, because Wallace has sent me an outline of his doctrine? I would far rather burn my whole book, than that he or any other man should think that I had behaved in a paltry spirit. Do you not think his having sent me this sketch ties my hands? . . . If I could honourably publish I would state that I was induced now to publish a sketch (and I should be very glad to be permitted to say, to follow your advice long ago given) from Wallace having sent me an outline of my general conclusions. We differ only in that I was led to my views from what artificial selection has done for domestic animals. I would send Wallace a copy of my letter to Asa Gray, to show him that I had not stolen his doctrine. But I cannot tell whether to publish now would not be base and paltry. This was my first impression, and I should certainly have acted on it had it not been for your letter.

"This is a trumpery affair to trouble you with, but you cannot tell how much obliged I would be for your advice.

"By the way, would you object to send this and your answer to Hooker to be forwarded to me? For then I shall have the opinion of my two best and kindest friends. This letter is miserably written, and I write it now that I may for a time banish the whole subject; and I am worn out with musing. . . ."

Then he pathetically concluded by saying, "My good dear friend, forgive me. This is a trumpery letter, influenced by trumpery feelings."

He did not mail the letter right away, and although he was "worn out with musing," he continued to ponder the problem. The following day he returned to the letter and wrote, "Forgive me for adding a P.S. to make the case as strong as possible against myself.

"Wallace might say 'You did not intend publishing an abstract of your views till you received my communication. Is it fair to take advantage of my having freely, though unasked, communicated to you my ideas, and thus prevent me forestalling you?' The advantage which I should take being that I am induced to publish from privately knowing that Wallace is in the field. It seems hard on me that I should thus be compelled to lose my priority of many years' standing, but I cannot feel at all sure that this alters the justice of the case. First impressions are generally right, and I at first thought it would be dishonourable in me now to publish."

To add to Darwin's difficulties, his infant child had just died of scarlet fever, and four days later he replied to a letter from Hooker by saying, "I have just read your letter, and see you want the papers at once. I am quite prostrated, and can do nothing, but I send Wallace, and the abstract of my letter to Gray, which gives most imperfectly only the means of change and does not touch on reasons for believing that species do change. I dare say all is too late. I hardly care about it. But you are too generous to sacrifice so much time and kindness. It is most generous, most kind. I send my sketch of 1844 solely that you may see by your own handwriting that you did read it. I really cannot bear to look at it. Do not waste much time. It is miserable in me to care at all about priority."

Emotionally tortured, torn between his desire for recognition and his fear of being dishonorable, and, most of all, ashamed of what he called his "trumpery," Darwin passed the days at Down House, while his two good friends worked out a solution that would resolve the difficulty fairly and honorably. On July 1 they presented four documents at a meeting of the Linnaean Society. The first was a letter that they had jointly signed. In this, they explained how Darwin had happened to receive Wallace's paper and described his first impulse to publish it. In not permitting him to do this, they said that "we have explained to him that we are not solely considering the relative claims to priority of himself and his friend, but the interests of science generally." The second document contained extracts from Darwin's unpublished paper of 1844, which Hooker stated that he had read the year it was written and "the contents of which we had both of us been privy to for many years." The third document was an abstract of the letter Darwin had written to Asa Gray in October, 1857, in which he had set forth his views. The fourth was Wallace's paper. In their covering letter, Lyell and Hooker affirmed that both men had reached their conclusions independently and that neither man had known what the other was doing.

Both Lyell and Hooker attended the meeting at which these documents were presented, and each made a few remarks stressing their importance and advising those present to give careful consideration to what they heard. But, surprisingly, little discussion took place. Hooker said later that "the interest excited was intense, but the subject was too novel and too ominous for the old school to enter the lists, before armouring. After the meeting it was talked over with bated breath: Lyell's approval and perhaps in a small way mine, as his lieutenant in the affair, rather overawed the Fellows, who would have otherwise flown out against the doctrine. We had, too, the vantage ground of being familiar with the authors and their theme."

Hooker gave a report of the meeting to Darwin, and it was now up to Darwin to tell Wallace what had happened. He did this in a letter in which he also enclosed one from Hooker. Then he took up his pen to thank the two friends who had stood by him in his time of difficulty. To Hooker, he said, "I have always thought it very possible that I might be forestalled, but I fancied that I had a grand enough soul not to care; but I found myself mistaken and punished; I had, however, quite resigned myself, and had half written a letter to Wallace to give up all the priority to him, and should certainly not have changed had it not been for Lyell's and your quite extraordinary kindness. I assure you I feel it, and shall not forget it." And to Lyell, he said, "I have never half thanked you for all the extraordinary trouble and kindness you showed me about Wallace's affair. Hooker told me what was done at the Linnaean Society, and I am far more than satisfied, and do not think that Wallace can think my conduct unfair in allowing you and Hooker to do whatever you thought fair. I was certainly a little annoyed to lose all priority, but had resigned myself to my fate."

Hooker now took Darwin firmly in hand. In a kindly fashion, he showed Darwin that he had had one lucky escape and that he was not as indifferent to recognition as he had thought; his pangs over his possible loss of priority to the discovery revealed that. If he did not want to be "forestalled" again, he should get his book into print. But instead of the long, practically endless work that he had envisioned, why did not Darwin write something shorter, perhaps an abstract? Shaken by his recent experience, Darwin agreed and said that fall, "I am working almost steadily at my Abstract, but it grows to an inordinate length; yet fully to make my view clear (and never giving briefly more than a fact or two, and slurring over difficulties), I cannot make it shorter. It will yet take me three or four months; so slow do I work, though never idle. You cannot imagine what a service you have done me in making me make this Abstract; for though I thought I had got it all clear, it has clarified my brains very much, by making me weigh the relative importance of the several elements." This "Abstract," as Darwin kept referring to it, was the full text of the *Origin of Species*.

While Darwin had been pacing the floor at Down House, trying to make up his mind what to do about Wallace's paper, Wallace had been in New Guinea, searching for more specimens. He had hurt his ankle climbing among the trunks and branches of fallen trees, and the wound had turned into an obstinate ulcer that would not heal. He was confined to his hut, unable to move without a crutch, and the men working for him "were more or less ill, some with fever, others with dysentery or ague; at one time there were three of them besides myself all helpless, the cook alone being well, and having enough to do to wait upon us."

He had recovered and was hunting for birds and insects by July 1, when Lyell and Hooker were presenting his paper to the Linnaean Society. On July 29 he left New Guinea with no regrets, boarding the schooner that would take him back to Ternate. "Continual rain, continual sickness, little wholesome food," he wrote, "with a plague of ants and flies surpassing anything I had before met with, required all a naturalist's ardour to encounter; and when they were uncompensated by great success in collecting, became all the more insupportable. This long-thought-of and much-desired voyage to New Guinea had realized none of my expectations. Instead of being far better than the Aru Islands, it was in almost everything much worse. Instead of producing several of the rarer Paradise Birds, I had not even seen one of them, and had not obtained any one superlatively fine bird or insect. I cannot deny, however, that Dorey [the place where he was staying] was very rich in ants. . . . They swarmed on my table as I was at work setting out my insects, carrying them off from under my very nose, and even tearing them from the cards on which they were gummed if I left them for an instant. They crawled continually over my hands and face, got into my hair, and roamed at will over my whole body, not producing much inconvenience till they began to bite, which they would do on meeting any obstruction to their passage, and with a sharpness which made me jump again and rush to undress and turn out the offender. They visited my bed also, so that night brought no relief from their persecutions." The voyage to Ternate was also a disappointment. Instead of the steady southerly and easterly winds he had expected, the wind, when it blew at all, came from the west, and the voyage that should have taken only five days dragged on for seventeen. When he arrived in Ternate, he could not have been in a poorer state of mind to receive bad news. And Darwin's letter was almost there.

Many of his friends at Ternate were curious about his trip to New Guinea and wanted to see what he had brought back, so Wallace covered the long table on his veranda with a piece of calico, unpacked his specimens of birds, and made a display of the better ones on the table. One Sunday he invited his acquaintances to a reception, and even he was rather pleased with the results. "I myself," he wrote, "was surprised at the beauty of the show when thus brought together and displayed on the white table, which so well set off their varied and brilliant colours."

He was in better humor, therefore, when Darwin's letter arrived, but Darwin should have had no fears in the first place. Darwin was a generous man, and so was Wallace. Darwin had worried about asserting his priority; Wallace would have worried if he had not. To the news from England, Wallace expressed only surprise and delight. Writing to his relatives, he said, "I have received letters from Mr. Darwin and Dr. Hooker, two of the most eminent naturalists in England, which have highly gratified me. I sent Mr. Darwin an essay on a subject upon which he is now writing a great work. He showed it to Dr. Hooker and Sir Charles Lyell, who thought so highly of it that they had it read before the Linnaean Society." After this he added with great modesty, "This insures me the acquaintance of these eminent men on my return home."

Wallace's reaction to what Darwin had done brought a measure of peace to Down House that January. In reply to Wallace, Darwin wrote, "I was extremely pleased at receiving three days ago your letter to me and that to Dr. Hooker. Permit me to say how heartily I admire the spirit in which they are written. Though I had absolutely nothing whatever to do in leading Lyell and Hooker to what they thought a fair course of action, yet I naturally could not but feel anxious to hear what your impression would be. . . .

"Most cordially do I wish you health and entire success in all your pursuits, and, God knows, if admirable zeal and energy deserve success, most amply do you deserve it."

A possible dispute between two great men had been avoided. Joseph Hooker and Charles Lyell, both of them calm and both of them lovers of justice, deserve much of the credit for the solution they devised. But the greater share should go to Alfred Wallace and Charles Darwin, men who sought truth not only in science but also in their personal affairs.

II

There were three men whose esteem Darwin most coveted. Two of them, of course, were Lyell and Hooker, to whom he had turned in his crisis. The third was Thomas Henry Huxley, fourteen years his junior.

Huxley was born on May 4, 1825, in Ealing, a few miles west of London. His father was a schoolteacher, and Huxley, for the first eight years of his life, received his education at home. He then entered the school where his father taught. He had as low an opinion of his formal education as Darwin had of his. "My regular school training," he wrote, "was of the briefest, perhaps fortunately; for though my way of life has made me acquainted with all sorts and conditions of men, from the highest to the lowest, I deliberately affirm that the society I fell into at school was the worst I have ever known. We boys were average lads, with much the same inherent capacity for good and evil as any others; but the people who were set over us cared about as much for our intellectual and moral welfare as if they were baby-farmers. We were left to the operation of the struggle for existence among ourselves. . . ." The only cheerful memory he retained of his school years was defeating a larger boy, a bully. But even that recollection was marred by the injustice that followed. He, the victor, emerged from the battle with a black eye, while his opponent had none. Therefore, the disciplinary wrath of the school authorities descended on his head alone.

About two years after Huxley entered the school, the headmaster died. His sons attempted to carry on, but the number of students rapidly dwindled, and soon the institution was dissolved. Huxley's father, now out of a job, moved back to his hometown of Coventry, where he obtained a position in a savings bank, and Huxley's schooling came to an end. This was not the misfortune it might have seemed. He had an enormous capacity for self-education, and he was now free to use it. At the age of twelve he was reading Hutton's book on geology and was soon, for example, teaching himself German, speculating on the cause of the colors in a sunset, and learning far more than he had at school.

For a time, he thought of becoming a mechanical engineer, but both his sisters had married doctors, and one of his brothers-in-law began teaching him medicine and, after a short time, helped him procure a position as an assistant to a doctor in the East End of London. Although his life until then had not been easy, it had been protected. But describing the East End, he said, "I saw strange things there—among the rest, people who came to me for medical aid, and who were really suffering from nothing but slow starvation. I have not forgotten—am not likely to forget so long as memory holds—a visit to a sick girl in a wretched garret where two or three other women, one a deformed woman, sister of my patient, were busy shirt-making. After due examination, even my small medical knowledge sufficed to show that my patient was merely in want of some better food than the bread and bad tea on which these people were living. I said so as gently as I could, and the sister turned upon me with a kind of choking passion. Pulling out of her pocket a few pence and halfpence, and holding them out, 'That is all I get for six and thirty hours' work, and you talk about giving her proper food.' "

Having now definitely decided to be a doctor, Huxley was formally apprenticed to his other brother-in-law and took courses at Sydenham College in preparation for the entrance examinations to the University of London. He did well in his studies, receiving several certificates of merit and the first prize in botany, and was given one of the free scholarships offered by Charing Cross Hospital. "I am sorry to say," he later remarked, "that I do not think that any account of my doings as a student would tend to edification. In fact, I should distinctly warn ingenuous youth to avoid imitating my example. I worked extremely hard when it pleased me, and when it did not, which was a very frequent case, I was extremely idle (unless making caricatures of one's pastors and masters is to be called a branch of industry), or else wasted my energies in wrong directions. I read everything I could lay hands upon, including novels, and took up all sorts of pursuits to drop them again quite as speedily." The only course that he remembered with particular pleasure was one in physiology. (The professor who gave it helped him publish a short paper on the structure of a hair.)

In looking back on his career as a student, Huxley probably did himself a grave injustice, for he received his degree without difficulty and cast about for a position that he could fill. Setting up practice himself was out of the question—he did not have the necessary capital—but a friend suggested that he apply to the director general for the medical service of the navy. "I thought this a rather strong thing to do," Huxley said, "as Sir William was personally unknown to me, but my cheery friend would not listen to my scruples, so I went to my lodgings and wrote the best letter I could devise." To his surprise, he shortly received an appointment for an interview, which ended with the director general's asking him to take the naval examination. After passing it, he was assigned to Haslar Hospital. It was a fortunate stroke of fate.

Huxley's chief at Haslar was Sir John Richardson, who was distinguished as a naturalist and as an Arctic explorer, but he seemed to pay no attention to Huxley. "I was extremely disgusted to find that 'Old John,' as we irreverent youngsters called him," Huxley wrote, "took not the slightest notice of my worshipful self, either the first time I attended him, as it was my duty to do, or for some weeks afterwards. . . . But one day, as I was crossing the hospital square, Sir John stopped me and heaped coals of fire on my head by telling me that he had tried to get me one of the resident appointments, much coveted by the assistant-surgeons, but that the Admiralty had put in another man. 'However,' said he, 'I mean to keep you here till I can get you something you will like,' and turned upon his heel without waiting for the thanks I stammered out."

Time dragged on, and nothing further happened, until one day Huxley's chief casually stopped him again and asked him if he would like to be an assistant surgeon on the *Rattlesnake,* a ship that was being sent to Australian waters to make surveys and to study geography, geology, and natural history. The captain of the *Rattlesnake* wanted a doctor who was also a scientist, and Huxley's chief was prepared to recommend him. Huxley leaped at the chance. He once said of his medical education, "I am now occasionally horrified to think how little I ever knew or cared about medicine as the art of healing. The only part of my professional course which really and deeply interested me was physiology, which is the mechanical engineering of living machines; . . . what I cared for was the architectural and engineering part of the business, the working out the wonderful unity of plan in the thousands and thousands of diverse living constructions, and the modifications of similar apparatuses to serve diverse ends." This is what he would have a chance to do on board the *Rattlesnake.*

The ship left Spithead on December 3, 1846. Like Darwin, Huxley found his quarters cramped. Writing to his sister, he said that "my total length, as you are aware, is considerable, 5 feet 11 inches, possibly, but the height of the lower deck of the *Rattlesnake,* which will be my especial location, is at the outside 4 feet 10 inches. What I am to do with this superfluous foot I cannot divine. Happily, however, there is a sort of skylight into the berth, so that I shall be able to sit with the body in it and my head out." The stern of the ship, however, contained a large workroom with bookcases, tables, and plenty of light, and Huxley was allowed to use this freely. They reached Madeira on December 18 and Rio on January 23, where they laid over, he reported home, "for the purpose of effecting some trifling repairs, which, though not essential to the safety of the ship, will nevertheless naturally enhance the comfort of its inmates. This you will understand when I tell you that in consequence of these same defects I have had water an inch or two deep in my cabin, wish-washing about ever since we left Madeira."

At Rio, which he thought must be one of the most beautiful places in the world, he and the ship's naturalist collected butterflies and birds and dragged for specimens in the water. From there, they sailed to the south of Africa, where, in the manner of Darwin's *Beagle,* the *Rattlesnake* surveyed the coastline, and Huxley mailed to the Linnaean Society two papers that he had written on the sea life he had been studying. The *Rattlesnake* next went to Mauritius, about which Huxley wrote to his mother: "In truth it is a complete paradise, and if I had nothing better to do, I should pick up some pretty French Eve (and there are plenty) and turn Adam. N.B. There are *no* serpents in the island."

Fortunately, he did not find the right "French Eve," for at Sydney, Australia, he met Henrietta Anne Heathorn and fell in love with her immediately. "I really don't know whether she is pretty or not," he wrote his mother. "But I never met with so sweet a temper, so self-sacrificing and affectionate a disposition, or so pure and womanly a mind, and from the perfectly intimate footing on which I stand with her family I have plenty of opportunities of judging." Obviously the couple could not be married right away—Huxley's salary was too small, and he had no independent income—but Nettie, as he called her, was willing to wait the four years that it would take him at the earliest to become a surgeon. Even then his promotion would depend largely on the scientific papers he published as a result of the voyage.

Altogether the *Rattlesnake* remained in Australian waters about three years, making one short cruise and three long ones out of Sydney. In 1849, Huxley wrote his mother about the ship's work: "We started from here [Sydney] last May to survey what is called the inner passage to India. You must know that the east coast of Australia has running parallel to it at distances of from five miles to seventy or eighty an almost continuous line of coral reefs, the Great Barrier as it is called. Outside this line is the great Pacific, inside is a space varying in width as above, and cut up by little islands and detached reefs. Now to get to India from Sydney, ships must go either inside or outside the Great Barrier. The inside passage has been called the Inner Route in consequence of its desirability for steamers, and our business has been to mark out this Inner Route safely and clearly among the labyrinth-like islands and reefs within the Barrier." Then he explained, "And a parlous dull business it was for those who, like myself, had no necessary and constant occupation. Fancy for five mortal months shifting from patch to patch of white sand in latitude from 17 to 10 south, living on salt pork and beef, and seeing no mortal face but our own sweet countenances considerably obscured by the long beard and moustaches with which, partly from laziness and partly from comfort, we had become adorned." This was quite different from Darwin's trip on the *Beagle*. Darwin had had no official duties aboard ship and was, therefore, free to spend much of his time on land. Huxley, however, as assistant surgeon was required to be near the men in his medical charge.

On the second long cruise the *Rattlesnake* conveyed an expedition that put ashore at Rockingham Bay on the northeastern coast of Australia to go overland to Cape York, on the northernmost peninsula in Australia, where it would be picked up by another ship. The leader asked Huxley to accompany them, and Huxley wrote that "if the Service would have permitted of my absence I should have certainly done so." The thirteen men started out, but they soon ran into trouble, and the leader, accompanied by a native guide, pushed on to Cape York to get help. He was in sight of the provisions ship, when a group of natives killed him. His guide somehow escaped, reached the vessel, and led a relief party to the place where they had left the other eleven men. When they arrived, they found only two survivors, and those two were also being attacked by the natives. Most certainly, the navy's restrictions saved Huxley's life.

On the third cruise, landing parties, with Huxley included, were several times almost attacked by the natives on the Louisiade Archipelago. On one occasion a member of the gun crew was cut off from the ship by a group of natives. As a distraction, he took off his clothes and offered them as presents. Then he amused the natives by performing a naked and impromptu dance in the burning heat. These antics gave a relief party time to come to his rescue.

Instead of completing its survey to the westward, the ship's mission was cut short by the death of its captain, and it was ordered back to London. Huxley received the news with mixed feelings. "Time was," he wrote his mother, "when I should have looked upon our return with unmixed joy; but so many new and strong ties have arisen to bind me with Sydney, that now when the anchor is getting up for England, I scarcely know whether to rejoice or grieve. . . . I have none the less affection for you or any other of those whom I love in England—only a very great deal for a certain little lassie whom I must leave behind me without clearly seeing when we are to meet again." On May 2, 1850, the *Rattlesnake* raised its anchor for the last time in the harbor of Sydney, rounded Cape Horn, and arrived in Chatham, England, on November 9, 1850.

Although he had been unable to go ashore as much as Darwin, Huxley had conducted intensive investigations in marine zoology, studying jellyfish, crustaceans, mollusks, and other forms of marine life. As he told the head of the naval hospital, he had brought back with him "the zoological notes and drawings which I have made during our cruise. They are somewhat numerous (over 180 sheets of drawings), and I hope not altogether valueless, since they have been made with as great care and attention as I am master of—and with a microscope, such as rarely, if ever, made a voyage around the world before." And, he pointed out, "they relate for the most part to animals hitherto very little known, whether from their rarity or from their perishable nature. . . ."

He wanted time—and, therefore, the resources—to work on this material. "It is not to be supposed," he told his former chief, "that one could occupy one's self with the animals for so long without coming to some conclusion as to their systematic place, however subsidiary to observation such considerations must always be regarded, and it seems to me (although on such matters I can of course only speak with the greatest hesitation) that just as the more minute and careful observation made upon the old 'Vermes' of Linnaeus necessitated the breaking up of that class into several very distinct classes, so more careful investigation requires the breaking up of Cuvier's 'Radiata' (which succeeded the

'Vermes' as a sort of zoological lumber-room) into several very distinct and well-defined classes. . . ." Huxley was doing what Lamarck had done—carefully studying and establishing new relationships among some of the lower forms of life.

The papers he had already written had, for the most part, met an indifferent fate, but one of particular importance had been printed. Entitled "On the Anatomy and the Affinities of the Family of Medusae," it attempted to place in the same class forms of life that superficially were extremely dissimilar. The significant feature of the paper was not its conclusion, but the method by which Huxley reached it. Discarding the old techniques of classification, he looked for more subtle and yet more important likenesses—in this case the formation of the stomach. Edward Forbes, one of Britain's leading naturalists and then paleontologist of the Royal Geological Survey of Great Britain, expressed the opinion of many of Huxley's contemporaries, when he wrote to him, saying, "I have had great pleasure in examining your drawings of animals observed during the voyage of the *Rattlesnake,* and have also fully availed myself of the opportunity of going over the collections made during the course of the survey upon which you have been engaged. I can say without exaggeration that more important or more complete zoological researches have never been conducted during any voyage of discovery in the southern hemisphere. The course you have taken of directing your attention mainly to impreservable creatures, and to the orders of the animal kingdom respecting which we have least information, and the care and the skill with which you have conducted elaborate dissections and microscopic examinations of the curious creatures you were so fortunate as to meet with, necessarily give a peculiar and unique character to your researches, since they thereby fill up gaps in our knowledge of the animal kingdom. This is the more important, since such researches have almost always been neglected during voyages of discovery."

With recommendations such as this—several other scientists were also willing to speak on his behalf—Huxley received an appointment as assistant surgeon assigned to a ship lying at Woolwich with the implicit understanding that he could spend his time working over his collections in London. This arrangement was to continue for six months, at the end of which time the Admiralty would review what Huxley had accomplished and decide whether to renew its understanding with him.

The years that followed were difficult ones. No one doubted Huxley's scientific ability, although some were jealous of his sudden reputation. Soon after his return to England, he was elected to the Royal Society, a signal honor for a person his age, and he shortly thereafter received the society's Royal Medal. But the Admiralty often appeared to hesitate over a renewal of his appointment, and this required what seemed to be endless correspondence and interviews, and he could not find anyone willing to give him a grant for the publication of his work. Several times he applied for professorships, but always unsuccessfully. In May, 1852, he wrote one of his sisters, "The way is clear before me, if my external circumstances will allow me to persevere; but I fully expect that I shall have to give up my dreams. Science in England does everything—but *pay*. You may earn praise but not pudding. . . . It is a charming piece of irony altogether. It is two years yesterday since I left Sydney harbor—and of course as long since I saw Nettie. I am getting thoroughly tired of our separation, and I think she is, though the dear little soul is ready to do anything for my sake, and yet I dare not face the stagnation—the sense of having failed in the whole purpose of my existence—which would, I know, sooner or later beset me, even with her, if I forsake my present object."

By April, 1853, he was almost ready to abandon his effort to be a scientist. "I may give up the farce altogether—" he wrote, "burn my books, burn my rod, and take to practice in Australia. It is no use going on kicking against the pricks. . . ." By the beginning of 1854 his dealings with the Admiralty had reached a crisis. They had withheld the grant he wanted for his publication and, to put an end to his requests, ordered him to active duty. When Huxley argued that his work was not finished, the Admiralty simply stopped his pay. To support himself, he took odd editorial jobs and wrote articles. Although the labor required was incommensurate with the income, he persisted, and in 1854 his fortune suddenly shifted. Nettie's family decided to return to England, so the long separation was about to end. Forbes resigned his professorship in London to take a better one in Edinburgh and helped Huxley secure two of his former lectureships. The Geological Survey offered him employment on a fee basis—he later became the survey's naturalist—and he received several other lectureships, all in the same year. It seemed as though the dam had at last broken.

Nettie arrived in England in May, 1855. Huxley had known that she had been ill—she had caught a chill while visiting a mining camp, and the doctor to whom she had gone prescribed for her unwisely—but he had had no idea that she was so badly off. One doctor, whose opinion he asked, told him that she could not live more than six months. Another, however, took a more temperate view. With good care, he thought she could recover completely. In either case, Huxley was determined to marry her as soon as possible. By now he had a wide acquaintance in the scientific world, and one of his friends was Joseph Hooker, to whom he wrote early in July, "I terminate my Baccalaureate and take my degree of M.A.-trimony (isn't that atrocious?) on Saturday, July 21. After the unhappy criminals have been turned off, there will be refreshment provided for the sheriffs, chaplain, and spectators. Will you come? Don't if it is a bore, but I should much like to have you there." And from Darwin, whom he had also come to know well, he received this word: "I hope your marriage will not make you idle; happiness, I fear, is not good for work."

But in the years following his marriage (Nettie recovered, and they led a happy life) he worked hard—often to the point of complete exhaustion —to establish firmly the place he had at last won for himself. He carried on his teaching assignments and his research, he published numerous papers, and he involved himself, as Darwin never did, in public projects such as the reorganization of part of the British Museum's collections.

His character in many respects was like Darwin's. He had the same impeccable honesty. When he did not take an active position in support of a friend's admittance to a society, he told the friend why. When he reviewed a publication unfavorably, he wrote to the author directly. But in one characteristic, Huxley differed widely from Darwin. On the last day of 1856, as he contemplated his future plans, he wrote in his journal, "To smite all humbugs, however big; to give a nobler tone to science; to set an example of abstinence from petty personal controversies, and of toleration for everything but lying; to be indifferent as to whether the work is recognized as mine or not, so long as it is done:—are these my aims? 1860 will show."

To most of those aims, Darwin could have subscribed—sublimation of self, tolerance except for controversy and lying—but there was one that was foreign to his nature. Huxley wanted to "smite all humbugs, however big." Darwin was not a fighter. Huxley was.

III

No one of Hooker's temperament was needed to defend Darwin's and Wallace's theory when their papers were presented to the Linnaean Society. Although Hooker reported that after the meeting the subject was "talked over with bated breath," that was about all that happened. An exciting, fundamental scientific theory had been presented to a learned society and printed in its annals, but it provoked little discussion except by an Irish prelate, who mentioned the theory to the Dublin Geological Society, calling the whole idea nonsense and undeserving of comment except for Lyell's and Hooker's sponsorship. And at the end of the year, the president of the Linnaean Society wrote that the past twelve months had been unmarked by any outstanding scientific discoveries. Nobody seemed to understand that the traditional world was being upset.

This lack of reaction did not disturb Darwin. He went ahead with his plans to complete what he kept referring to as his "Abstract," which Lyell had persuaded his publisher, John Murray, to print. Although Lyell required several more years before he really accepted Darwin's theory, from the first he thought it warranted publication and was willing to do anything to help. Darwin, in a letter to Lyell, had some reservations about what Murray's reaction would be when he saw the manuscript. "Would you advise me," he asked, "to tell Murray that my book is not more unorthodox than the subject makes inevitable. That I do not discuss the origin of man. That I do not bring in any discussion about Genesis, &c. &c., and only give facts, and such conclusions from them as seem to me fair." Darwin fully understood where his theory must eventually lead, but he had no intention of bringing theological discussions into his text. In the spirit of Buffon, he wanted to state the scientific truth as he saw it, but he was not going to invite controversy with either the Catholic or the Protestant Church. But Murray seems not to have had any trepidations. He bought the book on what Darwin considered good terms and prophesied that it would have a reasonable, although not outstanding, sale. He had only one point on which he was adamant. He was not going to publish a 500-page book and call it an abstract. That part of the title had to be eliminated. Darwin demurred, because he looked "at it as the only possible apology for *not* giving references and facts in full," but he finally deferred to Lyell and Murray.

The book appeared at the end of November, 1859, and Darwin heard immediately from his friends. Lyell told him, "I have just finished your volume, and right glad I am that I did my best with Hooker to persuade you to publish it without waiting for a time which would probably never have arrived, though you lived to be the age of a hundred, when you had prepared all your facts on which you ground so many grand generalizations. It is a splendid case of close reasoning and long substantial argument throughout so many pages. . . ." And Hooker said, "I am a sinner not to have written you ere this, if only to thank you for your glorious book— what a mass of close reasoning on curious facts and fresh phenomena—it is capitally written, and will be very successful. I say this on the strength of two or three plunges into as many chapters, for I have not yet attempted to read it. [He had had it only a few days.] Lyell, with whom we are staying, is perfectly enchanted, and is absolutely gloating over it." Huxley joined in with the other two friends. "I finished your book yesterday, a lucky examination having furnished me with a few hours of continuous leisure . . . no work on Natural History Science I have met with has made so great an impression upon me, and I do most heartily thank you for the great store of new views you have given me."

There were favorable reviews, too (just by chance, Huxley was asked to write the review for the *Times*), but the storm was gathering. Darwin sent a copy to Adam Sedgwick, the professor at Cambridge who had taught him what geology he knew when he had sailed in the *Beagle* and who had kindly taken the amateur on a field trip. Sedgwick was bitter. "If I did not think you a good-tempered and truth-loving man," he wrote, "I should not tell you that (spite of the great knowledge, store of facts, capital views of the correlation of the various parts of organic nature, admirable hints about the diffusion, through wide regions, of many related organic beings, &c. &c.) I have read your book with more pain than pleasure. Parts of it I admired greatly, parts I laughed at till my sides were almost sore; other parts I read with absolute sorrow, because I think them utterly false and grievously mischievous. You have *deserted*—after a start in that tramroad of all solid physical truth—the true method of induction, and started us in machinery as wild, I think, as Bishop Wilkins's locomotive that was to sail with us to the moon."

After discussing causation as the will of God and saying that he could prove God worked for the good of his creatures, Sedgwick continued: "We all admit development as a fact of history: but how came it about? Here, in language, and still more in logic, we are point-blank at issue. There is a moral or metaphysical part of nature as well as a physical. A man who denies this is deep in the mire of folly. 'Tis the crown and glory of organic science that it *does* through *final cause,* link material and moral; and yet it *does not* allow us to mingle them in our first conception of laws, whether we consider one side of nature or the other. You have ignored this link; and if I do not mistake your meaning, you have done your best in one or two pregnant cases to break it. Were it possible (which, thank God, it is not) to break it, humanity, in my mind, would suffer a damage that might brutalize it, and sink the human race into a lower grade of degradation than any into which it has fallen since its written records tell us of its history."

Although he closed his letter with expressions of personal friendship that he truly meant, Sedgwick had clearly stated the virulent opposition that Darwin could expect to meet. It was not simply a case of a scientific disagreement that could be argued out on a scientific basis, granted that even such discussions can become bitter. Logic had already been superseded by emotion. Lyell saw in Darwin's theory the need to set aside many of his long-cherished beliefs, but Sedgwick saw his world destroyed. If people believed Darwin, then God was gone, and man was debased, debased not merely in the sense that he might lose dignity by being descended from apes, but debased in the sense that his existence was meaningless. In these terms, the battle against Darwin took on the aspects of a holy war, for the barbarian was beating at the walls of civilization.

Sedgwick put his views in writing, and others did, too. One zoologist said he would read the book but would never believe in it. Another scientist wrote Darwin that his review would be hostile, but that he would not "calumniate the author." A member of the staff of the British Museum said to Darwin, "You have just reproduced Lamarck's doctrine, and nothing else, and here Lyell and others have been attacking him for twenty years, and because *you* (with a sneer and a laugh) say the very same thing, they are all coming around." Another man whom Darwin respected said he had produced "the law of higgledy-piggledy." And Agassiz, according to Asa Gray, had been reading it. "He says it is *poor—very poor.*"

Unlike the papers that had appeared in the proceedings of the Linnaean Society and gone almost unnoticed, the *Origin of Species* had created a storm. The first edition sold out immediately, and in early January, 1860, Murray brought out a second, doubling the printing order to 3,000 copies. As the book gained in notoriety, the reviews continued, and while some of them were favorable, others hurt Darwin personally. Speaking of one that appeared in the *Edinburgh Review,* he said, "It is extremely malignant, clever, and I fear will be very damaging. He [the reviewer] is atrociously severe on Huxley's lecture, and very bitter against Hooker. So we *three* enjoyed it together. Not that I really enjoyed it, for it made me uncomfortable for one night; but I have got quite over it to-day." It was, he said, "painful to be hated in the intense degree" that the reviewer apparently hated him.

What most troubled Darwin was the vitriolic nature of the attacks made on him. He had carefully avoided any mention of man or any application of his theory to contemporary theology. These were separate questions, and he thought they should be examined separately. He had merely stated certain ideas that seemed to him provable and was willing, as men like Sedgwick were not, to sort out the physical from the philosophical. Furthermore, being religious himself, he did not understand why his theory should conflict with faith in God. It merely changed some aspects of orthodox theology—nothing more. In an impassioned letter to Asa Gray, he told of his hurt over some of the reviews and of his religious conceptions. "With respect to the theological view of the question," he wrote, "this is always painful to me. I am bewildered. I had no intention to write atheistically. But I own that I cannot see as plainly as others do, and as I should wish to do, evidence of design and beneficence on all sides of us. I cannot persuade myself that a beneficent and omnipotent God would have designedly created the Ichneumonidae [a family that includes certain flies] with the express intention of their feeding within the living bodies of caterpillars, or that a cat should play with mice. Not believing this, I see no necessity in the belief that the eye was expressly designed.

"On the other hand," he continued, "I cannot anyhow be contented to view this wonderful universe, and especially the nature of man, and to conclude that everything is the result of brute force. I am inclined to look at everything as resulting from designed laws, with the details, whether good or bad, left to the working out of what we may call chance.

Not that this notion *at all* satisfies me. I feel most deeply that the whole subject is too profound for the human intellect. A dog might as well speculate on the mind of Newton. Let each man hope and believe what he can. Certainly I agree with you that my ideas are not at all necessarily atheistical. The lightning kills a man, whether a good one or a bad one, owing to the excessively complex action of natural laws. A child (who may turn out an idiot) is born by the action of even more complex laws, and I can see no reason why a man, or other animal, may not have been aboriginally produced by other laws, and that all these laws may have been expressly designed by an omniscient Creator, who foresaw every future event and consequence. But," he ended, "the more I think the more bewildered I become. . . ." Evolution, he believed, did not destroy God. There was room for both in men's minds.

One of his correspondents who agreed with him—and perhaps stated the thought more clearly—was Charles Kingsley, the British clergyman and author. Darwin had sent Kingsley a copy of the *Origin,* and in his acknowledgment of the present, Kingsley wrote, "All I have seen of it *awes* me; both with the heap of facts and the prestige of your name, and also with the clear intuition that if you be right, I must give up much that I have believed and written. In that I care little. Let God be true, and every man a liar! . . .

"From two common superstitions, at least, I shall be free while judging of your book:—

"(1.) I have long since, from watching the crossing of domesticated animals and plants, learnt to disbelieve the dogma of the permanence of the species.

"(2.) I have gradually learnt to see that it is just as noble a conception of Diety, to believe that He created primal forms capable of self-development into all forms needful *pro tempore* and *pro loco,* as to believe that He required a fresh act of intervention to supply the *lucunas* [minute bone cavities] which He himself had made. I question whether the former be not the loftier thought."

All too few people shared Kingsley's liberality or his belief that Darwin may have exposed a "loftier" view of God, and the battle between Darwin's supporters and opponents continued to rage. It came to a head at the meeting of the British Association for the Advancement of Science, held that June at Oxford. From the point of view of Darwin's supporters, the proceedings opened quietly enough, but on Thursday, June 28, an Oxford professor read to one of the sections a paper entitled "On the final causes of the sexuality of plants, with particular reference to Mr. Darwin's work on the *Origin of Species.*" The paper in itself was not as important as its references to Darwin, for these provided the presiding officer with an opportunity to call on Huxley to speak. Huxley tried to avoid any debate, stating "that a general audience, in which sentiment would unduly interfere with intellect, was not the public before which such a discussion should be carried on." He hoped to keep any arguments about Darwin's theory on a purely scientific level and not to let them degenerate into an appeal to popular opinion, but Darwin's opponents wanted just the opposite. One of them was Richard Owen, an excellent anatomist and the head of the natural history section of the British Museum. From the first, he had conceived a violent, unreasoning dislike for Darwin's book, and his learning made him a formidable contender. Not wishing to let the opportunity slip away, now that Darwin's theory had come up, he asked for the floor and said that it was his "conviction that there were facts by which the public could come to some conclusion with regard to the probabilities of the truth of Mr. Darwin's theory." He then gave some views of his own on the wide differences between the brain of a gorilla and the brain of a man. This was just the type of situation that Huxley had hoped to avoid— the careless unsubstantiated attack before an audience unqualified to judge the merits. But he could not let Owen's comments go unnoticed. Being himself knowledgeable about gorillas' brains, he replied by flatly contradicting what Owen had said and promising that he would "justify that unusual procedure elsewhere," a promise he redeemed by publishing an article on the subject. Nothing further was said, and the session ended quietly, but Huxley, in the minds of many, had become Darwin's principal champion.

Friday passed peaceably, but Saturday, as Darwin's supporters had heard, was the day when a major assault would be made. Samuel Wilberforce, the Bishop of Oxford, intended to enter the lists. The bishop, known to the less reverent as "Soapy Sam" because of his persuasiveness and his aptitude for political expediency, was an able debater, and he had been closeted with Owen, learning Owen's paleontological arguments against evolution. Huxley had no desire to attend the meeting at which the bishop planned to speak. "I had heard of the Bishop's intention to utilize the occasion," he wrote. "I knew he had the reputation of being a first-rate controversialist, and I was quite aware that if he played his cards properly, we should have little chance, with such an audience, of making an efficient defense. Moreover, I was very tired, and wanted to join my wife. . . ." On Friday, when he was walking in the street, he happened to encounter Robert Chambers, who some years before had written the anonymous book *Vestiges of Creation* that had so interested Wallace. In reply to a remark of Chambers' about the next day's meeting, Huxley said that he was not going to attend, because he could "not see the good of giving up peace and quietness to be episcopally pounded." Chambers reproached him by saying he was deserting their cause, and Huxley, overcome by Chambers' vehemence, answered, "Oh! If you take it that way, I'll come and have my share of what is going on!"

The next day the audience assembled in the lecture room where the meeting was scheduled to be held, but the crowd was too great—some 700 to 1,000 persons—and the meeting had to be adjourned to a larger room. Finally, everything was ready. Against the windows that lined the west wall sat the ladies, their handkerchiefs fluttering. The remainder of the audience crammed the rest of the room except for a spot along the east wall, where the speaker's platform was placed. On the platform were seated some notables, including the presiding officer, Hooker, Huxley, and the bishop. The speaker was an American, and the topic of his paper was the "Intellectual Development of Europe Considered with Reference to the Views of Mr. Darwin." Again, the paper itself was not of much consequence. The audience had come to hear not it, but rather the remarks that the bishop was expected to make. While the speaker spent over an hour expressing his views, the audience shifted restlessly. When he finally had finished, one of the audience rose from the floor and started attacking Darwin on theological grounds. He was shouted down. Up jumped a clergyman, who began speaking in the same vein. He, too, was shouted down. Another man took the floor, saying that Darwin would have done much better if he had only been wise enough to consult him. He started to give a mathematical analysis of evolution, but the audience also shouted him down, and the presiding officer ruled that no one could speak who was not prepared to discuss the subject scientifically. Some of the crowd began calling for the bishop, but the bishop rose only to say that his friend, the professor of biology who also sat on the platform, had something to say first. Obviously the bishop was delighted to build up the dramatic tension. The professor did not have much to add. He thought that Darwin's theory deserved thorough discussion but that he himself did not have sufficient knowledge to do so. Then he resumed his seat, and it was the bishop's turn.

The bishop's speech, which lasted half an hour, quickly proved that Owen had been a poor tutor. The bishop had not mastered his facts, but being a good speaker, he still held his audience. Even one of Darwin's adherents admitted that the bishop talked "in such dulcet tones, so persuasive a manner, and in such well turned periods, that I who had been inclined to blame the President for allowing a discussion that could serve no scientific purpose, now forgave him from the bottom of my heart." Sneeringly and sarcastically, but skillfully avoiding the alienation of his listeners, the bishop moved from point to point. He wanted to show that little evidence existed in support of Darwin's theory, that most of it was speculation. A while before, a sheep had been born in the north of England with an extra vertebra, and some enthusiasts had seized on this as a demonstration of Darwin's variation. The bishop touched on this and then asked rhetorically, "What have they to bring forward? Some rumored statement about a long-legged sheep."

Shortly after this remark he turned directly to Huxley and said in a bantering voice, "I should like to ask Professor Huxley, who is sitting by me, and is about to tear me to pieces when I have sat down, as to his belief in being descended from an ape." Then slowly, "Is it on his grandfather's or his grandmother's side that the ape ancestry comes in?"

Huxley tensed. Then he struck his hand on his knee and turned to a neighbor. "The Lord has delivered him into mine hands," he said. Afterward he explained that his neighbor "stared at me as if I had lost my senses. But, in fact, the Bishop had justified the severest retort I could devise, and I made up my mind to let him have it."

The bishop continued for a short time longer, then ended his talk, as one of the audience reported, "with a solemn peroration that Darwin's views were contrary to the revelations of God in His Scriptures." Huxley did not rise immediately. Instead he wisely waited until the audience called for him. Then he addressed them by saying first, "I am here only in the interest of science, and I have not heard anything that can prejudice the case of my august client." After that he quietly and decisively showed that the bishop was unequipped to discuss evolution scientifically by exposing the mistakes he had made. Then he touched on the question of the Creation. "You say that development drives out the Creator," he remarked to the bishop. "But you assert that God made you; and yet you know that you yourself were originally a little piece of matter no bigger than the end of the pencil-case."

At last, he brought up the bishop's insulting question and answered it. "I asserted, and I repeat," he said, "that a man has no reason to be ashamed of having an ape for his grandfather. If there were an ancestor whom I should feel shame in recalling, it would be a *man,* a man of restless and versatile intellect, who, not content with an equivocal success in his own sphere of activity, plunges into scientific questions with which he has no real acquaintance, only to obscure them by an aimless rhetoric, and distract the attention of his hearers from the real point at issue by eloquent digressions, and skilled appeals to religious prejudice."

Although other people, including Hooker, also spoke expressing their views, the debate of the day had been the one between Huxley and the bishop. Huxley had stated his choice clearly and publicly: He would prefer to be descended from an ape than from an unreasoning man like the bishop. In 1856 he had written his resolution in his journal to "smite all humbugs, however big" and had added, "are these my aims? 1860 will show." The year 1860 had shown.

IV

No one, not even Huxley's most enthusiastic supporters, thought for a moment that his reply to the bishop would end the great debate between the adherents of Darwin's theory and those who opposed it. But they did realize that they had achieved a moral victory of considerable proportions, because they had shown that they would not be put down by pompous orthodoxy and that even a bishop could not intimidate them.

The first wave of criticism was based largely on emotional reactions to the *Origin*. In a single book, not only had Darwin propounded an astounding scientific idea, but he had also undermined the religious faith of many people and struck a harsh blow at their opinions of themselves. It was a shocking experience to start a book thinking that you were a special creation of God and end the book knowing that you were not. Even in his last years, Darwin received crank letters, often unsigned and often obviously from old ladies, wishing that the Almighty would carry him off to the Pit. Sedgwick's reaction, when he saw his theology gone, was typical of the reaction of many readers.

In December, 1860, Darwin wrote Hooker that "I have got fairly sick of hostile reviews. . . . I can pretty plainly see that, if my view is ever to be generally adopted, it will be by young men growing up and replacing the old workers, and then the young ones finding that they can group facts and search out new lines of investigation better on the notion of descent than on that of creation." But in addition to those two stalwart defenders Hooker and Huxley, Darwin had other allies, men like Asa Gray, who wrote a series of articles in Darwin's defense that were printed in the *Atlantic Monthly* and were later published as a pamphlet. "I believe that your pamphlet," Darwin wrote, "has done my book *great* good; and I thank you from my heart for myself."

All this while, Wallace had continued his travels in the Malay Archipelago, covering mile after mile and wandering from island to island, as his collections grew in size. Finally, in the spring of 1862, he returned to London and went to live with his brother-in-law. Waiting for him were the packing cases and boxes containing the specimens he had reserved for his own use, and he began to open them and study them. His agent had already wisely invested the proceeds for the collections he had sold before Wallace's return, and these investments brought in 300 pounds a year. Wallace was not rich, but he was well enough off to have leisure.

When Darwin learned that Wallace was back in England, he invited him to Down House, and although the two never became close personal friends, they saw each other frequently after that and corresponded regularly. Wallace, of course, in spite of his shyness, soon became acquainted with the principal scientific figures of his day and later wrote his impressions of Darwin and two of Darwin's closest supporters, while also giving a picture of himself. "Although Huxley," he wrote, "was as kind and genial a friend and companion as Darwin himself, and that I was quite at ease with him in his family circle, or in after-dinner talk with a few of his intimates (and although he was two years younger than myself), yet I never got over a feeling of awe and inferiority when discussing any problem in evolution or allied subjects—an inferiority which I did not feel either with Darwin or Sir Charles Lyell. This was due, I think, to the fact that the enormous amount of Huxley's knowledge was of a kind of which I possessed only an irreducible minimum, and of which I often felt the want. In the general anatomy and physiology of the whole animal kingdom, living and extinct, Huxley was a master, the equal—perhaps the superior—of the greatest authorities on these subjects in the scientific world; whereas I had never had an hour's instruction in either of them, had never seen a dissection of any kind, and never had any inclination to practise the art myself. Whenever I had to touch upon these subjects, or use them to enforce my arguments, I had to get both my facts and my arguments at second hand, and to appeal to authority both for facts and conclusions from them. And because I was thus ignorant, and because I had a positive distaste for all forms of anatomical and physiological experiment, I perhaps over-estimated this branch of knowledge and looked up to those that possessed it in a pre-eminent degree as altogether above myself.

"With Darwin and Lyell, on the other hand, although both possessed stores of knowledge beyond my own, yet I did possess *some* knowledge of the same kind, and felt myself in a position to make use of their facts and those of all other students in the same fields of research quite as well as the majority of those who had observed and recorded them. I had, however, very early in life noticed, that men with immense *knowledge* did not always know how to draw just conclusions from that knowledge, and that I myself was quite able to detect their errors of reasoning." In the last sentence, Wallace described himself almost perfectly. With little formal education and lacking the knowledge of many of his contemporaries, he was able to remain free of detail and, being unconfused by it, come to his important conclusions.

On the other hand, Huxley, with his immense fund of facts, was a much abler defender of Wallace's and Darwin's ideas then Wallace. Huxley had already demonstrated his skill at debate and in dealing with polemics, and he also had the learning to handle the more unemotional scientific attacks on evolution that began to develop. Here, for a number of reasons, even he was often hard pressed. In the first place, there were some deficiencies in Darwin's theory, deficiencies that the evolutionists later had to correct, for the theory, while generally valid, was understandably not correct in all its points. Second, he was hampered, as Lamarck had been, by the inadequacy of the paleontological record. It was possible to argue with some justification that if the evolutionists were right in their reasoning, more fossils should be found to bear out their theory. Special emphasis was laid on this fact in connection with man, because the human remains available just were not enough to support the evolutionists.

Another important weakness in Darwin's case was his inability to explain the cause of variations. In this, his book contained a slight parallel to the paper Wallace had written in Sarawak. Wallace had presented a clear and truthful statement on evolution, a paper of considerable significance, but unconvincing because it provided no mechanism capable of controlling and governing the change. The *Origin*, of course, was not nearly so simple. Darwin had introduced the element of natural selection, and he had supported his arguments with a large amount of documentation. But to be fully accepted, the evolutionists had eventually to develop some explanation of the cause of change that was better than anything Darwin was able to bring forth.

Some of the most difficult attacks to refute came, however, from a totally unexpected source—the physicists. Earlier scientists, like Buffon, had worked hard to lengthen the time that the earth had existed, and the struggle to gain acceptance for more and more millions of years had been successful. This was essential to Darwin, for he argued that variations came slowly and that, therefore, the process of evolution had consumed much time. Now the physicists abruptly shortened it. William Thomson, Lord Kelvin, professor of natural philosophy at the University of Glasgow, was unquestionably one of England's leading scientists, a man known and respected throughout the world. He had no special interest in biology, but he did have one in the age of the earth and the sun. Measurements taken in mines indicated that the heat increased according to the depth, and from this phenomenon, Kelvin deduced that both the earth and the sun were cooling. His calculations and those of other physicists put the age of the earth roughly between 20,000,000 and 40,000,000 years. This was not nearly enough time for chance variation to work as Darwin had envisioned its working and thus provided his opponents with an opportunity to reintroduce the idea of design, for something other than pure fortune was necessary to create such astounding results in so few years. This posed a real problem for Darwin's supporters and for geologists like Lyell. Kelvin was no Bishop of Oxford, but a sincere and dedicated scientist. What is more, given the knowledge of physics at the time, his reasoning was right. Unable to refute Kelvin, Darwin simply thought that somehow Kelvin must be wrong, and even Huxley, brilliant as he was, could see nothing to do but, in effect, admit that time had been compressed and so had the process of evolution.

In the face of his opposition, Darwin made changes in subsequent editions of the *Origin* in an attempt to counter scientific criticism, and the theory gained more and more credence. The person who most bothered him, however, was his old friend Lyell, who still was not completely converted to his ideas. From the first, Lyell had recognized that Darwin's words were important and had urged him to publish them, but that did not necessarily mean that he agreed with them all. In 1863, Darwin wrote Asa Gray, "You speak of Lyell as a judge; now what I complain of is that he declines to be a judge. . . . I have sometimes almost wished that Lyell had pronounced against me. When I say 'me,' I only mean *change of species by descent.* That seems to me the turning-point. Personally, of course, I care much about Natural Selection; but that seems utterly unimportant to the question of Creation *or* Modification." A few months later, he wrote Hooker, "The Lyells are coming here on Sunday evening to stay till Wednesday. I dread it, but I must say how much disappointed I am that he has not spoken out on species, still less on man. And the best of the joke is that he thinks he has acted with the courage of a martyr of old. I hope I may have taken an exaggerated view of his timidity, and shall *particularly* be glad of your opinion on this head." Darwin had on his side a foremost zoologist, Huxley, and a foremost botanist, Hooker. He desperately awaited the conversion of Lyell, the geologist whom he regarded the most highly.

In the tenth edition of the *Principles of Geology,* Lyell capitulated entirely and officially adopted Darwin's views. Darwin regarded this as "a great triumph," but it was Wallace who saw it in a truer, and more generous, light. Writing in the *Quarterly Review,* he said, "The history of science hardly presents so striking an instance of youthfulness of mind in advanced life as is shown by this abandonment of opinions so long held and so powerfully advocated; and if we bear in mind the extreme caution, combined with the ardent love of truth which characterizes every work that our author [Lyell] has produced, we shall be convinced that so great a change was not decided on without long and anxious deliberation, and that the views now adopted must indeed be supported by arguments of overwhelming force." Aside from acknowledging Lyell's open-mindedness, Wallace also saw a practical advantage for Darwin, and he added, "If for no other reason than that Sir Charles Lyell in his tenth edition has adopted it, the theory of Mr. Darwin deserves an attentive and respectful consideration from every earnest seeker after truth."

Gradually, as Lyell had done, others were coming around to Darwin's way of thinking, and although discussion and debate continued and Lord Kelvin's thesis proposed a real problem, evolutionism began to occupy a respectable place in science. When the Royal Society awarded its Copley Medal to Darwin in 1864, it put the mark of recognition on him and his theory. After that he could be seriously challenged only if the challenger had a basic scientific reason for disputing him. At this point, Darwin might have been excused if he had decided to stop working. He had made his trip on the *Beagle,* he had developed his theory and seen it become well established as part of the science of his day, and he had an independent income that made it completely unnecessary to earn his living. Furthermore, his health continued to be bad. But Darwin was not a man to rest. He still had many notes and the material for more books; he also had many ideas that he wished to explore.

The Variation of Animals and Plants Under Domestication was published in 1868. This volume was an effort on Darwin's part to expand the *Origin,* which he had originally regarded only as an abstract, by examining the variations that had been caused by man in the breeding of domesticated plants and animals. Among the animals he considered were dogs, horses, pigs, cattle, and sheep. The book was commercially successful, and Darwin wrote Hooker, "What is the good of having a friend, if one may not boast to him? I heard yesterday that Murray has sold in a week the whole edition of 1500 copies of my book, and the sale is so pressing that he has agreed . . . to get another edition in fourteen days! This has done me a world of good, for I had got into a sort of dogged hatred of my book. And now there has appeared a review in the *Pall Mall* which has pleased me excessively, more perhaps than is reasonable. I am quite content. . . ." His contentment, however, was not thoroughly justified by the book he had produced. He had attempted to write on a subject with which science was not prepared to deal, and therefore, he had inadequate information on which to work. The result was a theory of a process called Pangenesis, which attempted to explain "how the characters of the parents are 'photographed' on the child, by means of material atoms derived from each cell in both parents, and developed in the child." His son later commented— and correctly—that it "never met with much acceptance."

In the *Origin* he had made only the slightest reference to man, although readers like the bishop quickly caught the implication. But in 1871 he brought out a book in which he directly tackled the question. It was entitled *The Descent of Man,* and the changed atmosphere in which it appeared was mentioned by the *Saturday Review,* which said, "He claims to have brought man himself, his origin and constitution, within that unity which he had previously sought to trace through all lower animal forms. The growth of opinion in the interval, due in chief measure to his own intermediate works, has placed the discussion of this problem very much in advance of that held by it fifteen years ago. The problem of Evolution is hardly any longer to be treated as one of its first principles; nor has Mr. Darwin to do battle for a first hearing of his central hypothesis, upborne as it is by a phalanx of names full of distinction and promise in either hemisphere."

In attempting to trace the relationship between man and other animals, Darwin was greatly hindered by the absence of fossils, the conclusive evidence that might have supported him. So he had to turn in other directions. One of these was to show the similarities between men and apes— he never claimed, as many people said he did, that man was descended from apes—but if his theory was correct, men and apes had relationships. He showed, among other things, that they were subject to some of the same parasites and the same diseases, and he pointed out the resemblances in their method of giving birth and nursing their young. He then discussed man's vestigial organs, such as his scalp muscles, hair, and wisdom teeth. But he did not believe that this evidence was sufficient. There still remained other aspects to be considered, such as speech, love, pain, and the affection of mothers for their offspring. By drawing on his experiences and anecdotes he had heard, he tried to give examples of each of these truly human characteristics as shown in a lower form by animals. Agreeing that man's moral sense might set him apart, Darwin said that self-sacrifice and social cooperation were evident among animals, as well as among humans. Religion he dismissed quickly on two points. Not all races were religious—he had observed that among the Fuegians years ago—and many religions had indulged in practices, such as human sacrifices, that were beneath the morality of animals.

At the time of writing this book he and Wallace were beginning to have scientific differences. Darwin ascribed the development of races to sexual selection; Wallace claimed that natural selection could account for it. Both men were concerned about the brain, and Wallace, more than Darwin, realized that the human brain somewhat changed the principle of natural selection. When Wallace first announced this idea, Darwin was delighted. Here was the reason why man was defenseless and hairless, among other animals rather physically inept. But how did the brain develop? Wallace proposed that man had learned to stand erect and then had grown a brain before he needed it. This implied some sort of design, some plan for the future, which Darwin rejected, because it brought mysticism back into nature. The differences between Darwin and Wallace, however, did not affect their personal relationship, and they remained friends.

During these years that the theory was gaining acceptance, Huxley remained one of its principal champions in spite of his heavy schedule. In addition to his teaching, Huxley was an active member of the Fishery Commission, a duty that required much of his time. As he explained to Darwin, "I don't know that I fear, with you, caring too much for science— for there are lots of other things I should like to go into as well, but I do lament more and more, as time goes on, the necessity of becoming more and more absorbed in one kind of work, a necessity which is created for any one in my position, partly by one's reputation, and partly by one's children. For directly a man gets the smallest repute in any branch of science, the world immediately credits him with knowing about ten times as much as he really does, and he becomes bound in common honesty to do his best to climb up to his reputed place. And then the babies are a devouring fire, eating up the present and discounting the future; they are sure to want all the money one can earn, and to be the better for all the credit one can win."

As he had mentioned to Darwin, he had other interests besides science, and one of these was education. In his lectures as a professor he had experimented with new approaches to the study of science, and he had realized that improvements were needed in elementary and secondary teaching. When he was asked by the British Association to serve on a committee to examine the teaching of science in the schools, he readily agreed to accept. Not content with mere report writing, he then gave a series of lectures on science to young boys. In reply to the request that he do so, he clearly stated what he had in mind. "Upon due reflection," he wrote, "I am not indisposed to undertake the course of lessons we talked about the other day, though they will cost me a good deal of trouble in various ways, and at a time of the year when I am getting to the end of my tether and don't much like trouble.

"But the scheme is too completely in harmony with what . . . I have been trying to bring about in schools in general—not to render it a great temptation to me to try to get it into practical shape. . . . You see my great object is to set going something which can be worked in every school in the country in a thorough and effectual way, and set an example of the manner in which I think this sort of introduction to science ought to be managed." These lectures, which he afterward repeated for an audience of women, also formed the basis of a popular book. Because of his evident and constructive interest in education, he became a member of the London school board, a position that enabled him to exert considerable influence on British teaching. There was a strong parallel between his career and Cuvier's. Both were eminent in their specialties, but both also felt a grave responsibility toward the society in which they lived and were thus willing to accept public positions. Huxley, however, refused to become involved in politics. He was asked to stand for Parliament, but he refused.

In contrast with Huxley, Wallace preferred a quiet, uncomplicated life. His ambition was to live in the country, enjoy his garden and his greenhouse, give an occasional lecture, and write a few reviews. When he returned from the Malay Archipelago, the wise investments made by his agent enabled him to lead this sort of life. He had an income then of approximately 300 pounds a year, and by selling some more of his collections and making the same sort of investment, he could have raised that to 500.

But Wallace had a friend who "had for some years saved part of his income and invested it in various foreign securities at low prices, selling out when they rose in value, and in this way he assured me he had in a few years doubled the amount he had saved. He studied price-lists and foreign news, and assured me that it was quite easy, with a little care and judgment, to increase your capital in this way." Lured by his persuasive friend, Wallace gradually sold out his former investments and bought those that his friend recommended. "This change," Wallace said, "went on slowly with various success for several years, till at last I had investments in various English, American, and foreign railways, whose fluctuations in value I was quite unable to comprehend, and I began to find, when too late, that almost all my changes of investment brought me loss instead of profit. . . ." He had another friend who had located two potential slate quarries and was forming a company to open them up. After examining the properties and hearing the opinions of some experts, Wallace said that "I was persuaded to take shares, and to be a director of these companies, without any knowledge of the business, or any idea how much capital would be required. The quarries were started, machinery purchased, call after call made, with the result in both cases that, after four or five years of struggle, the capital required and the working expenses were so great that the companies had to be wound up, and I was the loser of about a thousand pounds."

Wallace also had another friend who was a mining engineer, "a Cornishman, and familiar with tin, lead, and copper mining all his life, and he had the most unbounded confidence in good English mines as an investment. . . . And so I was persuaded to buy shares in lead-mines, and gradually had a large portion of my capital invested in them." But neither he nor his adviser had foreseen the increased imports of lead from Spain and the United States, which would force down the price of English lead. This investment, too, turned out to be a disaster.

Wallace also had another friend—but this friend was Charles Darwin. Wallace had reached the point where his income was barely sufficient to support his wife and two children. Unsuccessfully he applied for various positions, but he confided his problem to only one acquaintance. That friend, however, shortly afterward visited Darwin and told him about Wallace's difficulties. Darwin talked to Huxley, and between them they thought that it might be possible to obtain a pension from the government in recognition of Wallace's contribution to science. After careful writing and rewriting and after obtaining the signatures of other scientists, they presented a memorial to Gladstone, who was then Prime Minister. As a result of this action, Wallace was placed on the civil service pension list. The income he received, although not large, was sufficient, along with what he earned by lecturing and writing, to allow him to end his days comfortably.

This act of kindness was not the only one on Darwin's part. When Huxley, too, was having financial problems, Darwin headed a drive to raise private funds in his support. But Darwin's primary interest was in his science. He wrote on the expression of emotions in man and animals, on the subject of insectivorous plants, on the power of movement in plants, and other topics. These books alone, as well as his analysis of coral reefs, would have made him a figure in the scientific world of his day, but of course they did not approach in importance the *Origin*. That book had shaken man's thinking for all time.

When Darwin died on April 19, 1882, still unwell but having published the last of his books only a few months before, his family wanted to bury him quietly at Down. That would have been his own wish, to remain where he had done so much work in spite of constant illness, where he had thought out his theory of evolution. But the nation refused to accept such a burial for the man who had brought Great Britain so much honor. Twenty Members of Parliament signed a petition for interment in Westminster. "I quite sympathize with your feeling," one of them wrote Darwin's son, "and personally I should have greatly preferred that your father should have rested at Down. . . . Still, from a national point of view, it is clearly right that he should be buried in the Abbey." The grave they chose for him was in the north aisle of the nave. Only a few feet away was the grave of the only man in English history who equaled him in scientific brilliance and calm of spirit. That grave was Isaac Newton's.

Three years after Darwin's death, Huxley retired. In addition to his research, his work in education, and his defense of evolution, he had occupied many posts and held office in several scientific societies. For his years of service, the government awarded him a pension that provided for his needs. In 1890 he built a house in the seacoast town of Eastbourne and lived there for the rest of his life. At Eastbourne he at last led a quieter existence than any he had known before. Each morning he breakfasted at eight, spent an hour and a half puffing on his pipe and writing, and then visited his garden or walked on the terrace. After that he wrote some more, had lunch, and took a longer walk to the water. Occasionally he went to London, for he retained two of his many former positions, the deanship of the Royal College of Science and a trusteeship of the British Museum. But the old fire was still there, and he was as ready as ever to defend evolution from those who attacked it. The fame and reputation of his opponents made no difference to him, and when Gladstone proposed a too literal interpretation of the Creation as described in the Bible, one of the first to leap into the argument was Huxley.

But attitudes were softening. In 1892 Huxley's old adversary, Richard Owen, died. Huxley planned to attend his funeral, but overwork and bad weather prevented him from doing so. Nevertheless, with some embarrassment, he did go to a meeting to decide whether a memorial should be erected in Owen's memory. "I have no earthly objection to saying all that I honestly can of good about Owen's work—and there is much to be said about some of it—on the contrary I should be well pleased to," he wrote before the meeting. "But I have no reparation to make; if the business were to come over again, I should do as I did. My opinion of the man's character is exactly what it was, and under the circumstances there is a sort of hypocrisy about volunteering anything, which goes against my grain. The best position for me would be to be asked to second the resolution for the statue. . . ."

This was arranged, and Owen's grandson, who was at the meeting, was so pleased with Huxley's seconding speech that he asked him to write a concluding chapter to a biography of Owen. It was to contain "a 'critical' estimate of him and his work." Huxley believed he should agree to the grandson's request, and he later wrote Hooker, "I am toiling over my chapter about Owen, and I believe his ghost in Hades is grinning over my difficulties. The thing that strikes me most is, how he and I and all the things we fought about belong to antiquity. It is almost impertinent to trouble the modern world with such antiquarian business."

In 1894 the British Association was meeting at Oxford for the first time since 1860, and Huxley was specially invited to come and speak. The meeting was the largest ever held, and when Huxley rose to his feet, the room rang with applause. Later he wrote Hooker, "I wish, as everybody wished, you had been with us on Wednesday evening at Oxford when we settled accounts for 1860, and got a receipt in full from the Chancellor of the University, President of the Association, and representative of ecclesiastical conservatism and orthodoxy. . . . It was queer to sit there and hear the doctrines you and I were damned for advocating thirty-four years ago at Oxford, enunciated as matters of course—disputed by no unreasonable man!— . . . by the Chancellor."

In 1894 the Royal Society voted to award him its Darwin Medal. (Wallace had received it in 1890; Hooker in 1892.) Huxley had always believed that such honors should be given to younger men to stimulate them in their work. Yet he was pleased and wrote to a friend, "Didn't I tell the P.R.S., Secretaries, Treasurer, and all the Fellows thereof . . . that the Darwin Medal was to be given to the young, and not to useless old extinct volcanos? I ought to be very angry with you all for coolly ignoring my wise counsels. But whether it is vanity or something a good deal better, I am not. One gets chill in old age, and it is very pleasant to be warmed up unexpectedly even against one's own injunctions."

The following year, active almost to the end, he died quietly at his home in Eastbourne. He was widely mourned throughout Great Britain and the world, for those who knew him respected him, not only as a scientist, but also as a man. As one of his contemporaries wrote soon after his death, "I think the younger men do not know, that which (apart from science) I should put forward as his strongest claim to reverence and gratitude; and that is the steadfast courage and consummate ability with which he fought the battle of intellectual freedom, and insisted that people should be allowed to speak up their honest convictions without being oppressed or slandered by the orthodox. He was one of those, perhaps the foremost, who won that priceless freedom for us. . . ."

All this time Wallace had not been idle, although he later said that he might have liked to have been. After the strenuous years in Brazil and the Malay Archipelago, he wanted to rest. But his finances, even with the pension Darwin had secured for him, would not let him. Following his return to England, he wrote about his experiences in the East and continued to produce scientific works. One thing that interested him was the excellent studies of mimicry being done by his old friend Bates, and he carried Bates' work further. He was also fascinated by the geographic distribution of animals. "It is evident that, so long as the belief in 'special creations' of each species prevailed, no explanation of the complex facts of distribution *could* be arrived at or even conceived; for if each species were created where it is now found no further inquiry can take us beyond that fact, and there is an end to the whole matter." Now that evolution was being accepted, a whole new field was opened up, and it was one to which Wallace gave much time. (Wallace's line, marking the division between the life of Australia and that of the Orient, is still referred to by biologists.)

In 1886 he was invited to lecture at the Lowell Institute in Boston, as Lyell and Agassiz had been before him. His subject was "The Darwinian Theory," and one of the Boston papers reported, "The first Darwinian, Wallace, did not leave a leg for anti-Darwinism to stand on when he had got through his first Lowell lecture last evening. It was a masterpiece of condensed statement—as clear and simple as compact—a most beautiful specimen of scientific work. Mr. Wallace, though not an orator, is likely to become a favorite as a lecturer, his manner is so genuinely modest and straightforward." Because of his simplicity and the clarity with which he could express complex ideas, he contributed greatly to the acceptance of evolution in the United States.

After he finished at Boston, he crossed the country to California, where one of his brothers was living. There he met the American writer and conservationist John Muir and also saw the destruction of the redwoods, which appalled him. He liked the United States and Americans, but on his return to England, he wrote prophetically, "Over the larger part of America everything is raw and bare and ugly, with the same kind of ugliness with which we also are defacing our land and destroying its rural beauty. . . .

Both countries are creating ugliness, both are destroying beauty; but in America it is done on a larger scale and with a more hideous monotony."

In England, many people told him that they could not understand the *Origin of Species*, but they could comprehend his lectures on the subject. This reaction made him determine to write "an account of the Theory of Natural Selection as may enable any intelligent reader to obtain a clear conception of Darwin's work, and to understand something of the power and range of his great principle." In the book, *Darwinism*, he described the vast change that had occurred during recent years in the public's thinking. "Darwin," he said, "wrote for a generation which had not accepted evolution, and which poured contempt on those who upheld the derivation of species from species by any natural law of descent. He did his work so well that 'descent with modification' is now universally accepted as the order of nature in the organic world; and the rising generation of naturalists can hardly realize the novelty of this idea, or that our fathers considered it a scientific heresy to be condemned rather than seriously discussed. The objections now made to Darwin's theory apply, solely, to the particular means by which the change of species has been brought about, not to the fact of change. The objectors seek to minimise the agency of natural selection and to subordinate it to laws of variation, of use and disuse, of intelligence, and of heredity." In his last sentences, he brought out the question that Darwin had never been able to answer: What caused the changes? Until this was learned, the theory could not be thoroughly understood.

In 1899, Wallace moved to the small town of Parkstone. Here he had a garden—his gardening, he said, had always been "pure enjoyment" to him—and a small pond in which he could grow water lilies and other aquatic plants. As he intended never to move again, he allowed himself the luxury of planting orchids, which he had always wanted to grow. But the time had not yet come for him to rest. He continued writing, devoting much of his work to social problems with which he had always been concerned. For as a young surveyor he had witnessed the hardships and injustices brought about by land enclosures, and he had never forgotten the experience.

In 1908, the fiftieth anniversary of the reading of Darwin's and Wallace's papers, the Linnaean Society created the Darwin-Wallace Medal and selected Wallace as the first recipient. Wallace had always modestly stepped aside in favor of Darwin, and in his acceptance of the medal he explained why. "How different from [Darwin's] long study and preparation—this philosophical caution—this determination not to make known his fruitful conception till he could back it up with overwhelming proofs—was my own conduct.

"The idea came to me . . . in a sudden flash of insight; it was thought out in a few hours—was written down with such a sketch of its various applications and developments as occurred to me at the moment—then copied on thin letter paper and sent off to Darwin—all within one week. *I* was then (as often since) the 'young man in a hurry': *he*, the painstaking and patient student seeking ever the full demonstration of the truth that he had discovered, rather than to achieve immediate personal fame.

"Such being the actual facts of the case," Wallace said, "I should have had no cause for complaint if the respective shares of Darwin and myself in regard to the elucidation of Nature's method of organic development had been henceforth estimated as being, roughly, proportional to the time we had each bestowed upon it when it was thus first given to the world—that is to say, as twenty years is to one week. For, he had already made it his own." If Darwin today is far better known than Wallace, it is not only because of the excellence of his work but also because Wallace wanted it that way.

Even when he was ninety years old, Wallace still led an active life. His heart was filled with awe at the mystery he and Darwin had uncovered. Shortly before his death, he sat with a visitor in his study, looking out on the garden, woods, and sea that made up the view. "Just think!" he said, "All this wonderful beauty and diversity of nature results from the operation of a few simple laws." In his work, however, he concentrated more and more on the social problems of his times, and at the age of ninety wrote *Social Environment and Moral Progress*, a book that was well reviewed. He almost immediately contracted to write a larger one on the social order, but it was never finished. On November 7, 1913, in his ninety-first year, he quietly died in his sleep.

Almost everyone thought that his body should be placed in Westminster next to Darwin's, but his family would not agree. Instead, they buried him in a simple country cemetery on a hill covered with pines and open to the winds from the oceans over which he had traveled so many miles. As a memorial to him, they placed the stump of a petrified tree on the square stone marker—a reminder of how far he had delved into the past of the earth.

But England, if it could not have his body, still claimed his spirit. Since his family had no objection, his friends arranged to have a medallion of him placed in Westminster next to one honoring Darwin. It was unveiled in November, 1915. The Dean of Westminster Abbey gave the sermon, and among his remarks, he spoke these words as an epitaph to Alfred Russel Wallace: "It is the great men who work for the work's sake without regard to recognition, and who, as we might say, achieve greatness in spite of themselves."

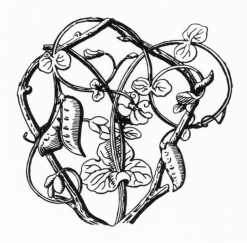

14

Science in a Monastery

GREGOR MENDEL: 1822–1884

I

In 1822, Charles Darwin was attending school at Shrewsbury and finding it highly unsatisfactory, Alexander Humboldt was in Paris, working on his notes and specimens, and Charles Lyell was studying law in London. On July 22 of that year, a second child and first son was born to Anton and Rosine Mendel in the small town of Heizendorf in Austrian Silesia. (Johann later added the name Gregor.) Except to the child's parents and a few of their friends, the event of his birth could not have seemed less important or significant.

His father, after eight years of service as a soldier during the Napoleonic Wars, had returned home to take over the family farm. Although many of the inhabitants of Heizendorf burned lime—Heizendorf lime was used for many miles around—or worked for the sawmill on the river, Anton Mendel devoted his time to improving his holdings, which consisted of a house, a large garden, and some forty-three acres of pasture and meadowland. Having no skill except a knowledge of agriculture, this was his only means of bettering his position in the world. He tore down the old house, erected a new one in its place, and planted a fruit orchard that ran from the house down the slope to the river. But he owned almost no cash, because whatever he earned went right back into the farm.

As a boy, Mendel lived a simple life. He played with his two sisters, helped his father with the farmwork—he particularly enjoyed grafting the fruit trees—and went to the district school, which supplied all the education most of the children of Heizendorf would ever need. A few, however, went on to a higher school at Leipnik (now Lipník nad Bečvou, Czechoslovakia), and after talking to some of these students, Mendel wanted to do the same thing. His father, hard pressed financially and hopeful that his son would eventually take over the farm, was reluctant but finally agreed. Since Mendel did well in his studies, he persuaded his parents after one year to let him enter an even more advanced school at Troppau (now Opava), which was about twenty miles from Heizendorf.

Because his father and mother were unable to pay the full tuition fees and board, they made an arrangement with the school to receive a discount by sending Mendel occasional quantities of bread and butter, which he used to reduce the number of school meals he ate. But even on this basis, the expense was too much for the slender resources of Anton Mendel. His son had entered Troppau in 1833 with the understanding that he would go through the six grades it had to offer, but in 1838, two years after Darwin had returned from his voyage on the *Beagle,* Anton Mendel could no longer afford even the reduced payments. One day while he had been working, a tree trunk rolled over him, crushing his chest, and from that point on, he found it difficult to keep up the farm. If Mendel wanted an education, he would have to pay for it himself. The young student, therefore, took a special course that qualified him to act as a tutor, but the additional work proved too much for him. In 1839 he became so ill that he had to return home, where he remained for many months. By September he had recovered sufficiently to go back to school, and he was graduated with good marks in the following August.

He had some thought of entering the priesthood—it was one of the few ways someone like himself could ever hope to lead an intellectual life—and he decided to go to Olmütz (now Olomouc) to study at the Philosophical Institute. His first year was extremely difficult. He had hoped to obtain employment as a tutor but soon found out that no one was interested in employing a peasant's son from Heizendorf. Somehow he scraped together enough money to finish the scholastic year, but that appeared to be as far as he would be able to go. In August, 1841, Anton Mendel, worn out by hard work and ill health, sold his farm to his son-in-law. In return for the land, livestock, and house, he was to receive a small cash payment and a lifetime pension. If Mendel wanted to enter the priesthood, the son-in-law was to pay a small amount toward his education. Otherwise, he was to be given free living quarters and the use of some of the land. The son-in-law was also to give the younger daughter, Theresia, a dowry. The terms of the sales contract showed Anton Mendel's concern for his family. He did the best for them that he could, but none of the amounts involved was large. As far as Mendel was concerned, it seemed highly improbable that he could continue studying. There was just not enough money. Theresia, however, had an answer to the problem. In an act of deep generosity, she offered to renounce her promise of a dowry if the son-in-law would increase the payments for Mendel's education. Mendel was able, therefore, to return to Olmütz, and this time he acquired some tutoring jobs. But again, he became seriously ill, most likely from overwork, and when he had completed the two-year course, he realized that he could no longer continue in this fashion. He either had to find a better means of supporting himself or resign himself to returning to Heizendorf and working as a farmer. Since the last choice was repugnant to him, he applied to the Augustinian Monastery at Altbrünn for admittance as a novice and was accepted in October, 1843.

Altbrünn was formerly a separate township but later became one of the four divisions of Brünn, the capital of Austrian Moravia and now Brno, Czechoslovakia. Lying at the conflux of the Svratka and Svitava rivers, it had served as Napoleon's headquarters during the Battle of Austerlitz. Two hills dominated the town. One of them, the Spielberg, was crowned by a castle, which had been converted into a prison, and when Mendel arrived in Altbrünn, it housed political offenders. The monastery itself was a two-story building that had been used as a nunnery until it was taken over by the Augustinians. The approach from the public square led through a gate and down an alley lined with lime trees. To the right stood the monastery's church, connected to the building by a walled-in corridor, and in the back of the building was the library, which served also to support the clock tower. Beyond the monastery were gardens and orchards running as far as the wall that surrounded the monastery's property.

The prelate was Cyrill Franz Napp, a man who combined intellectualism with business ability. He had been elected to his office at a young age (the Augustinians always tried to select a young prelate, because the monastery was compelled to pay a heavy tax on the death of each prelate), and he had set out to remedy its poor financial position. Under his direction, sufficient funds were raised to repair the church and add to the monastery building, and although he had an unimpressive appearance—he was small in stature and walked with a limp—the government quickly recognized his effectiveness and awarded him a number of important positions, so that he became an influence in Moravian affairs. Within the walls of his monastery he seemed aloof and cold. He always insisted on being addressed formally, and he rarely spoke directly to the friars and novices, only through the men who had immediate charge of them. Yet he seems to have been alert to recognize their individual talents, and more than one of them found a successful career through the prelate's plans on his behalf.

Mendel entered the monastery in 1843, but the prelate did not see fit to send him to the Brünn Theological College until 1845. His courses there consisted of ecclesiastical history, moral theology, languages such as Hebrew and Syriac, and other subjects designed for a member of a religious order. It was an education that, for his ultimate purposes, turned out to be as useless as Darwin's.

Mendel did well at his studies and was commended, not only for his intellectual work, but also for his behavior. In 1847, before he had been graduated but after he had taken his vows, he was ordained a priest, an action taken by the prelate because of a shortage of persons qualified to conduct services. This advancement got Mendel into trouble. Although he was always modest, he took advantage of his new promotion and stopped wearing his student's cap while listening to the lectures at the seminary. Little escaped the sharp eye of the prelate, and as soon as he noticed what Mendel was doing, he delivered a curt rebuke, as usual not personally, but through the prior. Even though Mendel had attained the priesthood, he said, he was still a student and must conform to the requirements laid down for students.

After Mendel's graduation in June, 1848, when the revolutions that so delighted Humboldt's liberal spirit were sweeping Europe, Mendel became a parish priest. This was the duty he had been trained for, but he soon discovered that he disliked it. One of his difficulties lay in his speaking German as his native tongue, while many of his parishioners spoke only Czechoslovakian. Another was his inability to witness pain or suffering. He simply could not bring himself to visit the bedsides of the seriously ill or to give comfort to those who were dying. Indeed, his reaction to such scenes was so violent that he became ill, and the prelate realized he must find some other career for the young man under his supervision.

A seventh class had just been established at the school at Znaim (now Znojmo) a town some thirty-five miles to the southwest of Brünn, and the school needed a substitute teacher to hold classes in Latin, Greek, German, and mathematics. In Austria at that time, teachers were required to take a qualifying examination, but the prelate would not let such a technicality stand in the way. Using his influence with the bishop and with the school system, he obtained the appointment for Mendel.

Mendel started his new job in the fall of 1849, and although he was eventually assigned to conduct less advanced classes than had been originally intended, his work seems to have been satisfactory. His only mistake was to make a sarcastic and youthful remark about the corpulence of the bishop, a comment that may have come back to that dignitary. Otherwise, he seems to have been highly regarded, and the headmaster wanted to make him a permanent member of the staff. To do this, however, Mendel would have to take the required teacher's examination, even though he had not had a university education, and in May, he received the first questions to which he was to give written answers, being allowed from six to eight weeks to do so.

The subjects that had so far most interested Mendel were the natural sciences, and although he had had little formal education in any of them, these were what he wanted to teach. He told the examiners that he had done enough self-study to make himself eligible to answer the questions in these fields. He, therefore, received problems in physics and geology. In physics he was asked to describe the properties of air and tell how winds were formed. The question in geology centered on the differences between Plutonian and Neptunian rocks. The examiner in physics was satisfied with Mendel's paper, noting that Mendel wanted to teach only in the lower schools, but the examiner in geology took a much sterner view. He said Mendel had done poorly in expressing his ideas and had included many errors. At the end of his paper, Mendel had attached a bibliography of the books at his command. Among them was Humboldt's *Cosmos,* but significantly absent was Lyell's *Principles.* Although this omission probably did not affect the outcome, it showed that Mendel was hopelessly out-of-date in his chosen subjects.

Although the geology examiner's report was extremely adverse, Mendel was permitted to continue with the next stage of the examination. In August, 1850, he reported to Vienna to take further tests in physics and natural history, this time without the privilege of consulting any books. The physics problem had to do with magnetism, and Mendel was able to answer only the first part of it successfully. With the second part of the question, he could do almost nothing. The question in natural history was to classify the mammals and describe their economic values. Here Mendel proved to be an almost complete failure. He clearly had little conception of technical classification or its terminology, and the examiners reported that, at least on the basis of his answer, he was unequipped to teach even the most elementary courses. Nevertheless, they gave him an opportunity to redeem himself in the oral examinations. But he did not do so. The examiners were impressed by his character, but not by his knowledge. Despite his sister's sacrifice, he was pathetically uninformed.

After Mendel returned to Brünn, he received another temporary appointment as a teacher, but it was obvious that he should have the necessary papers. The prelate wrote the examiners to find out what had happened, and the chairman of the examining board was frank in his reply. Mendel must have more education, and what was even more important, the chairman thought that the investment of time and money would be worthwhile. After securing the bishop's permission, the prelate sent Mendel to Vienna in 1851 to enter the university, giving him at last a chance to secure the type of education he had wanted so long and for which he had suffered so much.

At Vienna, Mendel took courses in zoology, mathematics, botany, and physics. For the first time he learned the systematic study of plants, how to use a microscope, a considerable amount of paleontology (the examiner in geology had especially commented on his deficiencies in this field) how to construct the apparatus needed for experiments in physics, and the mathematics necessary to solve physics problems. When he returned to Brünn in the summer of 1853, he still did not have the usual teachers' papers, but he at least knew the subjects that he wanted to teach.

While Mendel was at Vienna, the Brünn Modern School had been formed with the purpose of providing its students with a more scientific education than was generally available at that time. In the spring of 1854 the school lost its teacher of physics and natural history, and the headmaster asked Mendel to take over these courses, again as a substitute, in the lower grades. No one had ever doubted Mendel's qualities as a person. The block that had stood in the way of his becoming a good teacher was simply his lack of education. Now that that obstacle had been removed, he became a popular and effective instructor.

Years later his pupils remembered him as a stocky, healthy man with a pleasant, even disposition. Above everything else, he wanted his students to be interested in what they were studying, and he cared for this far more than for the facts they might have collected. Marks to him were more a necessary evil than a sign of what a student knew, and at the end of each term he gave his classes a chance to improve their grades if they wanted to take it. This chance consisted of having members of the classes give examination questions to each other until they had succeeded in improving their standing. He was not, however, merely easygoing, for he had the ability to maintain strict discipline without using threats or punishments. When, for example, he became concerned over his students' habit of killing birds, he simply ordered them to surrender their slingshots, delivered a lecture to them, and put an end to the practice.

His life seemed completely ordered, and he appeared to have at last found a suitable career, but he still had not passed the examination required of permanent teachers. For the first few years that he was back in Brünn, he studied by himself, using the monastery's extensive library and building on the knowledge that he had acquired in Vienna. In 1856 he declared himself ready and, during the spring, returned to Vienna once more to undergo the ordeal. The first time he had failed because he did not have the education. No one knows why he failed the second time, but fail he did. At the time his colleagues thought he had had a quarrel with the examiner in botany and had refused any diplomatic settlement of their differences. But Mendel would not discuss what had happened. He never tried to take the examination again, and to the end of his teaching career he remained a substitute.

II

Brünn was no intellectual center such as Paris or London. It did have the Wernerian Society, which was attempting to collect the information needed to publish a geologic map of Silesia and Moravia, and a section of the Agricultural Society of Moravia and Silesia. Both these groups, although neither was outstanding, provided Mendel with some stimulus, and he also had a number of good friends on the faculty of the school. But these hardly seem sufficient to account for the experiments that Mendel began to make on his own accord. For he developed an intense interest in heredity, one of the problems that had so absorbed Darwin and that formed one of the weaknesses of his theory.

Mendel began by breeding gray and white mice in his room, crossing them to see what would happen. He never thought enough of the results of these experiments to write down anything about them, and it is likely that he engaged in them purely for the pleasure of it. In any case, he shortly abandoned them and turned to plants. Describing his subsequent work, he later said, "That, so far, no generally applicable law governing the formation and development of hybrids has been successfully formulated can hardly be wondered at by anyone who is acquainted with the extent of the task, and can appreciate the difficulties with which experiments of this class have to contend. A final decision can only be arrived at when we shall have before us the results of detailed experiments made on plants belonging to the most diverse orders.

"Those who survey the work done in this department will arrive at the conviction that among all the numerous experiments made, not one has been carried out to such an extent and in such a way as to make it possible to determine the number of different forms under which the offspring of the hybrids appear, or to arrange these forms with certainty according to their separate generations, or definitely to ascertain their statistical relations.

"It requires some courage to undertake a labor of such far-reaching extent; this appears, however, to be the only right way by which we can finally reach the solution of a question the importance of which cannot be overestimated in connection with the history of the evolution of organic forms."

For a young man who could not pass the teachers' examinations, this was a truly remarkable statement. It would have been remarkable if it had been made even by one of Europe's leading scientists. Mendel had seen exactly what had to be done if the problem of inheritance were ever to be solved. Instead of collecting miscellaneous information from the breeders of plants and animals and then trying to interpret it, he had recognized the need for controlled experiments—with three points clearly in view. One, he wanted to know "the number of different forms under which the hybrids appear." Second, he hoped to find out in which generations they appeared. And third, he intended to establish the statistical relation between them, an extremely modern concept. Much of his ultimate success came from his having defined his problem so clearly.

As an initial step, he had to obtain a place where he could conduct his experiments, and the prelate was certainly not going to give him one of the monastery's profitable large gardens. Behind the library, however, was a small plot of land, about 120 feet long and 20 feet wide. It was cut off from the other gardens by a hedge and a path, and the prelate said that he could use it, although he must certainly have looked upon this as more a game than a serious scientific effort.

Next, Mendel had to choose the type of plants with which he would experiment, and for several reasons, he selected peas. They had characteristics that were easily recognizable and seemed constant; the hybrids were fertile, so they could be readily bred; and the construction of their flowers made it relatively easy to control their fertilization. From several seedsmen, he obtained "some thirty-four more or less distinct varieties of peas," and these he subjected to a two-year trial to make certain that they bred true. (One batch of seed, he noticed, produced a few plants that were markedly different from all the others that came from the same batch. This at first disturbed him, but he soon discovered that some seeds from another variety sold by the same man had become accidentally mixed into the package.) At the end of the two years' trial Mendel chose twenty-two varieties to work with.

Meanwhile, he had carefully selected the characteristics that he would observe during hybridization. These were seven in number and included whether the ripe seed was round or wrinkled, the shape of the pods, the position of the flower, the size of the plant—whether tall or short—and several other qualities, all of which could be easily seen and all of which, as far as Mendel knew, were constant in each variety.

Linnaeus' scientific studies had carried him to the remote northern expanses of Lapland, deep into Sweden's mines, and to the gardens of Holland. Humboldt's had taken him up the far reaches of the Orinoco, across the high ridges of the Andes, and through the heartland of Mexico. In the pursuit of knowledge, Huxley had explored the reefs of Australia and the passageways on the route from Sydney to India. Wallace had ventured into the depths of Brazil and the remote islands of the Malay Archipelago. And Darwin had gone completely around the world. Even Cuvier, Lamarck, and Buffon, who traveled less than many, had the entire Jardin des Plantes in which to work, not only its garden, but also its enormous collections. Mendel's great expedition, however, took him no farther than a tiny patch of soil behind the wall of the monastery's library.

Here he planted his carefully selected peas, letting them cling to the branches of trees or to strings that he had stretched across the area or allowing them to find support from sticks that he had driven into the ground. When the flowers appeared, he would force some of them open with his forceps, remove the pistil and stamen, and collect the pollen on a fine brush. Then he would open the flower of another plant, brush its pistil with the pollen, and afterward tie a paper or cloth bag around it to prevent its also being fertilized by an insect. (In addition, he kept some of each variety potted in a greenhouse. These served as a control to show whether the plants outside had become accidentally fertilized.) When the seeds had matured, he collected them carefully, labeled them, and held them ready for the next planting.

The years drifted on. Every growing season the somewhat corpulent priest could be seen behind the library, planting his peas, watching over them as the first green sprouts emerged from the ground, helping them reach the strings that he had stretched everywhere, opening the flowers with his forceps, putting the pollen on other flowers, and recording the results he obtained. Darwin opened Wallace's letter and decided the time had come to publish an abstract of his theory. The *Origin of Species* came off Murray's presses and was distributed to the booksellers. Huxley, angered by the bishop's insult, rose to his feet and delivered his response in the hall at Oxford. Great events were taking place in the world of science, but few were greater than those occurring in the garden patch at the monastery. Each year Mendel went patiently through the same routine, quietly tending his peas and keeping his detailed records. Slowly his findings showed certain patterns, which he arranged in tables.

He talked about his experiments with some of his friends in Brünn, and although they were interested, they did not seem to recognize their importance. To them, the schoolteacher was simply discovering some miscellaneous and perhaps not too useful facts about the hybridization of plants, information that might be helpful to seedsmen but hardly of much consequence otherwise. Nevertheless, they had no objection to his presenting a paper on the subject at a meeting of the Society for the Study of Natural Science, which they had founded in 1862. During the winter of 1864–1865, between his classes at the Brünn Modern School, Mendel spent his time checking his tables and writing his paper. The final presentation, although covering only a few pages, was too long for one meeting, so the membership permitted him to be the speaker at two meetings, those held on February 8 and March 8, 1865.

Standing in front of his small audience, Mendel, his eyeglasses squarely in place, began reading. "Experience of artificial fertilization, such as is effected with ornamental plants in order to obtain new variations in color, has led to the experiments which will here be discussed," he began modestly. "The striking regularity with which the same hybrid forms always reappeared when fertilization took place between the same species induced further experiments to be undertaken, the object of which was to follow up the developments of the hybrids in their progeny." Because he was effective in the classroom, Mendel probably delivered his material as well as possible, but there is little evidence that he aroused his audience. Like the members of the Linnaean Society when they first heard the papers of Darwin and Wallace, the members of the Brünn Society for the Study of Natural History did not understand the significance of what they were listening to. The simple priest, the man who could not pass the examination to teach natural history in the lower classes, was laying the basis for modern genetics, unraveling part of the mystery that was baffling men like Darwin, Wallace, and Huxley.

By examining Mendel's tables, it was possible to draw up what later became known as Mendel's laws. Instead of accepting the "blending" of characteristics, which many people, including Darwin, accepted at the time, Mendel showed that the characteristics of the parents remained separate, that some were dominant and others recessive, and that two plants that seemed to resemble each other might be quite different genetically, for one might be able to pass on only one characteristic, while the other might be able to pass on either the dominant or the recessive characteristic. With this knowledge, Mendel could predict, in certain instances, the outcome of interbreeding. If he used two varieties of peas, one being able only to pass on the dominant characteristic and the other only the recessive characteristic, the results of this interbreeding would resemble the dominant parent. But when these plants were interbred among themselves, three-quarters of the offspring would resemble the dominant ancestors, and one-quarter would be like the ancestors with the recessive characteristic. The differences between Mendel's projections and the actual results were so small that they could be explained by the size of the sample he used. Although he dealt with thousands of plants in the course of the experiment, the number, nevertheless, statistically permitted some error in the outcome.

If Darwin had been at that small meeting at Brünn, he would have been thrilled at hearing Mendel's report. Here at last was an orderly explanation of the process of inheritance and variation—one that leads directly to chromosomes and genes and modern knowledge of this feature of life. But Darwin, of course, was not there, and neither was anyone else who comprehended the meaning of what Mendel had said. The Brünn Society for the Study of Natural Science ordered the paper printed in its proceedings, which were then, as usual, sent to some 120 other libraries and scientific societies in Europe in exchange for their publications. The recipients placed it on their shelves. For anyone who cared to look, there was the answer to an important question that had been bothering the evolutionists.

III

By 1866, the year that Mendel's paper appeared in the society's proceedings, Otto von Bismarck, the personification of everything that Humboldt despised in the Prussian spirit, had successfully fought the Danes and gained possession of the duchies of Schleswig and Holstein for Prussia and Austria. Following that triumph, he engaged in a series of adroit and underhanded maneuvers, which, as he hoped they would, in 1866 provoked war with his former ally, Austria. The conflict that resulted was entirely one-sided. The Austrians had no chance of winning against the well-trained Prussian armies, and on July 12, 5,000 Prussian troops entered the city of Brünn.

The occupying forces demanded quarters and food. Large numbers of them stayed at the monastery, causing an expense that the monastery could ill afford. In the surrounding countryside, soldiers went off with grain and livestock to supply the conquering army, causing severe hardship to the peasants, to the landowners, and to several estates that belonged to the monastery. Worse even than that, they brought cholera with them. In Brünn alone, approximately 1,000 civilians and 2,000 soldiers died. Funerals were so common that the authorities forbade the mourners to toll the bells or march behind the coffins for fear of spreading panic. The war, however, lasted only seven weeks. At Prague, Bismarck forced his terms on the Austrian government, the invading wave receded, and life at Brünn and the monastery returned to normal.

The disruption caused by the Prussian invasion of Austria might at first have accounted for the absence of any reaction to Mendel's paper, but as the months passed and peace was restored, it became apparent that no one had any interest in it. Mendel himself lacked the ability or the desire to promote his ideas. When Wallace at Ternate suddenly recognized the importance of natural selection, he had immediately put his theory on paper and sent it to Darwin for his opinion, asking him to show it to others if he thought it merited such attention. Mendel, on the other hand, did nothing about his own paper after it had appeared in the proceedings of the Brünn Society for the Study of Natural Science. When nobody took the slightest notice of what he had said, he seemed to be content to leave it at that. But in December, 1866, after the Prussian troops had left, he took what for him was an unusual step: he addressed a personal letter to a stranger. The man he chose to write to was Karl von Nägeli, formerly a professor at Zurich and now at Munich. Knowing of Nägeli's interest in the process of change, Mendel wrote to him and told him about the results of his experiments and added that he was planning now to extend them to cover other plants. After almost two months had passed by, Nägeli finally replied in the tone of a professional talking to a mere amateur. Although Mendel had bred thousands of plants, Nägeli regarded his work on peas as inconclusive. He should conduct more experiments and extend his thinking to other plants, Nägeli said. To accomplish this, he had two suggestions to make: Mendel should send him samples of his pea seeds, so he could raise them himself (notes made by Nägeli at the time show that he did not think Mendel's theory would hold true), and Mendel might find it worthwhile to study the genus *Hieracium,* a group of weedy perennial herbs. (The tawny hawkweed, found in the northeastern United States, is one.)

In spite of the condescending tone of Nägeli's letter, Mendel was delighted to receive it and immediately sent 140 packets of seeds to Munich, each of them carefully labeled according to ancestry. Nägeli, as he had promised, planted some of them, but he never followed through with his plan to check Mendel's results independently. Yet at least no harm had been done, since Mendel could spare the seeds. His second suggestion, however, had serious consequences. In selecting peas for his original experiments, Mendel had made a wise choice. He had used plants whose flowers were easy to manipulate, whose hybrids were fertile, whose characteristics were marked, and whose genetic qualities—although he did not know this—were simple. Hieracia, however, posed a new set of problems. The flowers were small and, therefore, difficult to handle when Mendel tried to fertilize them, and part of the hybrids were sterile. Even worse, some of the plants were capable of reproduction without pollinization. Neither Nägeli, for all his superior attitude, nor Mendel knew this, but it rendered Mendel's subsequent experiments almost meaningless. As he carefully forced open the tiny flowers, collected the pollen on his brush, and gently touched it to the pistils of another plant, he was, in many instances, accomplishing nothing. The flower merely reproduced in its own way, and Mendel's action had no influence on the final results. From his point of view, therefore, he had walked into a nightmare world where the universal laws he thought he had discovered broke down. The predictions that he could so confidently make about the results of the hybridization of peas did not hold true. Although he was discouraged, Mendel in the true scientific spirit continued to persevere.

In 1868 the prelate died, and the members of the monastery convened to elect a successor. Mendel, the unassuming schoolteacher, seemed an unlikely choice—indeed, he thought so himself—but he was the person chosen. Immediately he wrote Nägeli to tell him of his good fortune, saying that his new duties would in no way interfere with his scientific experiments. So softhearted that he could not bring himself personally to say good-bye to his students, he asked the headmaster to make the announcement for him, but typical of his generosity, he requested that his last month's salary be divided among the three poorest boys.

As prelate, Mendel enjoyed considerable luxury for a peasant's son. He lived in the spacious prelate's apartment; he received a rather large income (this allowed him to pay all the cost of educating the sons of his younger sister, the one who had sacrificed her dowry on behalf of his education); and he could use any part of the monastery's grounds for his experiments, no longer confining himself to the small patch of ground against the library wall. He also had charge of all the monastery's agricultural work. The fruit trees particularly appealed to him, and remembering his experiences on his father's farm, he supervised much of the grafting and may even have made some attempts at cross-fertilization.

During the early years of his prelacy he conducted a variety of scientific experiments and observations. For some time he had been keeping records of the level of the groundwater in Brünn, measuring it at regular intervals from the top of the well in the monastery garden. His new position did not interfere with this. In the library, he set up a telescope and studied sunspots, making detailed drawings showing how they appeared to him through the lens, and out in the gardens, he placed numerous beehives, hoping that he could learn from the bees something more about the laws of descent. He designed a special cage that would permit him to control the fertilization of the queen (it did not always work), and he kept up a continual hunt for new varieties of bees that he could observe. He even obtained one from Brazil that had arrived in Austria in a shipment of lumber.

But he was having difficulty with his most important work. His hieracia kept on reacting in an unpredictable fashion, and their tiny flowers were creating a problem. Because they were too small for him to work on them in ordinary sunlight, he devised an instrument that combined a magnifying lens with a mirror. With the use of this, he could remove the pollen and fertilize the flowers, but it placed an extreme strain on his eyes. In the early summer of 1869, as he wrote Nägeli, he had to stop work almost entirely in order to rest his eyes and regain his normal sight. That summer he also delivered a preliminary report on his experiments to the Brünn Society for the Study of Natural History. Toward the end of it he said in some bewilderment, "If finally we compare the described result, still very uncertain, with those obtained by crosses made between forms of *Pisum* [peas], which I had the honor of communicating in 1865, we find a very real distinction. In *Pisum* the hybrids, obtained from the immediate crossing of two forms, have in all cases the same type, but their posterity, on the contrary, are variable and follow a definite law in their variations. In *Hieracium* according to the present experiments the exactly opposite phenomenon seems to be exhibited."

His duties as prelate began to press him. The monastery owned lands at some distance from Brünn—one holding, for example, was a large dairy—and Mendel had to visit them frequently. During his absences the gardener took care of his plants and in at least one instance overwatered and killed them. He had so little time, too. As he complained to Nägeli, he had now few opportunities to engage in the occupations that he really enjoyed. Yet new duties kept coming his way. He was elected to the Agricultural Society. The government appointed him to the commission to adjust land taxes in Moravia. He became the head of the Moravian Institute for Deaf-mutes. He was given a position on the administrative council of the Moravian Mortgage Bank and, in 1881, was made its chairman. This post paid a substantial salary, but it required a considerable amount of time. When he first became prelate, he had firmly said that he planned to continue his experiments in hybridization, but his resolution, like many good resolutions, gradually weakened. He still kept up some of his miscellaneous scientific work, like his observations of sunspots, but sometime in the early 1870's he stopped any attempt to carry on with the studies that eventually made him famous. Not only was it difficult to find the time, but no one seemed to care. His colleagues did not have much interest, Nägeli was unenthusiastic, and as for the 120 copies of his paper reprinted in the proceedings of the Brünn Society for the Study of Natural History, the society might just as well have thrown them in the river. They evoked no response whatsoever.

Mendel was one of those quiet, untroubled persons, whose ambitions are limited to the attainable, and he does not appear to have been perturbed by the lack of recognition. Aside from his correspondence with Nägeli, he did not try to bring his paper to the attention of any scientists outside Brünn. He did not even make a clear decision to give up his work. Under the pressure of his responsibilities on behalf of the monastery and perplexed by the behavior of the hieracia, he just began to spend less and less time on his experiments. He himself did not know when he ceased altogether. After that period his most valuable scientific work probably consisted of the meteorological observations that he took whenever he was in Brünn. Three times a day he wrote down the barometric reading, the humidity, and the temperatures from his registering thermometer and measured the rainfall. All this information was carefully tabulated and put into a form that would be useful to others.

His larger income made life more pleasant for him. He traveled a little, visiting Rome and going to Kiel for a meeting of beekeepers. When his

native town of Heizendorf was swept by a series of fires, he made a substantial donation toward the formation of a fire brigade. (In gratitude,
the fire brigade elected him an honorary member.) Although he had little
interest in music or the arts, he contributed generously to the Brünn Musical Society because the church organist was one of his chosen friends.
And of course, he educated his nephews, whom he greatly enjoyed having
with him at Brünn. In short, he was a distinguished citizen of his own
town, a man of public affairs, kindly and openhanded, but of no significance to the world as a whole.

His last years were marred only by a bitter and acrimonious dispute with
the Austrian government, which took up his time and energy. In 1874 a
law was passed providing for the taxation of monasteries to support the
other activities of the church. It was approved by the emperor and went
into effect the following year. Mendel, when he was asked to, dutifully
made out the inventory of the monastery's possessions, but he flatly refused to pay the tax bill that was subsequently submitted. Instead, he sent
in an amount that was somewhat less and insisted that it was a voluntary
contribution. His fellows in the monastery encouraged him to take this
stand, and other prelates looked on with interest to see what would happen.

The governor of Moravia almost immediately returned Mendel's "contribution" and advised the monastery that it could appeal the assessment
if the tax was too large. Mendel replied that the basic issue was not the
size of the tax, but the tax itself. He refused to recognize the state's right
to levy it. Since the state obviously could not give in to Mendel and maintain its authority elsewhere and since Mendel, thoroughly angry, refused
to compromise, the affair soon reached an impasse. In the spring of 1876,
instead of cultivating his plants, Mendel was resisting a warrant issued by
the municipality of Brünn permitting the seizure of the monastery's belongings to pay the sum owed the government. Mendel refused to cooper-
ate in any way with the officials who served the warrant. He would not
turn over his books; he would not hand them the keys to the strongbox;
anything they wanted, they would have to take by force.

This placed them in an impossible position. Although Mendel was in
violation of the law, he was, nevertheless, one of the dignitaries of the
town and of the church, and clearly they could not manhandle him. They,
therefore, retreated, but in reporting their action to the governor, they
advised him to sequester the monastery's revenues, advice the governor
promptly took. On the other hand, he did not like the situation and made
every effort to persuade Mendel to reverse his stand. When his hints that
Mendel might be honored by the government or receive an important political position failed to sway the prelate, he turned to threats. The minister for public worship and education was angry, he reported to Mendel,

and even the emperor was beginning to take an interest in the dispute. Nothing had any effect.

Sadly the other members of the monastery began to think that Mendel had made a mistake. In the first place, certain items that were excluded by law from the assessment had been reported by Mendel in his original inventory. Thus, the amount sequestered by the government was greater than it might have been if Mendel would only recognize the legality of the tax and file an appeal. In the second place, the more cooperative monasteries were being treated with greater consideration. Mendel had lost many of his friends in government. Now he was beginning to lose friends among his supporters in the monastery. He grew bitter and told his nephews of plots to put him in a lunatic asylum or perhaps even to kill him. In June, 1883, the Governor of Moravia pleaded with the bishop to talk to Mendel. By then it was clear that the government was not going to repeal the law or do anything but enforce it, but Mendel was too ill to be disturbed. The doctor reported that he was suffering from heart disease and dropsy. The financial affairs of the monastery were turned over to another official, and although he at first supported Mendel's position—he really had no choice—by fall he had protested the amount of the assessment, in this way tacitly acknowledging the legality of the tax.

That winter, although Mendel was too sick to carry on many of his duties, he was still able to make his meteorological observations. Every day he took the readings from his instruments and entered them in his book. On the morning of January 4, 1884, he rose as usual and walked out to the garden where he kept his beehouses and looked at the thermometer that was attached to one of the buildings there. He checked the rain gauge in the prelate's garden just as he always did, but before lunch, his heart suddenly became much worse, and the doctor knew that the end was near. He died two days later in the early morning hours of January 6, 1884.

By the standards of Brünn, the funeral parade was large. Various church officials, Protestant and Jewish as well as Catholic, took part. So did the teachers with whom he had worked so long, and so did his friends in the various societies to which he belonged. Even the fire brigade from Heizendorf sent a delegate. But there were no members of the international scientific world to which Mendel rightly belonged because of his paper on the peas. It contained the secret for which many men were searching, but it still lay on the shelves of the libraries to which it had been sent—unopened and unread.

I V

In the years during which Mendel was battling the government over its tax law and in the decades after his death, the ideas of the evolutionists were receiving increasing support from the paleontologists. Less than 200 years before, men of the intelligence of Voltaire had questioned whether fossils possessed any significance at all. Now scientists could no longer entertain any such doubts, for the meaning of fossils was fully understood. It had become a question of determining what the record said, whether it would substantiate evolution. Expeditions across the world were looking for fossils and more fossils, and men like Othniel Charles Marsh and Edward Drinker Cope were delving into the rich fossil beds of the American West. (The two men started out as friends but later became fierce and bitter competitors.) The record, of course, was not perfect, particularly with respect to man, but it indicated more and more that the evolutionists must be right, and the pattern appeared to be too perfect to be explained away by arguments like Louis Agassiz's.

On the other hand, the evolutionists were baffled in their attempt to produce a satisfactory explanation of how variations occurred. The idea of a general blending of characteristics led logically to an averaging out of qualities that did not reveal how variations could appear and then be naturally selected. The process would also consume an enormous amount of time, far more than the physicists then estimated the earth's age to be. The solution had to lie in some other direction.

One of those trying to penetrate the mystery was a Dutch botanist, Hugo de Vries, who was a professor at the university in Amsterdam. During his studies he observed some evening primrose plants growing in a meadow. From time to time he noticed the sudden appearance in their midst of what seemed to him to be new species, and in this phenomenon, he saw a possible answer to the unresolved questions perplexing the evolutionists. Instead of the slow, gradual changes that Darwin believed in, perhaps variations for some reason occurred abruptly. He was not sure why, but in his primroses, he saw the evidence before his eyes. To these changes, he gave the name "mutations." By one of those curious ironies that sometimes guide the development of mankind's thinking, he was not witnessing mutations as they are known today or even as he thought them to be. The evening primrose is genetically complicated—a hybrid that reverts to its ancestral types by a unique process—and it was these reversions that De Vries was really observing. But for practical purposes, that made no difference. De Vries had the right idea even if his experimental material would not bear him out when it underwent more advanced investigation.

He had been interested in genetics for some time, and he now decided that instead of solely relying on general observation and inference, he would conduct direct experiments. In addition, he searched the libraries to discover what else had been done before him. Mendel's paper had been mentioned a few times by other scientists—in one case, it was included in a bibliography by an author who had apparently never read it—but De Vries came across it during his hunt and decided to check Mendel's results against his own findings. On March 24, 1900, he read a paper to the German Botanical Society, describing what he had found from his hybridization. In his paper, he said that the principles he had discovered were essentially those worked out by Mendel years before. For the first time, thirty-five years after he had read it to the Brünn Society for the Study of Natural History, the significance of Mendel's paper was publicly recognized.

A month later on April 24, a German botanist, Karl Erich Correns, who was a professor at Tübingen, announced that he, too, had been studying genetics. He had started by examining the structure of cells and then had become interested in the reproduction of mosses. In the course of his investigations, he also had gone to the library and there had found Mendel's slim paper. His experiments had confirmed what Mendel had written.

Mendel had been neglected so long, but now recognition came in a flood, for in June of the same year an Austrian botanist, Erich von Tschermak, prepared a paper that appeared in the reports issued by the German Botanical Society. Unknown to either De Vries or Correns, he had also been working on problems of heredity, had come across Mendel's paper in the course of searching the library for information, and had confirmed Mendel's results and conclusions.

In England, William Bateson, a biologist, quickly recognized the importance of Mendel's pioneering work. Not only did he carry it further by applying it to animals, but he was the author of a book, *Mendel's Principles of Heredity,* in which he presented translations of Mendel's two papers and expanded his ideas. In his preface, he expressed his excitement. "In the Study of Evolution," he wrote, "progress had well-nigh stopped. The more vigorous, perhaps also the more prudent, had left this field of science to labour in others where the harvest is less precarious or the yield more immediate. Of those who remained some still struggled to push towards truth through the jungle of phenomena: most were content supinely to rest on the great clearing Darwin made long since.

"Such was our state when . . . it was suddenly discovered that an unknown man, Gregor Johann Mendel, had, alone, and unheeded, broken off from the rest—in the moment that Darwin was at work—and cut a way through.

"This is not metaphor, it is simple fact. Each of us who now looks at his own patch of work sees Mendel's clue running through it: whither that clue will lead, we dare not yet surmise."

In 1884, when Mendel had died, the city of Brünn had remembered him as the benevolent prelate who liked to putter in his garden, read his meteorological instruments, and raise his bees, a harmless, gentle man in spite of his quarrel with the government over the tax. When it was first proposed by the outside world that a memorial should be raised to him, not only were the people of Brünn surprised, but they had some difficulty recalling who he was. Indeed, some of them objected to having any monument at all in the public square, since it would interfere with the erection of booths for local fairs. But their differences were overcome, and on October 2, 1910, 150 scientists from many countries gathered at the unveiling of the statue, which showed a young priest standing against a background of pea vines, those peas he had cultivated so carefully in the little garden behind the library.

William Bateson spoke, and his words were an eloquent plea that science help bring the nations together. But nothing he wrote or said about Mendel's discovery was as prophetic as the sentence "Whither that clue will lead, we dare not yet surmise."

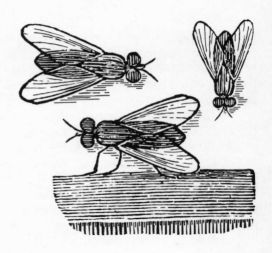

15

Today and Tomorrow

I

The insignificant little fruit fly, *Drosophila melanogaster*—an apparent pest, if anything—offers a cogent argument against permitting any form of life to become extinct. Before the early 1900's its disappearance from the world would have aroused little comment, merely a sigh of mild relief. But its loss would have been a sorry one, because *Drosophila melanogaster* is admirably designed for the study of certain aspects of heredity. It reproduces in profusion. It can be easily housed; thousands of flies can exist comfortably in a milk bottle stuck on a shelf. It can grow from an egg into sexual maturity in relatively few days. It has only four pairs of chromosomes, the parts of the nucleus that carry the genes, and each of them is large and distinguishable. And to make itself even more useful, it mutates frequently in the laboratory. Peas had served Mendel's purposes well; *Drosophila melanogaster* filled a similar, but more complicated role, for Mendel's successors.

One of the earliest of these was Thomas Hunt Morgan. In 1900, when De Vries, Correns, and Tschermak were publishing their papers about the discovery of Mendel's work, Morgan was teaching zoology at Bryn Mawr College, which he left a few years later in order to go to Columbia University. His first interest was embryology, but after moving to New York City, he began to entertain doubts about the theories of heredity that were being discussed by his colleagues. The only way he could resolve them was to conduct his own experiments, and there was *Drosophila melanogaster,* ready and waiting.

In the years that followed, Morgan and his associates, as well as many other leading scientists working independently, raised millions of these flies, caring for them as carefully as Mendel had cared for his peas, and in return the flies—and the other forms of life that were also studied —yielded many secrets about the process of heredity. Mankind learned about the existence of the X and Y chromosomes that determine sex; the arrangement of the genes on the chromosomes; how certain genes are linked together; about the phenomenon of crossover, in which one part of a chromosome can become attached to another; and the effect of mutations. Probing deeper and deeper, scientists discovered more and more about the construction of cells and the behavior of their component parts and finally uncovered the amazing role of DNA (deoxyribonucleic acid), which offers astounding possibilities for future study. The prophecy made by Bateson at the turn of the century, shortly after the discovery of Mendel's paper, is coming true. "An exact determination of the laws of heredity," he had written, "will probably work more change in man's outlook on the world, and in his power over nature, than any other advance in natural knowledge that can be clearly foreseen."

The studies of the geneticists revealed more than enough sources of variation to satisfy the requirements of the evolutionists. As expected, mutations were found to play an important role, but not in the manner that had been foreseen. At first, many scientists had believed that the changes brought about by mutations would be abrupt and drastic, causing sudden switches in the form of the species. Although such dramatic changes can occur, they are generally harmful, because they throw the other functions of the organism out of balance and thereby create an abortive monster, rather than a new form of life. Scientists learned instead that minor mutations, occurring at a fairly regular rate but subject to outside influences, such as ultraviolet light, produce the significant changes. The individual variations may be extremely minor, but with further breeding and the addition of other mutations, the total effect can be large. Darwin's theory of the blending of characteristics turned out to be somewhat true, although not in the form he had stated it. Characteristics remain separate, as Mendel had demonstrated with his peas, but a single gene may act differently in the presence of various other genes. Thus, the genetic world is not composed merely of readily discernible dominants and recessives, as Mendel's experiments might at first have made it appear. Instead, the findings that have resulted from his early discoveries have revealed highly complicated elements and incredible richness and demonstrated that mutations and recombinations of genes are sufficient to provide the change needed for evolution. The possibilities are mathematically enormous, and it is no longer possible to object to evolution, as its early critics did, on the ground of an insufficient source of variation.

Other evidence has also been uncovered to support Darwin, Wallace, and their followers. The study of vestigial organs, for example, helps verify their conclusions, and the fossil record has been continually enlarged by the scientists' diggings. In his day and in the light of his knowledge, Cuvier could argue effectively and convincingly that Lamarck's theory was not substantiated by the fossil remains that had been uncovered. He could not do this now. Although an element of chance enters the process of fossilization and sometimes obscures the track and although much searching remains to be done, the record as it has now been put together would have delighted Darwin, Huxley, and Hooker.

As a result of further research, many earlier ideas about evolution have had to be revised and refined. Following the publication of the *Origin of Species,* some enthusiasts used with increasing frequency the phrases "survival of the fittest" and "the struggle for existence," although Darwin himself generally preferred milder terms, such as "natural selection." But "survival of the fittest" had more romantic appeal for many persons, because it invoked a jungle world in which the "fittest" automatically won. Thus, it provided justification, if not for brutal physical acts, at least for brutal social acts. The business tycoon who had crushed his competitors could rest comfortably in the thought that the fittest had survived and that he was merely following a natural law as stated by science. In this form, the theory of evolution had a harmful effect on the philosophies and attitudes of many. Moreover, scientists have since discovered that such a simplistic view is not accurate, that evolution is far more complicated, and that, indeed, the meek may inherit the earth.

Many cases illustrate that the victory does not always go to the strong, nor the race to the swift. Two among them, both of which have become classics, show that sometimes what seems to be an advantage, a sign of "fitness," may under different conditions be a weakness. The peppered moth of Great Britain appears in two forms, one light and one dark. At one time, the dark form was at a considerable disadvantage, because against the bark of a light-colored tree it was readily visible to its predators. But the coming of industry changed its situation. Against a tree trunk covered with the soot of factory chimneys, it was better camouflaged than the lighter form, and therefore, in industrial areas it was more successful in escaping attack. In man, a particular gene affects the blood corpuscles in such a way as to increase the possibility of serious ailment. This undesirable gene, however, usually becomes a positive advantage when malaria strikes by creating a defense against the disease.

Since Darwin's day, numerous additional factors have been recognized as affecting the development of the species. Sexual attraction and the fertility rate are two of them, and particularly among humans, some are for practical purposes undefinable. The "fittest," if limited to terms of brutality, viciousness, slyness, competitiveness, and brute strength, are not those necessarily chosen to survive or those capable of making the greatest contribution to the human race. No one in recent times has demonstrated this more graphically than Adolf Hitler. Evolution reveals a mystery in which qualities such as cooperation, peacefulness, and other elements usually ignored by some of the early evolutionists may have an important role to play. As was true with Mendel's original theory of heredity and with most great theories like Darwin's, the end is not reached with the first statement. For the first statement is not a wall erected at the limits of truth; it is a gate that opens onto a path that vanishes in the distance. Thought builds on thought, theory builds on theory, but the final truth is unreached. Perhaps it is unreachable.

So it was with the work of the great naturalists. Each one built on the accomplishments of the others, somewhat as bricks are laid one on top of the other to form a building. Occasionally a single theory was of such significance, a theory like Mendel's or Darwin's, that it acted like a keystone, the one idea forming the central support for many others. In any science, however, an idea often serves its purpose at a given time and then becomes outmoded. But that is no reason for disparaging the original thinker, for he and his thoughts were a necessary part of the whole process. Linnaeus, in a world that was only a few steps away from the Middle Ages, a world in which a faked monster at Hamburg could receive serious consideration, brought to man's observation of the natural world a cool and orderly eye. If scientists today do not use Linnaeus' system of classification, it makes little difference in judging his worth, because in his time he provided a forward step. Without Linnaeus and without Buffon, who developed the Jardin du Roi into a scientific center, popularized science, and argued that the world was older than men had previously thought, could Lamarck have accomplished his studies of the "worms"? And Lamarck, helplessly entangled in his basic misconception that acquired characteristics could be inherited, what did he contribute? He fought unsuccessfully against the brilliant attacks of Cuvier, and his theory was later overthrown. Nevertheless, he helped launch a thought that in turn assisted in creating a fresh attitude that made the work of Darwin and Wallace possible. Neither of these two men simply reached into the darkness for their theories. Both of them had read Lamarck. Both of them had wondered about the ideas that were becoming increasingly current, the speculations that were taking place about the progressive development of life. Without Lamarck, perhaps it would not have been Darwin and Wallace who discovered evolution, but someone much later in history.

And would either of them have become the codiscoverers of evolution, if it had not been for Lyell? Not only did he lay the foundations of modern geology, but his concept of the continuity of geologic forces stimulated both men into considering the possibility that a similar continuity might be a factor in organic development as well. Yet Lyell, too, owed many debts. The catastrophes that Buffon had invented to account for the history of the world were, in themselves, insupportable, but they helped break down many dogmatic barricades. And Buffon was also effective in destroying the concept that the earth was as young as people had believed. Lyell had other debts, too. It is unlikely that his accomplishments would have been possible without the pioneering in geology done by Hutton, Playfair, and Smith. They had established a foundation on which he could build.

Thus, today's scientists, working in natural history or fields that are related to it, owe much to the studies of the great naturalists. The geologist exploring for oil or examining the structure of the Antarctic continent can trace the lineage of his thinking back to Linnaeus. The paleontologist looking for dinosaurs in the American West and the anthropologist searching for human remains in Africa are intellectual descendants of Darwin, Wallace, and Cuvier. Today Humboldt would be amazed to pick up the newspaper and read the daily weather report based on information provided by a network of stations such as even he had never imagined when he was making his recommendations to the Russian government. He would be equally startled to discover that a dollar sent to the Naval Oceanographic Office in Washington would promptly bring him by mail a world map showing the magnetic inclination for the year. This is a modern outcome of the readings that he took in the lonely windswept Andes, and he would be pleased with this development of his original ideas and methods. Because of his long life, he, almost more than any of the others, saw his ideas and his innovations accepted and then become outmoded, as knowledge moved ahead, and he recognized that intellectual obsolescence is the inevitable fate of the scientist and the price of scientific progress.

Of one thing, mankind can be sure. If the great naturalists of the past were alive today, they would be pleased that man is still pondering the problems they pondered, and they would not be disturbed that many of the ideas they advanced have since been rejected or refined, sometimes almost beyond recognition. They understood that change in ideas is as much a part of learning as evolutionary change is a part of life. But as they looked at the equipment and resources used today in studying their fields, they would warn us against complacency, against priding ourselves that we are anywhere near the end—the final road to ultimate understanding.

It was Huxley, the battler for truth, who said, "Each . . . answer to the great question, invariably asserted by the followers of its propounder, if not by himself, to be complete and final, remains in high authority and esteem, it may be for one century, or it may be for twenty; but, as invariably, Time proves each reply to have been only a mere approximation of the truth—tolerable chiefly on account of the ignorance of those by whom it was accepted, and wholly intolerable when tested by the larger knowledge of their successors." The only flaw in his statement is the period during which an answer may be held in high esteem. Even a single century is often too long.

II

The great naturalists concentrated on one subject, natural history, but they were representative of all significant thinkers—men who deal with broad concepts and seek simplicity, order, and truth. In this, they were like great musicians, artists, chemists, mathematicians, philosophers, or any other group who dedicate their minds and lives to similar ends.

Among themselves, they might differ bitterly, as the fierce, uncompromising struggle between Cuvier and Lamarck attests. On the other hand, wide similarities existed in their attitudes toward the major scientific problems of their times. This accounts for the surprising number of coincidental discoveries they made and explains why Darwin and Wallace arrived at the same conclusions independently and why three researchers discovered Mendel's paper almost simultaneously. As human learning moves forward, the stage becomes set for the next major step, and one or two of the brilliant minds of the day see and seize the opportunity. Darwin and Wallace lived in a time when the concept of evolution was slowly simmering in men's minds. Although no one had arrived at an acceptable theory, many people were discussing the possibility. Much of the basic work had been done, and the hour had struck when someone would put the pieces together. Darwin and Wallace both did it, using the same fundamental materials. If they had not, someone else would have eventually. This demonstrates the sweeping power of human thinking, but it does not detract from the importance of the leaders. They still deserve the credit and the fame given them.

Huxley described these men well, when he said that "most of us, shrinking from the difficulties and dangers which beset the seekers after original answers to these riddles, are contented to ignore them altogether, or to smother the investigating spirit under the featherbed of respected and respectable tradition. But, in every age, one or two restless spirits, blessed with the constructive genius, which can only build on a secure foundation, or cursed with the mere spirit of skepticism, are unable to follow in the well-worn and comfortable track of their forefathers and contemporaries, and unmindful of thorns and stumbling-blocks, strike out into paths of their own. The skeptics end in the infidelity which asserts the problem to be insoluble, or in the atheism which denies the existence of any orderly progress and governance of things: the men of genius propound solutions which grow into systems of Theology or of Philosophy, or veiled in musical language which suggests more than it asserts, take the shape of the Poetry of an epoch."

As Huxley said, it is not merely sufficient to ask the question or to doubt the dogma. The question must be asked with "that constructive genius, which can only build on a secure foundation." Skepticism alone, although refusing the comfort of tradition, degenerates into a sneering cynicism that defeats its purpose. Unable to place faith in accepted beliefs, it ends in believing in nothing, and its questioning turns into unconstructive nihilism. Such minds can usefully serve the society in which they exist by acting as spurs and goads, but they are not the minds that serve it best. Voltaire was a skeptic who did much good by raising doubts in a complacent, ingrown society. But it was Buffon, equally a questioner but not a skeptic, who recognized the importance of fossils. Unwilling to sneer, he could not sarcastically dismiss them as the leavings of pilgrims.

A quality that marked him—and marked all the great naturalists—was enthusiasm. Their private lives might be touched by tragedy—and often were. Buffon failed to obtain the intendancy for his beloved son and, helpless, watched him being cuckolded; Linnaeus in his later years was obsessed by a morbid philosophy; Darwin suffered continually from ill health; and Lamarck was haunted by poverty and the dislike of his students. Yet none of them was an unenthusiastic person as far as his field of study was concerned. They had boundless faith in the solvability of a problem and the importance of finding the answer. This is a characteristic that set them apart from the sometimes equally brilliant, but still lesser, minds of their contemporary skeptics. If they destroyed, they destroyed only to rebuild, and it was the rebuilding that truly concerned them.

As for the "thorns and stumbling-blocks" that impeded them, these came from two sources—one inside themselves; one outside. As for the first, no man can start fresh at every turning, strike down everything that has been learned before him, reexamine it for himself, and test its postulates. Time alone prevents him from doing this, because he cannot spend his life recapitulating all previous knowledge. But neither, if he is to be a significant thinker, can he afford to accept at its face value all that his own time tells him. The point at which he draws the line between acceptance and rejection is fine, and its exact degree may determine his ultimate greatness. After his voyage aboard the *Beagle,* Darwin could no longer reconcile himself to any form of special creation, although only a short time before he had hesitated about entering the church for fear its dogma might contradict the Bible. The principal alternative that his age offered him was some type of Lamarckism, but he could not totally accept that either.

After studying the distribution of fossils and species, he could, however, believe in at least one aspect of Lamarckism, the factor of progressive development. Thus, he freed himself intellectually to develop his own theory, using the best of his era's knowledge and discarding the worst.

Agassiz, on the other hand, drew the line at the wrong place and, therefore, just missed the greatness that he would otherwise have earned. His Ice Age was highly significant—Lyell's reaction testifies to the impact that it had—and his work in paleontology was outstanding. But he could not extricate himself from the teachings of Cuvier. Enthusiastic, brilliant, and an important influence for the good in American science, he fell short of being what he might have been by accepting what he should have rejected. He had, to an unfortunate degree, drawn the line in the wrong place.

Lyell narrowly escaped this fate. Sufficiently open-minded to encourage Darwin to publish his theory so it could be discussed, he hesitated to accept it and destroy thereby his long-cherished ideas. (In this, he was almost like Adam Sedgwick when he told Darwin that some human being must have thrown the tropical shell into the gravel pit at Shrewsbury. If it had been "really embedded there," he had commented, "it would be the greatest misfortune to geology, as it would overthrow all that we know about the superficial deposits of the Midland Counties.") But although Lyell took his own time—too much time, Darwin thought—he was finally ready to reject the old in favor of the new. As a consequence, his *Principles* continued to be up-to-date, and he retained the greatness that he had deservedly won.

The outside factor creating the "thorns and stumbling-blocks" was the imposition of blind authority, whether in the form of the Bishop of Oxford, the opinions of a professor like Sedgwick, the dogma of a group of theologians, the ideas held by the mass of the influential public, or the erroneous statements made by the possessors of massive accumulations of data. In all cases, the essential argument was the same: By virtue of his position, the holder of authority must be right. This argument was old—and fallacious—in the days of the great naturalists, and it is older—but no less fallacious—today. Yet it is still used frequently. As fields of knowledge, whether in science, government, or anything else, tend to become more technical and to require more information, they also tend to separate and become exclusive. Then the members who are higher up in the hierarchy are tempted to impose their authority on those farther down, and together they are likely to present a united front against the outsider. Men would do well to remember what Wallace said so simply: "I had . . . very early in life noticed, that men with immense *knowledge* did not always know how to draw just conclusions from that knowledge, and that I myself was quite able to detect their errors of reasoning." Without this ability to distinguish between knowledge and conclusions, Wallace might never have attained his remarkable results. He, like the other great naturalists, refused to be overawed by authority in any shape. Instead, they questioned the value of authority's conclusions and let their determination of this value form the basis of their criticism.

III

Those who add to man's knowledge often do so at considerable personal cost, for as pioneers in thinking they must rebel against tradition, and the world is rarely kind to its rebels. By its nature, society yearns for stability, particularly those parts of society that wield influence. Having the least to gain by revolution and the most to lose, they instinctively react against it. Thus, the great thinkers almost always meet with strong opposition, and although the stakes at which they are burned may not be surrounded with real fagots like Bruno's, the pain may still be enormous. Even in the nineteenth century, a comparatively enlightened age, the evolutionists continued to receive letters abusing them for having overthrown the established order, and Darwin was astonished at the personal animosity of some of the reviews of the *Origin of Species*.

In a way, this is a necessary reaction. Society must protect itself from the frauds and cranks by testing both the ideas and the sincerity of the innovators. It needs this defense to prevent chaos. But in return, once their ideas and theories have proved accurate, society owes a debt to the pioneers for the ordeal they have undergone. The payment of that debt has two aspects.

First, society has a responsibility not to remain idle. It should take the new ideas and develop them further, continuing to build on the fresh material that has been offered it. In the case of the great naturalists, none of them could have any cause for complaint on this account. Enormous intellectual progress has been made in every field in which they worked, and the progress is increasing at an accelerated rate.

But society also owes its pioneers a second obligation: to make good use of what they have shown to be true. The accumulation of knowledge, as Wallace said, is not a sufficient end in itself. What matters are the conclusions drawn from the knowledge. And here the naturalists have not fared so well. As a sum of their work, they removed man from the special, unrealistic niche he had created for himself and showed that he was not an exception isolated from the web of life, but an integral part of all life. As long as he could delude himself that he was a separate case, he had—like a small child who does not know enough—an excuse for certain aspects of his behavior. Not being a normal being, he was not bound by normal rules. But this excuse no longer exists, and he knows, or at least he should know, that he has a responsibility toward all other life and toward the environment that has made his existence possible. It is this responsibility that, in large measure, man is ignoring.

Among all forms of life, he has unique advantages. He has the power of speech and, thus, an unprecedented ability to transmit ideas and to accumulate knowledge as no other animal can. His hands are more miraculous than any tool he has devised and have played a large role in his emergence from the ranks of other life. No sensitive man can look at his hands without wondering where he might have been without them. Even more important, man has his highly developed brain, the only one like it in the animal kingdom. This gives him a power that is denied every other species. Other animals can remember the past and learn from it, but none like man. Other animals can look into the future, but none like man. Other animals can feel emotions such as love, hate, greed, and generosity, but none can translate these into actions in the way man can or control and channel them into constructive or destructive uses. He has been given special powers, but does he employ them wisely?

The good he accomplishes is apparent—his hospitals, his charities, his concern for the sick and weary, his interest in the arts and sciences. But unfortunately, the evil looms equally large. No other animal treats its species so well; neither does any other animal treat it so badly. Even the grizzly bear, one of the fiercest of animals, does not destroy its own kind with the evident relish that man sometimes exhibits. After a battle it tends to leave the defeated alone and to permit it to retreat from the field without further injury. It does not give itself up to the frenzied aggressiveness that man often shows.

Most animals live in a degree of harmony with their environment. They may change it—and not always for the good—but none forces change on it as man does. If man does not like a mountain, he removes it. If he does not like the way a stream flows, he dams it. Constantly he models and remodels his surroundings like a sculptor working with clay, but often to much less purpose. He is the creator of many of the droughts from which he suffers. He is the spreader of many of the diseases from which he dies. He pollutes the air he breathes. He contaminates the water he drinks. With the exception of the rat, it is difficult to think of a species that is more filthy in its habits.

It would make less difference if man's capacities were more limited, but he has the ability to impose his will on other forms of life. Drunk with his immense power, he even invents nuclear weapons with which he can threaten his fellows and browbeat them into following his wishes and, in the process, risk taking the whole world with him.

At the root of this arrogance is a disdain for the teachings of the great naturalists. By removing man from the special position that he had created for himself and by placing him in the natural world where he rightly belongs, they gave him a clue to understanding, not only his past, but also his present and his future. He is different, but he is not unique, and he, too, is subject to the forces of nature. In spite of his speech, his hands, and his brains, he has been given no guarantee of survival, only an opportunity to survive. Even before Buffon, naturalists knew that life-forms can become extinct, and as more and more fossils have been uncovered, it has become apparent that there are no certain exceptions. After extinction, it is often possible to tell why the crisis occurred, but predictions are more difficult to make. Size, strength, brains—all these have not invariably provided fitness in the old sense, and man might well ponder the cockroach's long existence and its relative immunity to radioactivity.

That thought may seem degrading, but the naturalists had no intention of debasing man. They were only interested in finding the truth, and they argued that in their dispassionate answers they had uncovered greater beauty and greater mystery than were contained in the concept of an omniscient spirit, capable of doing anything. Man's desire for mysticism should be satisfied by the thought that the most skillful surgeon or the most outstanding painter, as well as the most vicious criminal, was once a single cell from which that particular human developed. If that is not sufficient, he can contemplate one of the many other miraculous aspects of the life of which he is a part. But to appreciate these miracles requires humility, and this, if man can learn to accept it, may be the greatest heritage left by the great naturalists. For once man becomes humble, once he discards the illusion that he is an exception to nature's rules, he may be able to lift himself from the fire of emotional tumult and turn into something better than he has ever known.

He arose by chance, although the word "chance" might be capitalized, and chance will always play a part. But more than any other type of living being, he has an opportunity to direct his future and control his destiny. Unlike most animals, he can chose within limits what he wants to be and how he would like to shape the earth. But to make a wise choice, he must start by realizing that his animal heritage contains some good and some evil and that each individual must decide which aspect he will cultivate in himself. To claim that brutality, whether open or disguised by a veneer of civilization, is justified by the "survival of the fittest" is to deny what man now knows about evolution. To blame our worst emotions on our animal ancestors, thus feeling justified in permitting them play, is also to deny man's better knowledge. The same evolution that gave man his animal ancestry also gave him his brains and, therefore, the means to control his emotions. And it may well be that this control is one of the dominant factors in his survival so far.

He must also reestablish his relationship with nature. That relationship is not something invented by pastoral poets. As the great naturalists have shown, it is a hard scientific fact, and there is no escaping from it. Although man can temporarily shut himself up in concrete cities and spend his days walking on asphalt streets, he cannot flee from nature. As a living being, he needs food and water no matter where he is, and he needs the products of the soil, the lakes, and the sea. Even in the city, he can be struck down or helped by other forms of life, a virus against which there is no known defense, or a mold that will be used as an antibiotic. There is also an indication that at least some people require the natural world for emotional survival. This cannot be dismissed lightly as merely the fancy of a bird watcher. It is deeply rooted in human character, and to satisfy this need may, in the long run, be more vital to the progress of the human race than the construction of skyscrapers or the building of superjets.

Man simply does not know and is not qualified to make final judgments, for his ignorance is greater than his knowledge, and his knowledge is often greater than his understanding. More goes on in the world that cannot be explained than can be. And when man attacks nature in a sledgehammer fashion, as he so often does, he could be sowing the seeds of danger to himself. Perhaps in the future some great naturalist will uncover a law that will allow man to predict the consequences of his every action. But such a possibility is remote, and meanwhile, he would do well to tread with caution. This caution should be coupled with humility, more attentiveness to the teachings of biologists and others concerned with natural history, and greater awareness that the purpose of life is, after all, life itself. If man can learn to contemplate his existence with greater admiration for its magnificent mysteries and strive to live in greater harmony, not only with his own species, but with the whole natural world, he will have justified all that has gone into his making.

IV

In the beginning, man sought knowledge of nature to improve his chances of survival. The hunter who knew the ways of the best animals ate the best food and wore the best furs. But even then, as he transcribed his impressions of nature on the walls of his caves, he must have felt there was something more significant than his day-to-day relationship with the world around him. Nothing else would account for the strange and beautiful qualities of his paintings or the time that he spent making them. As he progressed in his development, he sometimes stifled, but never completely lost, his sense of wonder and his curiosity. Aristotle studying the marine life of the Near East, Galileo looking through his telescope at the moon, Kepler plotting the paths traced by the planets, Linnaeus traveling through the wilderness of Lapland, Cuvier working at the Jardin des Plantes, Humboldt peering into the smoking mouth of a volcano, Wallace lying on his bed at Ternate thinking about the origin of the species, or Mendel growing his peas in the monastery garden, these and the others all were participants in the same great adventure—the long hunt for knowledge that may eventually lead to the better life that all men seek.

Because of the magnitude of their accomplishments, they were, of course, among the most prominent, but for each of them, there were thousands of other figures, contributing in one way or another to the sum of man's knowledge. And the search has not been limited to those devoting their whole lives to it, as Humboldt and Darwin and Lamarck did. It is a hunt that has engaged the attention of every man at some time or other, whether he has only paused for a moment at night to gaze at the immensity of the heavens above him or stopped by the roadside to pick a daisy. As Huxley said, "The question of questions for mankind—the problem which underlies all others, and is more deeply interesting than any other—is the ascertainment of the place which Man occupies in nature and of his relations to the universe of things. Whence our race has come; what are the limits of our power over nature, and of nature's power over us; to what goal are we tending; are the problems which present themselves anew and with undiminished interest to every man born into the world."

The quest of the great naturalists was not only their quest, but ours. We are, each of us, a participant in the long voyage from the unknown to the less unknown, seekers for the answer to "the question of questions" for mankind. Where the search will lead, we cannot predict. Whether we will be successful, we cannot be sure. Only one thing seems certain. The ultimate truth will probably always elude us, no matter how long the human race endures, for truth, like the universe, appears to be infinite and has no boundaries. Therefore, the quest of the naturalists, just like the personal quest of each of us, will prove endless. It is the knowledge of this endlessness that demonstrates the courage of man and the dignity of his spirit.

Acknowledgments

It is unfortunate that the acknowledgments in a book usually have to contain expressions of appreciation that have no personal meaning, because they thus often go unread, and the author has no means of publicly thanking those to whom his personal debt is great.

In this case, my good friend, James Ross, with whom I have often discussed some of the topics in this book, and the Reinhold Publishing Corporation have given me permission to quote liberally from Richard A. Pimentel's *Natural History* in both the foreword, "About This Book," and in the appendices. William Targ of G. P. Putnam's Sons has given me the benefit of his gentle, but perceptive, judgment, and Theron Raines has as usual provided his encouragement and also his criticism. Bern Dibner, who among the other positions he holds, is director of the Burndy Library, Norwalk, Connecticut, has, with his usual graciousness, given me free access to the magnificent collection of scientific works under his supervision. I have drawn heavily on the Burndy Library for the illustrations in this book and have received much assistance, always generously given, from the librarian, Mrs. Adele Matthysse.

The patience of Mrs. C. R. Horton, Jr., in reading the rough drafts of my text seems to be as unending as the "quest" itself, and to C. R. Horton, Jr., I owe an equal debt, although of a slightly different nature.

The staffs of the Yale University Library, the Westport Public Library, and the Pequot Library, Southport, Connecticut, have, as they always have, treated me with the utmost consideration. It is impossible to thank them individually, but I would be lost without them.

The following have given me permission to quote from letters in their Audubon collections: the Library Company of Philadelphia, the Historical Society of Pennsylvania, and the American Philosophical Society. All of them are located in Philadelphia. The New York Historical Society, New York City, and the Princeton University Library have permitted me to reproduce photographs in their possession.

I am grateful, too, to the members of my family: Lucy D. S. Adams, Harriet and Jacques Transue, George W. Adams II, and Elliott D. S. Adams. Each in his own way has made substantial contributions to this book.

Notes

In a book of this scope, detailed notes would be burdensome, because they would take many pages and probably be of little interest to the general reader. So I have limited myself to fairly brief comments on each chapter. These include the principal sources I have used, specific references where I have made direct quotations, particular problems or matters of interest, and occasionally suggestions for further reading. After consideration, I thought that this format might be the most helpful I could adopt.

Except where otherwise indicated, the translations are my own.

Chapters One and Two

During the period with which these chapters deal, it is particularly difficult to distinguish between naturalists and other thinkers, for the sciences were not as specialized as they later became. That wonderful man Aristotle could deal with literary criticism, philosophy, the physics of the cosmos, and biology all at practically the same time. Of course, he was unusual for his own or any other day, but this interdependency of thought was characteristic of an earlier era. Religion, philosophy, art, and science were much more closely related than now. What modern artist, for example, could contribute to the knowledge of human anatomy as Leonardo did; what philosopher could change our attitudes toward the physical universe as Bruno succeeded in doing? Furthermore, the sciences themselves were so little developed that a discovery in one also advanced the others. The field biologist today does not think of himself as a mathematician, but he would find his field trips greatly complicated by the absence of the decimal system. An ecologist, studying the effects of human intrusion on an area, is greatly assisted by knowing that man is related to all life, not a separate creation capable of operating under completely separate rules. In these chapters, therefore, I have used an especially broad definition of the word "naturalist." (In choosing the people of Lascaux specifically to include in this category as representatives of prehistoric man, I was guided by the beauty and fame of their paintings.)

The reader who wishes to pursue further the subjects covered in these pages will find in the bibliography a number of general histories of science, all of which have proved valuable to me. Some of the more detailed works that may be of special interest are: the description of the Lascaux caves that can be found in Bataille's book, the interesting treatment of Aristotle's philosophy and science contained in Randall's; the description of Pliny's death in the moving letter written by his son to the historian Tacitus; Drake's book on Galileo's writings; Armitage's study of Copernicus, which is also a popular, but rather detailed, book on early astronomy; Dobell's book on Antony van Leeuwenhoek (Dobell explains that his name probably derives from Leeuwenpoort, or Liongate, the part of Delft where Leeuwenhoek's family resided); and Koestler's highly readable and philosophic study of Kepler. Those wishing to study the conflict between church and science, will find that White's *A History of the Warfare of Science with Theology in Christendom* remains a classic.

When the reader finishes these chapters, I hope that he will be aware that an uncritical attitude toward previously conceived assumptions—especially if those assumptions are backed by authority—presents the greatest impediment to human thinking. But I hope that he will not believe that today we have come far from the time when Galileo could be imprisoned for writing down what he saw rather than what he read in the authorities or the era when anatomists lectured from Galen while the dissectors at their sides were revealing completely contrary facts. Science has come some distance, yes, but perhaps not as far as we may think, and in other fields, we are even more unquestioning. In February, 1950, to cite just a single example from politics, an American Senator stood before an audience in Wheeling, West Virginia, and stated categorically that the paper he held in his hand contained a list of known Communists in the State Department. Although, in fact, no such list existed, he threw the country into a panic. Yet only a few years before, the Communists, with just as little evidence to support the assumption, were widely regarded as among America's best friends, "the heroes of Stalingrad" whom it was dangerous to criticize either publicly or within the government.

We often have the same delusions about business. Authority has told us that as an institution, business is hardheaded and practical, so we rarely question the efficiency of the business lunch or the pointless conference, both of which consume hours of time for little purpose. Or take the phrase "free enterprise," which is a shibboleth of our society. It is interesting to note how many of its loudest proponents end up, in practice, indicted under the anti-trust laws.

I cite these examples, neither in criticism nor intending the list to be complete, but merely as a reminder that we still live in an age of myths and acceptance of authority. So I hope the reader will regard with humility the obstructionists and uncritical thinkers that appear in these chapters and elsewhere in this book and will recall that they are human beings and that perhaps he himself, like me, is one of them without knowing it, at least part of the time and about certain subjects.

Any book has to have a point of view, and this one looks at mankind's progress through the eyes of the naturalists, most of whom are scientists. Therefore, its point of view is largely scientific and occasionally somewhat harsh on the church, but I hope that the reader will not forget the many benefits the church, both Protestant and Catholic, has given to the society in which we live. It may, at its worst, have delayed the advance of science. At its best, it encouraged art, preserved knowledge, and created faith in the dignity of the human individual.

Chapter Three

The life of Linnaeus exemplifies a problem that is common in dealing with many scientists: Their work may be significant, but it may also go out of date. Modern biologists still retain Linnaeus' binary nomenclature, but they do not employ his method of classification. So in the text I have attempted not to discuss it in detail but merely to indicate its importance and the role of Linnaeus in developing this branch of the natural sciences. Those who are interested in knowing more about the modern method of classification may wish to refer to Appendix B, which explains how plant and animal life is classified today.

One of the principal sources of information about Linnaeus' early life is the autobiographical sketches that he himself wrote. These sometimes contradict one another, but taken together, they provide an accurate picture of his struggle for recognition. Fries examined them closely and also searched all the records that he could find in Sweden. The results of his studies can be read in English in Jackson's book. Stoever's book, which has also been translated into English, provides certain information that does not appear in Fries. Hagberg's book, which has also been translated into English, gives a short and interesting evaluation of Linnaeus for those who wish to pursue the subject further.

The letters quoted are as follows: Smith, Vol. II, pp. 333–34, 96–97, 91–92, 204–05, 231–35, 229, 335–36, and 346. The letter of James Edward Smith, is in Stoever, pp. 311–12 and 314. The quotations from Linnaeus' Lapland journal are taken from Smith's translation.

Chapter Four

There are numerous books about Buffon that contain biographical sketches and criticisms of his work, but one of the most interesting is the two-volume *Correspondence inédite de Buffon,* annotated by Henri Nadault de Buffon. The letters reveal Buffon's personality at firsthand, but of even greater consequence are the notes, which are voluminous and constitute more than half of the book. In them, the editor has presented much contemporary material, as well as many insights into Buffon's life that are not available in more formal works.

Curiously enough, one of the most detailed accounts of Buffon's enlargement of the Jardin du Roi was written, not by a Frenchman, but an American, William Franklin Falls, who prepared *Buffon et l'agrandissement du Jardin du Roi à Paris* as a doctoral thesis. It also contains a detailed description of the Jardin du Roi at the time Buffon became intendant.

The quotations taken from Buffon's books may be found in the appropriate sections of any of the many editions of his complete works. These also contain his discourse to the French Academy and his exchange of correspondence with the faculty of theology.

The letters quoted are from Henri Nadault de Buffon as follows: Vol. I: 6–7, 12, 31–32, 41–42, 47, 48–49, 56, 75, 98–99, 105, 114, 121–22, 174; Vol. II: pp. 71 and 224.

The description of the relationship between Buffon and Joseph is taken from a manuscript by Humbert-Bazile and reproduced in *Correspondance inédite,* Vol. I, p. 222.

Chapter Five

The biographer of Lamarck faces a particularly difficult problem, because, like a ship passing through water, in his personal life Lamarck left few traces behind him. His scientific works still stand, of course, and his *Zoological Philosophy* is still read today. (I was interested in learning that the copy in the Yale Medical School Library is frequently consulted by students.) But not much is known about him as a person.

During his lifetime he was completely occupied with his work. He seems to have had few friends and to have written few letters, and even his contemporaries, including Buffon, who knew everything about everybody, apparently never pierced the veil that separated his professional existence from his private life. At his death, no one was greatly concerned about collecting any information that might have remained. Cuvier obtained some from Lamarck's son, and a few others jotted down personal reminiscences, but that was the extent of it.

Later, when he became famous, the circumstances were unfortunate. Evolution was accepted by the principal scientists, but Darwin's writings, which made it acceptable, also discredited Lamarck's theory. Those who resurrected him, therefore, did so primarily in an attempt to refute Darwin, and this was not a sufficiently disinterested motive to lead them into studying his personal life.

Curiously enough, it was an American, Packard, who wrote one of the first comprehensive works on Lamarck, and a Frenchman, Landrieu, was so moved by it that he decided to translate it into Lamarck's native tongue. In the process he discovered several additional sources of information that had not been available to Packard, and he ended by preparing an original study, which was published by the Zoological Society of France. This has provided me with much of the information in this chapter.

Landrieu, of course, checked as many facts as he could, but it was impossible to verify completely certain of the stories about Lamarck. For example, the description of his action on the battlefield rests solely on the authority of what his son told Cuvier. There seems to be no other substantiating evidence, although Landrieu was able to verify Lamarck's military service and rank. Even greater obscurity surrounds his decision to leave the army. His son told Cuvier about an accident, indicating that it occurred during some horseplay, but Landrieu discovered that about the same time several officers were under investigation for trying to force another officer to leave the regiment. In view of Lamarck's apparent unpopularity later in life, it is logical to assume that the two incidents were related.

Landrieu was also able to obtain other original information including the texts of his frantic appeals to the government, but the total still remains scanty.

In addition to relying heavily on Landrieu, I have also drawn on Buffon's correspondence for a description of Lamarck's tour through Europe (see *Correspondance inédite,* Vol. II, pp. 365–68), even though this correspondence makes hardly any mention of Lamarck. The quotations from Lamarck are from his published works as indicated in the text.

Chapter Six

There are a number of books about and eulogies of Georges Cuvier. Viénot's biography contains most of the pertinent facts and also casts additional light on Cuvier's tortured decision to support the proposed change in the election law. Coleman's book contains a close analysis of his work as a scientist.

The quotation describing the elephant fossils comes from the essay on that subject in *Recherches sur les ossements fossils de quadrupèdes* and the quotations describing his basic attitudes toward fossils and their reconstruction and importance occur in *Discours sur les révolutions de la surface du globe.* Cuvier's thoughts on the correlation of the parts appear in the introduction to *Animal Kingdom.* For this and other quotations from the same work, I have relied on the English edition published in 1863.

Audubon's description of his meetings with Cuvier are contained in his journal under the dates September 4, 1827, September 15, 1827, and September 22, 1827. Cuvier's extraordinary working habits are also described by Lyell in his *Life, Letters and Journals.* Like many others, Lyell was curious to know how one man could accomplish so much.

Chapter Seven

In choosing representative collectors for this chapter, I was faced with the same problem that has appeared elsewhere: There were many worthy candidates and not sufficient room for them all. Audubon's name is so familiar in both Europe and the United States, however, that I thought he should be included, particularly because he is an interesting person in himself and also because he provides a striking example of a man who makes a significant contribution to natural history without having had formal scientific training. Having made this choice, I believed that I could not ignore Alexander Wilson, who was truly the pioneer in American ornithology and whose character is so in contrast with Audubon's.

Those interested in the development of science in the United States will find Jaffe's book nontechnical and informative, and the extension of European science to other parts of the world is well described by Basalla, whose interesting and provocative article holds that European science in a newly opened country generally passes through three phases. In phase one, the new land provides material for European science to use; in phase two, it develops a colonial science of its own but is still dependent on Europe; in phase three, it creates its indigenous scientific tradition. Readers of Basalla's article will recognize that Wilson and Audubon are essentially "phase one" scientists.

The role of the gifted, but self-trained, naturalists is a curious and important one, and they have made many significant contributions. There are several reasons for this, one of which is the character of natural history. So much of it depends on direct observation of nature at work. This takes time, a sharp eye, experience, and knowledge, but it may not require either technical training or complex equipment. An amateur physicist, for example, is highly unlikely to discover a new form of matter, but an amateur ornithologist may uncover a fact about bird behavior or even a new species. It is not that one form of science is higher than the other; it is merely that they are different. Of course, in Basalla's phase one, the chances of the amateur naturalist's obtaining the eminence of Wilson and Audubon are much greater than at a later time. If Audubon were alive today and tried to repeat his work against the background of modern knowledge, he would likely be considered an artist, rather than a serious ornithologist worthy of membership in the leading scientific societies.

In passing, I should comment briefly on the historic quarrel between Wilson's and Audubon's followers, a quarrel which was made much of during Audubon's lifetime and even afterward. It sprang up after Wilson's death, when Audubon found himself in direct competition with the dead man's reputation, and it was fanned by Ord, who had reason to dislike Audubon personally and to envy him professionally. Little firsthand information is available about the meeting of Wilson and Audubon at Louisville in 1810, but there is no reason to believe that it was anything but friendly and casual. The disputes that followed were not between Wilson and Audubon, but between Wilson's adherents and Audubon, and it was one of those unpleasant events to which too much importance has been attached.

Although he was a dramatic and appealing figure, Wilson has been rather neglected by American biographers, but those who wish to know more about him will enjoy reading Cantwell's book, as well as his own writings.

Audubon has received better treatment, and a number of books have been written about him. One of these, published by G. P. Putnam's Sons, is my own.

The material quoted in this chapter can be found in the following sources. The letters of Wilson, which appear in Volume I of his *Memoirs and Remains,* are as follows: pp. 49, 55, 61, 80, 81, 91, 101, 102, 103, 104, 106, 144, 152, 178, 224, 234, and 235.

Audubon's description of his meeting with Wilson appears in the episode "Louisville" in the "Ornithological Biographies" included in *Audubon and His Journals.* Wilson's description of the ivory-billed woodpecker appears in the description of that bird contained in *American Ornithology.*

Other quotations are as follows: a letter by Audubon dated August 26, 1832, in the possession of the Historical Society of Pennsylvania; Audubon's "Labrador Journal," *Aububon and His Journals,* Vol. I, pp. 425–26; Lucy Audubon's quotation from p. 436 of her book, and Victor's description of his father's death is contained in a letter dated February 3, 1851, in the possession of the Library Company of Philadelphia.

Chapter Eight

Although Humboldt could be a heavy and discursive writer, he also had a clear eye for the world around him and a sensitivity toward what he saw. As a consequence, some of his works not only provide an excellent picture of his life, but also make good reading in themselves—provided the reader is willing to skip. His narrative of his travels on the Orinoco (again with skipping) is a remarkably fascinating travel book, delightful and easy for pages, although loaded in others with technical observations of no interest to the general reader. Aside from his own formal works, his letters to Varnhagen von Esne—and Esne's accounts of their conversations—provide additional insight. These appear in the *Letters of Alexander Humboldt.*

Among the several biographies about Humboldt, I found Kellner's especially helpful in its clear evaluation of his scientific work. Kellner also makes an effective point about Humboldt's influence as a cartographer: He marked the position of the village of Esmeralda just above the juncture of the Casiquiare and the Orinoco and thus placed it on the maps of Venezuela. It remains there even today, although the village itself has apparently disappeared long since. Such was the power of Humboldt!

Those readers who would like to pursue further the question of terrestrial magnetism—but do it in layman's language—will find an excellent summary in Chapter VII of the mariner's bible, Bowditch's *Practical Navigator.* (At least this is true of the edition of 1966; the editions sometimes vary radically.) The same book also contains an interesting description of the work of the Board of Longitude, founded in 1707 after 2,000 men were lost when a British squadron ran aground, because it did not know its position. The search for an accurate means of telling time, which was the key to finding longitude, was a long one and consumed the entire lifetime of John Harrison, the British chronometer maker who finally received the board's reward in his eightieth year.

In quoting from Humboldt's *Personal Narrative,* I have used the translation by Williams. The quotations in this chapter are as follows:

Personal Narrative: Vol. I, pp. 43, 110–11, 168, and 171; Vol. II, pp. 22–23; Vol. III, pp. 179–80, 307–8, 311, and 316; Vol. IV, pp. 143–44, 320–21, 348–50, 355, 436–37, 457–58, and 534–37; Vol. V, Part I, pp. 289–91 and 441–42; Vol. V, Part II, pp. 504–5 and 695; Vol. VII, pp. 263–71 and 464. *Vues des Cordillères*: Vol. I, pp. 74–75 and 80–81. *Essai politique*: Vol. I, p. 1. *Personal Narrative*: Vol. VII, p. 287; Vol. I, pp. x–xi, xi–xiv, and xix.

Chapter Nine

Unlike many of the other naturalists, Lyell led a relatively quiet life, both physically and emotionally. Although he traveled, he traveled comfortably—except perhaps in Sicily—for he was able to afford the comforts denied others. He never had to worry much about his finances. Born into a well-to-do family, his future was assured with the rapid success of the *Principles.* Because of his devotion to his work, he avoided controversies and politics, knowing they would distract him from the geology he loved so much. Except for the knowledge that science was advancing faster than his thinking and for the death of his wife, his life was not touched by tragedy. Consequently, lacking the romantic appeal of other naturalists, he has not fared well at the hands of biographers, who generally prefer more dramatic material. His *Life, Letters and Journals,* however, reveals a gentle, cultivated man with a quiet sense of humor and extreme dedication to his work. The two volumes are well worth the reading. His second book on America is also delightful, not only for its picture of this country in 1845, but also for what it shows of Lyell. Because he separated his geologic observations from his personal reminiscences, it makes somewhat better general reading than his first travel book.

The quotations in this chapter are as follows: *Life, Letters and Journals*: Vol. I, pp. 8–9, 11–12, 16–17, 21, 61, 68–69, 125, 128, 146, 139, 168–69, 170–71, 189–90, 199–200, 213, 217–18, 226–27, 231, 256, 260–61, 269–70, and 311–12. *Elements of Geology*: p. iv. *Life, Letters and Journals*: Vol. I, pp. 316–17, 388, 395–96, and 396–97. *Travels in North America*: Vol. I, pp. 21–22, 23, 27–28, 56–57, 76, and 185; Vol. II, pp. 233–34. *Life, Letters and Journals*: Vol. II, pp. 188, 243, and 316–17. *Antiquity of Man*: pp. 391–95. *Life, Letters and Journals*: Vol. II, pp. 325, 329, 361–62, 363–64, 369, 387, 436–37, 451, and 452.

Chapter Ten

Agassiz's obstinate refusal to give Darwin's ideas the consideration they merited contrasts sharply with Lyell's attitude. Lyell was just as reluctant to overturn his long cherished beliefs, but he was willing to examine the evidence critically, and once having done so, he became convinced. Agassiz, on the other hand, was like so many thinkers in history, even great ones. He was enslaved by his prejudices and his deep respect for the authority of Cuvier. If he could have brought himself to reappraise what he had always considered true, he would have occupied a far more important place in the history of science. For with his brilliant mind and vast knowledge, he would have certainly become one of the first—and ablest—of Darwin's supporters. Unfortunately, he failed to do so, and he committed this error in the comparatively radical environment of the United States. In England, at least during his lifetime, he would have found more of the conservative scientists who tended to share his views.

Much of Agassiz's delightful character shows through in Elizabeth Cary Agassiz's biography of him and in the biography about her written by Lucy Allen Paton. Both books, of course, are one-sided. Lurie's biography provides a good picture of the man, handling impartially his faults and his virtues. A representative selection of Agassiz's writings is included in the book by Davenport, who has attempted to show the man and his style through his work.

The quotations in this chapter are as follows: Elizabeth Cary Agassiz: Vol. I, pp. 146–47, 147–48, 23, 32, 93–94, 63–64, 65, 68, 69–70, 137–38, 139–40, 165–66, 171–74, 180–81, and 185. Agassiz's *Address on Humboldt*: pp. 43–47. Elizabeth Cary Agassiz: Vol. I, pp. 220–21, 383–84, 389–94, 310–11, and 400; Vol. II, pp. 431, 435–36, 514–15, 535, 526–27, and 553–54. Agassiz's

Structure of Animal Life: pp. 1–7. Elizabeth Cary Agassiz: Vol. II, p. 635. Agassiz's *Address on Humboldt*: p. 57. Elizabeth Cary Agassiz: Vol. II, pp. 759, 762–63, and 780–81. Gray, *Louis Agassiz*: p. 44.

Chapter Eleven

Darwin was a fascinating person, not only for what he achieved, but for what he was—kind, generous, and hardworking. The literature on him is, of course, extensive, but the reader might be especially interested in looking at the books by Gertrude Himmelfarb, Loren Eisley, or Sir Gavin De Beer that are listed in the bibliography. His own writings, such as his autobiography and his account of the *Beagle*'s voyage, are both interesting and self-revealing.

The quotations in this chapter are as follows: Darwin, *Autobiography*: pp. 9, 9, 9, 15, 18, 18, 25, 26, 27, and 27–28. Darwin, *Voyage of the Beagle*: pp. 6, 24–25, 205, 206, and 211–12. Darwin, *Autobiography*: pp. 29–30. Darwin, *Voyage*: pp. 218, 223, 227, 141, 229, 230, 260, 260–61, 283, 303, 306, 311, 318–19, 331, 375, 378–79, 381, 384, 385, 394, 394, 411, 415, 420, 429, 444–45, and 502–3. Darwin, *Autobiography*: pp. 32–33, 42, 42–43, 33–34, 160, and 43.

Chapter Twelve

Certainly Alfred Wallace was one of the most unusual of scientists, not only for the way he arrived at his great discovery, but for the almost unbelievable manner in which he gave the major credit to Darwin. He always acknowledged that Darwin had assembled far more facts to support his theory and had thought it out more thoroughly. If Darwin is generally remembered as the discoverer of evolution and Wallace too often forgotten, Wallace himself was largely the cause. So great was his modesty, he even wrote a book entitled *Darwinism*.

The seafaring reader will immediately realize, as Wallace himself learned later, that the captain of the *Helen* fought the fire in the wrong way. By opening the hatches, he ventilated it, whereas he should have tried to smother it. Because the balsam was subject to spontaneous combustion, the kegs containing it were usually packed in wet sand. The captain was unaware of this, and when some kegs were brought to the ship at the last moment and no sand was available, he placed them in a bedding of rice chaff. The seafaring reader may also like to know that the *Jordeson*, which they boarded so hopefully in mid-Atlantic, turned out to be in terrible condition and nearly sank with them during a vicious storm in the English Channel. At one point the captain of the *Helen* remarked to Wallace, "We were not very safe in our two small boats, but I had rather be back in them where we were picked up than in this rotten old tub."

The works that a reader might wish to look at, if he wants to learn more about this extraordinary man, would include his own two travel books, *A Narrative of Travels on the Amazon and Rio Negro* and *The Malay Archipelago*, as well as his autobiography, *My Life*. Marchant's biography contains many additional documents referring to him, and Wilma George's looks at him with the perspective of a modern biologist.

The quotations in this chapter are as follows: Wallace, *My Life*: Vol. I, p. 136. Bates: pp. 18–19, 31, and 34. Wallace, *Travels*: p. 3. Bates: p. 7. Wallace, *Travels*: pp. 26, 28, 31, 33–34, and 36. Bates: p. 66. Wallace, *Travels*: pp. 42–43, 99, 110, 141, 144, 172–73, 182, 226, 236, 250, 259, 273, 274, 275, and 278. Wallace, *Malay*: pp. 18, 31, 32, 33, 35, 37, 116, 122–23, 131, 162, 170–71, 317, 369, and 228. Wallace, *My Life*: Vol. I: pp. 360–61 and 362.

Chapter Thirteen

The notes for the chapters in which Darwin and Wallace were first discussed contain some of the references that anyone wanting to know more about these two outstanding men might wish to read. A good conception of Huxley's remarkable character can be gained from his *Collected Essays* and from the *Life and Letters of Thomas Huxley,* by his son, Leonard Huxley. His letters to Darwin, contained in Darwin's *Autobiography,* are also revealing.

Unfortunately no verbatim report of the Oxford meeting was kept, and Huxley, of course, spoke without a prepared text or even notes. In reconstructing the meeting, I have relied on the reports assembled by him and by Darwin. For Huxley's reply to the bishop, I have used the account that he said presented the words most accurately.

A whole library could be built around the subject of evolution and the struggle for its acceptance. *The Mechanism of Evolution* by Dowdeswell is clear, concise, and relatively untechnical, and Eiseley's book *Darwin's Century* describes the battles of the evolutionists in an interesting fashion. Because of the overwhelming importance of the *Origin of Species,* we tend to forget Darwin's other scientific work. Much of it is described in *Darwin's Biological Work,* edited by Bell. The texts of Darwin's and Wallace's papers are reproduced in *Evolution by Natural Selection,* printed by the Cambridge University Press. The drama of the situation makes them fascinating reading even today.

By a curious irony, while I was working on this chapter, I caught a brief radio report that a teacher was suing in one of our states for the right to teach evolution in the public schools. Perhaps we are not as advanced as we think we are, and there are more Samuel Wilberforces in our current world than we believe. As for that gentleman, it is only fair to add that he entertained many liberal political ideas for his day and that he apparently harbored no grudge for his defeat at Huxley's hands. Huxley later wrote that "in justice to the Bishop, I am bound to say he bore no malice, but was always courtesy itself when we occasionally met in after years."

The quotations in this chapter are as follows: Darwin, *Autobiography*: pp. 196, 197–98, 198, 200, 201–2, 202–3, and 205. Wallace, *Malay*: p. 390. Wallace, *My Life,* Vol. I: pp. 364–65. Huxley, *Life and Letters,* Vol. I: pp. 5, 16–17, 22, 25, 25–26, 7–8, 28, 34, 37, 42, 48, 49, 62, 65, 108–9, 116, 139, and 162. Darwin, *Autobiography*: pp. 209, 218, 223, 224, 229, 231, 244, 249, 241–42, 253–54, 251, 252, 253, and 258. Wallace, *My Life,* Vol. II: pp. 39–40. Darwin, *Autobiography*: pp. 260, 269, 275, 282, and 289. Huxley, *Life and Letters,* Vol. I: pp. 269–70 and 332–33. Wallace, *My Life,* Vol. II: pp. 378, 379, and 380. Darwin, *Autobiography*: p. 349. Huxley, *Life and Letters,* Vol. II: pp. 395, 401, 409–10, and 430. Wallace, *Island Life*: p. 8. Wallace,

My Life, Vol. II: pp. 109 and 193. Wallace, *Darwinism*: p. v. Marchant, Vol. I: pp. 113, 249, and 255.

Chapter Fourteen

In 1899 a high school student was reading in the public library at Brünn and came across Mendel's paper on hybridization in the proceedings of the Brünn Society for the Study of Natural History. Puzzled by the combination of mathematics and botany, he took the paper to his teacher, who was equally puzzled. Just a few years later the student, who was Hugo Iltis, learned the significance of what Mendel had done. Subsequently, he wrote Mendel's biography, and he did so in time to talk to people who had known the prelate personally. This was fortunate, because otherwise we would have had little information about the man, so few writings did he leave behind him. Even the date of his birth is not known for a certainty. The church records show one; he celebrated another, two days later.

The reader may be struck by the vast gap between the quality of Mendel's education and the significance of his discoveries and realize that this is a recurring pattern. Of the main characters in this book, only a few of them had what could be termed good educations. Linnaeus, for example, was largely self-taught. Wallace left school at an early age. Darwin later said, and probably truthfully, that his education had been worthless to him. And so the list goes with a few notable exceptions like Agassiz. This may not be a mere matter of chance. One of Huxley's contemporaries, commenting on Huxley's brilliant career, attributed his performance in part to his lack of education. No case can be made for college dropouts, but there seems to be evidence that certain independent minds do better with a necessary minimum of academic training. Apparently they are then freer to go their own ways and think their own thoughts.

For those who may have forgotten what they learned in school about Mendel's discoveries, there is a brief discussion of them in Appendix D.

The quotations in this chapter are as follows: Bateson, 1909: pp. 317–18, 318, and 367. Bateson, 1902: p. 1.

Chapter Fifteen

The subjects mentioned in this chapter cover fields so broad that it is difficult to single out specific books to recommend to the reader who wishes to pursue any of them further. Some of those that might be helpful to him are, of course, listed in the bibliography, but there are also numerous others.

Many of the great naturalists were distinguished by the ability to write clearly and movingly on their subjects. Fortunately, that tradition has not been lost. Among today's biologists and other scientists concerned with natural history, a surprising number are truly outstanding writers as well. They not only make their subjects clear, but also have the philosophic frame of mind that enables them to apply their thinking to the world generally. Their books deserve great consideration by every man who is engaged in his own personal quest, because they will provide him with guideposts.

Although a book like this deals with facts, it cannot help being influenced by the personal philosophy of the writer, and out of fairness to the reader, perhaps this should be made known. As I look at man, I am impressed by what he is compared to what he was; I am unimpressed by what he is compared to what he might be. And as I contemplate the mysteries of the past, the present, and the future, I am reminded of Huxley's words: "Of all the senseless babble I have ever had occasion to read, the demonstrations of the philosophers who undertake to tell us about the nature of God would be the worst, if they were not surpassed by the still greater absurdities of the philosophers who try to prove that there is no God."

The quotations in this chapter are as follows: Bateson, 1902: p. 1. Huxley, *Man's Place in Nature*: pp. 72 and 71–82. Darwin, *Autobiography*, p. 25. Wallace, *My Life*, Vol. II: p. 39. Huxley, *Man's Place in Nature*: p. 71. The quotation in the previous paragraph appears in Huxley, *Life and Letters*, Vol. I: p. 444.

Bibliography

The following is in no way intended to be a detailed bibliography covering the subjects treated in this book. Such a bibliography would be a book in itself. Instead, it is merely a listing of some of those used. In many instances, when I have consulted several editions of the same work, I have listed the latest as being the most easily available.

ADAMS, ALEXANDER B., *John James Audubon.* New York, G. P. Putnam, 1966.

ADAMS, FRANK DAWSON, *The Birth and Development of the Geological Sciences.* New York, Dover Publications, 1954.

AGASSIZ, ELIZABETH CARY, ed., *Louis Agassiz: His Life and Correspondence.* Boston, Houghton, Mifflin, 1886. 2 vols.

AGASSIZ, LOUIS, *Address Delivered on the Centennial Anniversary of the Birth of Alexander von Humboldt.* Boston, Boston Society of Natural History, 1869.

———, *Contributions to the Natural History of the Acalephae of North America.* Boston, Memoirs. American Academy of Arts and Sciences, 1850.

———, *Essay on Classification,* Edward Lurie, ed., Cambridge, Mass., Belknap Press of Harvard University Press, 1962.

———, *Études sur les glaciers.* Neuchâtel, Jent et Gassmann, 1840.

———, *Geological Sketches.* Boston, Ticknor and Fields, 1866.

———, *Humboldt.* New York, Humboldt Library of Popular Science Literature, No. 43, 1833.

———, *The Intelligence of Louis Agassiz: A Specimen Book of Scientific Writings,* selected, with introduction and notes, by Guy Davenport. Boston, Beacon Press, 1963.

———, *An Introduction to the Study of Natural History.* New York, Greeley and McElrath, 1847.

———, *A Journey in Brazil.* Boston, Ticknor and Fields, 1868.

———, *Lake Superior.* Boston, Gould, Kendall and Lincoln, 1850.

———, *Methods of Study in Natural History.* Boston, Ticknor and Fields, 1863.

———, *Nouvelles Études et expériences sur les glaciers actuels.* Paris, V. Masson, 1847.

———, *On the Principles of Classification in the Animal Kingdom.* Charleston, S. C., Press of Walker and James, 1850.

———, *Outlines of Comparative Physiology.* London, H. G. Bohn, 1851.

————, "The Primitive Diversity and Number of Animals in Geological Times." *American Journal of Sciences and Arts,* Series 2, Vol. XVII (May, 1854).

————, *Principles of Zoology.* Boston, Gould and Lincoln, 1851.

————, *Report on the Florida Reefs.* Cambridge, Mass. Printed for The Museum, 1880.

————, *The Structure of Animal Life.* New York, Scribner, Armstrong, 1874.

ALBERG, ALBERT, *The Floral King: A Life of Linnaeus.* London, W. H. Allen, 1888.

ANTHONY, RAOUL LOUIS FERDINAND, *Cuvier et le chaire d'anatomie comparée du Muséum National d'Histoire Naturelle.* Paris, Archives du Muséum National d'Histoire Naturelle, 1932.

ARISTOTLE, *The Basic Works of Aristotle,* edited and with an introduction by Richard McKeon, New York, Random House, 1941.

ARMITAGE, ANGUS, *The World of Copernicus.* New York, New American Library, 1961.

ARTHUR, STANLEY CLISBY, *Audubon: An Intimate Life of the American Woodsman.* New Orleans, Harmanson, 1937.

ASIMOV, ISAAC, *A Short History of Biology.* New York, Natural History Press, 1964.

————, *The Wellsprings of Life.* New York, New American Library, 1960.

————, *The World of Carbon.* New York, Collier Books, 1962.

AUDUBON, JOHN JAMES, *The Birds of America.* New York, Dover Publications, 1967. 2 vols.

————, *Journal of John James Audubon Made During His Trip to New Orleans in 1820–1821.* Boston, The Club of Odd Volumes, 1929.

————, *Journal of John James Audubon Made While Obtaining Subscriptions to His "Birds of America," 1840–1843.* Boston, The Club of Odd Volumes, 1929.

————, *Letters of John James Audubon, 1826–1840.* Boston. The Club of Odd Volumes, 1930.

AUDUBON, LUCY, *The Life of John James Audubon, the Naturalist.* New York, G. P. Putnam, 1902.

AUDUBON, MARIA R., *Audubon and His Journals.* New York, Dover Publications, 1960.

BACHMAN, JOHN, *An Examination of Professor Agassiz's Sketch of the Natural Provinces of the Animal World.* Charleston, James Williams and Gitsinger, 1855.

BAILEY, L. H., *How Plants Get Their Names.* New York, Dover Publications, 1963.

BAIRD, SPENCER FULLERTON, *Correspondence Between Spencer Fullerton Baird and Louis Agassiz,* collected and edited by Elmer Charles Herber. Washington, Smithsonian Institution, 1963.

BARLOW, NORA, ed., *Charles Darwin and the Voyage of the Beagle.* London, Pilot Press, 1945.

BARNES, HARRY ELMER, *An Intellectual and Cultural History of the Western World.* New York, Dover Publications, 1965. 3 vols.

BASALLA, GEORGE, "The Spread of Western Science." *Science,* Vol. 156, No. 3775 (May 5, 1967), pp. 611–22.

BATAILLE, GEORGES, *Lascaux or the Birth of Art.* Switzerland, Skira, no date.

BATES, HENRY WALTER, *The Naturalist on the River Amazons.* Berkeley and Los Angeles, University of California Press, 1962.

BATES, MARSTON, *The Nature of Natural History.* London, Chapman & Hall, 1951.

BATESON, WILLIAM, *Mendel's Principles of Heredity.* Cambridge, Cambridge University Press, 1902.

————, *Mendel's Principles of Heredity.* New York, G. P. Putnam, 1907.

BECKER, CARL L., *The Heavenly City of the Eighteenth-Century Philosophers.* New Haven, Yale University Press, 1932.

BELL, P. R., ed., *Darwin's Biological Work.* New York, Wiley, 1964.

BERRILL, N. J., *Man's Emerging Mind.* New York, Fawcett World Library, 1965.

BETTANY, GEORGE THOMAS, *Life of Charles Darwin.* London, W. Scott, 1887.

BISHOP, PHILIP W. *See* Schwartz, George

BLANCHARD, ÉMILE, *Un Naturaliste du dix-neuvième siècle: Louis Agassiz.* Paris, Impr. de J. Claye, 1875.

BONNEY, THOMAS GEORGE, *Charles Lyell and Modern Geology.* London, Cassell, 1901.

BOORSTIN, DANIEL J., *The Lost World of Thomas Jefferson.* Boston, Beacon Press, 1960.

BOREK, ERNEST, *The Code of Life.* New York, Columbia University Press, 1965.

BOULE, MARCELLIN, *Georges Cuvier, fondateur de la paléontologie.* Paris, Archives du Muséum National d'Histoire Naturelle, 1932.

BRANN, EDWARD ROMMEL, *The Political Ideas of Alexander Humboldt.* Madison, Wisconsin, Littel Print Co., 1954.

BRIGHTWELL, MISS (CECILIA LUCY), *A Life of Linnaeus.* London, John Van Voorst, 1858.

BRINK, ALEXANDER R., ed., with assistance of E. Derek Styles, *Heritage from Mendel.* Madison, University of Wisconsin Press, 1965. Proceedings of the Mendel Centennial Symposium, Fort Collins, Colorado, 1965.

BRITISH MUSEUM, *Memorials of Linnaeus.* London, Printed by Order of the Trustees of the British Museum, 1907.

BROWN, Vinson, *Discoveries in Ancient Life.* New York, Science Materials Center, 1961.

BRUHNS, KARL CHRISTIAN, *Life of Alexander von Humboldt.* London, Longmans, Green, 1873.

BUFFON, GEORGES LOUIS LECLERC, *Correspondance inédite.* Recveilli et annotée par Henri Nadault de Buffon. Paris, Librairie de L. Hatchette et Cie, 1860. 2 vols.

————, *Discours sur le style prononcé è l'Academie Française,* Paris, E. Belin, 1866.

————, *Oeuvres complètes.* Paris, Dufour, Mulat et Boulanger, 1856–1858. 4 vols.

————, *Oeuvres philosophiques.* Paris, Presses Universitaires de France, 1954.

BURY, J. B., *History of Greece.* London, Macmillan, 1929.

BUTCHER, S. H., *Aristotle's Theory of Poetry and Fine Art.* London, Macmillan, 1932.

BUTLER, S., *Evolution, Old and New; or The Theories of Buffon, Dr. Erasmus Darwin, and Lamarck, as Compared with That of Charles Darwin.* London, 1911.

BUTTERFIELD, HERBERT, *The Origins of Modern Science.* New York, Free Press, 1965.

CADDY, FLORENCE, *Through the Fields with Linnaeus: A Chapter in Swedish History.* London, Longmans, Green, 1887.

CALLENDAR, CHARLES. *See* Tax, Sol

CANTWELL, ROBERT, *Alexander Wilson.* Philadelphia and New York, Lippincott, 1961.

CARRINGTON, RICHARD, *A Million Years of Man.* New York, New American Library, 1964.

CLODD, EDWARD, *Thomas Henry Huxley.* New York, Dodd, Mead, 1902.

COHEN, I. BERNARD, AND JONES, HOWARD MUMFORD, ed., *Science Before Darwin.* London, Andre Deutsch, 1963.

COLBERT, EDWIN H., *Evolution of the Vertebrates.* New York, Wiley, 1955.

COLEMAN, WILLIAM R., *Georges Cuvier, Zoologist.* Cambridge, Mass., Harvard University Press, 1964.

COOPER, LANE, *Louis Agassiz as a Teacher.* Ithaca, N.Y., Comstock Publishing, 1945.

CUVIER, GEORGES, *The Animal Kingdom Arranged in Conformity with Its Organization.* New York, G. & C. & H. Carvill, 1831. 4 vols.

————, *The Animal Kingdom Arranged in Conformity with Its Organization,* translated and abridged by H. M'Murtrie. New York, G. & C. & H. Carvill, 1832.

————, *Discours sur les révolutions de la surface du globe.* Paris, G. Dufour, 1828.

————, *A Discourse on the Revolutions of the Surface of the Globe.* London, Whittaker, Treacher, and Arnot, 1829.

————, *Éloges historiques.* Paris, E. Ducrocq, 1860.

————, *Essay on the Theory of the Earth,* with an account of Cuvier's geologic discoveries by Professor Jameson and observations by Samuel L. Mitchill. New York, Kirk & Mercein, 1818.

————, *Recherches sur les ossements fossiles des quadrupèdes.* Paris, G. Dufour, 1825. 5 vols.

————, *Recueil des éloges historiques.* Paris, Firmin Didot Frères, Fils et Cie, 1861.

————, AND BRONGNIART, ALEX, *Description géologique des environs de Paris.* Paris, G. Dufour, 1822.

DALL, DR. WILLIAM H., *Linnaeus as a Zoologist.* Washington, D.C., The Academy, 1907.

DAMPIER, SIR WILLIAM CECIL, *A Shorter History of Science.* New York, Meridian Books, 1957.

DARWIN, CHARLES, *The Autobiography of Charles Darwin and Selected Letters,* Francis Darwin, ed., New York, Dover Publications, 1958.

————, *Charles Darwin's Diary of the Voyage of H.M.S. Beagle,* Nora Barlow, ed. Cambridge, Cambridge University Press, 1934.

————, *The Descent of Man.* New York, D. Appleton, 1871.

————, *The Expression of the Emotions in Man and Animals.* London, J. Murray, 1904.

————, *Extracts from Letters Addressed to Professor Henslow.* Cambridge, Cambridge University Press, 1835.

————, *The Formation of Vegetable Mould, Through the Action of Worms.* New York, D. Appleton, 1882.

————, *Geological Observations on Volcanic Islands—Parts of South America.* London, Smith Elder & Co., 1846.

————, *Insectivorous Plants.* New York, D. Appleton, 1875.

————, *Journal of Researches into the Natural History and Geology of the Countries Visited During the Voyage of H.M.S. "Beagle" Round the World.* New York, Harper, 1846.

————, *The Life and Letters of Charles Darwin,* Francis Darwin, ed. London, J. Murray, 1887. 3 vols.

————, *More Letters of Charles Darwin,* Francis Darwin and A. C. Seward, ed. London, J. Murray, 1903.

————, *The Movements and Habits of Climbing Plants.* London, J. Murray, 1875.

————, *On the Various Contrivances by Which British and Foreign Orchids Are*

Fertilized by Insects and on the Good Effects of Intercrossing. London, J. Murray, 1862.

————, *Origin of Species and Descent of Man.* New York, Modern Library, no date.

————, *The Structure and Distribution of Coral Reefs.* Berkeley and Los Angeles, University of California Press, 1962.

————, *The Variation of Animals and Plants Under Domestication.* New York, D. Appleton, 1876.

————, *The Voyage of the Beagle,* annotated and with an introduction by Leonard Engel. Garden City, N.Y., Doubleday, 1962.

————, ASSISTED BY FRANCIS DARWIN, *The Power of Movement in Plants.* New York, D. Appleton, 1896.

DAVIS, WATSON, *The Century of Science.* New York, Duell, Sloan and Pearce, 1963.

DE BEER, SIR GAVIN RYLANDS, *Charles Darwin: A Scientific Biography.* Garden City, N. Y., Doubleday, 1965.

DE VRIES, HUGO, *Plant Breeding.* Chicago, Open Court Publishing, 1907.

————, *Species and Varieties.* Chicago, Open Court Publishing, 1905.

DIBNER, BERN, *Darwin of the Beagle.* New York, Blaisdell, 1964.

DOBELL, CLIFFORD, *Antony van Leeuwenhoek and His "Little Animals."* New York, Dover Publications, 1960.

DOBZHANSKY, THEODOSIUS GRIGORIEVICH, *Evolution, Genetics, and Man.* New York, Wiley, 1958.

DODSON, EDWARD O., *Evolution: Process and Product.* New York, Reinhold, 1960.

DOWDESWELL, W. H., *The Mechanism of Evolution.* New York, Harper & Row, 1960.

DRACHMAN, JULIAN M., *Studies in the Literature of Natural Science.* New York, Macmillan, 1930.

DRAKE, STILLMAN, ed. and trans., *Discoveries and Opinions of Galileo.* Garden City, N.Y., Doubleday, 1957.

DUNBAR, CARL O., *Historical Geology.* New York, Wiley, 1949.

DUNN, LESLIE CLARENCE, *A Short History of Genetics.* New York, McGraw-Hill, 1965.

EHRLICH, BLAKE, *Paris on the Seine.* New York, Atheneum, 1962.

EHRLICH, PAUL R., AND HOLM, RICHARD W., *The Process of Evolution.* New York, McGraw-Hill, 1963.

EISELEY, LOREN, *Darwin's Century.* Garden City, N.Y., Doubleday, Anchor Edition, 1961.

ELTON, CHARLES S., *The Ecology of Invasions by Animals and Plants.* New York, Wiley, 1958.

EMERSON, RALPH WALDO, *Louis Agassiz.* Boston, Boston Society of Natural History, 1874.

FALLS, WILLIAM FRANKLIN, *Buffon et l'agrandissement du Jardin du Roi à Paris.* Paris, Archives du Muséum National d'Histoire Naturelle, 6e Serie, Tome X, 1933.

FAURÉ, ELIE, *Les Constructeurs.* Paris, G. Crès & Cie, 1921.

FENTON, CARROLL LANE, AND FENTON, MILDRED ADAMS, *Giants of Geology.* Garden City, N.Y., Doubleday, 1952.

FENTON, MILDRED ADAMS. *See* Fenton, Carroll Lane

FLOURENS, PIERRE, *Buffon, histoire de ses travaux et de ses idées.* Paris, Paulin, 1844.

————, *Cuvier, histoire de ses traveaux.* Paris, Paulin, 1845.

————, *Des Manuscrits de Buffon.* Paris, Garnier Frères, 1860.

FORD, ALICE, *John James Audubon*. Norman, Okla., University of Oklahoma Press, 1964.

FRAZER, SIR JAMES GEORGE, *The New Golden Bough*, edited and with notes and a foreword by Theodor H. Gaster. Garden City, N.Y., Doubleday, Anchor Edition, 1961.

GEORGE, WILMA, *Animal Geography*. London, Heinemann, 1962.

GOURLIE, NORAH, *The Prince of Botanists, Carl Linnaeus*. London, H. F. & G. Witherby, 1953.

GRAVIER, CHARLES JOSEPH, *Les Vers et les arthropodes dans le "Regne Animal."* Paris, Archives du Muséum National d'Histoire Naturelle, 1932.

GRAY, ASA, *Louis Agassiz*. Reprinted from the *Andover Review* for January, 1886.

GREENE, EDWARD L., *Linnaean Memorial Address*. Washington, D.C., The Academy, 1907.

HAGBERG, KNUT, *Carl Linnaeus*, trans. by Alan Blair. London, Jonathan Cape, 1952.

HALL, A. RUPERT, AND HALL, MARIE BOAS, *A Brief History of Science*. New York, New American Library, 1964.

HALL, MARIE BOAS. *See* Hall, A. Rupert

HAMILTON, W. J., JR., *American Mammals*. New York, McGraw-Hill, 1964.

HARDIN, GARRETT, *Nature and Man's Fate*. New York, New American Library, 1961.

HARDING, WALTER, *The Days of Henry Thoreau*. New York, Knopf, 1967.

HERRICK, FRANCIS HOBART, *Audubon the Naturalist*. New York, Appleton-Century, 1938.

HIMMELFARB, GERTRUDE, *Darwin and the Darwinian Revolution*. Garden City, N.Y., Doubleday, 1962.

HOLDER, CHARLES FREDERICK, *Louis Agassiz: His Life and Work*. New York, G. P. Putnam, 1893.

HOLM, RICHARD. *See* Ehrlich, Paul R.

HUMBOLDT, ALEXANDER VON, *Annales des voyages de la géographie, de l'histoire, et de l'archéologie*. Paris, Gide Fils, 1819–1870.

————, *Cosmos*. London, Longman, Brown, Green, and Longman's, 1847.

————, *Essai politique sur le royaume de la Nouvelle-Espagne*. Paris, Jules Renouard, 1827. 4 vols.

————, *Examen critique de l'histoire de la Géographie du Nouveau Continent*. Paris, Gide Fils, 1836–1839.

————, *Expéeriences sur le galvanisme*. Paris, De l'Imprimerie de Didot Jeune, 1799.

————, *The Island of Cuba*. New York, Derby & Jackson, 1856.

————, *Letters of Alexander Humboldt (1827–1858) to Varnhagen von Ense*. London, Strübner, 1860.

————, *Lettres américaines d'Alexandre Humboldt (1798–1807)*. Paris, E. Guilmoto, 1905.

————, *Personal Narrative of Travels to the Equinoctial Regions During the Years 1799–1804*, trans. by Helen Maria Williams. London, Longman, Hurst, Rees, Orme, and Brown, 1814. 8 vols.

————, *Selections from the Works of the Baron de Humboldt*, with notes by John Taylor. London, Longman, Hurst, Rees, Orme, Brown and Green, 1824.

————, *The Travels and Researches of Alexander von Humboldt*. Edinburgh, Oliver & Boyd, 1832.

————, *Voyage aux régions equinoxiales du nouveau continent, 1799, 1800, 1801, 1802, 1803, 1804*. Paris, À la Libraire Grecque, Latine, Allemande, 1816–1831.

————, *Vues des cordillères et monuments des peuples indigènes de l'Amérique*. Paris, Bourgeois-Maze, 1816. 2 vols.

HUTTON, JAMES, *Dissertations on Different Subjects in Natural Philosophy*. Edinburgh, A. Strahan and T. Cadell, 1792.

————, *An Investigation of the Principles of Knowledge, and of the Progress of Reason, from Sense to Science and Philosophy*. Edinburgh, A. Strahan and T. Cadell, 1794.

————, *Theory of the Earth, with Proofs and Illustrations*. New York, Hafner, 1960.

HUXLEY, JULIAN, *Evolution in Action*. New York, Harper, 1953.

HUXLEY, LEONARD, *Charles Darwin*. New York, Greenburg, 1927.

————, *Life and Letters of Thomas Henry Huxley*. New York, D. Appleton, 1900. 2 vols.

HUXLEY, THOMAS HENRY, *Autobiography and Selected Essays*. Boston, Houghton, Mifflin, 1909.

————, *Darwiniana (Essays)*. New York, D. Appleton, 1896.

————, *Evidence as to Man's Place in Nature*. New York, D. Appleton, 1880.

————, *Evolution and Ethics and Other Essays*. New York, D. Appleton, 1896.

————, *Man's Place in Nature*. Ann Arbor, University of Michigan Press, 1959.

————, *On the Origin of Species or the Causes of the Phenomena of Organic Nature*. New York, D. Appleton, 1863.

ILTIS, HUGO, *Life of Mendel*. New York, Hafner, 1966.

IRVINE, WILLIAM, *Apes, Angels, and Victorians*. New York, McGraw-Hill, 1955.

JACKSON, BENJAMIN DAYTON, *Linnaeus: The Story of His Life*, adapted from the Swedish of Theodor Magnus Fries. London, H. F. & G. Witherby, 1923.

JAFFE, BERNARD, *Men of Science in America*. New York, Simon & Schuster, 1958.

JARDINE, SIR WILLIAM, *Lions, Tigers etc.* Edinburgh, W. H. Zigars, 1843.

JOHNSON, FREDERICK H., *Guide to Niagara Falls and Its Scenery*. With *Geology and Recession of the Falls* by Lyell. Philadelphia, G. W. Childs, 1864.

JONES, HOWARD MUMFORD. *See* Cohen, I. Bernard

JOUBIN, LOUIS MARIE ADOLPHE OLIVIER ÉDOUARD, *Études de Cuvier sur les mollusques*. Paris, Archives du Muséum National d'Histoire Naturelle, 1932.

JOURDY, ÉMILE, *L'Heritage de Lamarck*. Paris, Zoologie, 1916.

KASTON, B. J. *See* Winchester, A. M.

KELLNER, L., *Alexander von Humboldt*. London, Oxford University Press, 1963.

KING-HEHE, DESMOND, *Erasmus Darwin*. New York, Scribner, 1963.

KLENKE, PROFESSOR, *Alexander von Humboldt: A Biographical Monument*. New York, Harper, 1853.

KOESTLER, ARTHUR, *The Watershed: A Biography of Johannes Kepler*. Garden City, N.Y., Doubleday, 1960.

LACÉPÈDE, BERNARD GERMAIN ÉTIENNE DE LA VILLE SUR ILLON, *Oeuvres du Comte de Lacépède*. Paris, Ludrange et Verdière, 1826–1833. 11 vols. Contains eulogy by Cuvier.

LACROIX, ALFRED, *Georges Cuvier et la minéralogie*. Paris, Archives du Muséum National d'Histoire Naturelle, 1932.

LAMARCK, JEAN, *An Epitome of Lamarck's Arrangement of Testacea*. London, Longman, 1875.

————, *Flore française*. Paris, L'Imprimerie Royale, 1778.

————, *Histoire naturelle des animaux sans vertèbres*. Paris, Verdière, 1815–1822.

————, *Hydrogéologie*. Paris, L'Auteur au Muséum d'Histoire Naturelle, 1802.

————, *Philosophie zoologique*. Paris, Chez Dentu, 1809.

————, *Recherches sur les causes des principaux faits physiques*. Paris, Maradan, 1794.

————, *Système des animaux sans vertèbres*. Paris, Chez Deterville, 1802.

————, *Zoological Philosophy*. London, Macmillan, 1914.

LANDRIEU, M., *Lamarck, le fondateur du transformisme, sa vie, son oeuvre*. Paris, Mémoires de la société Zoologique de France, 1909.

LANKESTER, EDWIN, ed., *Memorials of John Ray*. London, Ray Society, 1846.

LEBASTEUR, HENRI, *Buffon*. Paris, H. Lecène et H. Oudin, 1889.

LEE, JAMES, *An Introduction to Botany*. Edinburgh, Mundell, Doig & Stevenson, 1806. Based on extracts from the works of Linnaeus.

LEE, SARAH BOWDITCH, *Memoirs of Baron Cuvier*. New York, J. J. Harper, 1833.

LINNAEUS, CARL VON, *Critica botanica*, trans. by Sir Arthur Hart. London, Ray Society, 1938.

————, *A Dissertation on the Sexes of Plants*. Translated by James Edward Smith. London, Printed for the Author, 1786.

————, *Lachesis lapponica; or A Tour in Lapland*. Translated by James Edward Smith. London, White and Cochrane, 1811.

————, *A System of Vegetables, According to Their Classes, Orders, Genera, etc.* Litchfield, England, Translated by a botanical society at Litchfield, England. Printed by J. Jackson, for Leigh and Sotheby, 1783.

LINNÉ, CARL VON. *See* Linnaeus, Carl von

LOVELL, HARVEY B. *See* Winchester, A. M.

LURIE, EDWARD, *Louis Agassiz: A Life in Science*. Chicago, University of Chicago Press, 1960.

LYELL, SIR CHARLES, *Eight Lectures on Geology*. New York, Greeley and McElrath, 1842.

————, *Elements of Geology*. Philadelphia: Hayes & Zell, 1857.

————, *The Geological Evidences of the Antiquity of Man*. London, J. Murray, 1863.

————, *Life, Letters and Journals of Sir Charles Lyell*. London, J. Murray, 1881. 2 vols.

————, *A Manual of Elementary Geology*. New York. D. Appleton, 1853.

————, *On the Structure of Lavas Which Have Consolidated on Steep Slopes*. London, Taylor & Francis, 1859.

————, *Principles of Geology*. London, J. Murray, 1835.

————, *A Second Visit to the United States of North America*. London, J. Murray, 1855. 2 vols.

————, *Travels in North America*. London, J. Murray, 1845. 2 vols.

————, AND MURCHISON, SIR RODERICK, "On the Excavation of Valleys as Illustrated by the Volcanic Rocks of Central France." *New Philosophic Journal* (July, 1829).

MARCHANT, JAMES, *Alfred Russel Wallace*. London, Cassell, 1916. 2 vols.

MARCOU, JULES, *Reply to the Criticisms of James D. Dana*. Zurich, Geological Pamphlets IV, 1859.

MASON, STEPHEN FINNEY, *Main Currents of Scientific Thought: A History of the Sciences*. New York, Schuman, 1953.

McKEON, RICHARD, *Introduction to Aristotle*. New York, Modern Library, 1947.

MOORE, RUTH, *Man, Time, and Fossils*. New York, Knopf, 1953.

NEWMAN, JAMES R., *Science and Sensibility*. New York, Simon & Schuster, 1961. 2 vols.

NORDENSKIOLD, ERIK, *The History of Biology*, trans. by Leonard Bucknall Eyre. New York, Tudor, 1959.

NYE, RUSSEL BLAINE, *The Cultural Life of the New Nation*. New York, Harper & Row, 1963.

ODUM, EUGENE P., *Fundamentals of Ecology*. Philadelphia, Saunders, 1959.

PACKARD, ALPHEUS SPRING, *Lamarck, the Founder of Evolution*. New York, Longmans, Green, 1901.

PATON, LUCY ALLEN, *Elizabeth Cary Agassiz*. Boston, Houghton, Mifflin, 1919.

PERNON, JEAN FRANÇOIS, *Lamarck; influence de la cécité sur la génie*. Université de Paris, "Bibliographie" p. 56, 1928. Thesis.

PETERSON, HOUSTON, *Huxley, Prophet of Science*. London and New York, Longmans, Green, 1932.

PIMENTEL, RICHARD A., *Natural History*. New York, Reinhold, 1963.

PITTENDRIGH, COLIN S. *See* Simpson, George Gaylord

PLAYFAIR, JOHN, *Illustrations of the Huttonian Theory of the Earth*. Edinburgh, W. Creech, 1802.

RANDALL, JOHN HERMAN, JR., *Aristotle*. New York, Columbia University Press, 1960.

REID, GEORGE K., *Ecology of Inland Waters and Estuaries*. New York, Reinhold, 1961.

ROSE, HUGH, *The Elements of Botany*. London, T. Cadell, 1775. A translation of the *Philosophic botanica* and other treatises of Linnaeus.

ROSTAND, JEAN, *L'Évolution des espèces*. Paris, Hachette, 1932.

ROYAL ANTHROPOLOGICAL INSTITUTE AND INSTITUTE OF RACE RELATIONS, *Man, Race, and Darwin*. London, Oxford University Press, 1960.

SCHONLAND, B. F. J., *The Flight of the Thunderbolts*. London, Oxford University Press, 1950.

SCHWARTZ, GEORGE, AND BISHOP, PHILIP W., ed., *Moments of Discovery, the Origins of Science*. New York, Basic Books, 1958. 2 vols.

SIMPSON, GEORGE GAYLORD, *This View of Life*. New York, Harcourt, Brace & World, 1964.

————, PITTENDRIGH, COLIN S., AND TIFFANY, LEWIS H., *Life: An Introduction to Biology*. New York, Harcourt, Brace, 1957.

SINGER, CHARLES, *A Short History of Science to the Nineteenth Century*. London, Oxford University Press, 1941.

SINNOTT, EDMUND W., AND WILSON, KATHERINE S., *Botany: Principles and Problems*. New York, McGraw-Hill, 1955.

SMITH, SIR JAMES EDWARD, *A Selection of the Correspondence of Linnaeus, and Other Naturalists*. London, Longman, Hurst, Rees, Orme, and Brown, 1821. 2 vols.

STIRTON, RUBEN ARTHUR, *Time, Life, and Man*. New York, Wiley, 1963.

STODDARD, RICHARD HENRY, *The Life, Travels and Books of Alexander von Humboldt*. New York, Rudd and Carleton, 1858.

STOEVER, D. H., *The Life of Sir Charles Linnaeus*. London, B. and J. White, 1794.

STRINGHAM, EMERSON, *Alexander Wilson: A Founder of Scientific Ornithology*. Kerrville, Texas, 1958.

STYLES, E. DEREK. *See* Brink, R. Alexander

TAX, SOL, ed., AND WITH CALLENDER, CHARLES, *Evolution After Darwin*, Vol. III, Chicago, University of Chicago Press, 1960. Proceedings of the University of Chicago Centennial.

TELLER, JAMES DAVID, *Louis Agassiz, Scientist and Teacher*. Columbus, Ohio State University Press, 1947.

TIFFANY, LEWIS H. *See* Simpson, George Gaylord

UNIVERSITY OF PITTSBURGH, *A Book That Shook the World*. Pittsburgh, University of Pittsburgh Press, 1961.

VAN DOREN, CARL, *Benjamin Franklin*. New York, Viking, 1938.

VIÉNOT, JOHN, *Le Napoléon de l'intelligence—Georges Cuvier.* Paris, Fischbacher, 1932.

WALLACE, ALFRED RUSSEL, *Australia and New Zealand.* London, Stanford, 1893.

————, *Australasia.* London, Stanford, 1883.

————, *Bad Times.* London, Macmillan, 1885.

————, *The Claims of Labour.* Edinburgh, Co-operative Printing Co., 1886.

————, *Contributions to the Theory of Natural Selection.* London, Macmillan, 1870.

————, *Darwinism: An Exposition of the Theory of Natural Selection.* London, Macmillan, 1881.

————, *The Darwin-Wallace Celebration.* London, Linnaean Society, 1908.

————, *The Geographical Distribution of Animals.* London, Macmillan, 1876.

————, *Island Life.* New York, Harper, 1881.

————, *The Malay Archipelago.* New York, Dover Publications, 1962.

————, *My Life,* New York, Dodd, Mead, 1905.

————, *A Narrative of Travels on the Amazon and Rio Negro.* London, Reeve and Co., 1853.

————, *Natural Selection and Tropical Nature.* London, Macmillan, 1891.

————, *Tropical Nature and Other Essays.* London, Macmillan, 1878.

————, AND CHARLES DARWIN, *Evolution by Natural Selection.* Cambridge, Cambridge University Press, 1958.

WENDT, HERBERT, *Out of Noah's Ark.* Boston, Houghton, Mifflin, 1959.

WHITE, ANDREW DICKSON, *A History of the Warfare of Science with Theology in Christendom.* New York, Dover Publications, 1960. 2 vols.

WICHLER, GERHARD, *Charles Darwin: The Founder of the Theory of Evolution and Natural Selection.* Oxford, N.Y., Pergamon Press, 1961.

WILLIAMS, HENRY SMITH, *The Great Astronomers.* New York, Newton Publishing, 1932.

WILSON, ALEXANDER, *American Ornithology,* with a continuation by Charles Lucien Bonaparte. Edinburgh, Constable, 1831.

————, *Memoirs and Remains.* Paisley, Scotland, Alex. Gardner, 1876. 2 vols.

WILSON, KATHERINE S. *See* Sinnott, Edmund W.

WINCHESTER, A. M., ASSISTED BY KASTON, B. J., *Biology and Its Relation to Mankind.* Princeton, Van Nostrand, 1962.

————, AND LOVELL, HARVEY B., *Zoology.* Princeton, Van Nostrand, 1955.

Biographical Sketches

The following brief sketches of some of the major and minor figures that appear in this book may be helpful to the reader by serving in effect as a cast of characters to which he may occasionally wish to refer.

Adelard of Bath (*c*. 1090–*c*. 1150)   One of the great translators from Arabic into Latin, Adelard brought the work of Al-Khowarizmi, who used Arabic numerals, to the attention of Europe. He also translated Euclid from Arabic into Latin.

Agassiz, Alexander (1835–1910)   The son of Louis Agassiz, he specialized in marine zoology and for part of his life worked with the United States Coast Survey. He was also active in the copper-mining industry, from which he made a large fortune. This did not, however, prevent him from continuing with his scientific studies.

Agassiz, Jean Louis Rodolphe (1807–1873)   Born in Switzerland, Agassiz did his first great scientific work in paleontology, and his work on fossil fish won the respect of men like Cuvier, who befriended him. He made important contributions to glacial geology. He eventually left Switzerland and moved to the United States, serving as a professor at Harvard. In spite of his brilliance, he was never able to accept the concept of evolution and remained one of its consistent opponents.

Agrippa, Marcus Vipsanius (63 B.C.–12 B.C.)   A military commander, he was also a friend of Octavian (later Augustus) and urged him to go to Rome immediately after Julius Caesar's death. He continued in Augustus' service and married his daughter. He was also a geographer and conducted a general survey of the world.

459

Al-Khowarizmi (*c.* 830)   A Persian, he adopted the Arabic numerals of the Hindus in his mathematics. He was also one of the first to use the word "algebra" in its modern mathematical sense.

Al-Kindi (813–80)   Working at Baghdad, he produced a large number of scientific works. Some of them dealt with meteorology, optics, the tides, and the reflection of light.

Anaximander (610 B.C.–547 B.C.)   A student of Thales, he was one of the first geographers and was interested in both astronomy and cartography. His maps were probably the best of their kind during his time.

Arago, Dominique François Jean (1786–1853)   A French physicist, he was made a prisoner while on a government geodetic survey. His heroism in preserving his scientific papers during his imprisonment won for him the lifelong friendship of Humboldt. His principal scientific work was in optics and magnetism. As a political liberal, he was also active in public life.

Aristotle (384 B.C.–322 B.C.)   Born in Macedonia, he went to Greece as a young man, became an admirer of Plato, moved to Asia Minor, and then became the tutor of Alexander the Great. When Alexander ascended the throne, Aristotle returned to Athens and founded his Lyceum. His investigations and teachings covered almost the entire scope of human knowledge. He did excellent work in the biological sciences, and Darwin considered him one of the greatest biologists.

Artedi, Peter (1705–1735)   A student friend of Linnaeus, he later joined Linnaeus in Holland. He specialized in fish, but his work was ended by his premature death. Linnaeus undertook to edit and publish the studies he had made.

Audubon, John James (1785–1851)   Born in the French colony of San Domingo, Audubon emigrated to the United States as a young man and became a naturalized citizen. After an unsuccessful career as a businessman, he became an ornithologist and produced his classic work, *The Birds of America.*

Averroës (1126–1198)   He was born at Córdoba, Spain. In his writings, he argued that the world was eternal, although he, like other thinkers of his time, believed that space was finite. His views did not permit a single act of creation of the world and, therefore, ran contrary to the beliefs of the Christians, Jews, and Arabs.

Avicenna (980–1037)   A physician who was born at Bukhara, he wrote a book, *Canon of Medicine,* which greatly influenced medieval Europe. He was also a philosopher.

Bache, Alexander Dallas (1806–1867)   As superintendent of the United States Coast Survey, he developed a comprehensive plan for the survey of the coast. He also arranged to make the facilities of the government available to Agassiz on many occasions.

Bacon, Francis (1561–1626)   In his writings, he was a severe critic of adherence to the classical traditions and proposed that scientists depend more heavily on experiment and observation. His philosophy toward natural research had an important effect on subsequent thinkers.

Bacon, Roger (*c.* 1214–1294)   A Franciscan, he taught at both Paris and Oxford. He was a collector of knowledge, rather than a creator of knowledge, but he recognized the need for direct experimentation and observation. In this, he was unusual for his age, which was given over to Scholasticism.

Baird, Spencer Fullerton (1823–1887)   His work covered a wide range of subjects in American natural history, and as secretary of the Smithsonian Institution, he influenced the development of American science. Among the people he knew were Audubon and Agassiz.

Bartholin, Thomas (1616–1680)   A professor of anatomy at Copenhagen, he did much to build up the prestige of the university, attracting students from all over Europe. He was one of the discoverers of the lymph system.

Bartram, John (1699–1777)   He was one of the pioneer botanists in the United States and served as a collector for many Europeans. On the outskirts of Philadelphia, he founded a famous botanical garden, which attracted many American scientists. His work was continued by his son, William Bartram (1739–1823), who wrote *Travels* describing a collecting expedition to Florida.

Bates, Henry Walter (1825–1892)   A British naturalist, Bates accompanied Wallace to Brazil, remaining in that country for several years after Wallace left. During his travels, he collected more than 14,000 specimens, 8,000 of which proved to be previously unknown. His studies of mimicry were outstanding. He served as assistant secretary of the Royal Geographical Society.

Bateson, William (1861–1926)   An English biologist, Bateson was an enthusiastic supporter of Mendel. He arranged for the publication of Mendel's papers in Great Britain and conducted extensive experiments of his own, applying Mendel's principles to both animals and plants.

Berthollet, Claude Louis (1748–1822)   A French chemist, he studied the properties of such substances as ammonia and chlorine. His work on oxygen led to Humboldt's experiments in Paris.

Boerhaave, Hermann (1668–1738)   An outstanding Dutch physician, he was interested in improving the training of doctors. To this end, he wrote a practical, straightforward book, which in its approach to the subject was like a modern text. He had a mechanical conception of the life process. He also helped Linnaeus publish his *Systema naturae*.

Bonaparte, Charles Lucien (1803–1857)   A nephew of Napoleon I, he began publishing a four-volume book on American ornithology when he was twenty-two. After returning to his home in Italy, he took part in the political agitation that swept the country in 1847. Two years later, he was forced to leave and spent most of the rest of his life working in zoology.

Bonnet, Charles (1720–1793)   He lived in his native Switzerland and, because of eye difficulties, spent much of his life speculating, rather than observing. He believed strongly in the traditional Christian attitudes. As a young man, he did some excellent work in insect biology and discovered parthenogenesis. This led him to his theory of "preformation," according to which each female held within her the "germs" of all the individuals that would come from her line.

Bonpland, Aimé Jacques Alexandre (1773–1858)   A French botanist, Bonpland is chiefly remembered as Humboldt's companion during his Latin American travels. He helped Humboldt with some of the scientific publications that resulted from the trip and then returned to South America, where he remained for the rest of his life.

Borda, Jean Charles de (1733–1799)   Borda was a French mathematician and made important contributions to navigation. His encouragement led Humboldt to study terrestrial magnetism during his travels in Latin America.

Borelli, Giovanni Alfonso (1608–1679)   An Italian and a follower of Galileo, he tried to adapt Galileo's methods to the natural sciences and did so successfully, particularly in his study of muscles.

Boyle, Robert (1627–1691)   In association with Robert Hooke, he studied air and other gases. He is remembered principally for Boyle's law on the relation of the volume of gas to the pressure exerted on it. He also showed that air is used in combustion and respiration and then went further to demonstrate that only a part of it is so used.

Brahe, Tycho (1546–1601)   A Danish astronomer, Tycho gained favor with the crown and, as a result, a large income. This permitted him to buy the best astronomical instruments. His resulting observations were extremely extensive and accurate. Toward the end of his life, he employed Kepler as an assistant. His excellent records were helpful to Kepler in developing his own theories.

Bruno, Giordano (1548–1600)   As a young man, he entered a monastery in his native Italy but soon left the church and spent the rest of his life propounding his ideas about the nature of the universe. His theories, although primarily speculative in nature, were remarkably close to the actual truth. Because of his beliefs, he was burned at the stake.

Buckland, William (1784–1856)   Both a clergyman and a geologist, he taught geology at Oxford, where Lyell was one of his students. Although a leader in his field during the early part of his career, he fell behind his times and, toward the end of his life, spent much of his time justifying the Bible in terms of geology.

Buffon, Georges Louis Leclerc, Comte de (1707–1788)   A French naturalist, he converted the Jardin du Roi at Paris into a leading scientific center. He also wrote *Natural History,* which became a leading reference work in the field and helped make the study of natural science popular. His views over the Creation and the Flood brought him into conflict with the church.

Camerarius, Rudolph Jacob (1665–1721)   A German botanist and physician, he conducted intensive investigations of the sexual reproduction of plants.

Cavendish, Henry (1731–1810)   Cavendish was an English physicist and chemist. Although his work covered a wide range of subjects, he is principally remembered for his studies of gases. He was able to determine the weights of equal volumes of gases, and he estimated the proportion of hydrogen and oxygen in water.

Chambers, Robert (1802–1871)   A publisher in Scotland, Chambers was also the author of several books, many of them dealing with Scottish history. In one, however, he discussed the possibility of evolution. Entitled *Vestiges of Creation,* it was more imaginative than scientific, but it stimulated discussion of the subject and greatly influenced Alfred Russel Wallace.

Cooper, Thomas (1759–1839)   Driven from England because of his liberal views, he went to the United States, where he was tried and convicted under the Alien and Sedition Acts. He was a friend of Joseph Priestley, and the two conducted experiments together. His principal field was chemistry, and he taught the subject at a number of American colleges and universities.

Cope, Edward Drinker (1840–1897)   An American paleontologist, Cope conducted extensive searches in the fossil beds of the West. He was responsible for finding hundreds of previously unknown vertebrates, thus greatly enriching the record that supports evolution.

Copernicus, Nicolaus (1473–1543)   One of the world's greatest astronomers, he was born in Poland. After extremely careful observations, he realized the earth could not be the center of the universe. He spent years working on the development of his theory but published the results only shortly before his death.

Correns, Karl Erich (1864–1933)   Correns was a German botanist who became interested in cells and then in the reproduction of molds. From this, his interest extended to heredity. His research on the printed material available led him to Mendel. He was the second person to announce the importance of Mendel's work.

Crateuas (*c.* 111 B.C.–*c.* 64 B.C.)   A pharmacologist interested in medicinal herbs, he produced a book on botany in which he systematically used pictures to illustrate the plants that he was discussing.

Cusa, Nicholas of. *See* Nicholas of Cusa

Cuvier, Georges (1769–1832)   At a young age, he joined the staff of the Jardin des Plantes in Paris as professor of zoology. His special interest was comparative anatomy, and he became so skillful that he was able to develop means of reconstructing extinct animals. Many regard him as the founder of modern paleontology. He refused, however, to believe in evolution and consistently attacked Lamarck's theories in that field. He also held many public offices under Napoleon and his successors.

Dana, James Dwight (1813–1895)   An outstanding American geologist and zoologist, Dana was a professor at Yale. He was one of those who quickly recognized the importance of Darwin's theory of evolution. He was one of the first scientists Agassiz called on when he came to the United States, but later the two men had serious scientific differences.

Darwin, Charles Robert (1809–1882)   Darwin is known throughout the world for his theory of evolution. A quiet and patient Englishman, he took so long to complete his studies that he almost lost his priority to Wallace. His theory was so important that it overshadows the other excellent work he did, such as his studies of coral reefs.

Daubenton, Louis Jean Marie (1716–1800)   A French naturalist, he was one of Buffon's principal collaborators. A misunderstanding took place between them, and the relationship broke up, but he was invaluable to Buffon in producing some of the earlier volumes of *Natural History*.

Da Vinci, Leonardo (1452–1519)   Possessed of one of the great intellects of all times, he was best known in his own day for his art and for his anatomical studies. His notebooks reveal the comprehensiveness of his thinking, but because they were not published during his life, they did not exercise the influence they might have had on his contemporaries.

Democritus (*c.* 460 B.C.–*c.* 370 B.C.)   One of the Greek philosophers, he believed that all matter was composed of "atoms" and the space that surrounded them. The "atoms" themselves were indivisible. The similarity between his theory and modern conceptions is more apparent than real.

Descartes, René (1596–1650)   A mathematician and a philosopher, he upheld a mechanical approach to the universe and to the natural sciences. He wished to avoid conflict with the church and, therefore, carefully tempered his writings. This made them acceptable to many readers who might otherwise have been unaware of the new attitudes in science.

De Vries, Hugo (1848–1935)   While teaching at Amsterdam, De Vries noted what he called "mutations" among some primroses. This led him to study their heredity. In the course of his research, he found Mendel's original paper and announced that his experiments generally supported Mendel's conclusions. This announcement was made in 1900 and was the first time that Mendel's work had been recognized.

Dillenius, Johann Jakob (1684–1747)   Born in Darmstadt in Germany, he was invited to England and, after working there for several years, became professor of botany at Oxford. He knew and encouraged Linnaeus, while remaining critical of much of his work.

Dioscorides, Pedanius (probably first century A.D.)   A surgeon in the Roman Army, he wrote a book about medicinal herbs that remained the authority for many centuries.

Döllinger, Ignaz (1770–1841)   Born in Bavaria, Döllinger was a respected and able professor of anatomy with a special interest in evolutionary history. Among his noted students was Agassiz.

Dufay (du Fay), Charles François de Cisternay (1698–1739)   A French physician, he became intendant of the Jardin du Roi in Paris, which he attempted to build into a leading scientific center. On his deathbed, he chose Buffon to succeed himself, a choice that eventually led to the realization of his visions. He is also remembered for his outstanding work in electricity.

Erasistratus (flourished *c.* 300 B.C.)   A native of Chios, he taught physiology at Alexandria. One of his principal interests was the nervous system.

Euclid (*c.* 323 B.C.–285 B.C.)   He studied at Athens and then went to Alexandria. He is, of course, well known even today for his geometry.

Forbes, Edward (1815–1854)   A British naturalist, Forbes conducted intensive investigations of the marine life of the Mediterranean and the waters of Great Britain. He was also active in the fields of paleontology and geology. He was one of the first to recognize Huxley's brilliance and helped him obtain employment and thus continue as a scientist.

Forster, Johann Georg Adam (1754–1794)   Born in Germany, Forster accompanied his father on one of Cook's voyages around the world and won fame for himself by the book he subsequently published describing the journey. He greatly influenced Humboldt by stimulating his desire to travel.

Franklin, Benjamin (1706–1790)   An American statesman and diplomat, Franklin encouraged the study of science in the United States. He was one of the first scientists to work on the Gulf Stream, and he also proposed the experiment that proved lightning was electricity.

Galen (*c.* 130–*c.* 200)   A physiologist from Pergamum, he was a teleologist and believed that everything was made by God according to a master plan. This approach to science coincided with the theological attitudes of the Middle Ages, so Galen was treated with far more respect than his ideas merited.

Galilei, Galileo (1564–1642)   Galileo was one of the most famous scientists of all time. His observations of the heavens completely refuted the theories of Aristotle. He is also remembered for his work with pendulums and falling bodies. He eventually came into conflict with the Inquisition.

Galvani, Luigi (1737–1798)   Galvani taught anatomy at the university at Bologna, his native city. In addition to being an outstanding teacher, he studied the effects of electricity on the muscular reactions of animals, principally frogs.

Garden, Alexander (1730–1791)   A physician who practiced in Charleston, South Carolina, Garden was also a botanist and zoologist. The gardenia was named for him. He remained a Loyalist during the American Revolution and was forced to leave the country.

Gauss, Karl Friedrich (1777–1855)   Gauss was a German mathematician who devoted much of his life to the study of magnetism. He knew Humboldt, and he may have been responsible for encouraging Humboldt to renew his studies in this field. His own work became so advanced that Humboldt had difficulty understanding the mathematics involved.

Gay-Lussac, Joseph Louis (1778–1850)   A Frenchman who was interested in the properties of the atmosphere, he made many balloon ascents in order to take samples at higher altitudes. He and Humboldt became friends after Humboldt's return from Latin America, and they conducted many experiments together.

Geber (probably the eighth century)   A Syrian and an alchemist, he did excellent work in chemistry and prepared many substances that are known today.

Geoffroy Saint-Hilaire, Étienne (1772–1844)   A prominent French scientist assigned to the Jardin des Plantes, he was interested in comparative anatomy and especially in the work of Daubenton. Although he made many contributions, he was speculative and often unreliable. He supported Lamarck against Cuvier, but he could not contend with Cuvier's knowledge of anatomy.

Gerard of Cremona (1114–1187)   He lived for many years in Toledo, Spain, and is credited with having translated almost a hundred books from Arabic into Latin. One of these was Avicenna's *Canon of Medicine,* which was considered the standard work on the subject.

Gray, Asa (1810–1888)   An American botanist, he was a professor at Harvard and an expert on the flora of the United States. His studies of plants brought him into correspondence with Darwin. He was one of the first people to whom Darwin confided his theory of evolution. Gray was one of its ablest defenders in the United States.

Grew, Nehemiah (1641–1712)   He practiced medicine in London and by means of a microscope conducted extensive investigations in plant anatomy. Like Malpighi, he observed the vascular system in plants and noticed that plant tissue was composed of cells.

Hales, Stephen (1677–1761)   A graduate in theology from Cambridge, Hales took orders in the Church of England. He also continued his early interest in the natural sciences and conducted quantitative experiments in biology, becoming an outstanding plant physiologist.

Hall, James (1811–1898)   Hall was an American geologist and paleontologist, who spent most of his professional life as a geologist for the State of New York. He cooperated with Agassiz in trying to establish better standards for scientific education in the United States.

Haller, Albrecht von (1708–1777)   A child prodigy, Haller, who was Swiss, devoted most of his life to writing poetry and studying biology. He was particularly interested in physiology and anatomy. He was also a sharp critic of Linnaeus.

Halley, Edmund (1656–1742)   An English astronomer, he plotted the course of the comet that bears his name. He was interested in meteorology and also published a map showing the world's winds. One of his greatest services was encouraging Isaac Newton to write the *Principia.*

Harriot, Thomas (1560–1621)   After being graduated from Oxford, he tutored Sir Walter Raleigh in mathematics and also instructed his sea captains. Raleigh sent him to make a scientific report on Roanoke Island. The report was one of the first works describing the natural history of the New World.

Harvey, William (1578–1657)   After taking a degree at Cambridge, he traveled abroad and then returned to England to practice medicine in London. By simple mathematics, he demonstrated that Galen's theory of the circulation of the blood was an impossibility. He then showed the true functions of the heart, veins, and arteries.

Helmont, Jan Baptista van (1557–1644)   A native of Brussels, he studied theology and subsequently medicine. He was firmly opposed to Galen and Aristotle, but he was better at attacking their theories than at developing new ones to take their place.

Herophilus (flourished 300 B.C.)   An anatomist at Alexandria, he performed public dissections of human bodies. (He was later accused of performing them on living people, but this accusation seems unbased on fact.) He did much work with the nervous system.

Herschel, John Frederick William (1792–1871)   Although he originally intended to be a lawyer, Herschel's interest soon switched to astronomy, optics, and chemistry. He became one of Great Britain's leading scientists. His influence extended beyond his field, for he attempted to encourage the study of all science and to give science new dignity in the minds of people generally. His father, William Herschel, had also been an outstanding astronomer.

Hippocrates (c. 460 B.C.–c. 377 B.C.)   A native of Greece, he was the most celebrated physician in antiquity. He traveled widely and advocated a humanitarian attitude toward patients. The Hippocratic school of medicine adopted a rational approach to medical and, consequently, to scientific problems. He was the author of the famous aphorism "Art is long and life is short."

Hooke, Robert (1635–1703)   An associate of Robert Boyle, he studied the physical properties of air, including its compressibility and weight, and helped lay the basis for modern chemistry and physics.

Hooker, Joseph Dalton (1817–1911)   Hooker was an outstanding British botanist and the director of Kew Gardens. His work included studies of the plants of Great Britain, India, and the United States. He was an early supporter of Darwin and helped Lyell arrange the presentation of Darwin's and Wallace's papers on evolution.

Humboldt, Alexander von (1769–1859)   A Prussian, Humboldt spent most of his inheritance on an extensive journey through Latin America that provided the basis for his scientific career. He investigated many subjects, such as geology, the distribution of plants, and magnetism. Because of his long life and his outstanding personal character, he knew many of the great scientists of the nineteenth century. He spent much of his time and slender resources encouraging younger men.

Hutton, James (1726–1797)   A native of Scotland, Hutton first became a doctor and then gave himself to the management of a farm he had inherited. When he put this in sufficiently good condition to rent profitably, he moved to Edinburgh and spent the rest of his life studying geology. He recognized the importance and role of sedimentation, erosion, and volcanic action, and his ideas eventually led to the downfall of Werner's Neptunism. Because his writing style was poor, his ideas became known primarily through a book by John Playfair, who explained them more dramatically and clearly.

Huxley, Thomas Henry (1825–1895)   An outstanding British zoologist, Huxley helped in the revision of Cuvier's system of classification and made other important contributions to science. He was an early supporter of Darwin, and because of his vast knowledge and his ability to express his thoughts well, he became one of evolution's most formidable defenders.

Jefferson, Thomas (1743–1826)   Although he is best remembered, of course, as President of the United States, he was also a scientist. Among his scientific accomplishments, he served as president of the American Philosophical Society and wrote a book on the natural history of Virginia.

Jussieu, Antoine Laurent de (1748–1836)   A French botanist, he taught at the Jardin des Plantes in Paris. Although not a particularly original observer, he performed a great service to science by setting up a natural system of classification in opposition to Linnaeus.

Jussieu, Bernard de (1699–c. 1777)   A member of a family of distinguished French botanists, Jussieu taught the subject at the Jardin du Roi, where he specialized in classification. One of his students was Lamarck.

Kelvin, William Thomson, first Baron (1824–1907)   A professor of physics at the University of Glasgow, Kelvin worked in many fields, including electricity and thermodynamics. He also radically redesigned the mariner's compass and developed other aids to navigation. His theory of the cooling of the earth, however, presented a real problem for the early evolutionists. By substantially reducing the time the earth could have been in existence, it did not permit enough years for the variation of the species to have taken place.

Kepler, Johannes (1571–1630)   An astronomer, he studied the motions of the planets and proved that they moved in ellipses, not circles, and that their motion was not uniform. By providing a mechanical interpretation, he helped destroy science's faith in Aristotle.

Lacépède, Bernard Germain Étienne de la Ville (1756–1825)   He was one of the professors at the Jardin du Roi. Buffon's brother and son jointly selected him to continue writing *Natural History* after Buffon's death, not knowing that Buffon did not approve of Lacépède's work and had specifically chosen another man.

Lamarck, Jean Baptiste Pierre Antoine de Monet de (1744–1829)   After a rather undistinguished scientific career, he became professor of invertebrate zoology at the Jardin du Roi in Paris. Although he was self-taught in the subject, he saw relationships between various forms of life and developed a theory of evolution. He believed, however, that acquired characteristics could be inherited, and his theory collapsed under the attacks of Georges Cuvier.

Leeuwenhoek, Antony van (1632–1723)   A Dutch businessman, he became expert at making his own microscopes. With them, he observed many hitherto unknown details which he reported in a series of letters to the Royal Society in London.

Leibniz, Gottfried Wilhelm (1646–1716)   A German mathematician, he was highly respected in Europe, and his advice was sought by many of the Continent's leading men. He developed a theory of living monads, which made up all life. Although the theory was highly speculative, it contributed to biology by making scientists more aware of life and its infinite variety.

Linnaeus, Carl (1707–1778)   After studying in Holland, he returned to Sweden and eventually secured a professorship at the University of Uppsala which he held for the remainder of his life. His system of classification was widely accepted, and he also introduced binary nomenclature, the use of two names, one designating the genus and the other the species.

Lucretius (c. 94 B.C.–c. 55 B.C.)   A Roman poet, he also wrote a book *On the Nature of Things*, which represents the Epicurean attitude toward nature.

Lyell, Charles (1797–1875)   A native of Great Britain, Lyell first took up the study of law and then turned to geology. Accepting the theories of Hutton, he looked on the geologic process as continuous. His book *Principles of Geology* was the standard authority of the day, which he kept revising to account for the discoveries of himself and others. He was one of those who encouraged Charles Darwin.

Maimonides (1135–1204)   A court physician, he spent most of his life in Cairo, although he had been born in Spain. He criticized Galen's medical writings, and his views on cosmology influenced St. Thomas Aquinas.

Malpighi, Marcello (1628–1694)   Born near Bologna, he was one of the early scientists to work with a microscope. He was a practical observer and studied many aspects of animal bodies and did pioneering work in the anatomy of plants.

Malthus, Thomas Robert (1766–1834)   A British economist and clergyman, Malthus studied and wrote about the controls that limit the growth of populations. His book was read by both Wallace and Darwin and led them to thinking about natural selection.

Marsh, Othniel Charles (1831–1899)   Marsh taught paleontology at Yale and led many expeditions to the West in search of fossils. His findings helped support the evolutionists. Among his significant discoveries were the remains of early American horses. Until then, it was believed that horses had originated in Europe.

Mela, Pomponius (flourished middle of first century A.D.)   Born in Spain, he became a prominent geographer in the Roman world. For the most part, however, he borrowed heavily from Eratosthenes and merely added details discovered by the Romans in their explorations.

Mendel, Gregor Johann (1822–1884)   Mendel spent his adult life in a monastery in Brünn (Brno, Czechoslovakia). There he conducted experiments with the hybridization of peas. His results provided an important basis for modern genetics, but the paper he wrote on the subject went unnoticed for many years.

Michael the Scot (c. 1175–c. 1235)   He translated the works of a number of Arabic writers into Latin. One of these was Averroës, who held that the world was eternal, a belief that questioned the teachings of Jews, Moslems, and Christians. Michael was considered by many to be a wizard because of his learning.

Mitchill, Samuel Latham (1764–1831)   A physician and member of Congress, Mitchill was interested in many aspects of science. (Jefferson called him the "Congressional Dictionary.") He founded the *Medical Repository,* one of the first important scientific publications in the United States.

Morgan, Thomas Hunt (1866–1945)   Morgan, an American, was one of the early geneticists to experiment with the breeding of fruit flies and to use them for the study of genes. His work brought him a Nobel Prize.

Murchison, Roderick Impey (1792–1871)   Son of a wealthy Scottish family, Murchison entered the army and fought in Spain at the age of sixteen. The end of the Napoleonic Wars caused him to abandon the army as a career, and in his early thirties, he took up geology. He accompanied Lyell on a tour of the Continent. His most important work was concentrated on the Devonian and Silurian systems.

Musschenbroek, Pieter van (1692–1761)   After studying in Leiden, where he was born, he held various professorships and then returned to the university at Leiden to teach mathematics. He remained there for the rest of his life. He is credited with inventing the Leyden jar.

Nägeli, Karl Wilhelm von (1817–1891)   Nägeli was a Swiss botanist whose special interest was heredity. He uncovered many significant facts in this field, but he is more often remembered as the man who failed to understand the importance of Mendel's work, when Mendel sent him his paper. By failing to encourage Mendel, he may have been an influence in Mendel's discontinuance of his work.

Newton, Isaac (1642–1727)   Newton was one of the greatest scientists of all time. His discovery of universal gravitation and the development of his laws of motion represented a tremendous step forward. He also influenced all scientific thinking by his concentration on rules that applied under every circumstance.

Nicholas of Cusa (1401–1464)   Born near the German city of Trier, he had a brilliant career in the church, becoming a bishop and later a cardinal. He waged continuous warfare against the church's more superstitious practices, such as the trials of witches. Although not a scientist, he was convinced that the earth was not in the center of the cosmos and wrote convincingly about his beliefs.

Owen, Richard (1804–1892)   A prominent British biologist, he made many contributions to his field and for a long time headed the natural history section of the British Museum. He was, however, in hearty disagreement with Darwin and a leading opponent of evolution.

Palissy, Bernard (c. 1510–c. 1590)   A French potter, he often turned to nature for his designs. He found many fossils and recognized them for what they were, the remains of former life. In this, he was a pioneer.

Perrault, Claude (1613–1688)   Best known as an architect (he designed the Colonnade of the Louvre), he was also a doctor of medicine and an experimenter in biology. He attempted to find mechanical causes for various animal functions and, with Borelli, was one of the pioneers in creating a modern attitude toward biological research.

Playfair, John (1748–1819)   Although primarily a mathematician and physicist, Playfair became interested in the geologic theories advanced by his fellow Scotsman James Hutton. A better writer than Hutton, he wrote a book based on Hutton's ideas and with full credit to him. It was largely through this book that Hutton became known.

Pliny the Elder (23–79)   A military officer, he also wrote many books, including a history of the wars between the Germans and the Romans. He was the author of *Natural History,* an encyclopedic work that contained most of the knowledge of his time. He was undiscriminating, however, and often failed to distinguish between folklore and fact.

Priestley, Joseph (1733–1804)   A Unitarian minister, he was also a chemist who worked with gases. He is best remembered as the discoverer of oxygen, although one other scientist, who delayed publication of his work, probably discovered it before him. Finding life in England unpleasant because of the hostility to his liberal political views, Priestley moved to the United States.

Pythagoras (*c.* 582 B.C.–*c.* 497 B.C.)   A Greek philosopher, he settled in Crotona in the southern part of Italy about 530 B.C. There he established a secret society devoted to the study of his philosophy. He was also greatly concerned with mathematics, and his name is widely remembered today because of the Pythagorean theorem.

Rafinesque, Constantine Samuel (1783–1840)   Rafinesque, whose father was French, was born in Constantinople, lived in France, and then moved with his family to Italy before coming to the United States. He was a botanist and also produced a book on the fish of the Ohio River. His work was marred by his credulity and his overanxiety to find new species. He also had an intimation of the principles of evolution, although his thinking in this field did not go far enough to be useful.

Ray, John (*c.* 1627–1705)   His father was a blacksmith who sent him to Cambridge, where he became interested in mathematics and natural science. He wrote on many subjects, including religion. In conjunction with his friend Francis Willughby, he worked on zoology. His book on botany was a standard reference work of his time.

Rhazes (865–925)   One of the great Arab physicians, he studied at Baghdad. His descriptions of smallpox and measles have been regarded as medical classics, and he wrote a book containing almost everything that was known about Persian, Syriac, and Indian medicine.

Richardson, John (1787–1865)   A British naval surgeon, he was also an Arctic explorer. He obtained for Thomas Huxley an assignment to go to Australia, which provided the basis for Huxley's career. He was also one of those who encouraged Huxley after his return to England.

Rivinus, Augustus Quirinus (1652–1723)   A native of Leipzig whose original name was Bachmann, he wrote a large work on botany in which he attacked the former methods of classifying plants and attempted to create a new one. He was, however, better at criticizing than creating.

Robert of Chester (*c.* 1110–*c.* 1160) An Englishman who lived in Spain for a number of years, he translated the Koran. He also translated Al-Khowarizmi's *Algebra* into Latin.

Rudbeck, Olof (1630–1702)   An outstanding anatomist, he taught the subject at Uppsala, Sweden. He was one of the discoverers of the lymph system. He also made extensive natural history collections in Sweden. These were later enlarged by his son, Olof Rudbeck, the Younger, but were lost in a fire that swept Uppsala.

Rumford, Count. *See* Thompson, Benjamin

Say, Thomas (1787–1834)   A zoologist, he was one of the leaders of the Long-Say Expedition, which was sponsored by the American government and explored the West in 1819. He made a similar expedition in 1823. Interested in insects, he wrote *American Entomology*.

Sedgwick, Adam (1785–1873)   Sedgwick taught geology at Cambridge, and one of his students was Darwin, who was then thinking of entering the ministry. What he learned from Sedgwick was important to Darwin when he began the voyage on the *Beagle*. Later, however, Sedgwick became a conservative force in British geology.

Seneca (*c.* 4 B.C.–A.D. 65)   A Roman philosopher, he was Nero's tutor and supported Nero in his early days as emperor. Finally, he broke with him, and Nero had him put to death. His work *Natural Questions* was primarily a compilation of material drawn from earlier sources, but his belief that nature was created expressly for the service of man made him popular with the later ecclesiastical authorities.

Silliman Benjamin (1779–1864)   Silliman, who taught at Yale, was a geologist and chemist. He was an excellent teacher and influenced many students. In addition, he helped American science by founding and editing one of the first important scientific journals, *The American Journal of Science and Arts*.

Smith, William (1769–1839)   An English surveyor, Smith became interested in the similarities of the geologic strata that he studied in connection with the building of canals. He matched their fossil contents and proved their relationships, thus developing the science of stratigraphy.

Steno, Nicolaus (1638–1686)   The son of a wealthy goldsmith in Copenhagen, he went to Italy and became physician to the Duke of Tuscany. He was an anatomist and also did remarkable, but relatively unnoticed, work in paleontology. He later became a religious fanatic.

Strabo (*c.* 63 B.C.–*c.* A.D. 24)   A Roman geographer, he prepared a general survey of the world. Because he lived in Rome and was able to collect the information available there, he had more material to work with than his predecessors had had. He was hindered, however, by his deficiency in mathematics.

Swammerdam, Jan (1637–1680)   Although his scientific career was brief—it was interrupted by a quarrel with his father and by his subsequently becoming a religious mystic—he contributed greatly to the knowledge of insect anatomy. His important work was done in his father's house in Amsterdam.

Thales (*c.* 640 B.C.–*c.* 546 B.C.)   A native of Miletus, he was a successful merchant and traveled abroad. From the knowledge of astronomy he gained in Egypt and Mesopotamia, he successfully predicted an eclipse of the sun visible in Miletus in 585 B.C. He did considerable work in mathematics. He was particularly interested in finding general natural laws.

Theophrastus (*c.* 372 B.C.–*c.* 287 B.C.)   A student of Plato and Aristotle, he became a botanist and left behind him one of the best arranged biological books of antiquity. He also conducted experiments to determine the sex of plants.

Thompson, Benjamin (1753–1814)   A native of New England, he fled the United States during the American Revolution and joined the British. He then asked leave to serve the Duke of Bavaria in Munich, after which he returned again to England. His principal scientific work was in ballistics, heat, and light.

Tournefort, Joseph Pitton de (1656–1708)   Destined by his father to be a priest, he gave up theology on his father's death and became a botanist and doctor of medicine. He taught in Paris and devised the best method yet known for the classification of plants.

Valliant, Sébastien (1669–1772)   He wrote a paper on the sex of plants. Linnaeus came across a review of this paper while he was a student at Uppsala, and it stimulated him to undertake his studies in this field. These in turn helped him with his system of classification.

Vesalius, Andreas (*c.* 1514–1564)   The circumstances of his death are unknown, because he disappeared during a pilgrimage to Jerusalem. A native of Brussels, he spent most of his adult life in Italy, where, through actual observation, he discovered the errors in Galen's anatomy and substituted an anatomy of his own.

Vicq-d'Azyr, Félix (1748–1794)   A French physician, he held many government posts in medicine but, nevertheless, found time to study his favorite subject, comparative anatomy. One of his significant contributions was tracing the same organ in many different animals. His work did much to stimulate Georges Cuvier.

Voltaire, François Marie Arouet de (1694–1798)   Although Voltaire was a skeptic and attacked many of the institutions in France, he could not bring himself to believe in the geological significance of fossils. He thought they were remains left by pilgrims and other travelers. He and Buffon quarreled on this point.

Wallace, Alfred Russel (1823–1913)   Having determined to make his living as a collector of specimens, Wallace traveled extensively in Brazil and the Malay Archipelago. During his journeys, he independently developed a theory of evolution similar to Darwin's. Although Darwin had been working on his theory longer—a fact that Wallace graciously acknowledged—he stands with Darwin as a codiscoverer.

Werner, Abraham Gottlob (1750–1817)   Professor at the mining school at Freiberg, Werner was one of the most influential geologists of his day. He built the school into a leading European center, but he also propounded the theory, known as Neptunism, that most rocks were of aqueous origin. Although he did not publish his ideas, he was so popular as a teacher that they soon became both widely spread and warmly defended.

Willis, Thomas (1621–1675)   The son of a farmer, he attended Oxford and then practiced medicine. He was particularly interested in the brain and the nervous system. In his book on the subject, he obtained the services of his friend Sir Christopher Wren to do some of the illustrations.

Willughby, Francis (1635–1672)   During his lifetime, he supported John Ray and left him a legacy on his death. This permitted Ray to continue his studies uninterrupted. Willughby himself concentrated on zoology, while Ray at first confined himself to botany.

Wilson, Alexander (1766–1813)   The son of a Scottish weaver and smuggler, Wilson came to the United States to avoid prosecution in Scotland. After working as a teacher, he decided to become an ornithologist and, after great hardship, produced *American Ornithology,* which for years was the authority in its field.

APPENDIX B

Classification

The following description of classification, which may be of special interest in connection with the life of Linnaeus and other naturalists concerned with classification, is taken from *Natural History* by Richard A. Pimentel, Reinhold Book Corporation, a Subsidiary of Chapman-Reinhold, Inc., New York, 1963. It appears on pages 95–99 and is reproduced with permission.

There are over a million species of living organisms in the world today. Needless to say, it is impossible for anyone to know all of them. Yet, for various reasons, man is a great labeler. He appears to have a passionate desire to name things, a characteristic that seems to obscure and all too often to satisfy his ignorance. Probably since the time of the earliest humans, names have been applied. Perhaps, in order to simplify things and arrange them in his mind, ancient man attempted many schemes of classification.

Man's efforts to name organisms led to the science of taxonomy, the grouping of organisms. Early schemes were purely matters of convenience, using such things as habits and habitats to group animals together. According to that now-defunct system whales, seals, and porpoises would be grouped with fishes. Today, biologists do their best to determine animal *ancestry* and *relationships* and to use that information for purposes of classifying. In modern taxonomy, the whales, seals, and porpoises are classified with mammals. Even today, however, the complexity of known phylogeny may necessitate a classification of pure convenience; known evolution may be too intricate to be shown by modern or any relatively simple means of classification. In spite of this possibility, the modern biologists' attempts to use relationships to form groups have resulted in the most convenient, especially for learning and remembering, and most informative scheme to date.

477

Taxonomic Categories

The basic unit of taxonomy is the single kind of organism, or *species*. (The term "species" is both singular and plural; the word "specie" means coined money.) A species may seem to be a very definite thing. Everyone recognizes dogs, cats, cows, and horses as species because each group is unique and easily distinguished. However, these well-known animals present a warped view of conditions in nature. Perhaps the best way of contemplating a species is to think of its existence in view of the death of many of its ancestors. For example, the African and Indian elephants are two similar but different species that are related through common ancestry; if time could be ignored and the ancestors and all intermediate types to these two species were living today, one would find it impossible to separate the elephants into two species. For this reason, if one considers the known possibility of two living, geographically isolated groups of organisms that possess similar form and habits, the problem of determining what is and what is not a distinct species can be appreciated. Although past life does not exist to create problems in species definition, some very closely related living organisms cause the same sort of difficulty. What then is a species? The common idea, gathered from the less complex kinds of species, is that a species is a group of organisms freely reproducing with one another but reproductively isolated from all other groups of organisms. For many purposes this is a satisfactory way of thinking of a species.

Categories above the species are strictly for convenience and may not be accepted by all biologists. For example, within a single family the number of genera recognized by different biologists may range from five to ten. This occurs because individual higher categories are never equivalent when applied to different groups, no matter how hard a biologist might try for uniformity. Uniform higher categories are impossible, because evolution does not produce units of distinct and discontinuous size; rather, the consequence of evolution is a continuous variation in the size and complexity of different units. In spite of this, larger categories are valuable when they represent natural groups; hence, the primary criterion for any of these larger groups is common ancestry and the larger the category, the more organisms are included. Similar species with common ancestry are grouped into *genera* (singular *genus*), genera into *families* (singular *family*), families into *orders,* orders into *classes,* classes into *phyla* (singular *phylum*), and phyla into *kingdoms.* Depending on the classification scheme, there are two kingdoms, Animalia and Plantae; three kingdoms, those two, plus Protista; or four kingdoms, the preceding three, plus Monera. It should be noted that botanists tend to use the term *division* instead of phylum. Technically speaking, the term "phylum" should be reserved for animals and the term "division" for plants; however, phylum is acceptable and is used here for plants, animals, monerans, and protistans.

Many categories below the species level may be recognized. However, only *subspecies* and *variety* have much use and meaning. The subspecies designation is restricted mostly to animal species. In its usual meaning it refers to a geographic race that has some structural or other difference from the rest of its species. A variety, a plant subunit of the species, can be a structural variant without regard to distribution, a structural variant forming a geographic race, a structural variant sharing the range of other variants of the same species, or a color or habit (form of growth) variant.

The species and other categories already mentioned are the basis of a framework within which one can start with a very large group, such as a phylum, and work down through finer groupings, all attempting to show relationship and usually assuming *common ancestry,* until the individual organism is distinguished. In some cases, and to obtain additional groups, the species and higher categories are further subdivided or grouped by the addition of the prefixes *sub-* and *super-* (respectively, something less than and something more than the group so designated). Also, *infra-* may be used as a unit just below *sub-*. The subspecies is an example of this type of division. Also, such categories as *tribe* and *variety* assume particular places in the hierarchy of biological classification. In certain detailed taxonomic studies special categories (e.g., cohort, brigade, legion, and section) are created and defined to fulfill special needs. These latter categories always must be defined, because they do not possess a standardized position in the taxonomic hierarchy.

An example of the categories generally used to classify modern man are as follows:

Kingdom Animalia
　Subkingdom Eumetazoa
　　Phylum Chordata
　　　Subphylum Vertebrata
　　　　Superclass Tetrapoda
　　　　　Class Mammalia
　　　　　　Subclass Theria
　　　　　　　Order Primates
　　　　　　　　Suborder Anthropoidea
　　　　　　　　　Family Hominidae
　　　　　　　　　　Genus *Homo*
　　　　　　　　　　　Species *sapiens*
　　　　　　　　　　　　Subspecies *sapiens*

A general term to refer to any taxonomic category is useful. A single taxonomic category is called a *taxon* (plural, *taxa*).

Nomenclature

Nomenclature is the scientific naming of organisms. Scientific names for species (generally considered "the scientific name") are binomial, consisting of both the generic and specific names. Man belongs to the genus *Homo* and species *sapiens*. His scientific name, a combination of the generic and specific names, is *Homo sapiens*. Parenthetically we must avoid possible confusion. There are two meanings of "specific name." So far we used this term to indicate a single word in a binomial. However, "specific name" also can mean "the binomial scientific name" of a species. For example, the specific name of man is *Homo sapiens*. Moreover, unless one is referring separately to binomial components, the scientific name always is two words.

When written or printed, scientific names must conform to certain set procedures. Notice that the generic name is capitalized and the second word is uncapitalized. This standard procedure is always followed in this book and is essential for animal designations. In some botanical names it also is proper to capitalize the second word; however, it is always correct to capitalize only the first word, the generic name. In addition, specific names must be either underlined, italicized, or printed in boldface type. Often the last name, or an abbreviation of the last name, of the biologist who proposed the organism's name is appended to the scientific name, as in *Homo sapiens* L., the L. being an abbreviation of Carl von Linne ("Linnaeus"), who proposed the scientific name for man. Sometimes the biologist's name is included in parentheses; this means that there has been a change in the name originally applied (see "Name Changes" below). Finally, the names may come from Latin, Greek, or any other language, or have meaningless derivation; however, all must be latinized, as *californica* or *californicus* for California and *washingtonii* or *washingtonia* for Washington. Higher taxa names have the same origin as specific names and are always capitalized but require no special printing or writing. The taxon designation is capitalized only when combined with a scientific name (e.g., Family Hominidae).

Subspecific or varietal recognition necessitates the formation of three names, a trinomial. The subspecies of modern man is *Homo sapiens sapiens*—more simply, *Homo s. sapiens*. The specific name is abbreviated in the previous manner when it is the same as the subspecific name. Further abbreviation is possible if a name follows its nonabbreviated form. For example, if the scientific name of Neanderthal man (assuming Neanderthal and modern man belong to the same species, a premise most biologists do not accept) were to follow in written text the above scientific name for modern man, the Neanderthal's could be written *H. s. neanderthalensis*. However, if the Neanderthal's scientific name did *not* follow that of modern man or of another member of the same genus and species, the correct nomenclature would be *Homo sapiens neanderthalensis*.

The writing of varietal names is somewhat different. For example, a particular variety of the California poppy is *Eschscholtzia californica* var. *crocea*. Notice that the word "variety" is abbreviated and that the variety name, like the subspecific, is written in the same manner as specific names. Abbreviation of part of variety names, actually individual genus or species names, is possible only if the variety follows other members of the same species or genus. For example, after *Eschscholtzia californica*, a poppy, these abbreviations are possible: *E. c.* var. *peninsularis* for *Eschscholtzia californica* var. *peninsularis* and *E. caespitosa* var. *hypecoides* for *Eschscholtzia caespitosa* var. *hypecoides*, a different species. In no event are any of these abbreviations possible unless they follow directly a complete writing of the word or words that are abbreviated.

Name Endings

Certain taxa of plants and animals tend to have uniform endings because of rules for naming. Although exceptions to these rules are permitted on the basis of pre-rule common usage, the following taxa usually have the endings shown:

	Plants	*Animals*
Order	-ales	
Suborder	-ineae	
Superfamily		-oidea
Family	-aceae	-idae
Subfamily	-oidea	-inae
Tribe	-inae	-ini

Name Changes

In general, scientific names are quite stable. However, there are circum stances under which scientific names can be changed. The two main sources of redesignations are *taxonomic revisions* and the *law of priority*. In part, the law of priority states that the first name given a species shall be its scientific name.

Changes due to taxonomic revision generally reflect scientific progress. They are based upon new interpretation of biological relationships as a result of study of one or more species. This can cause one or more of three possible name changes: (1) A species must be transferred from one genus to another, so the generic name becomes different. (2) It is discovered that what had been considered two species is a single species, so one specific name must be dropped, or synonomized, and the first given name be established for the species as a whole (law of priority). (3) What was thought to be a single species is found to be two or more species, in which case new specific names are given to each of the new species. All of these examples are "scientific changes of names."

Reassignments due to the law of priority alone are the common example of "nomenclatorial changes in names." These changes often are criticized be cause they do not stem from new knowledge or scientific progress. The tech nicalities in relation to the law of priority and to other bases for nomenclato rial changes in names are extremely complex. However, a simple example of a replacement according to the law of priority would involve a generic and/or specific name's being superseded because a properly and earlier applied name is found. In spite of the fact that these alterations do cause difficulty and exasperation, they are an aspect of the very thing that yields the great stability characterizing most scientific names.

Geologic Table

The following geologic table, which may interest the reader who would like to follow the development of life and of geologic features, is taken from *Natural History* by Richard A. Pimentel, Reinhold Publishing Corporation, a subsidiary of Reinhold-Chapman, Inc., New York, 1963. It appears on pages 109–19 and is reproduced with permission.

PHANEROZOIC EON

Eras	Periods and Epochs	Physical Events (North America)	Life
(MODERN LIFE)	QUATERNARY — Recent / .01	Postglacial climate; glaciers melting; great stream, flood, and ground water actions; ocean wave and shore current erosion; winds important in dry areas.	Rise of man through new stone, bronze, and iron ages. Expansion and restriction of ranges of living organisms to present distributions.
	Pleistocene / 1	Rejuvenation to high relief—northeast and Pacific Coast uplift, western mountain vulcanism; general growth; Great Valley a geosyncline since Jurassic; extensive continents. Four glacial and three interglacial warm climates; alpine glaciation and erosion; continental glaciation and effects; many lakes, especially in Great Basin; rivers flooded by melting ice; western canyons excavated; extensive glacial and stream actions. Pronounced western mountain building, including vulcanism.	Stone age men and first modern man. (Cro-Magnon). Modern types of plants and animals are dominant. Extinction of many trees and large animals.
	Pliocene / 1	Climate cooling but semiarid; first half marked zonation, and last half like now; western mountain erosion and area sedimentation; some western peneplaination; Great Plains sedimentation.	North and South America connected after isolation since Eocene (?) and mammals known to mingle—extension and expansion of many species. North American horses and elephants approach modern forms.

CENOZOIC	TERTIARY	Epoch		Physical history	Life
			12	World-wide elevation and restricted seas; most active growth of western mountains; vulcanism especially in Cascades; Rockies and Basin Ranges refaulted; Western Great Basin shears from Sierras; Coast Ranges folding, faulting, and vulcanism.	Rise of present organism distribution.
		Miocene	12	Climate with temperature fluctuations in the continuing cooling trend; some erosion due to mountains; California, Gulf and Atlantic Coasts submerged and deposits accumulated; continental erosion. Seas generally restricted; western mountains start forming, widespread vulcanism including northwestern lava fields, start of Cascadian Revolution and growth to Recent.	Advances in mammals, especially horses and elephants; apes appear; peak for mammals. Reduction of forests and retreat of polar flora.
		Oligocene	11	Rapid decline from old warm climate, warm and humid to cooler and drier; erosion in high western mountains and associated local sedimentation; Gulf submerged and sedimentation. Restricted seas, but lands generally lower; some localized western uplift near end.	Archaic mammal extinction; rise of advanced mammals (anthropoids, hoofed and carniverous) and birds. Subtropical forests widely distributed.

PHANEROZOIC EON

Eras	Periods and Epochs	Physical Events (North America)	Life
CENOZOIC (cont.) 63	TERTIARY (cont.) 62 — Eocene 22	Last of maximum warm climates in a cycle of slight cooling then return, start of cooling cycle at end; high mountain stream erosion, perhaps some glaciation in highest Rockies; California and Gulf Coast sedimentation. Most extensive Tertiary seas in California; California mountains active, especially vulcanism; continued Rockies growth.	Dominance of early mammals. Coming of modern invertebrates, birds and mammals. Expansion of modern plants with sub-tropical forests to polar regions.
	Paleocene 5	Continued slight cooling then return to Cretaceous conditions; physiography much like Eocene but climate cooler and drier with semiarid areas. Seas not as widespread and mountain growth less active, except Rockies.	Reptiles subordinate. Dawn and spread of modern mammals. Modernization of plants.
	Upper Cretaceous	Climates more uniform and warmer than now but slight cooling at end. Seas split North America through Great Plains; Atlantic and Gulf Coasts and much of California submerged, widespread sedimentation;	Great extinction of older groups at the end and into the Paleocene, extinction of ruling reptiles and earliest birds. Mollusks abundant. Continued decrease of gymnosperms; eruption of flowering plants, dominance

MESOZOIC (MIDDLE LIFE)			Physical	Life
CRETACEOUS		27	toward the end. submerged and lowlands of Rockies rise by some vulcanism, then uplift of intermontane plateaus of west and Rockies growth; also Great Plains and eastern uplift and Appalachian Highlands arching.	Dinosaur peak, but extinction of some ruling reptiles and earliest birds. Increase of mollusks and dawn of modern invertebrates. Expansion of modern gymnosperms; first absolute fossils of flowering plants; decrease of gymnosperms at end.
	Lower Cretaceous	45 72	Temperature generally uniformly high, but climatic diversity and seasonal changes, perhaps some glacial and arid areas, mostly warm and fluctuating. Continent generally low except for continued elevation in Pacific borderlands; seas encroach from Arctic into Canada and from Gulf into Great Plains, also from Pacific into borderlands.	
JURASSIC		46	Temperature much like Lower Cretaceous, but generally less climatic diversity. Shallow seas in Pacific borderlands and Great Plains, a long erosion cycle for most of the continent. Pacific borderland mountain building from Central America to Alaska, active vulcanism including intrusion of Sierra batholith.	Dawn of birds; spread of archaic mammals: marine, flying, and giant reptiles common. Modern type crustaceans; age of cephalopods (octopus and squid allies); development of higher invertebrates. Older gymnosperms dominant to the dawn of modern types.

PHANEROZOIC EON

Eras	Periods	Physical Events (North America)	Life
MESOZOIC (cont.) 230	TRIASSIC 49	Period of temperature rise to Jurassic, but climate more arid than Jurassic, mostly semiarid and arid with widespread deserts, probably wet-dry cycles in temperate climates. Continent rising, east becoming land, but continent generally low and some sea encroachment along Pacific.	Dawn of mammals; ruling reptiles dominant: primitive amphibian extinction. Marine invertebrates decline. Older gymnosperms increase.
	PERMIAN 50	Climatic mystery, apparently a violent drop in temperature almost to present conditions and rapid rise almost to past warmth; widespread aridity and Southern Hemisphere glaciation, perhaps some glaciation in the eastern United States; different areas with desert, semiarid, wet-dry cyclic, warm, and frigid climates. Seas invade Texas, southwest, and then Great Plains and area of western mountains, or Cordilleras. Third cycle of world-wide uplift and mountain building, including Appalachian Revolution.	Widespread extinction of older forms of life. Rise of primitive reptiles, mammal-like reptiles, and modern insects. Fossil evidence for most living orders of vascular plants other than the flowering plants. Decline of lycopods and horsetails.

PALEOZOIC (OLD LIFE)			
PENNSYLVANIAN or UPPER CARBON-IFEROUS	30	Gradual temperature decline from Mississippian, climate very moist, warm to tropical with little seasonal variation; subtropics move farther northward. Alternate emergence and submergence with extensive epicontinental shallow seas developing many times; great swamps in east contain flora that fossilized to form extensive coal deposits.	Ancient forms of life become rare. Giant insects. More coal-forming plants and continuation of many Mississippian types. Many fern-like plants and gymnosperms forming forests. First definite moss and liverwort fossils.
MISSISSIPPIAN or LOWER CARBON-IFEROUS	35	Generally uniformly warm and mild climate but local moist and wet-dry cycles. Topography low, shallow seas invade much of west and east to continental rise at end; active movements in southern Appalachians and site of Rockies from Utah to Texas; continued folding of New England Acadian mountains; start of great eastern coal deposits.	Dawn of reptiles; amphibians numerous; sharks numerous; rise of insects; many corals. Early coal-forming plants dominant, especially nonflowering vascular plants, including lycopods, horsetails, seed ferns, etc.
DEVONIAN	60	Temperature drop, then rise to warmer Mississippian conditions; climate generally desert to warm and humid mild, perhaps some glaciation. Widespread seas advance to cover 40% of North America, but withdraw at end. Acadian Mountains form by vulcanism and folding in second uplift cycle.	Dawn of amphibians; age of fishes, many armored types; perhaps first insects; corals and crinoids abundant. First known trees, but mostly primitive plants. First brown algae, "moss," and higher fungi macrofossils.

PHANEROZOIC EON

Eras	Periods	Physical Events (North America)	Life
PALEOZOIC (*cont.*)	SILURIAN 20	Uniformly warm, representing first peak in continuously warming trend that started in Precambrian; climate generally mild and uniform, much like Ordovician, to late desert conditions. Two complete cycles of sea advance and retreat with advances featuring widespread seas; land generally low.	First air-breathing animals invade the land (lungfishes and arthropods). Marine arthropods (sea scorpions) dominant. First insects. Rise of fishes. Many algae, probably still dominant. Expansion of land plants, including vascular plants; first psilopsids.
	ORDOVICIAN 95	Gradual temperature rise to Silurian conditions; climate relatively warm and uniform apparently to area of present Arctic Seas. Greatest North American submergence (over 60%) to sea withdrawal at end. Mountain formation along northern Atlantic Coast of the United States.	First vertebrate fossils (armored fishes). Climax of age of invertebrates and rise of modern types; corals and trilobites abundant; many mollusks, especially cephalopods. First red algae fossils. Probable divergence of vascular and other land plants. Algae still the dominant plants.
	CAMBRIAN	Rapid temperature rise from conditions much like now; perhaps early glaciation to warm with local arid areas.	Most to all plant and animal phyla definitely present; all vascular plant subphyla present? Mostly ancient, now extinct representa-

		tives of present life; ancient lamp shells and arthropods (trilobites) dominant. Continued marine algae dominance.
620	100	
	Sea invades much of continent and partially withdraws by the end. Land generally low.	

CRYPTOZOIC EON

Possible Subdivisions	Physical Events (North America)	Life
Proterozoic Era?	Climate of repeated glacial and warm moist interglacial periods; near end temperature conditions to the lowest ever known, then start of rapid rise that also characterized the Cambrian. Great sedimentation to second great period of mountain building followed by erosion—loss of many fossils. Dawn of Actualistic Period of geological history—geological processes subject to same laws and conditions as now.	Age of primitive life; marine algae probably the dominant life. Perhaps the final origin of most phyla; definite protozoans, sponges, coelenterates, segmented worms, other worms, and perhaps lamp shells; also bacteria, algae, fungi, and vascular plants (spores) seem to be represented. Probably a time of the early development of all phyla.
1500?		
Archezoic Era?	Probably hot to very warm with dense cloud cover and torrential rains to more moderate conditions. First great mountain formation (volcanic) and erosion, some sedimentary deposits. Like Proterozoic in many respects.	Dawn of life?
2000?		

PRECAMBRIAN

ACTUALISTIC ←   2120

PREACTUALISTIC

CRYPTOZOIC EON

	Possible Subdivisions	Physical Events (North America)	Life
			Premise that early life used H_2S and CO_2 in photosynthesis, releasing oxygen to form early version of present atmosphere; H_2S removed.
PRECAMBRIAN (cont.) — PREACTUALISTIC (cont.) — Azoic Era? — 1000? 3000 5120	Azoic Era?	Birth of the solar system, earth, oceans; first great erosion cycle. Preactualistic Period of geological history—although same fundamental laws operated as now, conditions were so different that natural phenomena were not the same; earliest part had barren rocky lithosphere, and hydrosphere and atmosphere mainly of ammonia, hydrogen sulfide, and water plus some carbon dioxide; photochemical reactions formed the organic compounds which characterized later Preactualistic, prior to the dawn of life.	Inorganic materials to organic compounds that became the basis for life. Probably no living creatures during this era; perhaps the dawn of virus-like compounds.

Mendel's Discoveries

If the reader has forgotten what he knew about Mendel's discoveries, he may find the following outline helpful.

For this purpose, it is not necessary to use more than two contrasting characteristics. One of them can be a dark color in a flower and a dominant characteristic. It can be represented by "D." A light color and a recessive characteristic can be represented by "1."

Because hereditary characteristics come in pairs, the pure-strained dark flowers can offer D or D. The pure-strained light-colored flowers can offer 1 or 1. When they interbreed, the characteristics will combine, and each resulting flower will be D1. In appearance, they will be dark, because D is a dominant characteristic. But genetically they will be different from the pure-strained dark flowers, because each one will also have the recessive characteristic 1.

A D1 plant will breed with a D1 plant on this basis. The pollen grains will be either D or 1. (The characteristics have to be divided, because only one can be carried by each pollen grain.) Mathematically, therefore, four grains should be equally divided into two D's and two 1's, and the egg cells receiving them could be expected to be divided on the same basis. The resulting plants would be: one "DD," two "D1," one "11," as shown in the following table:

Pollen Grains	Egg Cells	Resulting Plant
D	D	DD
1	1	11
D	1	D1
1	D	D1

Three out of the four plants would be dark in color, and one would have reverted to the light color. Obviously this ratio is more likely to appear if a large, rather than a small, number of flowers is bred, just as a person flipping a coin is more likely to find that heads has come up nearly as often as tails if he tosses the coin many times.

There are, of course, factors that make the study of genetics much more complicated than this. But Mendel's discovery that (1) each characteristic remains separate, (2) that some are dominant and some recessive, and (3) that their recombination can be studied statistically formed the basis for modern genetics.

Index

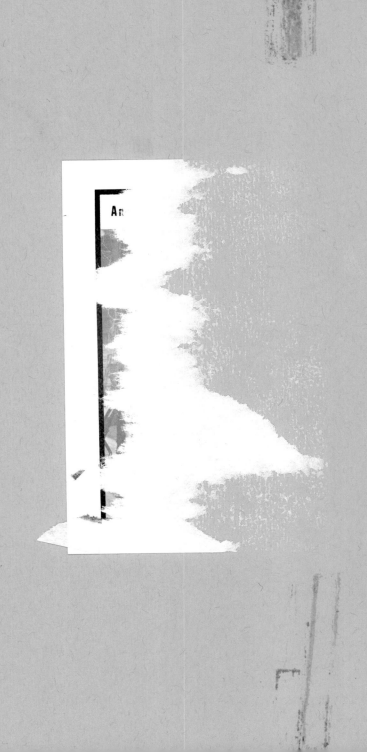